THE QUANTITATIVE
ANALYSIS
OF SOCIAL PROBLEMS

THE QUANTITATIVE ANALYSIS OF SOCIAL PROBLEMS

Edited by
EDWARD R. TUFTE
Department of Politics
Princeton University

ADDISON-WESLEY PUBLISHING COMPANY
Reading, Massachusetts · Menlo Park, California · London · Don Mills, Ontario

This book is in the Addison-Wesley Series in
BEHAVIORAL SCIENCE: QUANTITATIVE METHODS

Frederick Mosteller, Consulting Editor

ISBN 201-07610-1
DEFGHIJKLM-AL-79876543

To Susanne

PREFACE

If you want to understand and solve social problems, a good first step toward these goals is to master the quantitative ideas in this collection of papers. The readings show what quantitative analysis is good for and how it can be criticized and improved. Included, then, are a number of well-executed studies of important social, economic, and political problems: equality of educational opportunity, voting behavior, poverty, automobile accidents, smoking and health, and so forth. Other papers center on data analysis, research design, and statistical criticism. Many of the papers either are published here for the first time or have been relatively inaccessible. Thus the collection should prove enlightening to those who want access to the more quantitative studies of social problems as well as to those studying statistics and data analysis in the social sciences.

The collection is divided into five parts:

1. Statistical Evidence and Statistical Criticism.
2. Experimental and Quasi-Experimental Studies.
3. Economic and Aggregate Analysis.
4. Survey Data.
5. Data Analysis and Research Design.

The first three readings are careful and judicious assessments of quantitative work. They discuss controversial and sometimes difficult studies: *Sexual Behavior in the Human Male* by Kinsey, Pomeroy, and Martin; a political tract called "Catholic Voters and the Democratic National Ticket"; and studies of the relationship between smoking and lung cancer. The fourth paper in this section, growing out of some of the criticisms of the research on smoking and health, suggests a number of ground rules for statistical criticism. All these readings are valuable, it seems to me, because, by their example, they help us to arrive at sensible evaluations of quantitative studies. The discussion by Cochran, Mosteller, and Tukey of *Sexual Behavior in the Human Male* reaches a balanced conclusion about a flawed but highly significant study. The paper by Cornfield, Haenszel, Hammond, Lilienfeld, Shimkin, and Wynder pulls together many different types of evidence about the consequences of smoking. Their work is especially valuable because of its stress on the logic of inference and the logic of counterexplanation.

The next three sections contain quantitative studies of particular economic, political, and social problems. The readings are rather arbitrarily divided into three categories on the basis of the origin of the data. The important point is that a wide range of techniques are useful for collecting and analyzing data that bear on a variety of substantive problems. For example, the study by Haddon and others of pedestrians killed by automobiles represents an imaginative use of a controlled quasi-experimental method for a problem that initially seems hardly amenable to the collection of data on a control group.

Included in the section of survey studies are "Relation of School Factors to Achievement" and "Integration and Achievement," which are excerpted from *Equality of Educational Opportunity*, often called the "Coleman Report" after its principal investigator. The Report is a massive document with a wide range of findings about how schools in the United States operate and fail to operate. The reader is urged to consult the original study. Furthermore, the reader should take heed that the material is very difficult from a statistical point of view. The Report's findings, often striking at the conventional educational wisdom, have led to a good deal of controversy—both political and statistical.* The section of the Report reprinted here includes most of the findings generating dispute. It also contains a useful discussion of regression procedures (found at the beginning of the selection and in the "Technical Appendix").

The final section contains readings on data analysis and research design. Two of the papers—Tukey and Wilk on data analysis and Abelson and Tukey on the assignment of numerical values to ordered information—have been virtually inaccessible and should be especially useful to data analysts. The final selection in this section, written by the editor, partially summarizes and applies some of the thoughts of the other papers to specific research in political science.

---

* See Samuel Bowles and Henry Levin, "The Determinants of Scholastic Achievement— An Appraisal of Some Recent Evidence," *Journal of Human Resources* 3 (Winter, 1968), 3–24; James S. Coleman, "Equality of Educational Opportunity: Reply to Bowles and Levin," *ibid.* 3 (Spring, 1968), 237–246; and Bowles and Levin, "More on Multicollinearity and the Effectiveness of Schools," *ibid.* 3 (Summer, 1968), 393–400.

Few of the papers collected here deal with the political and moral problems associated with the empirical analysis of matters relevant to social policy. At least two books, however, are especially helpful in clarifying these issues: Lee Rainwater and William Yancey, *The Moynihan Report and the Politics of Controversy*, and Irving Louis Horowitz, ed., *The Rise and Fall of Project Camelot: Studies in the Relationship between Social Science and Practical Politics*.

Many first-rate studies were not included simply because of lack of space. This book contains only a very few selections bearing on economic questions despite the vast amount of quantitative work done in that field. Convenient access is provided to the econometric literature, however, by *Readings in Economic Statistics and Econometrics*, edited by Arnold Zellner.

This collection has grown out of courses at Princeton University taught in the Department of Politics and the Woodrow Wilson School of Public and International Affairs. I am indebted to my students in these courses, several of whom raised questions that encouraged me to seek out some of the material found here. I hope that this collection may encourage their pursuit of both relevance and rigor.

Princeton, New Jersey   E.R.T.
December 1969

CONTENTS

1 / STATISTICAL EVIDENCE AND STATISTICAL CRITICISM

STATISTICAL PROBLEMS
OF THE KINSEY REPORT

WILLIAM G. COCHRAN
FREDERICK MOSTELLER
JOHN W. TUKEY

This is the report of a committee appointed by the Commission on Statistical Standards of the American Statistical Association to review the statistical methods used in *Sexual Behavior in the Human Male*. We shall refer both to the book and to its authors (Kinsey, Pomeroy and Martin) as KPM. The committee wishes to emphasize that this report is confined to statistical methodology, and does not concern itself with the appropriateness or the limitations of orgasm as a measure of sexual behavior. The treatment of specific problems has necessitated an examination of some of the statistical and methodological problems of such studies, and the organization of frames of reference in which the statistical methods can be discussed. The committee hopes that both detailed and general considerations will be of service to Dr. Alfred C. Kinsey and his co-workers; to the National Research Council's Committee for Research on Problems of Sex, who requested the appointment of this committee, and to others facing similar statistical or methodological problems.

We have endeavored to write this report in a way that would minimize the possibility of misunderstanding. To do this, it is necessary to deal with many detailed aspects of the work, one at a time. By judicious selection of topics and attitudes, it would have been possible to write two factually correct reports, one of which would leave the impression with the reader that KPM's work was of the highest quality, the other that the work was of poor quality and that the major issues were evaded. We have not written either of these extreme reports.

Even within the present report, a reader who is trying only to support his own opinions could select sections and topics to buttress either view. In the details of this report the reader will find numerous problems that we feel KPM handled admirably. If he pays attention only to these, he would find support for the opinion that the work is nearly impeccable and that the conclusions must be substantially correct. There are other problems which we believe KPM failed to handle adequately, in some cases because they did not devote the necessary skill and resources to the problems, in other cases because no solutions for the problems exist at present. The reader who concentrates only on the parts of our report

Reprinted by permission of the authors and the American Statistical Association from *Journal of the American Statistical Association* **48** (December, 1953), 673–716. The present version has been slightly abridged by the editor. The full report, including the appendices, was published as a monograph by the American Statistical Association in 1954.

in which such problems are discussed would find support for the opinion that KPM's work is of poor quality.

Our own opinion is that KPM are engaged in a complex program of research involving many problems of measurement and sampling, for some of which there appear at the present to be no satisfactory solutions. While much remains to be done, our overall impression of their work to date is favorable.

Many details are discussed in the body and appendices of this report. The main conclusions are as follows:

1.   The statistical and methodological aspects of KPM's work are outstanding in comparison with other leading sex studies. In a comparison with nine other leading sex studies (four supported in part by the same NRC Committee) KPM were superior to all others in the systematic coverage of their material, in the number of items which they covered, in the composition of their sample as re-gards its age, educational, religious, rural-urban, occupational, and geographic representation, in the number and variety of methodological checks which they employed, and in their statistical analyses. So far as we can judge from our present knowledge, or from the critical evaluations of a number of other qualified specialists, their interviewing was of the best.

2.   KPM's interpretations were based in part on tabulated and statistically analyzed data, and in part on data and experience which were not presented because or their nature or because of the limitations of space. Some interpreta-tions appear not to have been based on either of these. We feel that unsubstan-tiated assertions are not in themselves inappropriate in a scientific study. The accumulated insight of an experienced worker frequently merits recording when no documentation can be given. However, KPM should have indicated which of their statements were undocumented or undocumentable and should have been more cautious in boldly drawing highly precise conclusions from their limited sample.

3.   Many of KPM's findings are subject to question because of a possible bias in the constitution of the sample. This is not a criticism of their work (although it is a criticism of some of their interpretations). No previous sex study of a broad human population known to us, medical, psychiatric, psychological or socio-logical, has been able to avoid this difficulty, and we believe that KPM could not have avoided the use of a nonprobability sample at the start of their work. Something may now perhaps be done to study and reduce this possible bias, by a probability sampling program.

In our opinion, no sex study of a broad human population can expect to present incidence data for reported behavior that are *known* to be correct to within a few percentage points. Even with the best available sampling techniques, there will be a certain percentage of the population who refuse to give histories. If the percentage of refusals is 10 per cent or more, then however large the sample, there are no statistical principles which guarantee that the results are correct to within 2 or 3 per cent. The results may actually be correct to within 2 or 3 per cent, but any claim that this is true must be based on the undocumented opinion that the behavior of those who refuse to be interviewed is not very different from that of those who are interviewed. These comments, which are not a criticism of KPM's research, emphasize the difficulty of answering the question: "How accurate are the results?", which is naturally of great interest to any user of the results of a sex study.

4.   Many of KPM's findings are subject to question because of possible inaccuracies of memory and report, as are all studies of intimate human behavior among broad segments of the population. No one has proposed any way to remove the dangers of recall (involving both memory and report) and KPM were superior to the nine studies referred to above in their attempts to control and measure these dangers. We have suggested still further expansions of their methodological checks.

Until new methods are found, we believe that no sex study of incidence or frequency in large human populations can hope to measure anything but reported behavior. It may be possible to obtain observed or recorded behavior for certain special groups, but no suggestions have been made by KPM, the critics, or this committee which would make it feasible to study observed or recorded behavior for a large human population. These remarks are intended as a comment on the present status of research techniques in sex studies and not as a criticism of KPM's work.

5.   KPM received only limited statistical help, in part because the work was pursued during the War years when such expert help was difficult to find for non-military projects. In view of the limited statistical knowledge which was available to them, as made clear by the failure of their sample size experiment, KPM deserve much credit for the straight thinking which brought them safely by many pitfalls. Their need of adequate statistical assistance continues to be serious. Substantial assistance might come through the development of a statistical clinic at Indiana University, or through the addition of a statistical expert to KPM's own staff. Unfortunately the sort of assistance which might resolve some of their most complex problems would require understanding, background, and techniques that perhaps not more than twenty statisticians in the world possess.

6.   A probability sampling program should be seriously considered by KPM. The actual gains from an extensive program are limited, to an extent unknown at present, by refusal rates and indirectly by costs, particularly by the costs of maintaining the present quality of the individual histories by KPM's approach. A step-by-step program, starting with a very small pilot study, is recommended.

7.   In addition to proposing a probability sampling program we have made numerous suggestions in this report for the modification and strengthening of KPM's present approach. The suggestions include expanded methodological checks of their sampling program, a further study of their refusal rate, some

modification of their methods, of analyses, further comparisons of reported vs. observed behavior, and stricter interpretations of their data. We have been informed by KPM that many of these improvements, including some expansion of their techniques for obtaining data, have already been incorporated in the volume dealing with sexual behavior in the human female.

Chapter I. Background and Organization

1. *Organization Involved*

This committee, consisting of William G. Cochran, Chairman, Frederick Mosteller, and John W. Tukey, was appointed by President S. S. Wilks in September 1950 as a committee of the Commission on Statistical Standards of the American Statistical Association. This action was initiated by a request from the Committee for Research on Problems of Sex of the National Research Council, as indicated by the following excerpt from a letter dated May 5, 1950, from Dr. George W. Corner, a member of the NRC Committee, to Dr. Isador Lubin, Chairman of the Commission on Statistical Standards of the American Statistical Association.

> ■ In accordance with our telephone conversation of yesterday, I am writing to state to you the desire of the Committee for Research in Problems of Sex, of the National Research Council, that the Commission on Standards of the American Statistical Association will provide counsel regarding the research methods of the Institute for Sex Research of Indiana University, led by Dr. Alfred C. Kinsey.
>
> This Committee has been the major source of financial support of Dr. Kinsey's work, and at its annual meeting on April 27, 1950, again renewed the expression of its confidence in the importance and quality of the work by voting a very substantial grant for the next year.
>
> Recognizing however that there has been some questioning, in recently published articles, of the validity of the statistical analysis of the results of this investigation, the Committee, as well as Dr. Kinsey's group, is anxious to secure helpful evaluation and advice in order that the second volume of the report, now in preparation, may secure unquestioned acceptance. ■

Some correspondence ensued, in which Wilks indicated the willingness of the American Statistical Association to provide counsel as requested.

Kinsey, in a letter to Wilks dated August 28, stated that

> ■ we should make it clear that we deeply appreciate the willingness of the American Statistical Association to undertake such an examination of our statistical methods, that we will give it full cooperation in having access to all of our data as far as the peculiar confidential nature of our data will allow, and that we understand, of course, that the committee shall be free to publish its findings of whatever sort. ■

In the same letter, Kinsey also made a number of suggestions about the constitution and work of the committee, to the effect that the persons on the committee should be primarily statisticians with experience in human population studies, that they should plan to review the statistical criticisms which have been published about the book on the male, and that they should compare methods used by Kinsey and his associates in their research with methods in other published research in similar fields.

With respect to the research on the human female, Kinsey wrote as follows:

■ It should, however, be made clear that all the data that will go into our volume on *Sexual Behavior in the Human Female* are already gathered, that the punch cards have already been set up and most of them punched, and that statistical work is proceeding on that volume now. While the recommendations of the committee may modify further work, it can affect this forthcoming volume only in the form in which the material is presented, the limitations of the conclusions, and the careful description of the limitations of our method and conclusions. ■

2. *Committee Procedure*

Although no specific written directive was issued to the committee, the letter quoted earlier from Corner to Lubin sets forth the task assigned to the committee. In one respect the scope was deliberately reduced as compared with that envisaged in the letter. The committee decided not to undertake any examination of the researches and data relating to the human female, in order to avoid disruption of Kinsey's proposed schedule of work.

In October, 1950, the committee spent five days at the Institute for Sex Research of Indiana University, accompanied by Mr. Robert Osborn as assistant. Subsequent meetings of the committee were held at Chicago (December 1950), Princeton (January 1951), Cambridge (May 1951), Baltimore (July 1951) and Princeton (October 1951).

In their review of previous studies of sexual behaviour, the committee received major assistance from Dr. W. O. Jenkins, who prepared a series of reports which appear in Appendix B. Mr. A. Kimball Romney prepared a helpful index of the principal criticisms made of the statistical methodology used in the book *Sexual Behavior in the Human Male*.

3. *Structure of This Report as a Whole*

KPM's program of research is a major undertaking, involving more than ten years' work. Any discussion of it which aims at thoroughness must itself be lengthy. In order to keep the main body of our report down to a reasonable length, we have relegated much of the documentation of our conclusions, and all detailed discussion, to the following series of appendices.*

---

*   Space limitations have made it impossible to reprint these appendices. However, some of the references to them have been retained, so that the reader can judge the extent of documentation and detail provided by the committee's report. [Ed.]

A. Discussion of comments by selected technical reviewers.
B. Comparison with other studies.
C. Proposed further work.
D. Probability sampling considerations.
E. The interview and the office as we saw them.
F. Desirable accuracies.
G. Principles of sampling. . . .

Many of the problems faced by KPM occur in most types of sociological investigation. Some are likely to be encountered in almost any kind of scientific investigation. For this reason, we have thought it advisable to present certain of the methodological issues in rather general terms. . . .

Contents of This Report

4. *Structure of the Main Body*

In preparing the main body, we have stressed easy reference and have kept related matters together at the expense of fluency of arrangements and lack of repetition. Thus our main conclusions in a form intended for the general reader take 3 pages in the digest above, while more detailed conclusions, expressed for a more technical audience, take 3 pages in Chapter XI. A particular subject summarized there is also likely to be discussed once in Chapter II, where we try to point out what KPM did, once again in one of Chapters IV to IX, where we assess KPM on an absolute scale, and yet again in Chapter X, where we compare KPM with previous workers in the field. This is repetitive, but we hope that it will permit ready reference and avoid treating subjects out of context.

After this introductory chapter on background structure, the remainder of the main body falls into three parts:

i) Chapters II and III. In the first of these, we describe, respectively, what choices KPM had to make and what they chose. In Chapter III we outline some essential principles of sampling, which seem not to have been clearly enough formulated or widely enough understood. These chapters are introductory.

ii) Chapters IV to XI. In the first six of these, we try to compare KPM's work with an absolute standard. The order chosen (interview, sample, methodological checks, analytical techniques, complex examples, interpretation) is that in which the problems arise in an evolving study such as KPM's. Chapter X compares KPM with previous works on the basis of Appendix B, while Chapter XI summarizes the conclusions of this part.

iii) Chapter XII. This discusses briefly various suggested expenditures of further effort.

Chapter II. Major Areas of Choice

5. *What Sort of Behavior?*

The purpose of Chapter II is to record in summary form the major choices made by KPM.

Certainly the choice of orgasm as the central sort of sexual behavior for study was a major one, leading to consequences whose statistical aspects will be discussed in various places, but this choice is not a matter of *general* quantitative methodology, and hence falls outside the scope of this committee's task.

6. *Whose Behavior?*

KPM had to choose the population to which this study should apply. This decision does not seem to have been made clearly. From the basis for the "U.S. Corrections" (p. 105) we should infer it to be "all U.S. white males." If it were the population to which the U.S. Corrected sample actually applies on the average (the *sampled* population, see Section 18), it would be a rather odd white male U.S. Population. It would have age groups, educational status, rural-urban background, marital status and all their combinations according to the 1940 census, but it would have more members in Indiana than in any other state, and it would have been selected to an unknown degree for willingness to volunteer histories of sexual behavior. We do not regard this description of the sampled population as an automatic criticism, as some critics do. We make it here as a factual statement, noting that the careful and wise choice of the sampled population, although difficult, is a relatively free choice of the investigator. . . .

Further, KPM chose to study the behavior of many (at least 163 in tabular form) segments of this large population, feeling, apparently, both that comparisons among segments would be illuminating and that data for (clinical) application to individuals should come from a reasonably homogeneous segment. KPM's choice of a broad population created many problems, particularly in sampling. Whether they would have been well advised to confine themselves to a more restricted population, e.g., the state of Indiana, is debatable. For our part, we are willing to take their choice as given, and to discuss briefly elsewhere some alternatives for further work (Chapter IX-D).

7. *Observed, Recorded, or Reported Behavior*

KPM, interested in actual behavior, had, in principle, the choice of studying observed, recorded, or reported behavior. But since they selected a broad population and orgasm as the type of behavior, their only feasible choice seems to have been *reported* behavior. This situation does not seem likely to change in the foreseeable future.

The choice of reported behavior implies that the question: "On the average, how much difference is there between present reported and past actual behavior?" is seriously involved in any inferences about actual behavior which are attempted from KPM's results. The difference might well be large, leading to a large systematic error in measurement. However, use of observed or recorded behavior in order to avoid this difference does not seem to us a feasible way to measure nationwide incidences and frequencies for KPM's broad population, because it would have produced systematic errors in sampling possibly larger than the error in measurement.

8. *Interview or Questionnaire, and Types Thereof*

Having settled on reported behavior, KPM had to decide whether this report should be oral or written, and what methods should be used to elicit it. Their choice was oral, in a face-to-face interview whose flavor was designed to be that of a doctor or family friend. The choice of oral rather than written report:

1) made it possible to obtain *apparently* satisfactory answers from many more subjects (the percentage of complete illiteracy in the U.S. is small, but the percentage of illiteracy on complex subjects not usually written about is undoubtedly substantial).
2) permitted and encouraged variation of the form of the questions to suit the subject and the situation.

Those, like some critics, who believe in a repeatable measurement process, regardless of whether or not it measures something that is always relevant, find (2) bad. Those who, like KPM, feel that appropriately flexible wording improves communication and thus improves the quality of report despite the variability resulting from changes in the form of questions, find (2) good.

Given an interview rather than a questionnaire, the remaining choices of KPM follow a consistent pattern. In nearly every case their approach resembled the clinical interview more closely than the psychometric test.

9. *Which Subjects?*

Here there are various choices, pertaining to:

1) selection of individuals one at a time or in clusters.
2) keeping age, education, marital status, etc., segments in the sample proportionate to those in the population or making them of more nearly equal size.
3) selecting individuals on a catch-as-catch-can basis, a partly randomized basis, or according to a probability sampling plan.

They chose:

1) to select individuals in clusters.
2) to keep age, education, marital status, etc., segments more nearly equal in the sample than in the population.
3) to use no detectable semblance of probability sampling ideas.

The pros and cons will be discussed later.

10. *What Methodological Checks?*

There are choices as to the types of checks and the number of each to be made. The types of checks made by KPM, including

1) take-retake,
2) husband-wife,
3) duplicate recording of interview,
4) overall comparison of interviews,
5) others

seem to cover all those easily thought of. The numbers of checks made are discussed later. Duplicate recording of interviews occurred in an unknown, but presumably small, number of cases. No comparisons from duplicate recordings were reported, perhaps because most occurred in connection with the training of interviewers.

11. *How Analyzed and Presented?*

In analyzing frequency and incidence of activity, KPM chose to report both raw and "U.S. Corrected" data and to make simple comparisons. Just what was done in general was clearly stated, but the steps involved in detailed computations were not explained. No attempt was made to find helpful scales or composite variables.

With the exception of "U.S. Corrections," most of the analysis of the tabular data is confined to straightforward description. Some attention is paid to the problem of sample-population relation in the form of standard errors (presumably underestimated because they were based on the assumption of random sampling). However, this approaches lip service, since many apparent differences are discussed with no attention to significance or nonsignificance. (Again we do not regard this as an automatic criticism, particularly since accurate indication of significance would have been difficult.)

In analyzing cumulative activity, KPM's main tool was the accumulative incidence curve, a technique which they developed independently.

12. *How Interpreted?*

The main choices concerned

1) extent of warning about possible differences between reported behavior and actual behavior,

2) extent of warning about possible differences between the sampled population (see Section 18) and the entire U.S. white male population,
3) extent of warning about sampling fluctuations,
4) extent of verbal discussion *not* based on evidence presented,
5) certainty with which conclusions were presented.

Under (1) the emphasis was on methodological checks in order to indicate, as far as they could, how small this difference seemed to KPM to be. Under (2) there was little discussion. Under (3) the warnings were made early, incompletely, but not often. Under (4) the extent of discussion was substantial, most of it aimed at social and legal attitudes about sexual behavior, and descriptions or practices not covered by the tables. Under (5) the conclusions were usually presented with an air of solid certainty.

In general the observations seem to have been interpreted with more fervor than caution, although occasional qualifications may be found.

Chapter III. Principles of Sampling

13. *Introduction*

It is difficult, if not impossible, to assess the quality of any sample and its analysis without comparing it with a set of principles. This is particularly true of KPM's works. The present chapter endeavors to set down, in compact form, a few of the principles of sampling which are especially relevant to a consideration of KPM's sampling. As we have noted (Section 6), KPM chose to select individuals in groups or clusters, to divide the population into segments and keep segment sizes more nearly equal in the sample than in the population, and to use no semblance of probability sampling ideas. The discussion in this chapter concentrates on these aspects of sampling. . . .

Whether by biologists, sociologists, engineers, or chemists, sampling is often taken too lightly. In the early years of the present century, it was not uncommon to measure the claws and carapaces of 1,000 crabs, or to count the number of veins in each of 1,000 leaves, and to attach to the results the "probable error" which would have been appropriate had the 1,000 crabs or the 1,000 leaves been drawn at random from the population of interest. If the population of interest were all crabs in a wide-spread species, it would be obviously almost impossible to take a simple random sample. But this does not bar us from honestly assessing the likely range of fluctuation of the result. Much effort has been applied in recent years, particularly in sampling human populations, to the development of sampling plans which, *simultaneously*,

 i) are economically feasible,
 ii) give reasonably precise results, and
iii) show within themselves an honest measure of fluctuation of their results.

Any excuse for the practice of treating non-random samples as random ones is now entirely tenuous. Wider knowledge of the principles involved is needed if scientific investigations involving samples (and what such investigation does not involve samples?) are to be solidly based. Additional knowledge of techniques is not so vitally important, though it can lead to substantial economic gains.

14. *Cluster Sampling*

A botanist who gathered 10 oak leaves from each of 100 oak trees might feel that he had a fine sample of 1,000, and that, if 500 were infected with a certain species of parasites, he had shown that the percentage infection was close to 50 per cent. If he had studied the binomial distribution, he might calculate a standard error according to the usual formula for random samples, $p \pm \sqrt{pq/n}$, which in this case yields 50 ± 1.6 per cent (since $p = q = .5$ and $n = 1,000$). In doing this he would neglect three things:

i) probable selectivity in selecting trees (favoring large trees, perhaps),
ii) probable selectivity in choosing leaves from a selected tree (favoring well-colored or alternatively, visibly infected leaves, perhaps), and
iii) the necessary allowance, in the formula used to compute the standard error, for the fact that he had not selected his leaves individually.

Most scientists are keenly aware of the analogs of (i) and (ii) in their own fields of work, at least as soon as they are pointed out to them. Far fewer seem to realize that, even if the trees were selected at random from the forest, and 10 leaves were chosen at random from each selected tree, (iii) must still be considered. But if, as might indeed be the case, each tree were either wholly infected or wholly free of infection, then the 1,000 leaves tell us *no more* than 100 leaves, one from each tree, since each group of 10 leaves will be all infected or all free of infection. In this event, we should take $n = 100$ in calculating the standard error and find an infection rate of 50 ± 5 per cent. Such an extreme case of increased fluctuation due to sampling in groups or clusters would be detected by almost all scientists, and is not a serious danger. But less extreme cases easily escape detection.

We have just described, as one example of the reasons why the principles of sampling need wider understanding, an example of *cluster sampling*, where the individuals or sampling units are not drawn separately and independently into the sample, but are drawn in clusters, and have tried to make it clear that "individually at random" formulas do not apply. Cluster sampling is often desirable, but must be analyzed appropriately. KPM's sample was, in the main, a cluster sample, since they built up their sample from groups of people rather than from individuals.

15. *Possibilities of Adjustment*

Often the population is divided into segments of known relative size, perhaps from a census. It is sometimes thought that the best method of sampling is to take the same proportion from every segment, so that the sample sizes in the segments match the corresponding population sizes. Such samples do have the advantage of simplifying computations by equalizing weights, and they sometimes lead to a reduction of sampling error. But modern sampling theory shows that optimum allocation of resources usually requires *different* proportions to be sampled from different segments, whether the purpose is to estimate average values over the population or to make analytical comparisons between results in one group of segments and those in another.

When there are disparities in the relative sizes of segments in the sample as compared with the population, whether accidental or planned, these disparities must be taken into account when we attempt to estimate averages over the whole population. One way in which this can be done is by adjustments applied to the segments. Such adjustments proceed as follows. Suppose that we know

  i) the true fraction of the population in each segment, and
 ii) the segment into which each individual in the sample falls.

Then we can weight each individual in the sample by the ratio

$$\frac{\text{fraction of population in that segment}}{\text{fraction of sample in that segment}}.$$

(It is computationally convenient to weight each segment mean with the numerator of this ratio; the result is algebraically identical to that described above.)

The result of adjustment is a new "sampled population"—one such that the relative sizes of its various segments are very nearly correct (according to (i) above). Since the weight is the same for all the sample individuals in a given segment, adjustment does nothing to redress any selectivity which may be present *within* segments. If we adjust in this way, we remove one source of systematic error without affecting other sources at all. The philosophy of such adjustments is discussed further in Section G-12, and it is concluded that they may generally be appropriately made (within the limits discussed in sections C-16–C-18). Their chief danger is the possible neglect of the possibilities that they may be

  i) entirely too small,
 ii) too large,
iii) in the wrong direction,

because of unredressed selectivity *within* the segments. When this possibility exists, extreme caution in presenting the results of adjustment is indicated.

16. *Probability Samples*

When probability samples are used, inferences to the population can be based entirely on statistical principles rather than subject-matter judgment. Moreover, the reliability of the inferences can be judged quantitatively. A probability sample is one in which

  i) each individual (or primary unit) in the sampled population has a known probability of entering the sample,

ii) the sample is chosen by a process involving one or more steps of automatic randomization consistent with these probabilities, and

iii) in the analysis of the sample, weights appropriate to the probabilities (i) are used.

Contrary to some opinions, it is *not* necessary, and in fact usually not advisable in a pure probability sample for

i)   all samples to be equally probable, or

ii) the appearance of one individual in the sample to be unrelated to the appearance of another.

In practice, because some respondents cannot be found or are uncooperative, we usually obtain, at best, approximate probability samples and have approximate confidence in our inference.

17. *Nonprobability Samples*

Samples which are not even approximately probability samples vary widely in both actual and apparent trustworthiness. Their trustworthiness usually increases as they are insulated more and more thoroughly from selective factors which might be related to the quantities being studied. Insulation may be obtained by:

i)   adjustments applied to the segment means in the sample,

ii) examination of the sample as drawn for signs of selection on a particular factor,

iii) partial randomization.

Adjustment for segments, as explained in Section 15 above, corrects for any selective factor operation *between* segments, but corrects not at all for selective factors operating *within* segments. If adjustment is to be used, deliberate selectivity between segments may be exercised without danger, *so long as it does not imply selectivity within segments.*

Negative results when the sample is examined for signs for selection on a particular variable are comforting, and strengthen the reliability of the sample. The amount of this strengthening depends very much on the *a priori* importance of the variables checked to what is being studied.

Deliberate (partial) randomization is a step toward a probability sample, and may be very helpful on occasion.

18. *Sampled Population and Target Population*

We have found it helpful in our thinking to make a clear distinction between two population concepts. The *target* population is the population of interest, about which we wish to make inferences or draw conclusions. It is the population which we are trying to study. The *sampled* population requires a more careful definition but, speaking popularly, it is the population which we actually succeed in sampling.

The notion of a sampled population can be more clearly described for probability sampling. In order to have probability sampling, we must know the chance that every sampling unit has of entering the sample, and the weight to be attached to the unit in the analysis. The sampled population may be defined as the population generated by repeated application of these chances and these weights. The frequency of occurrence of any particular sampling unit in the sampled population is proportional to the product

(chance of entering the sample) × (weight used in analysis).

This product is made constant for a probability sample. Thus, with probability sampling, the sampled population consists of all sampling units which have a non-zero chance of selection.

The sampled population is an important concept because by statistical theory we can make quantitative inferential statements, with known chances of error, from sample to sampled population. It must be carefully distinguished from the target population, the population of interest, about which we are tempted to make similar inferential statements.

Even with probability sampling, the sampled and the target population usually differ because of the presence of "refusals," "not-at-homes," "unable to classify," and so on. The consequence of these disturbances is that certain sampling units, although assigned a known chance of selection by the sampling plan, did not in fact have this chance in practice.

With non-probability sampling, the situation is much more obscure. By its definition as given above, the sampled population depends on the existence of a sampling plan (which may be only a vague set of principles in the investigator's head) and on the "chances" that any sampling unit had of being drawn. These chances are not well known—if they were, we should have a probability sample. But in many cases, it is reasonable to behave as if these chances exist and to attempt to estimate them, because they provide the only means of making statistical inferences beyond the non-probability sample to a corresponding "sampled population." The difficulty comes in specifying, or sometimes even thinking about, the nature of the sampled population. It is certain to be a weighted population where, for example, Theodosius Linklater may appear 1.37 times, while Basil Svensson appears only 0.17 times.

Insofar as we make statistical inferences beyond the sample to a larger body of individuals, we make them to the sampled population. The step from sampled population to target population is based on subject-matter knowledge and skill, general information, and intuition—but not on statistical methodology.

Chapter IV. The Interview Area

19. *Interview vs. Questionnaire*

The committee members do not profess authoritative knowledge of interviewing techniques. Nevertheless, the method by which the data were obtained cannot be regarded as outside the scope of the statistical aspects of the research.

For what our opinion is worth, we agree with KPM that a written question-naire could not have replaced the interview for the broad population contemplated in this study. The questionnaire would not allow flexibility which seems to us necessary in the use of language, in varying the order of questions, in assisting the respondent, in following up particular topics and in dealing with persons of varying degrees of literacy. This is not to imply that the anonymous question-naire is inherently less accurate than the interview, or that it could not be used fruitfully with certain groups of respondents and certain topics. So far as we are aware, not enough information is available to reach a verdict on these points.

20. *Interviewing Technique*

Many investigators have faced the problem of attempting to obtain accurate information about facts which the respondent is thought to be unwilling to report. It is natural to inquire whether KPM, in their interviewing technique, took advantage of accumulated experience as to the best methods for extracting the facts. But it is also well to inquire how much definite experience has been accumulated.

The KPM interview impressed us as an extraordinarily skillful performance. Direct questions are put rapidly in an order which seems to these respondents hard to predict, so that it is difficult to tell what is coming next. Despite the air of briskness, we did not receive the impression that we were being hurried if we wished to reflect before replying, and supplementary questions or information were given if this seemed helpful to the memory. The coded recording of the data was done unobtrusively by the interviewer, so that the interview appeared to be a friendly conversation rather than any kind of an inquisition. These, of course, are personal impressions.

KPM evidently think highly of the virtues of this technique, because it was adopted despite limitations which it imposes on the scope and rate of progress of the study. The technique makes great demands on the interviewer. The long period of training and the personal qualities required have restricted and will continue to restrict the interviewers to a very small number This limits the speed with which data can be accumulated and also puts restrictions on the type of sampling that can be employed.

The type of interview used by KPM differs markedly from the less directive methods which are sometimes recommended for dealing with taboo subjects. If the subject is likely to feel that his answer to a certain question will affect his prestige in the eyes of the interviewer, a less directive approach would be to conduct the interview in such a way that he gives the desired information without realizing that he is answering the awkward question. The KPM method is the antithesis of this. Research on interviewing techniques has not yet produced any substantial body of evidence as to the superiority of either the less directive methods or the KPM technique.

With regard to specific inaccuracies in the KPM data, we believe that the interview gives an opportunity both for positive and negative bias. The KPM assumption that everyone has engaged in all types of activity seems to some likely to encourage exaggeration by the respondents. (KPM feel (personal communication) that their cross-checks are highly effective in detecting such exaggeration.) On the other hand, our impression from the interview was that a successful denial of certain types of activity would be possible if the subject was prepared to do so, although we do not know the full extent of the KPM cross-checks which would lead them to be suspicious of such a denial. KPM assert (personal communication) that they regard cover-up as a more likely source of bias than exaggeration. Our opinions on this statement are divided.

As KPM point out (p. 48), the subject's willingness to talk about certain types of activity is influenced by the attitudes of the social group to which he belongs. Until evidence to the contrary is presented, the presumption (made by some of the critics) that his final responses will also be influenced is one that cannot be cast aside. The size of these influences is still a matter of opinion. A corresponding element of doubt is present in almost all comparisons between different social levels, both those which provide some of the most interesting comparisons in the book, and those in many other studies.

Chapter V. The Sampling Area

21. *KPM's Sampled Population*

As noted above, KPM's sample was deliberately disproportionate, partly in order to cover individual segments defined by age, education, religion, etc., in an adequate manner, partly because of geographical convenience. If the results for individual segments were to be based on samples of at least moderate size, such disproportion was necessary and wise. Its effects on overall results are less clear. It seems impossible to be sure what effect it had on the variability of the final result, and its use is certainly not a demonstrable error as far as variability is concerned.

In their U.S. corrections, KPM provided adjustments for disproportion between segments defined by age, education, and marital status. As noted above (Section 17) we feel that such adjustments are usually appropriate. Due to absence of population data, they did not adjust for religion. The geographical imbalance of their sample was so great that an overall geographic adjustment was not feasible. Thus they compensated for some disproportions, and left others to produce what effects they would.

Their only examination of the sample for signs of selection within segments is their comparison of 100 per cent groups (groups where all members were interviewed) with partial groups (groups where only part of the members were sampled). This gives some insight into the effect of volunteering as a selective factor. Beyond this, KPM report no serious effort to measure the actual effect of volunteering, or to discover what percentage of the population they would be able to persuade to be interviewed.

They made no use of randomization. They might have attempted to sample, say, college seniors from two colleges drawn at random from a large list of colleges, but they are of the opinion (personal communication) that this would have slowed up the work to an unmanageable extent.

All in all, the absence of any orderly sampling plan contrasts strikingly with their usual methodical mode of attack on other problems.

As stated briefly above (Section 6), the "sampled populations" corresponding to

1) KPM's raw means, and to
2) KPM's "U.S. corrected" means,

respectively, are startlingly different from the composition of the U.S. white male population. (For example, although these sampled populations have the U.S. average combination of education and rural-urban background, they have half of their members living in Indiana.) Since a complete probability sample seems to have been out of the question at the beginning of the KPM investigation, some such "sampled population" was to be expected, although it might have been somewhat less distorted. Provided that further statistical analyses of the sort indicated in Appendix C, Chapter II-C were made, it would be possible to make adequate rigorous inferences from the sample to this ill-defined "sampled population."

The inference from these vague entities to the U.S. white male population depends on:

a) the inferrer's view as to what these "sampled populations" are really like, and
b) the inferrer's judgment as to how (reported) sexual behavior varies within segments.

It is not surprising that experts disagree.

The inference from KPM's sample to the (reported) behavior of all U.S. white males contains a large gap which can be spanned only by expert judgment. This is a common phenomenon in social fields, but is still unfortunate. A considerable bridge across this gap would be furnished by a small probability sample.

22. *Could KPM Have Used Probability Sampling?*

If probability sampling could have been used, its use would have avoided one of the main gaps in KPM's present chain of inference. We have, therefore, considered this possibility carefully.

The difficulties in applying probability sampling to KPM's study lie in the expenditure of time required to make the contacts necessary to persuade a predesignated man to give a history. By adapting the mechanism of the probability sample to KPM's situation, these difficulties may perhaps be reduced (see Appendix D, Chapter V-D). It would almost certainly have been impractical for KPM to have used a probability sample in the early years of their study. If KPM's apparent "opinions" (p. 39 of KPM) as to the effectiveness of their present techniques of contact are correct, starting a probability sample would have been practical at any time since the appearance of the male volume in 1948.[1] However, KPM (personal communication, 1952) feel that such an interpretation of their written statement is unwarranted.

Since it would not have been feasible for KPM to take a large sample on a probability basis, a reasonable probability sample would be, and would have been, a small one, and its purpose would be:

1) to act as a check on the large sample, and
2) possibly, to serve as a basis for adjusting the results of the large sample.

A probability sampling program planned to serve these purposes is discussed in Appendix D, Chapter VII-D. Such a program should proceed by stages because of the absence of information on costs and refusal rates.

This conclusion about probability sampling does not excuse KPM from the responsibility for choosing geographical disproportion in order to save travel time and expense. The wisdom or unwisdom of this choice seems to depend on one's view as to the magnitude of geographical differences. Again, it is not surprising that experts disagree.

Chapter VI. Methodological Checks

23. *Possible Checks*

The primary check, if it could be made, is the comparison of *average* actual behavior with *average* reported behavior. *Variability* in the difference between actual and reported behavior is secondary in interest, because high variability merely implies the necessity of larger numbers of cases, while large average differences between actual and reported behavior represent a systematic error that cannot be adjusted without rather complete knowledge. Unfortunately this primary check does not at present seem feasible in studying human sexual behavior as it occurs in our culture.

Of secondary importance are checks of the single actual report with the average actual report, where averages may be taken over fluctuations, time, spouses, and/or interviewers. In this second category, the following possible comparisons suggest themselves:

1. Reinterviews of the same respondent
2. Comparison of spouses
3. Comparison of interviewers on the same population segment
4. Duplicate interviews by the same interviewer at various times.

24. *KPM's Checks*

The only comparison of observed and reported behavior which KPM found feasible was the date of appearance of pubic hair, which agreed quite successfully. This is a physical characteristic, different in character and emotional loading from the behavior of main interest. Some subjects may have had to rely upon general information, plus some assistance from the interviewer, in naming a date for themselves. Thus this check furnishes rather weak support.

At the level of rechecks on respondents, some information is available but more is needed. Similarly, comparisons of spouses have been made for a relatively selected group. The checks themselves are encouraging, but more cases are needed.

Some attempts have been made to compare the staff interviewers but since there is some selection in the assignment of cases, these comparisons do not meet the problem as squarely as interviews of the same respondent by different interviewers, or the recorded interview technique.

A comparison of early versus late interviews by Kinsey is given in KPM, but it is hard to tell, for example, whether the 12.4 per cent drop (from 44.9 to 32.5 per cent) in the accumulative incidence for total pre-marital intercourse at age 19 (single males, education level 13+) from early to late interviews is due to differing groups sampled, instability in the interviewing process, or reasonable sampling variation for cluster sampling (KPM p. 146).

KPM have made serious efforts to check their work in the aspects where checking seems feasible. However, improved and more extensive checking is needed. Although duplicate recording of interviews is mentioned, no data have been published. Even if they must be based on very few cases, such comparisons should be made available.

Chapter VII. Analytical Techniques

25. *Variables Affecting Sexual Behavior*

After introductory chapters (5 and 6) on early sexual growth and activity, KPM proceed to examine the effects of the following variables:

Age
Marital status
Age of adolescence
Social level
Comparison of two generations
Vertical mobility in the occupational scale
Rural-urban background
Religious background

In this chapter we attempt to appraise, in general terms, the analytical techniques used by KPM in their study of these variables.

26. *Definition of the Variables*

Some of the variables: age of adolescence, social level, occupational level, rural-urban background and religious background, involve problems of definition. These seem to have been in the main thoughtfully handled and presented by KPM. For instance, KPM discuss the relative merits of educational level attained by the subject and of the occupational class of the subject and of his parents as a measure of social level (pp. 330–32). In their opinion, educational level is the most satisfactory criterion and this was adopted for the analysis. In the case of religious affiliation, KPM distinguish between active and inactive profession of religious faith, though the definition of the two terms is not made entirely clear.

The definition which looks least satisfactory is that of age of adolescence (p. 299), where the problem is formidable. The criteria employed by KPM appear difficult for the reader to interpret.

27. *Assessing Effects of Variables*

With a multiplicity of variables which may interact on each other, the task of assessing the importance of each variable individually is not easy. Examination of the variables one by one, ignoring all other variables except the one under scrutiny, may give wrong conclusions, because what appears on the surface to be the effect of one variable may be merely a reflection of the effects of other variables.

A thorough attack on this problem calls for a multiple-variable approach in which all effects are investigated simultaneously. This requires a high degree of statistical maturity and of skill in presentation.

The method utilized by KPM is a compromise. In general, with some exceptions, they regard age, marital status and educational level as basic variables, which are held fixed or compensated for in the investigation of each of the remaining variables. The other variables are disregarded for the moment. Although we have not examined the matter exhaustively, this policy seems to have been justified by events, because KPM claim from their analyses that the other variables, with the exception of age at adolescence, have had relatively minor effects.

28. *The Measurement of Activity*

In the KPM tables, activity is measured by "incidence" (per cent of the population who engage in the activity) as well as by frequency per week. In some tables, both mean and median frequencies are given, and also frequencies for the total and for the active population. There are advantages in presenting various measures. On the other hand, inspection suggests that all these measures are correlated: that is, to some extent they tell the same story. A complex internal analysis would probably show about how many measures are really needed to extract the information in the data and what individual measurements, or combinations of them, are best for this purpose. Perhaps a single one, or at most two, would suffice. As it is, both KPM and the industrious reader have to wade through tables and discussion of a number of different measurements, without being clear whether anything new is learned. Simplification would be pleasant, but is far from essential.

29. *Tests of Significance*

In the discussion of effects which they regard as real, KPM make little appeal to tests of significance. They often present standard errors attached to the mean frequencies for individual cells. Because sampling was non-random and was by groups, these standard errors, calculated on the assumption of randomness, are under-estimates, perhaps by a substantial amount. The standard errors have a kind of negative virtue, in the sense that if a difference is not significant when judged against these errors, it would not be significant if a valid test could be devised. The problem of devising a realistic estimate of the true standard errors is one of considerable complexity.

We have been unable to discover from the book the principles by which KPM decide when to regard an effect as real. The size of the effect is one criterion. Size should certainly be taken into account, since an effect may be significant statistically but too small to be of biological or sociological interest. They evidently attach some importance to the consistency with which an effect is exhibited in different parts of a table. As a criterion, consistency is of variable worth. Consistency over different age groups (where age denotes age at the time of the reported activity) is of little worth, since there is inevitably substantial correlation between sampling fluctuations of reported activities at neighboring ages because the same subject appears in neighboring age groups. More weight can be attached to consistency over different educational levels, because different groups of subjects are involved.

To summarize, statements about the data in their tables lie at the level of shrewd descriptive comment, rather than at the level of an attempt to make inferential statements from a sample to a clearly defined population (even though this could not be the U.S. white male population).

We do not propose to discuss the analysis for each variable separately. Two analyses which have attracted much attention will be considered later (Sections 33 to 37).

30. *U.S. Corrections*

In most sampling plans it is necessary to provide a set of weights for the segments of the sampled population to recover accurate estimates for the target population (i.e. the population about which inferences are desired). That such adjustments are usually appropriate, whether probability or nonprobability samples are employed, has already been pointed out (Section 17).

Since KPM have as their target population U.S. white males, we can reasonably expect them to apply weights in an attempt to correct for disproportionate representation in the sampled population of some segments of the target population.

KPM supply U.S. Corrections (pp. 106–9) and use them rather consistently throughout the work. There are no examples given explaining the application of the weights. The critics, and sometimes this committee, have had difficulty in verifying computations where they have been used. Of the 13 tables where corrections could be checked completely, one checked, 10 checked except for one age group each, and two were not checked by the correction mentioned in the text. Apparently the exposition could be improved.

The U.S. Corrections should be used, but it might be possible to make a more effective choice of segments (see A-43 and V-C and II-G).

KPM did not sufficiently warn the reader that U.S. corrected figures are not corrected for selection within segments, and may be seriously biased.

31. *The Accumulative Incidence Curve*

KPM have a useful device for summarizing incidence data by age. This accumulative incidence curve gives the percentage of individuals in the sample (reporting for a given age) to whom a particular event has occurred before that age. Although the explanation of the concept of accumulative incidence is not as clear as most of KPM's writing, the computations made are satisfactory. When there are no generation-to-generation changes in the population and no differential recall depending on age at report, this method is particularly justified, because it packs all the incidence data neatly into one grand summary. . . . No better method for overall comparisons seems to be available.

32. *Other Devices*

1.   KPM did some extensive sampling experiments on their data, with a view to discovering the sample size needed for the accuracy they desired. These experiments turned out to be almost valueless because KPM did not take account of the necessary statistical principles (see A-19).

2.   The committee had an opportunity to inspect the KPM facilities on a visit to Bloomington, Indiana. We observed that the data sheets were neatly filled out, that the files were well kept, that requests for original data were usually met in a matter of moments, and that the office was well equipped for handling the extensive data with which KPM deal.

3.   The KPM volume was written while data were still being collected. Apparently KPM chose to use all the data on hand at the time a particular point was being analyzed (personal communication from KPM). Thus different tables have different totals, a source of annoyance to critics and users of the book. The reasons for this should have been pointed out by KPM. The additional interviewing was deliberately selective with an aim to strengthen weak segments (personal communication from KPM). It seems to us that, if this strengthening was necessary for later analyses, it would have been worthwhile to add the new material to the early tabulations. This would also have increased comparability and avoided the problems raised by the existence of many different sampled populations.

Chapter VIII. Two Complex Analyses

33. *Patterns in Successive Generations*

In this chapter we discuss briefly two analyses by KPM which have attracted much attention. Our object is to give two specific illustrations of the kind of analysis which they chose to undertake, with comments on their competence.

The first analysis was made by dividing the sample into two groups: those over 33 years of age at the time of interview, with a median age of 43.1 years, and those under 33 years at the time of interview, with a median age of 21.2 years.

Our comments deal with three topics: (i) the statistical methodology employed (ii) KPM's summary of their tables (iii) the general problem of inference from data of this type.

34. *Statistical Methods*

In the comparisons, educational level and age at the time of the activity are held constant and in nearly all comparisons marital status also. The method used to compare the group means seems satisfactory except for some minor points, discussed in A-25, A-33 and A-43.

It would have been helpful to present classifications of the older and younger groups according to other factors which might influence sexual activity, e.g., rural-urban background, religious affiliation, marital status at age 20 or 25. The two groups would not necessarily agree closely in these break-downs, for there has been a slow drift towards the towns, and perhaps a drift towards "inactive" rather than "active" religious affiliation. For interpretive purposes it is advisable, in any event, to learn as much as possible about the compositions of the older and younger groups. Some critics have claimed that the older generation is "atypical."

35. *KPM's Summary of Their Tables*

The data are presented in 8 large tables (98–105). As a statistician learns from experience, a competent summary of a large body of data is not an easy task. KPM give a detailed discussion of the accumulative incidence data for each type of outlet, followed by a similar discussion of the frequency data.

These detailed comments on what the data appear to show seem sound, except that on two occasions where the younger group showed greater sexual activity, KPM ignored or played down the difference between the two groups (Section A-45).

Their general summary statement reads in part as follows:

■ The changes that have occurred in 22 years, as measured by the data given in the present chapter, concern attitudes and minor details of behavior, and nothing that is deeply fundamental in overt activity. There has been nothing as fundamental as the substitution of one type of outlet for another, of masturbation for heterosexual coitus, of coitus for the homosexual, or vice versa. There has not even been a material increase or decrease in the incidences and frequences of most types of activity. . . .

And the sum total of the measurable effects on American sexual behavior are slight changes in attitudes, some increase in the frequency of masturbation among boys of the lower educational levels, more frequent nocturnal emissions, increased frequencies of premarital petting, earlier coitus for a portion of the male population, and the transferences of a percentage of the pre-marital intercourse from prostitutes to girls who are not prostitutes. ■

Some critics have objected strongly to this statement, particularly the first paragraph, on the grounds that it gives a biased report by brushing aside the differences in activity, which are almost all in the direction of higher or earlier sexual activity by the younger group. The reporting does appear a little one-sided, in that the reader is encouraged to conclude that the differences are immaterial, although KPM do not state what they mean by a "material" increase. On the other hand, the catalogue of differences, given at the end of the second paragraph above, includes all differences noted either by KPM or the critics, except for an increased homosexual activity in the younger group at educational levels 0–8 and 9–12.

36. *Validity of Inferences*

Two objections have been made by some critics to any inferences drawn from a comparison of this type. The first is that the groups may not be representative of their generations. KPM have attempted to dispose of this objection, at least in part, by holding educational level and marital status constant. It might be possible to go further and hold other factors constant, or at least examine whether the samples from the two generations differ in these factors. But with non-random sampling the objection is not removed even if a number of factors are held constant, because one or both groups might be biased with respect to some factor whose importance was not realized. Various opinions may be formed as to the strength of the objection, but it can be removed only by the use of probability sampling accompanied by valid tests of significance.

Secondly, in a comparison of this type, the older generation is describing events which involve a much longer period of recall, with a possibility of distortion as events become distant. Further retake studies, if KPM can continue them for a sufficiently long period, may throw some light on the strength of this objection.

The joint effect of these objections is to render the conclusions tentative rather than definitely established.

35. *Vertical Mobility*

This analysis (pp. 417–47) shows a degree of ingenuity and sophistication which is not too common in quantitative investigations in sociology. The data are arranged in a two-way array according to the occupational class of the subject at the time of interview and the occupational class of the parents. KPM examine whether the pattern of sexual activity of the subject is more strongly associated with the parental occupational class than with that attained by the subject. They conclude (p. 419)

■ In general, it will be seen that the sexual history of the individual accords with the pattern of the social group into which he ultimately moves, rather than with the pattern of the social group to which the parent belongs and in which the subject was placed when he lived in the parental home.

The most significant thing shown by these calculations (Tables 107–115) is the evidence that an individual who is ever going to depart from the parental pattern is likely to have done so by the time he has become adolescent. ■

The amount of data which KPM present in this analysis is worth mention as evidence that they do not shirk work. Tables are given for 7 types of activity. Three age groups are shown in each table. When we classify by occupational level of subject and parent, this leads to 21 two-way tables. Five measures of the type of activity are given, so that a painstaking examination extends over 105 two-way tables.

KPM appear to have paid most attention to the frequency data. Their task is to determine whether this shows a stronger association with the occupational class of the subject or of the parent. In reaching a verdict, they rely on judgment from eye inspection. By a similar eye inspection, we agree with their verdict as a descriptive statement of what the data indicate, although different individuals might disagree as to how definitely their statement holds. Judgments made by one individual for the data on frequencies were that in 7 of the 21 two-way tables, association with subject and parent either was not present at all or looked about equal. In 9 it looked mildly more with the subject and in 5 it looked strongly more with the subject.

It would be of interest to undertake a more objective analysis. Analysis of variance techniques are available for this purpose, although some theoretical problems remain.

So far as interpretation is concerned, the principal disturbing factor is the possibility, which some critics have mentioned, that the subject's reports of his activity are influenced by the social level to which he belongs at the time of interview. KPM maintain that attitudes towards different types of activity are strongly affected by the social level of the subject. Whether they change when he changes his social level would be interesting to discover. Something might be learned by retakes for subjects who had moved in the social scale. To obtain an abundant body of data of this kind will, however, be a slow and difficult process.

Chapter IX. Care in Interpretation

38. *Sample and Sampled Population*

In sample surveys, the inference from sample to sampled population is often relatively straightforward, although not trivial. We can usually set limits so that the statement "the sample agrees with the sampled population within these limits" has approximately the agreed-upon risk. (We may have to work fairly hard to set these limits correctly.) But we have always to remember, and usually must remind the reader steadily, that these limits are not infinitely narrow.

KPM's caution on page 153 is a caution, but it is not repeated.

In general, their statements about small differences are more forthright than we would care to make.

39. *Sampled Population and Target Population*

When a respectable approximation of a probability sample is involved, the step from sampled population to target population is usually short and the inference strong. Otherwise, the inference is often tortuous and weak. It depends on subject matter knowledge and intuition, and on other barely tangible considerations. These considerations deserve to be brought to the reader's attention, and to be discussed as best the authors may.

This KPM did not do adequately. Their discussion of diversification (p. 92) and 100 per cent samples (p. 93) is only a beginning.

40. *Systematic Errors of Measurement*

Any quantitative study offers the possibility of systematic errors of measurement. It is generally agreed that these possibilities should be placed before the reader and discussed.

In KPM's study these possibilities concentrate on the difference between present reported and past actual behavior. KPM spent Chapter 4 on this question. Their discussion is generally good, except on some questions which arise in connection with generation-to-generation comparison (see Sections A-25 and A-44).

41. *Unsupported Assertions*

We are convinced that unsubstantiated assertions are not, in themselves, inappropriate in a scientific study. In any complex field, where many questions remain unresolved, the accumulated insight of an experienced worker frequently merits recording when no documentation can be given. However, the author who values his reputation for objectivity will take pains to warn the reader, frequently repetitiously, whenever an unsubstantiated conclusion is being presented, and will choose his words with the greatest care. KPM did not do this.

Many of the most interesting statements in the book are not based on the tabular material presented and it is not made at all clear on what evidence the statements are based. Nevertheless, the statements are presented as if they were well-established conclusions.

42. *Some Major Controversial Findings*

Some KPM findings about which much scientific discussion has centered relate to:

 i) stability of sexual patterns,
 ii) homosexuality, and
 iii) the effects of vertical mobility.

In all these areas KPM have made forthright and bold statements. As discussed in more detail in Sections A-45 to A-47 (also see A-25), there are reasons for caution in every one of the three areas.

Chapter X. Comparison with Other Studies[2]

43. *Interviewing*

Good sex studies have been made using both the personal interview and questionnaire techniques. Given that just one technique is to be employed, KPM's choice of personal interview seems necessary if illiterates or near-illiterates are to be sampled. At present, it is good practice in gathering this type of data to endeavor to have all subjects give information on as many relevant points of the study as possible. No study seems to have done better on this matter than KPM.

Whether it is always good practice to standardize the questions asked is debatable. KPM did not do this and give telling arguments against the practice. Some other studies have standardized the questions, both in personal interview and in self-administered questionnaires, and they have included good arguments in favor of their procedure. In training interviewers KPM seem to have gone to greater lengths (a year of training) in preparing for the *specific* interview used in the study, than any of the other personal interview studies. Information on training of interviewers is fairly hard to come by in all these studies.

Given the choice of personal interview, it is not possible at this writing to be logically certain whether the KPM technique is better or worse than that of the other interview studies, no matter whether one approves or disapproves of the tactics of a diagnostician or medical detective. Some discussion of how the KPM interview appeared to us is given in Appendix E. Numerous cross-checks on frequency and dates of occurrences appear within the KPM interview, while they seem to be lacking in most other studies. Setting aside points on which there is no evidence, KPM's interviewing is as good as or better than that of the other studies reviewed.

44. *Checks*

As for checks on the interviewing process, KPM unquestionably lead the field with 100 per cent samples, retakes, spouse comparisons, early vs. late groups, interviewer comparisons, and the pubic hair study. Some authors mention casual checks with no data supplied. Bromley and Britten compare interview and questionnaire results on different groups. Davis reports a study where 50 subjects were interviewed before and after questionnaire administration, and offers a breakdown by consecutive 100 questionnaires received. Dickinson and Beam's two books speak of comparing verbal reports and physical examination results as a way of verifying the record rather than as a check—no records seem to be published. Farris' comparison of reported vs. personally recorded masturbatory rates omits the critical comparative information. Hamilton finds that different question wordings give different responses, but leaves the matter here. Landis and Bolles use several independent judges for evaluation of scales— but, instead of comparing their results, argue that agreement will be good because of experience and training. They do not compare normal with handicapped subjects. Landis checks with the psychiatric case history as a means of eliminating subjects with discrepancies, and gives data on the agreement of independent judges' ratings. Terman offers spouse comparisons. When KPM's checks are viewed with those of the other leading sex studies in mind, it is clear that a new high level has been established.

45. Sampling

All studies used volunteer non-probability samples. Some were drawn from more specifiable target populations than others. For example, Bromley and Britten drew exclusively from college volunteers, while Davis used mail-question-naire respondents from lists of Women's Clubs and college alumnae. Others used well-to-do patients, or clinic groups. Aside from KPM, Bromley and Britten is the only study that seems to have attempted to get nationwide geographic representation (we have omitted M. J. Exner's 1915 study), while Davis has covered the eastern area, and Terman covers part of the California area. Although KPM's sample is heavily charged with college students, a broader representation of social and educational levels is offered than in the other studies. All studies reviewed have special features which make generalizations to specific populations difficult. Certainly KPM's sampling seems never worse and often better than that of the other studies.

46. Analysis

Most studies confined their analysis to simple descriptive statistics—percentages, means, and medians. A few added ranges, standard deviations, correlation coefficients, and attempted significance tests. About half used two-way breakdowns, usually on background characteristics, as a way of sharpening differences between groups. Three studies offered scales either based on judges' evaluations (Landis, and Landis and Bolles), or scoring of batteries of items (Terman). KPM restricted the use of scales to occupational classification and homosexual-heterosexual rating. They added the accumulative incidence curve, the U.S. corrections, and extensively used fine-grained (high-order) breakdowns. In general, KPM's analysis employed more devices and was more searching than the analyses offered by other studies.

47. Interpretation

We have already mentioned (33) that KPM are competent at the accurate and understandable verbal description of the meanings of a table whose entries are taken as correct. Some of the other authors have also done well, although the extent of their analysis is usually more limited. In inferring from sampled population to target population, all the studies are weak. The inferences left with the reader (if we are to judge) are much broader than the studies could possibly warrant. Every study has its own precautionary remarks to the effect that the reader must not extend the inferences beyond that of the population studied. Very little attempt is made to describe the target population, to help the reader with the step from sample to sampled population, or to remind him of sampling fluctuations. The precautionary remarks in the opening pages of a study are usually forgotten when the authors come to discuss matters of national policy, morals, legislation, therapy, and psychological and sociological implications toward the end of their book. The reader must then be left with the inference that the findings apply on at least a national scale. Bromley and Britten are more forthright than most. They argue overtly that their volunteer college sample is a representative of all U.S. individuals of college age. Of the 10 studies considered, only two, Davis and Farris, seem to have consistently exercised due caution about generalization from sample to population and warnings to the reader. . . .

Our reviewer was not asked to gather data that would give us a way of comparing the extent of unsupported statements in the other studies with those of KPM, so this aspect of interpretation remains uncompared by us. It would be very interesting if someone would collect such information, not only in connection with the present work, but with regard to general scientific writing in various fields. This would be no small task.

Chapter XI. Conclusions

48. *Interviewing*

1) The interviewing methods used by KPM may not be ideal, but no substitute has been suggested with evidence that it is an improvement.
2) The interviewing technique has been subjected to many criticisms, but on examination the criticisms usually amount to saying "answer is unknown," or "KPM have not demonstrated how good their method is."

These conclusions can be summarized by saying that we need to know more about interviewing in general.

49. *Checks*

1) The types of methodological checks considered by KPM seem to be quite inclusive.
2) A greater volume of checks—more retakes, etc. is desirable, as is more delicate analysis.
3) The results of duplicate recording of interviews should be published.

These conclusions can be summarized by saying that KPM's checks were good, but they can afford to supply more.

50. *Sampling*

Given U.S. white males as the target population, our conclusions are that:

1) KPM's starting with a nonprobability sample was justified.
2) It should perhaps already have been supplemented by at least a small probability sample.
3) If further general interviewing is contemplated, and perhaps even otherwise, a small probability sample should be planned and taken.
4) In the absence of a probability-sample benchmark, the present results must be regarded as subject to systematic errors of unknown magnitude due to selective sampling (via volunteering and the like).

51. *Analysis*

KPM's analysis is best described as simple and relatively searching. They did not use such techniques as analysis of variance or multiple regression, but they brought out the indications of their data in a workmanlike manner.

In more detail:

1) their selection of variables for adjustment seemed to be a reasonably effective substitute for more complex analyses,
2) they gave several measures of activity (giving the reader a choice at the expense of more tables to examine),
3) they made essentially no use of tests of significance, but cited many standard errors (which were inappropriate for their cluster samples),
4) they used U.S. Corrections and their (independently developed) accumulative incidence curve. More careful exposition of these devices would have been desirable.

To summarize in another way:

i) they did not shirk hard work, and
ii) their summaries were shrewd descriptive comments rather than inferential statements about clearly defined populations.

Their main attempt at inferences was a sample size experiment whose results (i) could have been predicted by statistical theory, (ii) were irrelevant to their cluster sampling.

They continued to add new interviews without redoing earlier tabulations, thus producing an unwarranted effect of sloppiness in the book, although their records were kept carefully and in unusually good shape.

52. *Interpretation*

1) KPM showed competence in accurate and understandable verbal description of the trends and tendencies indicated by their tables. In stating and summarizing what the sample seems to show, they were competent and effective.

2)   Their discussion of the uncertainties in the inferences from the numbers in the tables to the behavior of all U.S. white males was brief, insufficiently repeated, and oftentimes entirely lacking. In instilling due caution about sampling fluctuations and differences between sampled and target populations, they were lax and ineffective.

3)   Their discussion of systematic errors of reporting is careful and detailed (with the exception of some questions bearing on generation comparisons).

4)   Many of their most interesting statements are not based on the tables or any specified evidence, but are nevertheless presented as well-established conclusions. Statements based on data presented, including the most important findings, are made much too boldly and confidently. In numerous instances their words go substantially beyond the data presented and thereby fall below our standard for good scientific writing.

53. *Comparison with Other Studies*

In comparison with nine other leading sex studies, KPM's work is outstandingly good.

In more detail,

1)   their interviewing ranks with the best,
2)   they have more and better checks,
3)   their geographic and social class representation is broader and better,
4)   their volunteer non-probability sample problem is the same,
5)   they used more varied and searching methods of analysis,
6)   only two of the nine studies (Davis and Farris) were more careful about generalization and warned the reader more thoroughly about its dangers.

Thus, KPM's superiority is marked.

54. *The Major Controversial Findings*

It is perhaps fair to regard these four as KPM's major controversial findings:

1)   a high general level of activity, including a high incidence of homosexuality,
2)   a small change from older to younger generations,
3)   a strong relation between activity and socio-economic class,
4)   relations between activity and *changes* of socio-economic class.

All of these KPM set forth as well established conclusions. All are subject to unknown allowances for:

a)   difference between reported and actual behavior,
b)   nonprobability sampling involving volunteering.

While their findings may be substantially correct, it is hard to set any bounds within which the truth is statistically assured to lie. Once again, we wish to point out that the same difficulties are present in many sociological investigations.

Chapter XII. Suggested Extensions

55. *Probability Sampling*

Appendix D discusses the advantages, possibilities and difficulties of probability sampling in some detail.

In brief summary:

1) Costs and refusal rates together determine the wisdom of extensive probability sampling.
2) Information on costs and refusal rates is lacking.
3) Hence probability sampling should begin on a very small scale, say 20 cases.
4) A step-by-step program, starting at such a scale, seems wise, and is recommended to KPM.

56. *Retakes*

While retakes showed high agreement on vital statistics, and moderately high agreement on incidence, the data presented in KPM for frequencies show considerably less agreement. The data do not make clear how much better a retake agrees with a take than with a randomly selected interview for another subject with the same age, religion, social class, etc.

If the agreement is better, then retakes will provide evidence as to non-random agreement—evidence bearing on the much-discussed subject of the constancy of recall. In addition, take-retake differences are clearly so large as to make retakes of two old subjects at least as valuable as a take of one new subject in determining the average behavior of groups.

If the agreement is no better, then retakes will provide evidence that this was so, and every retake will be as valuable as a new take in determining the average behavior of groups.

In our opinion 500 retakes would help the standing of KPM's data more than 2,000 new interviews (selected in the same old way). It would of course be important to determine and report the selective factors which influenced the selection of the retaken subjects.

57. *Spouses*

Separate interviews of husband and wife are a useful supplement to retakes, in that they supply the nearest approach to two independent reports of the same action, although the information is restricted for the most part to marital coitus, and is weakened by the possibility of collusion. In the book, KPM present comparisons for 231 pairs of spouses.

In an expansion of this program, various elaborations could be suggested, The first objective should probably be to interview more pairs from the lower educational levels, in order that the agreement between spouses can be examined separately for different educational levels. As in the case of retakes, the data are not wasted so far as the main study is concerned, since they contribute both to the male and female samples.

58. *Presentation*

As the critics point out, parts of the book are hard to understand because of lack of clarity of presentation. In future editions, the following steps would remove the major ambiguities.

i)   KPM should explain why the numbers of cases change erratically from table to table. In future publication it would be worth substantial effort to avoid these changes.

ii)   Table headings and contents should be critically reviewed as to their lucidity.

iii)   Worked examples of the calculation of U.S. corrections should be given. References under the tables to the variables used for correction should be more precise.

iv)   More discussion should be given, with numerical illustration, of the meaning of accumulative incidence percentages.

v)   More information should be given about the questions asked, with their variations, in the interview. Although this would be extremely laborious to do for the complete interview, one or two blocks of related questions might serve the purpose. For such a block, KPM might describe (a) the variations used in the statement of the questions (b) the variations in the order of questions (c) the reasons for the variations. An illustration of this type would give deeper insight into the logical structure of KPM's interviewing technique and might go far to substantiate their claim (p. 52) that flexibility is one of the strengths of their technique.

vi)   Several critics make a strong plea that more information be given about the composition of the sample. The specific items requested vary with the critic, and some would be a major undertaking both in preparation and publication. A minimum that seems feasible would be to present a multiple classification of the subjects according to the following items *at the time of interview:* age, marital. status, occupation, educational status, religious affiliation, place of residence. In addition, more information is needed about the extent to which special groups (e.g., those in penal institutions, homosexual groups) contribute to the tables.

59. *Statistical analyses*

In Appendix C, a number of statistical analyses are outlined which would be a useful contribution to the methodology of studies of this kind. The analyses would require expert statistical direction.

As has been pointed out, the standard errors presented by KPM are invalid because they were computed on the assumption of random sampling of individuals. A method for calculating standard errors so as to take into account the actual nature of KPM's sampling is given in Chapter II-C. These standard errors would allow a realistic appraisal of the stability of KPM's means. They would indicate by how much the means determined from the present KPM sample are likely to vary from the means of a much larger sample of cases obtained by the KPM methods.

KPM described orgasm rates in terms of per cent incidence and mean or median frequency. However, other mathematical functions of these variables may be more appropriate, leading to simpler statements of the results. Approaches for investigating this question, and the related question of the use of some combination of the variables, are suggested in Chapters III-C and IV-C.

The question of applying adjustments to segment means has already been discussed (Section 17). A technique is presented (Chapter V-C) for reaching practical decisions on the appropriateness of adjustment and on the number of variables for which adjustment should be made.

60. *Relative priorities*

We give here our personal collective opinion as to how further effort on the male study might best be spent (we have not tried to evaluate priorities in comparison with the female study, or any other studies which KPM may contemplate).

If the interviewer time which it would require were available, we believe that the effort required for the proposed probability sample would be worthwhile.

So long as it did not interfere with the possibility of a probability sample, available interviewer time should be concentrated:

on retakes when working in or near old areas.
on husband-wife pairs when two interviewers are available.

If the probability sample has already been ruled out, and if fewer interviewer months are available, then an attempt to retake a random sample of previous subjects would be most desirable, whenever possible, husband and wife being taken whenever either is retaken.

Effort in the form of statistical analysis and presentation need not interfere with interviewing, and should be pressed to the extent that experienced and understanding personnel can be found.

NOTES

1. "The number of persons who can provide introductions has continually spread until now, in the present study, we have a network of connections that could put us into almost any group with which we wished to work anywhere in the country." (P. 39 of KPM.)

2.   The material in this chapter is our inference from the reviews supplied by W. O. Jenkins and presented in Appendix B. We have not personally read all the volumes concerned. The volumes are as follows:

Bromley, Dorothy D., and Britten, Florence H. *Youth and Sex*. New York: Harper and Brothers, 1938.

Davis, Katherine B. *Factors in the sex life of twenty-two hundred women*. New York: Harper and Brothers, 1929.

Dickinson, R. L., and Beam, Lura A. *The single woman*. Baltimore: Williams and Wilkins Co., 1934.

Dickinson, R. L., and Beam, Lura A. *A thousand marriages*. Baltimore: Williams and Wilkins Co., 1931.

Farris, E. J. *Human fertility and problems of the male*. White Plains, N.Y.: Author's press, 1950.

Hamilton, G. V. *A research in marriage*. New York: A. and C. Boni, 1929.

Kinsey, A. C., Pomeroy, W. B., and Martin, C. E. *Sexual behavior in the human male*. Philadelphia: W. B. Saunders Company, 1948.

Landis, C., et al. *Sex in development*. New York and London: Paul B. Hoeber, 1940.

Landis, C., and Bolles, M. M. *Personality and sexuality of the physically handicapped woman*. New York and London: Paul B. Hoeber, 1942.

Terman, L. M., et al. *Psychological factors in marital happiness*. New York: McGraw-Hill Book Co., 1938.

THE INTELLIGENT CITIZEN'S GUIDE TO THE ABUSES OF STATISTICS: THE KENNEDY DOCUMENT AND THE CATHOLIC VOTE*

AARON B. WILDAVSKY

Politicians and lobbyists have long sought to make advantageous use of the supposed preferences of some population group. The Negro vote, the farm vote, the Catholic vote, the labor vote, and many others are bandied about as political commodities designed to enhance the claims of a candidate for office or an interest group for preferment. So long as the use of election statistics and opinion polls was in its infancy, these claims (to guarantee support or threaten to withdraw it) could be accepted or rejected on intuitive grounds where no man could claim much greater competence than another. The appearance of presumably scientific studies of voting as well as the development of the arts of statistical manipulation have created new opportunities for the purveyors of bloc votes and new difficulties for the interested but necessarily amateur citizen and public official. How are they to evaluate these important political claims backed up by impressive and complicated displays of data?

Political scientists and sociologists have an interest in thwarting the suspect use of their work to gain political advantage. They have an obligation to provide defensive measures which the interested citizen may use to appraise demands resting upon the alleged behavior of various population groups. In this paper an actual attempt to parlay the predicted voting behavior of Catholics into a nomination for high political office in the United States is analyzed in such a way that the intelligent citizen is provided with criteria by which to judge similar attempts regardless of the group involved.

Probably the most important consideration in choosing presidential nominees is the expectation that they can win. For this reason presidential candidates claim victory, create public manifestations of support, and seek to demonstrate to the delegates that they can win while other likely aspirants can not. The use of public opinion polls to pin the "can't win" and "can win" label on candidates is by now a routine tactic in the convention wars. But the preparation of reports utilizing voting studies and electoral statistics, backed up by tables and charts, written in the language of the political scientist and the sociologist, and designed to aid a particular candidate is a relatively new phenomenon.

Reprinted by permission of the author and the publisher from Nelson W. Polsby, Robert A. Dentler, and Paul A. Smith, eds., *Politics and Social Life* (Boston: Houghton Mifflin, 1963), 825–844.

During the closing weeks of the 1956 preconvention campaign, a remarkable document was widely circulated among Democratic leaders. Its purpose was to mobilize support for Senator John F. Kennedy of Massachusetts as the Democratic candidate for Vice-President of the United States. The argument it advanced was a practical one: that the Democrats could win the 1956 election by running a Catholic for the vice-presidency; whereas they would be likely to lose if they did not do so. This conclusion was buttressed by a series of propositions relating the voting behavior of Catholics to the requirements of the Democratic party in national elections.[1]

If claims are to be made from the findings and raw material of political science, then consideration of what may and may not be accepted as proof is essential. In order to accomplish this purpose, the Kennedy document is summarized and subjected to critical scrutiny. It then becomes possible to establish a minimum list of critical standards which interested persons may use to decide whether such documents are to be taken seriously. The original document— *Catholic Voters and the Democratic National Ticket*—is reprinted in the Appendix and the reader may wish to consult it before proceeding further.

I. Internal Criticism

Catholic Voters and the Democratic National Ticket (hereafter referred to as the Document) puts forward four basic propositions which may be summarized as follows:

1) there is a Catholic vote
2) this vote is critical for Democratic success at national elections
3) the Democratic Party has lost and is still losing the Catholic vote
4) this lost vote may be recaptured by running a Catholic on the national ticket as Vice-President.

Although it is not possible to demonstrate that all these propositions are false, it can be shown that none of them is demonstrably true.

The first proposition holds "that there is, or can be, such a thing as a 'Catholic vote,' whereby a high proportion of Catholics of all ages, residences, occupations and economic status vote for a well-known Catholic candidate or a ticket with special Catholic appeal."[2] It is obvious that not all Catholics are part of this Catholic bloc, and easily demonstrable that some Catholics on some occasions vote against a Catholic candidate. Who, then, are the voters who make up this Catholic bloc? They can not be those who vote for a Catholic candidate because the latter belongs to the party they favor, or for any reason other than his Catholicism. We may say, then, that the Catholic voter is he who votes (or would vote) against his other tendencies (if he has any), or turns out when he otherwise would not, at a particular election for the sole and specific reason that a candidate identified as Catholic is found on the ballot.[3] In order to determine whether this condition is present we would need to know what the individual voter's intention was before the election and ascertain his reasons, if any, for changing it. We would also have to be able to identify those voters who switched before we could ask them any questions. Neither of these essential conditions has been met. Instead, the Document introduces the dubious concept of the "shifters" which we shall consider later on.

It is important to note that the explanation, the causal factor, for the existence of the Catholic vote is the presence of a well-known Catholic candidate or a ticket with a special Catholic appeal. For this reason we may define the conditions under which the phenomenon known as the Catholic vote *will not appear*. They are: (1) when two known Catholics are opposing each other, and (2) when two non-Catholics (neither of whom nor both of whom make a special Catholic appeal) are opposing each other. A third condition, in which a Catholic and a non-Catholic, or a candidate who makes a Catholic appeal versus one who does not, are opposed in a district where there are some Catholic voters, must be satisfied before the Catholic vote has even a theoretical opportunity for manifesting itself. And whatever relationship or pattern is offered as proof of the operation of the Catholic vote in case three situations must be shown not to occur in cases one and two. Yet this control is not utilized in the Document.

Although no proof or even probability of the existence of a Catholic vote is presented, surface indications (though certainly not proof) to the contrary are found within the Document. It is quite possible that considerations of nationality play a larger role in determining the votes of Catholics than does their religion. Information from the various polls cited indicates that there were significant variations in the way the Italian, Irish, and Polish ethnic groups voted, although they may have voted on the same side. There is, furthermore, no demonstrable relationship between the size of a state's Catholic population and its Presidential vote. If anything, though this is dubious, the figures presented in the Document indicate that Eisenhower (said to be the beneficiary of a shift in the Catholic vote)[4] did proportionately less well in states with a large Catholic population (Rhode Island, Massachusetts) than in those with a much lesser percentage of Catholic voters (Montana, California). And on the surface there would appear to be less reason to suspect the operation of a Catholic vote in 1952 when Catholic voters split 51 to 49 per cent among the two major parties than in 1948 when the split was 66 to 44.

These figures do suggest that Catholics who vote (not the Catholic voter as defined above) supported the Democratic Party in considerable number but are tending to vote Republican nationally. There is a world of difference between stating what may be regarded as an empirical truth—that in 1948 and in other years voting Catholics favored certain candidates and parties in large number— and proceeding from this to conclude that the causal factor at work was the presence of a Catholic on the ballot. Indeed, this can not be so, for there were no Catholics on FDR's winning combinations, and the suggestion that Al Smith's candidacy carried over for many years in influencing Catholic votes is given no substantiation. The Document commits the cardinal error of proceeding from gross statistical parallelisms (though even these are inaccurate) to causal relationships by loose inference rather than logical or empirical argument. Any attempt to predict the future must be based upon knowledge of the motive forces behind the parallelisms observed. Otherwise it becomes merely a matter of faith to separate out one particular factor of the many that might conceivably be responsible for the phenomenon.

The second proposition may be stated as follows: Since the Catholic vote is concentrated in "14 pivotal Catholic states" and "*whether these states go Democratic usually determines whether the Democrats win the [national] election,*" a Democratic victory in a national election depends upon its capturing this Catholic vote. In order to substantiate this proposition the Document employs a means of argument strikingly similar to the old story which goes, "For want of a nail the horse was lost, for want of a horse . . ." and so on until the nail decides the course of the war. However far-fetched this story may appear, it has the virtue of not claiming to identify the particular nail, as differentiated from all other similar nails, without which not only past but future wars were doomed to be lost. All that the Document actually demonstrates is that once upon a time the Democrats won national elections (and therefore needed no additional votes), and that now they are losing national elections and need more votes from somewhere—upstate, downstate, or middlestate; Catholic, Protestant, or Jewish; rich man, poor man, or any man—lest they continue to fall upon evil days.

Turning to Table 1, column three, we discover that the percentage of Catholic voters in each state is distorted by "applying Campbell's national average figures . . . to the official turnout figures for 1952. . . ." The national average is made up of highly disparate percentages for each state. A statistical procrustean bed may discomfort all of its occupants. Furthermore, figures on Protestant turnout are artificially deflated by the South, which is largely Protestant, and where even whites do not vote in great numbers. And the three states with over 50 per cent Catholic population gave Eisenhower a relatively low advantage, compared to those with only 20 per cent of voting Catholics.[5] These are, however, minor matters compared to the more serious errors which follow.

It is, first of all, incorrect to speak of any combination of states totaling more than a majority of the electoral vote as in any sense more critical, valuable, or pivotal than any other such combination. In a fairly close election one may choose any number of combinations of states whose defection to the other side would have reversed the course of events. And if one can properly speak of certain states being critical in a past election when the returns are in, there is no logical or empirical reason to believe that this will necessarily hold true for any succeeding election held at a four-year interval. For this reason there is no necessary connection between the margin by which Eisenhower won in 1952 and the number of votes needed to defeat him in 1956 when conditions may have utterly changed the extent and basis of his support.

Perhaps the basic fallacy underlying this section of the Document is the entirely unwarranted assumption that ". . . . *The Catholic voters in each of these* [pivotal] *cities can usually determine the size of the Democratic margin in those cities. . . .*" No evidence is offered to indicate how it is possible to say that any group provided the winning or losing "margin." Since Catholics are in a minority in these cities and not all of them vote Republican it would be equally or more logical to suppose that some majority or combination of minorities was more important. We are not dealing with homogeneous economic units where the last one in a series can be considered marginal. The concept of the Catholic margin demands that the votes of all other groups be kept as a constant—an unrealistic condition. It also demands that the authors of the Document be able to separate out what they define as the Catholic vote from Catholics who vote in their roles as wage earners, city dwellers, members of ethnic groups, or any of the myriad combinations thereof.

The third proposition is deceptively obvious. It holds that studies of the 1948 and 1952 presidential elections reveal that the Democratic Party has lost "the Catholic Democratic vote," to a critical degree. There is no denying that these works have recorded a decline in the percentage of Catholic voters supporting the Democratic Party. But this hypothetical Catholic vote can only be made up of those who would turn out to vote or who would vote against their other tendencies because a Catholic candidate or a ticket with special Catholic appeal appeared on the ballot. Now, there may be many reasons why voters who are Catholic did not vote for a Democratic candidate, but the appearance of a Catholic on the ballot cannot possibly be one of them, since both presidential tickets were made up exclusively of Protestants.

Perhaps, it may be alleged, the Catholic vote has been latent in the national arena, but we can observe it at work in congressional and senatorial elections. If it exists in these cases, then it is possible, although not certain, that it might be transferred to a presidential election. As "proof" of this contention we are presented with a selected list of Democratic Catholic legislators, from areas in which there are many voters who are Catholics, who ran ahead of the party's presidential candidate in their electorates. This represents the sum total of the data. Yet the study proceeds to the baseless conclusion that the sole and exclusive reason for the success of these Catholic candidates was their religion. Moreover, we are not told whether any of these Catholic candidates ran against other Catholic candidates, thus completely cancelling any alleged religious influence. (In electorates with a heavy Catholic population we would expect two Catholics to oppose each other quite frequently.) And where are those Catholics who lost? And, still worse, where are the non-Catholics who ran ahead of their tickets?

Before turning to the "shifters," one piece of arithmetical manipulation must be discussed. Table 4 lists the "Number of percentage points of two-party vote by which national ticket ran behind candidates listed." In every case where the Document permits us to check these figures they have been grossly exaggerated. Thus we discover that "Dodd won in Hartford by 8 per cent while Stevenson was losing by 1 per cent." Further on, we find that these figures have been added to reach the astounding conclusion that Stevenson trailed Dodd by 9 per cent. Let us assume that a local candidate received 80 per cent of the votes cast and his opponent 20 per cent, thus giving him a 60 per cent advantage. At the same time his party's presidential candidate lost that district by 80 per cent to 20 per cent giving him a losing margin of 60 per cent. Since the local candidate received 80 per cent and the presidential candidate 20 per cent, we would normally subtract the two figures and end up with a 60 per cent difference between them. The method employed by the Document, however, would add the two differences together and come up with an impossible grand total of 120 per cent.

Given the practical objective of the Document, it was essential that it isolate a group of voters known as the Catholic bloc, and indicate that they would be ready to vote for a Democratic national ticket under the appropriate circumstances. Using the Michigan nation-wide voting survey, they find that Eisenhower received around 49 per cent of the votes of Catholics in 1952 while the Republican candidate in 1948 received only 34 per cent. It is apparently on this basis (by subtracting the two numbers and dividing by 49) that they arrived at the following conclusion: "Approximately 30 per cent of these Catholics for Eisenhower were 'shifters'—that is, even on the basis of 1948 when the Catholic vote was already slipping away from the Democrats . . . they would have been expected to vote Democratic in 1952. These shifters . . . we shall call 'normally Democratic Catholics' . . . "[6] Without any justification, the Document assumes that all voting Catholics who voted for a Democratic President in 1948 are in some way regular adherents of the party. Those who supported Eisenhower in 1952 are further assumed to come from this number, rather than having been new voters or former Republican voters, although there is no reason why this is necessarily so. If these presumed shifters are equated with the Catholic vote, then one would have to account for their desertion of the Democratic party by the presence of a Catholic on the Republican ticket. Otherwise, they would not have been voting against their "normal" preference and could not be considered part of the Catholic voting bloc. The Document has failed to establish the identity of the shifters or to indicate in any way why some Catholics may have voted Democratic in 1948 and Republican in 1952.

The fourth proposition holds that the Democratic Party may recapture its lost Catholic vote, thus guaranteeing a national electoral victory, by running a Catholic for Vice-President. Even if we permit ourselves to believe that the first three propositions express actual relationships, there is no compelling reason for accepting the fourth. The assumption is that a Catholic vice-presidential candidate would cause the shifters to vote for a Democratic President. But since these shifters did not vote Republican for ascertainable religious reasons, one cannot make any inference regarding their future voting behavior without some knowledge of the underlying factors responsible for this past decision. If, to take one possibility, it is the social position of these voters which has changed their voting habits, it would be anyone's guess as to the effect of a Catholic candidate upon them. Their "natural" inclination would then be to vote Republican, and the task of the Document would be to show how this might be broken; a task it has not performed because it is as much in the dark about the causal factors as we are.

The great claim the Document makes is that

■ If Stevenson could have held in 1952 *only* those Catholics who had voted for Truman in 1948 but for Ike in 1952—or if he could recapture them in 1956—this would, as shown in Table 3, *add 132 electoral votes to the Democratic column, enough when combined with the Solid South to provide a majority of electoral votes*! ■

Turning to Table 3, we find it is based on questionable assumptions whose absence vitiates the intended conclusion. Column three contains the "Proportion of Eisenhower vote constituting margin by which he carried state" and column 4 the "Estimated per cent of Eisenhower vote in 1952, made up of 'Normally Democratic' Catholic voters who shifted." We are then supposed to compare the tables and see that a virtually complete shift of these voters to the Democratic nominee would give the party 132 electoral votes. But in order to reach this conclusion we must first assume that there are marginal voters, that they are Catholic, and that they are the same people known as Catholic shifters. And even so, the difference between the two columns is so slight that all other factors must be assumed to remain precisely the same or to cancel each other out in order not to affect the results. Eisenhower must draw the same percentage of voters from all other groups and a Catholic Vice-President must not alienate other Democratic voters.[7]

By making more modest (though less politically useful) claims, the authors of the Document could have done much better. Instead of adopting their terribly demanding definition of the Catholic vote, they might have conceived of it as referring to situations in which Catholicism is an independent variable of fluctuating salience with respect to the voting choice. Whatever the causes of Catholic defection from the Democratic Party, the Document could have tried to demonstrate that the presence of a Catholic candidate on the ballot would increase the saliency of religion to Catholics and thus lead more of them to vote for the Party. Then they might have claimed not that a Catholic candidate would guarantee victory but that he would gain more support from his religion than he would lose or, at least, that he would not necessarily lose support. But, as it stands, the Document does not even provide essential evidence for this lesser claim. The whole possibility of anti-Catholic voting is dismissed in the most cavalier and speculative way. In considering Al Smith's vote, for example, the Document uses one set of figures when discussing his losses and another set ("selected counties" at that) when talking about his gains. The comparison with the Democratic vote in 1924 is particularly unfortunate because it does not take into account the effects of LaFollette's independent candidacy. Turning to another example, we note that the measure of Catholic defection from the Democratic Party is the percentage of Catholic votes for Truman and for Stevenson. Yet there would have had to be a drop in this figure for most sizeable groups, since Truman won and Stevenson lost. Hence to establish that the defection of Catholics was any more significant than that of any other sizeable groups, one would have to show that it was disproportionately large. The Document does not do this.

In seeking to refute the "Al Smith myth" the authors of the Document have fashioned one of their own. They are not content to rest with Lubell and Harris on the proposition that the Al Smith campaign marked the beginning of an era in which the Democratic Party "created a new political base in the large Northern metropolitan areas." They read into this the assumption that this new political base was predominantly Catholic in nature, whereas it could just as well have been a combination of economic and social status, minority status, and many other factors. From this unwarranted assumption they proceed to another: ". . . A Catholic vice-presidential nominee could refashion this base as Al Smith did, and begin a new era of Democratic victories. . . ." Assuming that a Vice-President is equal in appeal (or lack of it) to a President, one would have to go further and assume that all or most of the conditions existing in 1928 and succeeding years would be present in 1956 before agreeing with the Document. And in that case we might repeat a situation where, according to the Document, "1928 [1956?] was a Republican year, regardless of who was on either ticket."

II. External Criticism

Thus far we have limited our criticism solely to internal evidence in the Document. It should not come as a surprise, however, to discover that when electoral statistics not contained in the Document are consulted, they contradict all of its significant findings. Ralph M. Goldman and John H. Romani demonstrate that "a comparison of the percentage points by which Catholic candidates led the [national] ticket in 1952 with the performance of non-Catholic candidates indicates that there is no significant difference. . . ." Moreover, the 1952 vote shows:

a) that most Congressmen, whether Catholic or non-Catholic, run ahead of the national ticket;
b) that Catholic candidates do not run better in Catholic areas than they do in non-Catholic areas;
c) that non-Catholics run as well as Catholics in Catholic areas.

Finally, Goldman and Romani point to John F. Kennedy's experience in Massachusetts in 1952 when he ran for the Senate while Adlai Stevenson was running for President. At that time Massachusetts' Catholic population was approximately 50.5 per cent although its distribution throughout the state was highly uneven, varying from 27.2 per cent in Barnstable County to 56.1 per cent in Bristol County. Yet Senator Kennedy, who is a Catholic, secured his highest margin over Stevenson (13.1 per cent) in the county with the lowest percentage of Catholics. "In the other counties he ran from 0.4 percentage point to 9.9 percentage points ahead of the ticket without any recognizable correlation with the percentage of Catholics in the counties." So far as one can tell from the bare election statistics in 1952 a candidate's religion was not a significant factor in his success or failure at the polls.[8]

Before analyzing the 1960 election returns, it seems advisable to ask what kind of election results would have been most favorable (on the surface) for the theses proposed in the Kennedy Document. These are the major possibilities:

Case 1. An overwhelming victory of landslide proportions would not have served to lend credence to the Document. Although there might have been a Catholic vote, there would undoubtedly have been many other substantial bloc votes in Kennedy's favor, no one of which was crucial. For if his margin of victory was sufficiently great it would undoubtedly have been possible to subtract the increase over the previous election in any one kind of vote, Catholic included, without changing the final result.

Case 2. A defeat for Kennedy would, of course, have constituted a direct refutation of the proposition that the appearance of a Catholic on the ballot would guarantee victory.[9] There could still have been a Catholic vote and this vote might have been recaptured by the presence of a Catholic candidate, but it obviously could not have been critical for Democratic success.

Case 3. An exceedingly small margin of victory would not have been promising for substantiation of the Document. Virtually any group could then claim that a shift of a few thousand votes in a few critical states made the difference between victory and defeat. While a Catholic vote might be important it would be unlikely to become all-important. Viewed in a practical light, there would not be much political leverage in claiming that one's party must have a candidate who appeals to Catholics *and* a dozen other groups.

Case 4. The returns which put the Kennedy document in the most favorable position would have been a substantial but not overwhelming victory. In this case there would have been a chance that the votes of some one group had changed sufficiently since the previous election to provide the margin of victory, and perhaps Catholics might meet that test. In any event, the possibility could not be ruled out without further examination of the evidence.

As we all know, Kennedy received 49.7 per cent to Nixon's 49.6 per cent out of a total vote of 68,832,670, a hair-breadth margin if there ever was one.[10] Validation of the Kennedy document, therefore, runs up against the difficulties outlined in case three above.

Two hard facts stand out from the welter of imponderables in the 1960 presidential election: (1) If we relax the criteria somewhat, there was probably a Catholic vote of some magnitude; (2) the increase in the votes of Catholics as compared to 1956 was not sufficient in and of itself to ensure Kennedy's victory. He also needed increases in the votes of Negroes, Jews, and other groups.

Both poll and electoral data strongly suggest that there was a Catholic vote in the 1960 election. According to the Gallup Poll, the percentage of Catholics supporting the Democratic candidate rose from 51 per cent in 1956 to 78 per cent in 1960. Moreover, 62 per cent of the Catholics who voted for Eisenhower in 1956 actually voted for Kennedy in 1960, while only 3 per cent of the Catholics who voted for Stevenson in 1960 switched to Nixon.[11] Although we do not know how many of the Catholics who voted for Eisenhower and Kennedy would also have voted for a Protestant Democrat in 1960, it seems safe to assume that by no means all would have done so. The presumption of a Catholic vote is further strengthened by the 1960 election returns which show that there is a high and positive correlation between the percentage of Catholics in a state and the percentage gain for the Democratic party over 1960.[12] While part of these results may be accounted for by other demographic variables such as ethnicity, it appears unlikely that the conclusion about the Catholic vote will be shaken.

These figures, it must be said, do not necessarily validate the claim that Catholics had been moving from the Democratic Party and that the presence of a Catholic candidate brought them back into the fold. Another Gallup Poll shows that 75 per cent of the Catholics who voted in the 1958 congressional election supported Democratic candidates,[13] a total just three percentage points less than Kennedy received in 1960. It is possible, therefore, that the relatively low vote of Catholics for Adlai Stevenson represents disapproval of him rather than of the party itself.

Unfortunately, we are not in a position to say whether or not Kennedy lost a considerable number of votes from Protestants.[14] Gallup tells us that Kennedy received 38 per cent of the votes by Protestants while Stevenson received only 37 per cent in 1956.[15] But we know from other surveys that Stevenson was extremely unpopular in 1956 and faced the handicap of running against the extraordinarily popular General Eisenhower.[16] Any Democratic candidate in 1960 was expected to do better than Stevenson. Since we are not permitted the luxury of running a laboratory test in which a Protestant Democrat runs against Nixon, there appears to be no way of determining how many voters who are Protestant would have gone Democratic if Kennedy had not been on the ballot.[17]

What we can do is to make a reasonably accurate determination of whether (other things being equal) the increased percentage of Democratic votes by Catholics was sufficient in itself to secure victory for Kennedy. First, we need an approximation of what the Democrats would have received in 1960 in each state if nothing had changed since 1956. This may be obtained by taking the percentage of the total vote which the party received in each state in 1956 and multiplying that figure by the number who voted in 1960. Second, we need the number of additional votes in each state gained by the increase in the votes of Catholics from 1956 to 1960. This may be secured by taking the increase in the percentage of Catholics who voted Democratic from 1956 to 1960 and multiplying that figure by the estimated turnout of Catholics.[18] Third, we need to take cognizance of third-party votes so that all ballots cast will be accounted for. The formula used here may now be stated as follows: the increase in the Catholic vote in each state may have been sufficient by itself to secure Kennedy's victory if the projection of the 1956 percentage upon the 1960 turnout in addition to the increase in the Catholic vote during that period is greater than 50 per cent of the total vote less the number of third-party ballots.[19] Correspondingly, if the 1956 projection plus the increase in the Catholic vote was less than one half the total vote minus the third-party vote, we may conclude that Kennedy could not have won simply on the basis of additional Catholic votes.[20]

Kennedy received 306 electoral votes, 37 above the required majority of 269. Thus the loss of any state or combination of states totalling more than 37 electoral votes would have been sufficient to defeat him or to throw the election into the House of Representatives in case no candidate received a majority.[21]

In order to simplify matters, we can restrict our attention to those states which Kennedy won and which were not in the Democratic fold in 1956.[22] Turning to Table A we see that (assuming a 10 per cent rise in turnout of Catholics) the increase in the votes of Catholics was sufficient to secure Kennedy's election in only seven states with a combined total of 87 electoral votes, while it was not sufficient in nine states having 148 electoral votes. If we assume no increase in Catholic turnout, Kennedy loses an additional three electoral votes from Delaware. And even if we make the unwarranted assumption of a 20 per cent increase in turnout, he still loses 89 electoral votes in six states. Allowing a large margin for error, it seems clear that Kennedy needed more than the increase in the votes of Catholics to win.[23]

Two brief examples may be cited to support this conclusion. Illinois and Texas together account for 51 electoral votes. Out of the approximately 4.7 million votes cast in Illinois, Kennedy's margin of victory was 8,858. Where a shift of 4,500 votes by any group would have been enough to spell the difference, it would not be difficult to find any number of groups which could be considered necessary for the victory. Gallup reports that on a national basis the votes of Jews increased from 75 per cent to 81 per cent Democratic over 1956 and the votes of Negroes from 61 per cent to 68 per cent.[24] Even if we reduce this increase by two thirds, it is evident that Kennedy needed additional votes from Jews and Negroes to win in Illinois. In Texas, Kennedy's margin was 46,233 out of 2.3 million votes cast and it is apparent that there was a shift by at least 25,000 Negro voters.[25]

What, then, do the 1960 election returns have to teach us about the requirements for future Democratic presidential candidates? If a candidate wants to get elected President on the Democratic ticket he had better get many more votes from Catholics, Jews, Negroes and other groups traditionally providing support for his party than was the case in 1956. If the best he can do is to get 38 per cent of Protestant voters, he had better look for exceedingly strong support from other groups. And common sense suggests that if a candidate can increase his support among Protestants he need not be so dependent upon other groups. As a postscript to Kennedy's victory we might add that it is also advisable to be personally attractive, energetic, photogenic, wealthy, skillful, determined, and run against Richard Nixon rather than Dwight Eisenhower.

■ **Table A.** Was the increase in the Catholic vote sufficient for a Kennedy victory?

State and electoral vote	Per cent Democratic in 1956	Number voting in 1960	Per cent Democratic in 1956 projected on 1960 turnout	Per cent Catholic population	Increase in Catholic vote 1956–1960 assuming 10 per cent greater turnout than per cent in population	50 per cent of Total vote minus 3rd party vote	1956 Projection plus increase in Catholic vote	Was Change in Catholic vote sufficient?
Connecticut 8	36.3	1,222,883	443,907	46.35	162,881	611,427	606,788	No[x]
Delaware 3	44.6	196,683	87,720	18.65	10,493	97,622	98,213	Yes[a]
Illinois 27	40.3	4,757,394	1,917,220	27.51	431,734	2,368,137	2,348,954	No[x]
Maryland 9	39.9	1,055,349	412,084	18.00	54,329	527,672	475,413	No
Massachusetts 16	40.4	2,469,480	997,670	50.49	356,667	1,229,184	1,354,337	Yes
Michigan 20	44.1	3,318,097	1,463,281	23.47	256,953	1,648,644	1,720,234	Yes
Minnesota 11	46.8	1,541,887	721,603	24.40	124,176	766,905	845,779	Yes
Nevada 3	42.0	107,267	45,052	18.63	5,050	53,634	50,102	No
New Jersey 16	34.2	2,773,111	948,404	37.51	297,416	1,362,284	1,245,820	No
New Mexico 4	41.8	311,118	130,047	36.23	28,508	154,201	158,555	Yes
New York 45	38.7	7,291,079	2,821,648	32.18	671,289	3,630,965	3,492,937	No
Pennsylvania 32	43.3	5,006,541	2,167,832	29.98	429,011	2,492,968	2,596,843	Yes
Rhode Island 4	41.7	405,534	169,108	57.97	67,225	202,767	236,333	Yes
South Carolina 8	45.4	386,687	175,556	1.28	1,318	193,344	176,874	No
Texas 24	44.0	2,311,670	1,017,135	18.71	114,173	1,133,796	1,131,308	No[x]
West Virginia 8	45.9	837,781	384,541	5.65	13,546	418,891	398,087	No

*   Figures for the number of Catholics in each state were taken from the 1960 *Catholic Almanac*, St. Anthony's Guild (New York, 1960). The percentage of Catholics in each state was figured by dividing the total number by the total population for that state listed in the 1960 *Statistical Abstract*.

[a]   This symbol indicates that Delaware would not have been included in the sufficient column if we had made no allowance for increased Catholic turnout.

[x]   This symbol indicates those states where the increase in Catholic votes would have been sufficient if we had assumed a 20 per cent increase in turnout.

III

Despite the advantage of being able to interpret election statistics and voting studies (a skill which many outside the academic community do not possess) there is no need for any interested and intelligent citizen to feel at the mercy of partisan arguments merely because they are accompanied by an imposing array of statistical devices. It should now be evident that a great deal can be learned from an examination of the internal evidence contained in a study which seeks to use this kind of data to make claims favorable to one or another candidate. A determination of validity or invalidity may be obtained by observing whether the necessary evidence has been presented, whether an appropriate methodology has been used, and whether logically permissible deductions from the data have been made.

Since candidates primarily seek to establish that they can win while other men cannot, any attempt to use election statistics and voting studies as a tactical weapon must follow roughly the same pattern as the Kennedy Document. The existence of a certain kind of voter must be established together with a candidate who appeals to that group. The candidate may be a member of that group or may be a person with whom they identify. It must then be shown that this candidate will attract votes otherwise unobtainable, that these votes are crucial to the party's success, and that they will in fact make the margin between defeat and victory. To claim less might be more modest but would defeat the essential purpose of demonstrating that the candidate is crucial to the party's chances. We can, therefore, restate the criteria used to evaluate the Kennedy document in terms of general tests which may be used to ascertain the validity of claims made along these lines. (Eligible citizens having common ethnic, religious, racial or other characteristics which motivate them to vote along identical lines are called "X voters." Candidates sharing these characteristics are said to have "X appeal.")

1.   The voting pattern offered as proof of the X vote must not occur when two candidates possessing X appeal run against each other or when two non-X's run, otherwise we would suspect more general factors at work.

2.   There being little advantage in claiming the votes of those who would support the party anyway, X voters must be those who would vote against any other tendencies they may have or who would turn out in appreciably greater numbers because of the presence on the ballot of a candidate with X appeal. Identifying these voters on the basis of raw election returns which do not tell us why a voter is motivated to vote the way he does is exceedingly difficult. An attempt may be made to surmount this difficulty by treating as X voters those who used to vote for the candidates' party but no longer do so. Unless it is demonstrated that these voters left the party because another party had a candidate with X appeal, however, there would be no reason to believe that they would return because of it. A voter may leave a party for one reason and return to it for another, but the factors responsible for the return must be found and validated.

3.   The percentage of X voters supporting a candidate with X appeal in an election must actually rise in rough proportion to the number of such voters in a given area. Since X voters are likely to be distributed unevenly over a state, large constituencies must be broken down to see if the county or district returns support the intended conclusion.

4.   Rather than relying solely on tables showing how well successful candidates with X appeal did in areas where there are many X voters, the losers as well as the winners must be cited. If there are some X appealers who won but also some who lost this does not prove very much. If candidates with an X appeal ran ahead of their national tickets but so did non-X candidates, the evidence must be deemed unsatisfactory.

5.   Tests must be made to see if at least some other major demographic characteristics of the electorate are better predictors of the vote than the presence of a candidate with X appeal. It may turn out that a candidate with X appeal also appealed to city dwellers, low-income people, or others and that these characteristics are more important than his X appeal.

6.   A body of voters cannot be shown to provide the margin for victory unless it can also be demonstrated that all other significant groups (whose number may be much larger) will not also change their distribution of votes. Since many things may happen in four years, this is a difficult task.

IV. A Debate Between a Purist and an Operator

The Purist.   These tests are admittedly severe. Yet one cannot have confidence in any study which fails to satisfy them. It may well be, consequently, that few or even no candidates will be able to demonstrate the kinds of claims discussed here. Yet there may be some small solace to be had. If it is extremely difficult to demonstrate that a candidate's race, religion, ethnicity or other such characteristic will bring victory to his party, it is equally difficult to demonstrate that some similar characteristic will lead his party to defeat. There is no need to blink at the appropriate conclusion: politicians may simply be forced to take their chances at the polls without using voting statistics as a suspect propellant.

The Operator.   This is naive. You talk as if people like Sorensen were supposed to have these studies made for an academic research organization instead of improving their candidate's chances for nomination or election.

The Purist.   This is just what I am complaining about. If we cannot stop politicians from manipulating voting behavior materials for their own advantage, at least we can expose their devious practices.

The Operator.   You claim that politicians distort the facts. but you are equally guilty of oversimplification. You have shown that the Kennedy document does not meet your overly rigorous standards of proof, but you have not shown that it is undeniably false. You should know that politicians work in a world of probabilities and not certainties. Didn't someone say that politicians theorize with a pistol to their heads, under great pressure of time and circumstance.

The Purist. That is their problem; one can sympathize with the difficulties they face without excusing them from meeting essential standards of proof. Are we to permit politicians to make misleading use of social science just because things are tough for them?

The Operator. I see that you have not understood me at all. Surely, you admit that national elections do appear to depend on what happens in the closely competitive states with large electoral votes which happen to have substantial Catholic populations. The Document claims that these key states can be won by Catholic votes without offsetting losses and (implicitly) that other major groups could not be won over in sufficient numbers to insure victory for the Democratic Party. Before you cry out that these claims have not been substantiated, I would grant that there are truly many logical combinations for a favorable result. But in the real world (which we are supposed to be talking about) politicians deal only with the most likely, realistic possibilities. The fact is that Democratic support from Jews and Negroes seemed to be at a near saturation point, and up-state Protestant farmers and suburban businessmen did not appear too promising. Under the circumstances, how can you suggest that it would be better to say nothing than to rely on weak evidence. You ought to give Kennedy and company a medal for making use of social science material instead of just guessing.

The Purist. What makes you think that the Document is better than "just guessing"? Its "other-things-being-equal" argument is highly fallacious. And Harry Truman showed us in 1948 how it was possible to win by welding together a combination of states which omitted the ones with the most electoral votes like New York and California. The virtue of guesswork is that it does not pretend to be anything else. This unjustified pretension to scientific validity is what I am against, and I hope that most social scientists will react the same way.

The Operator. You speak rather more hotly than objectivity would seem to require. But I will skip over that and attack you on a more familiar ground: you are leaving out the normal operation of our competitive political life. If other politicians did not like the Kennedy Document, they were perfectly free to criticize it or to come out with a rival analysis. The citizen does not have to be a social scientist to evaluate such claims; he can ordinarily choose among competing analyses, each biased, and choose the conclusions he prefers or the source he trusts. Isn't this the market-place-of-ideas which you fellows talk so much about?

The Purist. Perhaps social scientists should provide some of this criticism to restrain both sides from converting the market place into nothing more than a patent medicine show with rival hucksters. The use of electoral data for political purposes is on the increase and raises problems deserving consideration by the interested parties, including those who work professionally in the field.

The Operator. O.K. You do your work and I'll do mine.

The Purist. Agreed.

V. Conclusion

There can be little doubt that under *some* conditions during *some* elections *some* social characteristics of voters and candidates may have *some* relevance to the polling results. The question of the conditions under which specified social characteristics become relevant is most difficult and cannot be disposed of by slogans advertising the alleged potence of this or that group at the polls. We know that in a competitive political system various participants (parties, interest groups, leaders) put forward candidates and issues designed to capture the allegiance of various groups of people. Rarely is it possible to appeal to one group and one group alone not only because there are so many groups but also because each individual may have many social characteristics which are potentially relevant to his voting decision. A sense of history is helpful here because changes in the tides of affairs—war, depression, inflation—help determine which social characteristics are likely to be most salient at a particular time. It is quite possible, for example, that in the previously cited 1958 senatorial election in Massachusetts religion was largely irrelevant because the most relevant social characteristic, one shared by virtually all citizens, was local pride in giving a native son a boost towards the Presidency. As one observes the usual unthinking alternation between decrying social science as a black art of manipulation and ridiculing it as absurd, it is good to take a hard look at some of its more devious practices but also to observe with a sense of excitement the fascinating explanatory tasks ahead.

APPENDIX: The Kennedy Document

Catholic Voters and the Democratic National Ticket

1. *The significance and location of the Catholic vote.* The voter surveys of Lazarsfeld ("The People's Choice"), Lubell ("The Future of American Politics"), Bean ("How to Predict Elections") and others—as well as the statistics contained within on the 1928 election and the 1952 vote for Catholic candidates—all indicate that there is, or can be such a thing as a "Catholic vote," whereby a high proportion of Catholics of all ages, residences, occupations and economic status vote for a well-known Catholic candidate or a ticket with special Catholic appeal.

As Lubell has pointed out: "Catholic voting strength is currently at its peak, in view of the maturing of the offspring of the Italians, Poles, Czechs and other former immigrant elements."

But the Catholic vote is far more important than its numbers—about one out of every four voters who turn out—because of its concentration in the key states and cities of the North. These are the pivotal states with large electoral votes, which vary as to their party support and several of which are inevitably necessary for a victory in the Electoral College. And the strength of the Catholic vote within these states is considerably increased by the findings of Gallup, Campbell of the University of Michigan ("The Voter Decides") and others that Catholics consistently turn out to vote in greater proportion than non-Catholics.

The proportion of Catholics in the adult population and 1952 two-party vote in these key states, with a total electoral vote of 261 (266 is a majority) is shown in Table 1, compared with the margin by which Eisenhower carried these states.

These are the key Democratic states where elections are won or lost. Of these 14 pivotal Catholic states with their 261 electoral votes:

In 1940, 13 of these states with 240 electoral votes went Democratic, *without which the Democrats would have lost the election.*

In 1944, 12 of these states with 221 electoral votes went Democratic, *without which the Democrats would have lost the election.*

In 1948, 8 of these states with 125 electoral votes went Democratic, *without which the Democrats would have lost the election.*

In 1952, none of these states went Democratic; all 261 of their electoral votes went to Eisenhower, thus making possible the first Republican victory in 24 years.

Equally important are the major urban areas in these states and the concentration of Catholic voters in those areas. As shown by Table 2, *the Catholic voters in each of these cities can usually determine the size of the Democratic margin in those cities; the size of the Democratic margin in those cities usually determines whether these states go Democratic; and whether these states go Democratic usually determines whether the Democrats win the election.* For example, taking the past four elections:

In 1940, without net margins in New York, Chicago, Hudson County (Jersey City), Philadelphia-Pittsburgh, Providence and Milwaukee, the Democrats would have lost New York (47), Illinois (29), New Jersey (16), Pennsylvania (36), Rhode Island (4), and Wisconsin (12), or a total loss of 144 electoral votes.

In 1944, without their net margins in New York, Hartford and New Haven, Chicago, Baltimore, Detroit, Hudson County (Jersey City), Minneapolis-St. Paul, and Philadelphia, Democrats would have lost New York (47), Connecticut (18), Illinois (28), Maryland (8), Michigan (19), New Jersey (16), Minnesota (11),

■ **Table 1**

State	Proportion of Catholics in adult population	Estimated proportion of 1952 two-party vote made up of Catholic voters	Eisenhower's margin over 50 per cent of the 1952 two-party vote	Electoral vote
	%	%	%	
New York	32	40	6·0	45
Pennsylvania	29	39	3·0	32
Illinois	30	34	5·0	27
New Jersey	39	47	7·5	16
Massachusetts	50	57	4·4	16
Connecticut	49	55	5·9	8
Rhode Island	60	65	0·9	4
California	22	27	6·9	32
Michigan	24	30	5·8	20
Minnesota	24	27	5·6	11
Ohio	20	25	6·8	25
Wisconsin	32	38	11·2	12
Maryland	21	31	5·8	0
Montana	22	26	9·7	4

261
Needed to win: 266

Notes:

Column 1—Selected states: Not included are seven other States where the Catholics are an important part of the adult population: New Hampshire (37 per cent), Louisiana (34 per cent), New Mexico (46 per cent), Arizona (30 per cent), North Dakota (22 per cent), Maine (26 per cent), and Vermont (29 per cent). If these seven States were included, the total number of electoral votes would be 295. They are excluded from this analysis, however, either because they are not considered to be among the key swing States or because it would be speculative to translate the proportion of Catholics in their adult population into important voting strength for a Democratic Catholic candidate.

Column 2—Proportion of Catholics in population: These figures are taken from "The Official Catholic Directory" (1955, P. J. Kenedy & Sons). They pertain only to actual members of the church—and surveys have indicated that the actual number of those classified as Catholics would be approximately 10 per cent higher in each state. Survey analysts have found that the proportion of Catholics in the total population approximates the proportion of Catholics in the adult eligible-voter population.

Column 3—Proportion of Catholics in 1952 two party-vote: This column is calculated by applying Campbell's national average figures for the turnout of Catholics and non-Catholics to the official turnout figures for 1952 for each of the 14 States.

Column 4—Eisenhower's margin over 50 per cent in 1952: This figure represents the number of votes which must have shifted to the Democratic column for a Democratic victory in 1956.

■ **Table 2**

City	Estimated proportion of 1952 two-party vote made up of Catholic voters	Decline in Democratic proportion of two-party vote 1948 to '52
	%	%
New York	38	3·6
Buffalo	62	8·6
Rochester	38	9·8
Albany	38	Not available
Philadelphia	42	(gain) 8·0
Pittsburgh	46	5·0
Scranton	49	Not available
Chicago	49	4·2
Newark-Jersey	53	5·4
Trenton	46	Not available
Boston	55	11·8
Hartford	59	Not available
Baltimore	31	3·1
San Francisco	33	4·2
Los Angeles	22	5·2
Detroit	39	1·4
Minneapolis-St. Paul	30	9·0
Milwaukee	41	9·4
Cleveland	36	4·6
Cincinnati	25	5·5
Toledo	25	4·0

Note:

Column 2—Catholic voters in cities: These figures are derived by applying the appropriate State turnout figures for these dioceses in "The Official Catholic Directory" (1955, P. J. Kenedy & Sons).

and Pennsylvania (35), or a total loss of 172 electoral votes—*and the Republicans would have won the election.*

In 1948, without their net margins in Chicago, Los Angeles, Cleveland and Providence, the Democrats would have lost Illinois (28 electoral votes), California (25), Ohio (25), and Rhode Island (4), or a total loss of 82 electoral votes—*and the Republicans would have won the election.*

In 1952, as shown on Table 2, the Democratic vote in all of the major cities except Philadelphia fell sharply, and these cities for the first time in 24 years did not contribute a single electoral vote to the Democrats, thus making possible the first Republican victory in 24 years.

2. *Are the Democrats losing the Catholics?* Every analyst agrees they are, in terms of the national ticket. The Catholic Democratic vote was noticeably off in 1948—and showed a critical decline in 1952. Gallup, Roper, the University of Michigan Survey and others all reported this trend. Gallup said only 34 per cent of all Catholics considered themselves Republicans in 1950, but at least 44 per cent voted for Eisenhower in 1952. Harris of the Roper organization ("Is There a Republican Majority") said that Roper polls showed the following shifts to have been decisive in Eisenhower's election:

Catholics in general, normally over 65 per cent Democratic, went 47 per cent for Ike. German Catholics, previously 82 per cent Democratic, went 55 per cent for Ike. Poles, normally over 70 per cent Democratic, went 50 per cent for Ike. Irish, normally 65 per cent Democratic, went 53 per cent for Ike.

The Democratic era and political base begun by Al Smith, said Harris, ended in 1952. The "immigrant base," which had begun cracking in 1940, split wide open, probably permanently, he said. He predicted that the important Irish and German votes in particular would become largely an independent group, sharply affecting Democratic majorities in the Northern cities.

The University of Michigan nation-wide survey showed that of those voting for one of the two major candidates, over 66 per cent of the Catholics voted Democratic in 1948 but fewer than 51 per cent did in 1952. (There is striking similarity between these figures and those of Gallup and Roper.)

Thus Catholics in 1952, roughly 25 per cent of the voting population, went approximately one out of two for the Republican candidate, whereas in 1948 they had gone two out of three for the Democratic nominee; and, though they had constituted approximately $\frac{1}{3}$ of the Democratic vote in 1948, they were only 28 per cent of Stevenson's vote and constituted 21 per cent of Eisenhower's tremendous vote.

Approximately 30 per cent of these Catholics for Eisenhower were "shifters" —that is, even on the basis of 1948 when the Catholic vote was already slipping away from the Democrats (the Republicans carried New York, New Jersey, Pennsylvania, Connecticut, Michigan and Maryland), they would have been expected to vote Democratic in 1952.

These shifters—whom we shall call "normally Democratic Catholics"— constituted approximately 7 per cent of Eisenhower's total nation-wide vote. If Stevenson could have held in 1952 *only* those Catholics who had voted for Truman in 1948 but for Ike in 1952—or if he could recapture them in 1956— this would, as shown in Table 3, *add 132 electoral votes to the Democratic column, enough when combined with the Solid South to provide a majority of electoral votes!*

3. *Catholic Candidates.* What may be the clue as to the means of recapturing those votes—as well as further evidence of the national ticket's loss of Catholic votes in 1952—is provided by Table 4, showing how Democratic Catholic candidates for congressmen, senator and governor ran consistently ahead of their

■ **Table 3**

State	Estimated per cent of Eisenhower vote in 1952, made up of Catholic voters	Proportion of Eisenhower vote constituting margin by which he carried state	Estimated per cent of Eisenhower vote in 1952, made up of "normally Democratic" Catholic voters who shifted	Electoral votes
	%	%	%	
New York	35	11	11·0	45
Pennsylvania	36	6	11·0	32
Illinois	31	9	9·3	27
Massachusetts	51	8	15·3	16
Connecticut	48	11	14·4	8
Rhode Island	63	15	18·9	4
New Jersey	40	13		16
California	23	12		32
Michigan	27	10		20
Minnesota	23	10		11
Ohio	21	12		25
Wisconsin	30	18		12
Maryland	27	10		9
Montana	21	16		4

261
Needed to win: 266

Notes:

Column 2—Proportion of Eisenhower vote consisting of Catholics: This column is calcu-lated by applying to Table I the findings of the University of Michigan nation-wide survey (Campbell, "The Voter Decides") that roughly 49 per cent of voting Catholics voted for Eisenhower and roughly 51 per cent for Stevenson.

Column 3—Eisenhower's margin: The percentage listed is not to be confused with the percentage by which Eisenhower carried the State (which can be determined from Table 1, Column 4); but is the percentage of his own total vote represented by that margin, in order to make it comparable with figures portraying the percentage of his total vote made up of Catholics and previously Democratic Catholics.

Column 4—Catholics shifting to Eisenhower: This column is calculated by applying to Table 3, Column 2, and Table 1, Columns 3 and 4, the findings of the Michigan survey that over 66 per cent of the Catholic two-party voters in 1948 supported the Democratic ticket, as compared with fewer than 51 per cent in 1952. Figures are provided only for those States where a shift of the State to the Democratic column by means of a return of these Catholic voters is indicated.

■ **Table 4**

State or district	Candidate	Number of percentage points of two-party vote by which national ticket ran behind candidates listed (norm: 0.1 per cent to 1.6 per cent)
New York		
30th (Albany)	O'Brien	16·0
7th (New York City)	Delaney	15·0
10th (Brooklyn)	Kelly	5·0
9th (Brooklyn)	Keogh	3·0
14th (Brooklyn)	Rooney	11·0
New Jersey		
11th (Newark)	Addonizio	8·0
10th (Newark)	Rodino	21·0
14th (Jersey City)	Hart	4·0
Massachusetts		
	Kennedy	12·0
	Dever	8·4
Rhode Island		
	Pastore	12·0
	Roberts	7·0
Ohio		
	Lausche	26·0
	DiSalle	5·0
19th (Youngstown)	Kirwan	21·0
20th (Cleveland)	Feighan	25·0
Wyoming		
	O'Mahoney	19·0
Wisconsin		
4th (Milwaukee)	Zablocki	33·0
Pennsylvania		
2nd (Philadelphia)	Granahan	2·0
3rd (Philadelphia)	Byrne	2·0
5th (Philadelphia)	Green	1·0
28th (Pittsburgh)	Eberharter	11·0
Minnesota		
4th (St. Paul)	E. McCarthy	12·0

State or district	Candidate	Number of percentage points of two-party vote by which national ticket ran behind candidates listed (norm: 0.1 per cent to 1.6 per cent)
Michigan		
1st (Detroit)	Mackrowicz	6·0
13th (Detroit)	O'Brien	4·0
14th (Detroit)	Rabaut	8·0
15th (Detroit)	Dingell	7·0
16th (Detroit)	Lesinski	8·0
Connecticut		
1st (Hartford)	Dodd	9·0
Illinois		
2nd (Chicago)	O'Hara	1·0
5th (Chicago)	Kluezynski	6·0
6th (Chicago)	O'Brien	4·0
8th (Chicago)	Gordon	7·0
24th (East St. Louis)	Price	11·0
Montana		
	Mansfield	21·0

Note:

Columns 1 and 2—Catholic candidates, States and districts: These columns list only those members of Congress or Governors elected in 1952 who are known to be Catholics and elected by areas with large Catholic populations. There are, of course, many others where these facts could not be as easily determined.

national ticket, in a striking example of ticket-splitting on the part of Catholic voters.

Outside the South, according to Gallup and Roper, the Democratic presidential vote and the Democratic congressional vote ran approximately even, the same over-all percentage behind the Republican presidential and congressional candidates. Specifically, voters on the average cast Democratic ballots for President at a rate only $\frac{1}{10}$ of 1 per cent (Gallup) or 1.6 per cent (Roper) behind their votes for Democratic congressional candidates. But Table 4 shows how selected Catholic Democratic candidates ran much further ahead of the national ticket in their areas.

Some of the examples shown are particularly instructive. Had Stevenson run as well as Pastore (and Roberts), Lausche, Kennedy and Mansfield, he would, of course, have won an additional 49 electoral votes. His lags behind O'Brien in Albany and Delaney in New York City were greater than his lag behind Eisenhower for the state of New York as a whole; and the same is true of his lags behind Rodino in Newark, Zablocki in Milwaukee, Eugene McCarthy in St. Paul, and Price in East St. Louis.

Especially revealing of the picture of Catholic voters leaving the Democratic Party, except where a Catholic is on the ticket, are the following normally Democratic districts where Catholic voters are a major element:

Zablocki won in Milwaukee by 29 per cent while Stevenson was losing by 4 per cent.

O'Brien won in Albany by 7 per cent while Stevenson was losing by 9 per cent.

Delaney won in New York City by 2 per cent while Stevenson was losing by 13 per cent.

Addonizio and Rodino won in Newark by 4 per cent and 14 per cent respectively while Stevenson was losing by 4 per cent and 7 per cent.

Rabaut won in Detroit by 6 per cent while Stevenson was losing by 2 per cent.

Dodd won in Hartford by 8 per cent while Stevenson was losing by 1 per cent.

4. *How much would a Catholic vice-presidential nominee hurt the ticket?* On June 24, 1956, the Gallup Poll Feature was headlined "Qualified Catholic Could Be President." Nearly 3 out of 4 respondents said they would vote for a well-qualified Catholic nominated by their party for the Presidency itself. Of those who thought they would be opposed, a large share lived in the South—and if one of three Democrats stayed home (or even voted Republican) in the South due to a nominee's religious affiliation, few if any Southern electoral votes would be lost, even though Democratic margins in several states might be diminished.

A large share of the remainder appeared to be Republicans who would not support the Democratic ticket under any circumstances, and northern "liberal intellectuals" who will certainly vote Democratic without regard to the Vice-President's religion.

In short, even a Catholic nominee for President would be judged by most people on his qualifications for the office—and it is apparent that a Democratic Catholic vice-presidential nominee, though admittedly prejudice would be stirred, would lose no electoral votes for the ticket simply because a handful of Southerns or Republicans would not support him. Particularly in the key states and cities where he might be expected to concentrate his campaigning, his religion would be irrelevant to most.

5. *How about Al Smith?* This is the cry raised by professional pessimists opposed to a Catholic on the ticket. But, as Bean and others have shown, the "Al Smith myth" is one of the falsest myths in politics.

a) 1928 was a Republican year, regardless of who was on either ticket. It was a year for "Drys" like Hoover, not "Wets" like Smith. Professor William F. Ogburn, after a statistical study of 173 Northern counties, concluded that "prohibition sentiment was three times more decisive an influence in the election than the religious issue." Moreover, studies showed Midwestern and Southern voters opposing Al Smith as a Tammany product from the streets of New York, a portly cigar-smoking stereotype of the immigrant-base political boss. If Al Smith had been the Republican nominee and a Dry, he would have won the election regardless of his religion.

b) Of the states his two predecessors as Democratic nominees had both carried, Smith lost only 4 (Florida, North Carolina, Texas and Virginia, all of which the Democrats also lost in 1952 except for North Carolina), despite the usual assumption that Smith's Catholicism caused the Solid South and numerous other states to go Republican.

c) The nation has changed since 1928. There are more Catholics—their political role as seen above, is more crucial—their leadership in the Democratic Party and in statewide offices from California to Maine is both frequent and accepted—and the nation is considerably more tolerant on religious matters. Gallups' 1956 poll found an increasing acceptance of a Catholic President in just the last 15 years. The support for Frank Lausche for President among prominent Southern Democrats is most indicative. An Ambassador to the Vatican is not likely to be a major campaign issue, regardless of the candidates; and the question of Federal aid to parochial as well as public schools has been largely avoided by concentration on the problem of public school construction instead of operation.

d) Most important of all, and least known, is the fact that Al Smith helped the Democratic Party far more than he hurt it:

Of the states his two predecessors as Democratic nominees had both carried, Smith lost only 4 (Florida, North Carolina, Texas and Virginia, all of which the Democrats also lost in 1952 except for North Carolina), despite the usual assumption that Smith's Catholicism caused the Solid South and numerous other states to go Republican.

Smith carried Massachusetts and Rhode Island which had never previously returned a Democratic majority in the 20th century.

Smith carried a majority of the counties in every section of the country but one (East North Central); and increased the number of counties in the Democratic column in the North Eastern, Middle Atlantic, West North Central, Mountain and Pacific states. 122 Northern counties (77 of them predominantly Catholic) were captured from the Republicans.

Smith increased the Democratic vote by fantastic proportions in most states and particularly urban counties. For example:

	Democratic vote, in thousands	
	1924	1928
Massachusetts	281	792
Suffolk County	79	205
Connecticut	110	252
Rhode Island	76	118
New York	951	2,090
Bronx County	73	233
Pennsylvania	409	1,060
Philadelphia	54	276
Ohio	478	864
Cuyahoga County	24	166
Hamilton County	35	110
New Jersey	298	616
Hudson County	91	153
Minnesota	56	396
Hennepin	11	81
Michigan	152	397
Wayne County	23	157
Maryland	198	224
Illinois	577	1,300
Cook County	226	716

Thus Lubell has written: "The Republican hold on the cities was broken not by Roosevelt but by Al Smith." And Louis Harris concluded: "Al Smith marked the beginning of the Democratic era which ended in 1952 ... (He) created a new political base in the large Northern metropolitan areas."

Conclusion—Has the Democratic era ended? Has the party permanently lost its political base among the Catholics and immigrants of the large Northern cities that made a Democratic victory possible in 1940, 1944 and 1948? The above indicates that a Catholic vice-presidential nominee could refashion this base as Al Smith did, and begin a new era of Democratic victories, without costing even the few electoral votes Smith did.

His campaign would be largely concentrated in the key states and cities listed above, including also on his itinerary such cities with high Catholic populations as St. Louis, Gary, Omaha, Denver, Dubuque and Reno. No further state-by-state analysis should be needed—but it should be reemphasized as a major example that, by reducing Republican upstate majorities in New York by virtue of his vote in Rochester, Albany and Buffalo, and by increasing the declining Democratic vote in New York City, such a candidate could assure return of New York's 45 electoral votes to the Democratic column in 1956 for the first time in 12 years.

If he brought into the Democratic fold only those normally Democratic Catholics who voted for Ike, he would probably swing New York, Massachusetts, Rhode Island, Connecticut, Pennsylvania and Illinois—for 132 electoral votes. If he also wins the votes of Catholics who shifted to the Republicans in 1948 or earlier, he could also swing New Jersey, Minnesota, Michigan, California, Wisconsin, Ohio, Maryland, Montana, and maybe even New Hampshire—for a total of 265 electoral votes (needed to win: 266). Thus Ike could and would be defeated.

Special Appendix

Which would add the most strength to the Democratic ticket—an appeal to the Catholic vote, the Southern vote or the farm vote?

1. *Comparative electoral strength.* States with important Catholic votes which were lost by Stevenson in 1952 and might be recaptured in 1956 with a Catholic vice-presidential nominee (all analyzed in memorandum): New York, New Jersey, Massachusetts, Connecticut, Rhode Island, Pennsylvania, Maryland, Ohio, Illinois, Michigan, Wisconsin, Minnesota, Montana, California—total electoral votes, 261.

Southern and Border States which were lost by Stevenson in 1952 and might be recaptured in 1956 with a Southern vice-presidential nominee: Texas, Florida, Virginia, Missouri, Oklahoma, Tennessee (although this is almost certainly Democratic after Dixon-Yates) and Kentucky (which Stevenson carried)—total electoral votes, 88.

States with important farm votes, including those listed above, and stretched to include Western mining states, industrial states and livestock states which oppose high grain supports, which were lost by Stevenson in 1952 and might in 1956 be influenced to some degree, however slight, by a Farm Belt Vice-Presidential nominee: Idaho, Iowa, Wyoming, Nevada, Wisconsin, Oregon, Colorado, Montana, Utah, Indiana, Ohio, Michigan, Minnesota, Illinois, Washington, Oklahoma, Texas and Missouri—total electoral votes, 202.

2. *How important is the farm vote in the farm belt itself?* In the "farm revolt" of 1948, only three states of the Midwest can be said to have been swept into the Democratic column by virtue of votes cast by farmers—Iowa, Minnesota and Wisconsin—for a total of only 23 electoral votes. Truman lost Indiana, Kansas, Nebraska, North Dakota and South Dakota. The margin given him by the major urban areas of Illinois and Ohio overcame his deficit in the farm areas of those states; and practically all of his margin in Wisconsin consisted of his margin in Milwaukee, and practically all of his margin in Minnesota consisted of his margin in St. Paul-Minneapolis. Contrast this with the findings of the above memo that the key Catholic city vote was responsible for the Democratic victories of 1940, 1944 and 1948. Even in most farm states, there are more Catholic voters than farm voters, according to official census figures.

NOTES

*   I would like to thank Allan P. Sindler for bringing the Kennedy Document to my attention, Michael Margolis for helping me compile Table A, and Nelson W. Polsby, H. Douglas Price, and Raymond E. Wolfinger for useful criticisms.

1.   According to the well-informed James M. Burns, this survey was put together by Kennedy's assistant, Ted Sorensen, and "quietly let out to reporters as an analysis drawn up by 'backers' of Kennedy." (John Kennedy, *A Political Profile,* New York, p. 181.) It was used again in 1960 and, after the election, accepted as a correct prophecy by researchers for the Republican National Committee. (*The Washington Post*, April 9, 1961.)

2.   By a "ticket with special Catholic appeal" the Document apparently refers to the presence of a Catholic on the ballot as a Vice-Presidential candidate. No other standard for appealing to voters who are Catholics is mentioned. All quotations in this section are taken from the Document.

3.   The strategy of the argument demands that the "Catholic vote" be narrowed to those Catholics who voted Republican or who would not have voted at all. There would be no sales value in getting a Catholic candidate merely to keep people who were going to turn out and to vote Democratic anyway.

4.   This raises the question of how Eisenhower, a Protestant with a Protestant running-mate, could benefit from the Catholic vote under the terms of the definition. This point will be considered later on.

5.   A glance at Table 2 reveals that there is no connection between the number of Catholic voters in a city and the decline in Democratic vote from 1948 to 1952. Outside of Philadelphia where the Democratic vote increased, it is possible to construct the following table which is just as misleading as Table 2:

City	Per cent of Catholics %		Democratic decline %	
Detroit	39	Decrease	1·4	Increase
New York	38		3·6	
San Francisco	33		4·2	
Los Angeles	22		5·2	

It is always possible to claim that even if a Catholic candidate did not do too well in Catholic areas, a non-Catholic might have done worse. One way to check on this would be to compare the results from one election to another and see if the presence of a Catholic candidate has reduced the "spread" between the parties. Thus if a Republican Catholic lost it still might be true that his margin of defeat was less than that of his party in previous years. If this proved to be true for many districts, then one might suspect the presence of a Catholic voting bloc. But the Document presents no evidence of this kind. The burden of proof must rest with the proponents.

6.   The existence of "normally Democratic Catholics" who could be "expected" to vote Democratic is purely hypothetical. This is another instance where the Document begins by taking for granted the very thing it has to prove.

7. Part of the pattern of assumptions made in the Document is that the personality of the President will have no effect in persuading or dissuading Catholic voters from voting for or against him.

8. "More About 'Catholic Vote' in U. S. Elections." *U. S. News and World Report,* Vol. 41, August 17, 1956, pp. 42–46, 132–135. See also the comments by Louis H. Bean on pages 41–42. The authors present the tables from which their conclusions are drawn.

9. Although the Document specifies a Catholic on the ballot as Vice-President, there is no point in quarrelling with the appearance of a presidential candidate to take on the burden of argument.

10. The final election returns on a national and state basis are reported in an Associated Press dispatch of December 15, 1960. They are available in the *World Almanac* for 1961.

11. Public Opinion News Service, December 4, 1960. This poll was based on 3,312 interviews with Catholics taken before and after the election.

12. *U. S. News and World Report,* December 12, 1960. See the table by John H. Fenton substantiating this point. Thomas Flinn has done a county-by-county analysis of the vote in Ohio and reports a high and positive correlation between the percentage of Catholics in a county and the Democratic gain over 1956. Yet Nixon took Ohio by a substantial margin.

13. Public Opinion News Service, September 16, 1960.

14. The passage of time is not likely to make it any easier to solve this problem. Let us suppose that in future presidential elections a Protestant Democrat is shown to have retained the high proportion of Catholic voters who supported Kennedy. One explanation might be that Kennedy's candidacy had firmly attached them to the Democratic Party. An alternative explanation would be that Kennedy's Catholicism had been overestimated as a force attracting Catholic voters and that they would have voted Democratic anyhow when Eisenhower was no longer a candidate. Nevertheless, given considerable time and financial resources, some useful light could be shed on the 1960 election through a close examination of local returns in small, homogeneous, heavily Protestant constituencies where there is a clear baseline of support for the major parties. See the suggestion by V. O. Key in his "A Theory of Critical Elections," *Journal of Politics,* Vol. 17 (February, 1955), pp. 3–18.

15. Public Opinion News Service, December 7, 1960.

16. See Angus Campbell, Philip E. Converse, Warren Miller and Donald Stokes, *The American Voter* (New York, 1960), especially pp. 56–58, 525–30.

17. In an article on the 1960 presidential election the authors of *The American Voter* properly note "that the simple choice of a baseline will go a long way towards determining . . . the question of net religious effect. If we choose the 1958 vote as a baseline, it is hard to argue that Kennedy could have made any gains from his religion; if we choose the 1956 presidential vote, it is equally hard to argue that he lost ground on balance." They deal with this problem by arguing that it is absurd to choose the 1956 election which is the most disproportionately Republican in the series going back to 1928. Instead, they posit a "normal" presidential

election and decide that a Democratic candidate could expect to get 53–54 per cent of the two-party vote. They also posit expected votes of Catholics and Protestants for Democratic presidential candidates. Using this method, they conclude that Kennedy lost 2.2 per cent of the two-party vote, a large proportion of it in the South. [Philip E. Converse, Angus Campbell, Warren E. Miller, Donald E. Stokes, "Stability and Change in 1960: A Reinstating Election," *American Political Science Review*, LV (June, 1961), pp. 269–80.]

The above line of reasoning in this otherwise excellent article has disturbing ad-hoc qualities to it as the authors argue after the fact that 1960 represented a return to a normal or expected state of affairs.

In this paper I have chosen the 1956 election as a baseline precisely because it gives the greatest advantage to those who claim that the Catholic vote was decisive and thus hopefully makes the refutation all the more convincing. No claim is made here, however, concerning whether Kennedy did or did not lose votes. What is claimed is that any votes he may have gained from Catholics were not sufficient to secure his victory.

18. While methodological difficulties arise which make the results less than wholly accurate, they are accurate enough for the use to which they are put. One difficulty is that we do not have state-by-state breakdowns on the Catholic vote for 1956 and are forced to use the national average of 51 per cent. Gallup does give the 1960 figures by section (East 77 per cent, South 75 per cent, Midwest 81 per cent, Far West 74 per cent) so that the amount of distortion for any one state should be quite small. Since the argument can turn on any one of a number of combinations of states, as we shall see, it seems unlikely that the distortions would affect them all in the same direction. Another difficulty is that we lack figures for the 1960 turnout of Catholics. This can be overcome by using different assumptions and showing that they all validate the conclusion though in different degree. We begin by assuming that the turnout was simply equal to the percentage of Catholics in the total population. Then we increase the Catholic turnout by 10 per cent (which may be fairly reasonable) and again by 20 per cent (which is too high but serves to prove the point).

19. Caution is necessary here because it is possible that Kennedy might have lost support from some groups and made it up by increasing his vote from others and that these events would cancel each other in the totals.

20. It may be helpful to diagram these formulas. Let S stand for "the Catholic vote is sufficient," P for the Democratic percentage in 1956, T for the total vote in 1960, CV for the percentage increase in votes of Catholics from 1956 to 1960, Y for the turnout of Catholics in 1960, Z for the third party vote, > for greater than, < for less than, and a period ($\cdot$) for multiplication. Thus:

$$S \text{ if } (P \cdot T) + (CV \cdot Y) > (\tfrac{1}{2} \cdot T) - Z$$
$$\text{Not } S \text{ if } (P \cdot T) + (CV \cdot Y) < (\tfrac{1}{2} \cdot T) - Z$$

21. Fourteen electors in Mississippi and Alabama ran unpledged and later supported Senator Harry Byrd of Virginia. It is possible, therefore, that neither Nixon nor Kennedy would have received a majority.

22. Obviously, the Catholic vote did not help Kennedy win states which he lost. Also, if a state went Democratic in 1956 anything other than a decrease in votes would

keep it there. The following states (electoral votes are indicated in brackets) supported Stevenson in 1956 and Kennedy in 1960: Alabama (11), Arkansas (8), Georgia (12), Missouri (13), North Carolina (14). In Louisiana (10) the third party vote was so high, 21 per cent and the Republican vote so low, 28.6 per cent, that the percentage the Democratic Party gained while losing in 1956 would have been sufficient to win in 1960.

23. To be sure, the increase in the votes of Catholics was necessary for a Kennedy victory; he could not have won without it. But neither could he have won without a larger vote from other groups. It is difficult to answer the argument that Kennedy may have made himself overly dependent on Catholic votes by failing to draw more from Protestants.

24. Public Opinion News Service, December 7, 1960 and December 9, 1960.

25. See *The New York Times*, November 27, 1960, p. 51.

SMOKING AND LUNG CANCER: RECENT EVIDENCE AND A DISCUSSION OF SOME QUESTIONS

JEROME CORNFIELD WILLIAM HAENSZEL
E. CUYLER HAMMOND ABRAHAM M. LILIENFELD
MICHAEL B. SHIMKIN ERNST L. WYNDER

In 1957 a Study Group,[75] appointed by the National Cancer Institute, the National Heart Institute, the American Cancer Society, and the American Heart Association examined the scientific evidence on the effects of tobacco smoking on health and arrived at the following conclusion:

■ The sum total of scientific evidence establishes beyond reasonable doubt that cigarette smoking is a causative factor in the rapidly increasing incidence of human epidermoid carcinoma of the lung. ■

Concurrently, a report from the Medical Research Council[57] of Great Britain appeared which also drew the inference of a causal relationship between smoking and lung cancer from the statistical, clinical, and laboratory evidence available by midyear 1957.

The consideration of the accumulated scientific evidence has led to the acceptance of a similar viewpoint by responsible public health officials in Great Britain, the Netherlands, Norway, and the United States. This concensus of scientific and public health opinion does not mean that all problems regarding smoking and lung cancer have now been solved or that valid questions and reservations about some aspects of the subject do not remain. An excellent collection of primary references and opinions expressing both "sides" of the question was issued by a committee of the House of Representatives[42] which sought to examine the claims of filter-tip cigarette advertisements.

The general acceptance of the cigarette-lung-cancer relationship has not decreased research interest but has accelerated research in this and in such related fields as respiratory physiology and environmental carcinogens, and on the effect of tobacco smoke in a wide range of physiological and pathological reactions.

The result is that considerably more information has been published or has become available through other media. Included in the recent scientific evidence are the following:

1) Additional retrospective studies[68,69,73] on men with lung cancer and on matched controls have appeared. All show an association between cigarette smoking and epidermoid-undifferentiated lung cancer.

Reprinted by permission of Jerome Cornfield from *Journal of National Cancer Institute* **22** (1959), 173–203. The present version has been slightly condensed by the editor.

2) Additional retrospective studies on women[34,73] also show the association.

3) The first results of a third large prospective study,[20] which included 200,000 United States veterans who were observed for 30 months, duplicate closely the reported findings of the Hammond-Horn[38] and the Doll-Hill[18] studies.

4) Analyses by Kreyberg and others[19,46] substantiate that, epidemiologically, primary lung cancer must be divided into epidermoid-undifferentiated and adeno-carcinoma. The latter is much less related to smoking, and so far as is known at present, to other carcinogenic inhalants.

5) Additional findings have become available on the impingement of tobacco-smoke particles in the bronchi of animals, ciliary paralysis, and penetration of unidentified fluorescent materials into the bronchial cells.[40,41,45]

6) Additional data have been published[2,12] on the more frequent occurrence of hyperplastic and metaplastic changes in the lungs of smokers as compared with the lungs of nonsmokers. Hyperplastic and metaplastic changes have been produced in bronchi of dogs exposed to direct contact with tobacco "tars"[62] and in bronchi of mice exposed to tobacco smoke.[48]

7) Additional confirmations have been obtained on the induction of cancer of the skin in mice painted with tobacco-smoke condensates.[7,23,28,61,63]

8) Progress continues on the isolation and identification of chemical con-stituents in tobacco smoke, including compounds of the carcinogenic polycyclic type.[53,61,77,84,85]

The growing and consistent body of evidence has had no noticeable effect upon the viewpoint of a small but important group of individuals who would deny a causal role of cigarette smoking in cancer of the lung. Among these critics are Little[52] and Hartnett,[39] spokesmen for the American tobacco industry. Berkson[3,4] has been critical of many aspects of the statistical studies, and his reservations are, in part, also evident in papers by Neyman[60] and Arkin[1]. More general objections by Fisher,[25,26] Greene,[31] Hueper,[43] Macdonald,[54] Rigdon,[64] and Rosenblatt[67] have been published.

We have reviewed the criticisms that have been made regarding the cigarette-lung-cancer relationship in the light of new evidence. In this review we have sev-eral objectives: *a*) to point out recorded facts that directly answer some of the criticisms; *b*) to define more precisely some inadequacies of information, with the hope that this will lead to further research. The particular references we have used were selected because in our opinion the criticism was well stated; it is not our intention to reply to any specific publication or to any specific critic. Our view is that all valid questions should be answered. However, some questions may not be relevant, or there may be no information presently available for an answer. In the latter case, we believe that a distinction should be made between data that are unavailable and data that have been found to be contradictory.

For convenience, we have divided the criticisms and answers into five major topics, as follows: (I) Mortality and population data; (II) Retrospective and prospective studies; (III) Studies on pathogenesis; (IV) Other laboratory investigations; and (V) Interpretation.

I. Mortality and Population Data

The rising death rate from lung cancer in all countries that have sufficiently detailed mortality statistics is the most striking neoplastic phenomenon of this century. That this increase is a fact and not a spurious result of statistical classification is now commonly accepted. An entirely contrary view is held by only a few persons,[64] though there are dissenting opinions[29,43] regarding the extent and time relationship of this recorded increase.

Obviously, the case for the etiologic role of cigarette smoking would be seriously compromised if it could be demonstrated that the lung-cancer rate over the past half century had been stationary, particularly after 1920 when much of the rise in cigarette consumption, instead of other forms of tobacco, occurred.[59]

In a recent review, Rigdon and Kirchoff[65] document that primary lung cancer was first recognized as an entity during the early part of the 19th century, and that its occurrence has increased steadily since then, as manifested by the recorded relative frequency with which it was recognized in the clinic and at necropsy. This is undoubtedly correct but does not constitute evidence against a true increase in the incidence of the disease during the whole, or a more recent part, of the last 100 years.

Hueper,[43] accepting a true increase in the incidence of lung cancer, regards an increase dating back to 1900, or before the widespread use of cigarettes, as evidence against the cigarette–lung-cancer relationship. His contention would have crucial import only if it were maintained that cigarette smoking is the sole cause of lung cancer.

The vital statistics and the necropsy data that support the presumption of a real increase in lung-cancer risk certainly apply to the years after 1920. Because of the uncertainties associated with changes in diagnostic accuracy, no firm conclusions can be reached on whether the *rate* of increase in lung-cancer mortality has, in truth, accelerated since 1920.

Effect of Aging

Rosenblatt[67] has raised the question about the effect of the aging population on the lung-cancer rate. This particular point has been investigated by the use of age-adjusted rates. Dunn[22] has noted that only one sixth of the over-all increase in lung-cancer mortality among males in the United States (from 4 to 24 deaths per 100,000 males between 1930 and 1951) could be attributed to an aging population. Similar findings[16] have been presented for England and Wales where observations on lung-cancer mortality date back to 1900; the 1953 mortality rate for both sexes, 34 per 100,000 population, was 43 times the corresponding 1900 rate, 0.8 per 100,000 population. Allowance for increased average age of the population could account for only half this rise in lung-cancer mortality, with a 24-fold difference between 1900 and 1953.

Also, an aging population does not affect the age-specific death rates and cannot account for the phenomenon of increasingly higher lung-cancer mortality at all ages throughout the lifespan, which has occurred among successively younger groups of males born in the United States and England and Wales since 1850. A similar but less pronounced "cohort displacement" has been shown for females.

Diagnostic Factors

Little[52] and others[64] have raised the important question on whether better diagnostic measures and more complete reporting have resulted in a spurious increase in the recorded attack rate. Several special features of the increase in lung-cancer mortality would be difficult to account for on diagnostic grounds. These include the continuous rising ratio of male to female deaths, the increasing lung-cancer mortality rate among successively younger cohorts, and the magnitude of the current, continuing, increase in lung cancer-mortality.[16] By 1955, among white males, 50 to 64 years of age, in the United States, more deaths were attributed to lung cancer than to all other respiratory diseases combined.

Gilliam[29] has made a careful study of the potential effect of improved diagnosis on the course of the lung-cancer death rate. Even assuming that 2 per cent of the deaths certified in past years as tuberculosis or other respiratory disease were really due to lung cancer, he concluded that ". . . . all of the increase in mortality attributed to cancer of the lung since 1914 in United States white males and females cannot be accounted for by erroneous death certification to other respiratory diseases without unreasonable assumptions of age and sex differences in diagnostic error." His computations reduced the respective 26-fold and sevenfold increase in lung-cancer mortality among males and females, between 1914 and 1950, to the more modestly estimated dimensions of fourfold and 30 per cent, respectively. These estimates are certainly the lower bound on the magnitude of the true rate of increase during this period.

The Copenhagen Tuberculosis Station data, examined by Clemmesen et al.,[14] provide the greatest measure of control on the diagnostic improvement factor. In a tuberculosis referral service, used extensively by local physicians, where diagnostic standards and procedures including systematic bronchoscopy remained virtually unchanged between 1941 and 1950, the lung-cancer prevalence rate among male examinees increased at a rate comparable to that recorded by the Danish cancer registry for the total male population. This can be regarded as evidence that the reported increase in Danish incidence is not due to diagnostic changes.

Necropsy Data

Most necropsy data agree with mortality data on the increase in lung-cancer risk. To establish this point we referred to a necropsy series summarized by Steiner,[72] and returned to the original sources for evidence on the nature of changes over time. Since an existing compilation was chosen, the results do not represent a culling of autopsy series for data favorable to this thesis. The findings from 13 series are summarized in text-figure 1 as the proportion of lung cancers in relation to all necropsies. The relative frequency in terms of total tumors or total carcinomas yielded results which would lead to substantially the same inferences.

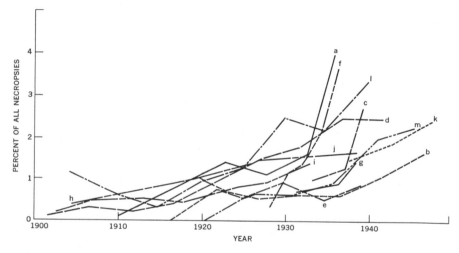

1   Relative frequency of carcinomas of the lung found at necropsy in 13 series. Complete references to material shown are listed in Steiner (72): (a) Frissel, (b) Gibson, (c) Halpert, (d) Jeuther, (e) Johnson, (f) Matz, (g) Menne, (h) Nagayo, (i) Perrone, (k) Saxton, (l) Steiner (1944), (m) Steiner (1950).

Mortality and necropsy data have their own virtues and weaknesses. Death certificates provide a complete report of deaths, but do not emphasize a high quality of diagnostic evidence, while the reverse holds true for necropsies. However, since both approaches lead to the same inferences, neither great variation in the quality of diagnostic evidence nor the unrepresentative nature of some of the necropsy observations can be viewed as plausible interpretations of the results. The alternative conclusion of a real increase in lung-cancer risk remains.

Urban-Rural Differences

Emphasis has been placed on the alleged incompatibility of the excess lung-cancer mortality, among urban residents, with the cigarette-smoking hypothesis.[43,44,54] Mortality data from several countries indicate strongly that lung-cancer rates are much higher in cities than in rural areas, and the observation that urban males in general have higher lung-cancer mortality than rural males is undoubtedly correct. The assertion of Macdonald[54] that ". . . . country people smoke as much, if not more, than do city people . . ." is not borne out by the facts.[35] Nevertheless, the evidence indicates that adjustment for smoking history could account for only a fraction of this urban-rural difference.[33]

However, this does not establish the converse proposition that control of residence history in the analysis of collected data would account for the excess lung-cancer risk among cigarette smokers. Evidence now in hand weighs strongly against this last assertion. Stocks and Campbell,[74] in their report on lung-cancer mortality among persons in Liverpool, the suburban environs, and rural towns in North Wales, showed that heavy smokers have higher lung-cancer rates when urban and rural males were studied separately. Mills and Porter[58] reported similar findings in Ohio. These results agree with the experience of the Hammond-Horn[38] study, which revealed markedly higher death rates for bronchogenic carcinoma among smokers regardless of whether they lived in cities or in rural areas. No contradictory observations are known to us.

Sex Differences

The sex disparity in lung-cancer mortality has also been cited[25,54] as grounds for discarding the cigarette-smoking hypothesis. In this connection it should be noted that persons advocating this line of argument have minimized sex differences in smoking habits to a degree not supported by available facts. A survey of smoking habits in a cross section of the United States population[35] demonstrated that men, on the average, have been smoking for longer periods than women. The sex differences in tobacco use were especially pronounced at ages over 55, when most lung-cancer deaths occur; 0.6 per cent of United States females in this age group have been reported as current users of more than 1 pack of cigarettes daily compared to 6.9 per cent of United States males. British data[76] also revealed much lower tobacco consumption among females, particularly for the years before World War II.

The present data contrasting the experience by sex would appear to support the cigarette-smoking hypothesis rather than discredit it. When differences in smoking habits are considered, it is possible to reduce the observed fivefold excess lung-cancer mortality among males to the 40 per cent excess mortality which prevails for many other causes of death.[33] One intriguing finding from these studies is that the estimated death rates for female nonsmokers agree closely with the death rates derived from retrospective studies on male nonsmokers.[34]

Evidence for Other Etiologic Factors

Etiologic factors of industrial origin, such as exposure to chromates and coal gas, are well established.[16] Excess lung-cancer risks among such groups as asbestos workers who develop asbestosis, appear likely.[16] One epidemiologic study[11] of British, World War I, veterans exposed to mustard gas and/or with a wartime history of influenza revealed virtually no excess lung-cancer risk among these groups.

The existence of other important lung-cancer effects associated with such characteristics as socioeconomic class cannot be questioned. Cohart[15] found that the poorest economic class had a 40 per cent higher lung-cancer incidence than the remaining population of New Haven, Connecticut. Results from the 10-city morbidity survey[21] have revealed a sharp gradient in lung-cancer incidence, by income class, for white males, which is consistent with Cohart's findings. Since cigarette smoking is not inversely related to socioeconomic status, we can agree with Cohart ". . . . that important environmental factors other than cigarette smoking exist that contribute to the causation of lung cancer." These and other findings are convincing evidence for multiple causes of lung cancer. It is obviously untenable to regard smoking of tobacco as the sole cause of lung cancer.

Two points should be made: The population exposed to established industrial carcinogens is small, and these agents cannot account for the increasing lung-cancer risk in the remainder of the population. Also, the effects associated with socioeconomic class and related characteristics are smaller than those noted for smoking history, and the smoking-class differences cannot be accounted for in terms of these other effects.

Special Population Groups

Haag and Hanmer[32] reported that employees in 9 processing plants of the American Tobacco Company, with an above-average proportion of smokers, had a lower mortality than the general population of Virginia and North Carolina for all causes and for cancer and cardiovascular diseases, but no higher mortality for respiratory cancer and coronary disease. They concluded: "The existence of such a population makes it evident that cigarette smoking *per se* is not necessarily or invariably associated with a higher risk of lung cancer or cardiovascular diseases or with diminished longevity."

The group studied by Haag and Hanmer was too small to yield significant results on respiratory cancer. Moreover, a major flaw in the conclusion has been pointed out by Case.[10] It is well known that mortality comparisons cannot be drawn directly between employee groups and the general population, since the death rates for many groups of employed persons are lower than death rates for the general population with age, sex, and race taken into consideration. This is true because there is a strong tendency to exclude from employment those persons who have acute or chronic diseases or who are seriously disabled from any cause and those employees who develop permanent disabilities from disease or other causes are usually discharged, retired, or dropped from the list of regular employees. Reasons of this nature undoubtedly account for the deficit in deaths from all causes noted in the group of employees under consideration.

A different picture is provided by the Society of Actuaries[71] who made a study for 1946 through 1954. The death claims for employees of the tobacco industry were reported to be slightly higher than, and the permanent disability claims were reported to be over three times as high as, those for employees in nonrated industries as a whole. This latter comparison indicates that the basic assumption of the Haag and Hanmer study is incorrect. Also, interpretation of group comparisons in this field should account separately for the experience of smokers and nonsmokers. We hope that Haag and Hanmer will supplement the report to provide data for smokers and nonsmokers in the study population.

II. Retrospective and Prospective Studies

The association between smoking and lung-cancer has now been investigated and reported by at least 21 independent groups of investigators in 8 different countries, who employed what is known as the retrospective method.[16,34,68,69,73,75] In these studies, patients with lung cancer, or their relatives, were questioned about their smoking history and other past events, and the answers compared with those of individuals without lung cancer who were selected as controls. Although these 21 studies have certain features in common, they varied greatly in the methods of selecting the groups, the methods of interview, and other important aspects.

The association between smoking and lung cancer was further investigated in two countries by three independent groups,[18,20,38] using the prospective method. In these studies, large groups were questioned on smoking habits and other characteristics, and the groups were observed for several years for data on mortality and causes of death. The three prospective studies also varied in several important details including the type of subjects, the selection of subjects, and the method of obtaining information on smoking habits.

In each of these studies, an association was found between smoking and lung cancer. In every investigation where the type of smoking was considered, a higher degree of association was found between lung cancer and cigarette smoking than between lung cancer and pipe or cigar smoking. In every instance where amount of smoking was considered, it was found that the degree of association with lung-cancer increased as the amount of smoking increased. When ex-cigarette smokers were compared with current cigarette smokers, it was found that lung-cancer death rates were higher among current cigarette smokers than among ex-cigarette smokers.

A number of investigators[3,36,54] have criticized the retrospective method but, for the most part, the specific points of criticism apply only to some of the studies and not to others. Some features of the three prospective studies on smoking also have been criticized. Again, certain of the points of criticism apply to one or another of the three prospective studies but not to all three. Specifically, doubts raised as to the validity of the early findings of the prospective studies have been eliminated by the persistence of the findings in the later phases of the same studies.

The validity of the findings on these extensive investigations has been questioned in regard to two major aspects: 1) the methods of selection of the study groups, and 2) the accuracy of information regarding smoking habits and the diagnosis of lung cancer.

Selection of Study Groups

Neyman[60] pointed out that a study based on a survey of a population at some given instant of time may yield misleading results. Suppose that a study is made on a day when all patients with lung cancer and a group of people without lung cancer are questioned about their smoking habits. If smokers with lung cancer live longer than nonsmokers with lung cancer, there would be a higher proportion of smokers in the lung-cancer group than in the control group—this would follow without questioning the proposition on which the model is based. However, only two of the retrospective studies were conducted in a way approximating an "instantaneous survey" procedure, so that this criticism does not apply to most of the studies. Furthermore, this difficulty is completely avoided in prospective studies.

Berkson[3] indicated that people with two specific complaints are more likely to be hospitalized than people with only one of these complaints. If a retrospective study were conducted exclusively on hospital patients an association would be found between these two specific complaints, even if there were no association between the same two complaints in the general population. This would influence the results if smokers with lung cancer are more likely to be hospitalized than non-smokers with lung cancer. However, Berkson showed that this difficulty is trivial if a high percentage of people with either one of these two conditions is hospitalized, which is the situation with lung-cancer patients. Furthermore, one retrospective study[74] included all lung-cancer patients who were in the study area, including those not hospitalized; another retrospective study[82] was based on individuals who died of lung cancer and other diseases regardless of whether they had been hospitalized or not. This difficulty does not arise in prospective studies.

In all but one of the 21 retrospective studies, the procedure was to compare the smoking habits of lung-cancer patients with the smoking habits of a control group who did not have lung cancer. Hammond,[36] Berkson,[3] and others have pointed out the grave danger of bias if the control group is not selected in such a way as to represent (in respect to smoking habits) the general population which includes the lung-cancer patients. Subsequent events have proved that this criticism is well founded, though the direction of the bias in most studies turned out to yield an underestimate of the degree of association between cigarette smoking and lung cancer. The reason was that in most of the retrospective studies the control group consisted of patients with diseases other than lung cancer. The choice of such a control group is tantamount to assuming that there is no association between smoking and diseases which resulted in hospitalization of the control subjects. This was an incorrect assumption since other studies have indicated an association between smoking and a number of diseases, such as coronary artery disease, thromboangiitis obliterans, and cancer of the buccal cavity.

Doll and Hill,[17] recognizing the possibility of bias in a control group selected from hospital patients, obtained an additional control group by ascertaining the smoking habits of the general population in a random sample of the area in which their hospital was located. The largest percentage of smokers (particularly heavy smokers) was found in the lung-cancer group, the smallest percentage of smokers was found in the general population sample, and an intermediate percentage of smokers was found in the hospital-control group. Similar results have been reported in a recent study of women.[34]

Berkson[3] pointed out that the criticisms in regard to selection bias in the retrospective studies are also applicable to the earlier findings in a prospective study. Suppose that, in selecting subjects for a prospective study, sick smokers are overrepresented in relation to well smokers and/or well nonsmokers are overrepresented in relation to sick nonsmokers. In this event, during the earlier period after selection, the death rate of the smokers in the study would be higher than the death rate of the nonsmokers in the study, even if death rates were unrelated to smoking habits of the general population. If smoking is unrelated to death from lung cancer (or other causes), the death rate of the smokers would tend to equalize with that of the nonsmokers as the study progressed. Thus, the bias would diminish with time, and a relationship due to such bias would disappear. This general principle is well known to actuaries and is one of the cornerstones of the life insurance business.

Hammond and Horn,[38] recognizing this possible difficulty, excluded from the study all persons who were obviously ill at the time of selection. As expected, the total death rate of the study population was low and very few deaths from lung cancer occurred during the first 8 months after selection. The total death rate, and particularly the death rate from lung cancer, rose considerably in the subsequent 3 years. What is more important, the observed association between cigarette smoking and lung cancer was considerably higher in the latter part than in the early part of the study, and the association between cigarette smoking and total death rates was also somewhat greater in the latter part of the study. This showed that the original bias in the selection of the subjects was slight and that it yielded an underestimate of the degree of association between smoking and death rates.

This particular problem was not encountered in the prospective studies of Doll and Hill[18] who could observe the death rates of all physicians in Great Britain (nonresponders as well as responders to the smoking questionnaire). The prospective study of Dorn[20] also had a defined population of veterans holding insurance policies, and nonresponders were observed as well as responders. Moreover, these two studies also showed that higher mortality from lung cancer among smokers was more evident during the later period than in the earlier period of observation. Thus, in the course of time, there was no disappearance of any selection bias factors that may have been introduced into the original study groups.

The subjects for the Hammond and Horn prospective study[38] were selected by volunteer workers with specific instructions on how it should be done. Mainland and Herrera[55] have suggested that the volunteer workers may have introduced a bias in the way they selected the subjects. The foregoing evidence of persistence and accentuation of the differences between smokers and nonsmokers, in time, effectively counters purposeful, as well as unknown, sources of such selection.

Accuracy of Information

Berkson[3,4] has remarked that the two major variables considered in all these studies—the ascertainment of smoking habits and the diagnosis of disease—are both subject to considerable error. The accuracy of diagnosis is not a major problem in retrospective studies because the investigator can restrict his study to those patients whose diagnosis of lung cancer has been thoroughly confirmed. This feature has been taken into consideration in several retrospective studies. It is more of a problem in prospective studies since all deaths that occur must be included, and certainly some of the diagnoses will be uncertain. However, in all three prospective studies, the *total death rate* was found to be higher in cigarette smokers than in nonsmokers and found to increase with the amount of cigarette smoking. If some of the excess deaths associated with cigarette smoking and ascribed to lung cancer were actually due to some other disease, then it means that: a) the association between cigarette smoking and lung cancer was somewhat overestimated, but b) the association between smoking and some other disease was somewhat underestimated. The reverse would be true if some of the excess deaths associated with cigarette smoking and ascribed to diseases other than lung cancer were actually due to lung cancer. Hammond and Horn[38] found that the association with cigarette smoking was greater for patients with a well-established diagnosis of lung cancer than for patients with less convincing evidence for a diagnosis of lung cancer. This suggests that inaccuracies in diagnosis resulted somewhat in an underestimate of the degree of association between smoking and lung cancer.

The study on physicians, by Doll and Hill,[18] in which presumably the clinical and pathologic evidence of the cause of death would be somewhat more than in the general population considered by Hammond and Horn and by Dorn, yields almost identical risks to lung cancer by smoking class.

In regard to information about smoking, Finkner et al.[24] have made a thorough study of the accuracy of replies to questionnaires on smoking habits. Their results indicate that replies are not completely accurate but that most of the errors are relatively minor—very few heavy smokers are classified as light smokers. Random and independent errors simply tend to diminish the apparent degree of association between two variables. A national survey of smoking habits in the United States[35] yielded results on tobacco consumption that were consistent with figures on tobacco production and taxation.

On two occasions several years apart, Hammond and Horn[38] and Dorn[20] questioned a proportion of their subjects. The results indicated close reproducibility in the answers.

Hammond[36] and others[54] have questioned the reliability of the retrospective method on the grounds that the illness may bias the responses given by the patient or his family when they are questioned about smoking habits, and that knowledge of the diagnosis may bias the interviewer. This possible difficulty was minimized in several of the 21 retrospective studies on smoking in relation to lung cancer. For example, in the study conducted by Levin,[49] all patients admitted to a hospital during the course of several years were questioned about their smoking habits *before* a diagnosis was made. Only a small proportion later turned out to have lung cancer, though many had lung disease symptoms or lung diseases other than lung cancer. Doll and Hill[18] also showed that patients whose diagnosis of lung cancer was subsequently established to be erroneous had smoking histories characteristic of the control rather than of the lung-cancer group. Furthermore, a larger percentage of cigarette smokers have been found among patients with epidermoid carcinoma of the lungs than among patients with adenocarcinoma of the lungs.[34,46,79] This could hardly have resulted from bias either on the part of the patient or on the part of the interviewer.

Multiple Variables

Arkin,[1] Little,[52] Macdonald,[54] and others have criticized the studies of cigarette–lung-cancer relationship on the grounds that only smoking habits were really investigated, and that numerous other possible variables were not considered.

This criticism may seem especially appropriate in view of the accepted fact that no single etiologic factor has been proposed for any neoplastic disease. The criticism may also be valid in relation to any one of the retrospective and prospective studies. However, in the aggregate, quite a number of other variables have been specifically investigated or can be inferentially derived. Of course, all studies considered the basic factors of age and sex; some dealt with geographic distribution,[74] occupation,[8] urban or rural residence,[74] marital and parous status,[34] and some other habits such as coffee consumption.[34]

The Doll and Hill[18] prospective study was confined to a single professional group, physicians. Thus there could be no great variation attributable to occupation or socioeconomic status. Stocks and Campbell[74] put particular emphasis on the study of air pollution and occupational exposure and included a number of other factors in addition to smoking. It is evident, in the Hammond-Horn[38] study and other investigations, that there is a consistent relationship between urban residence and a higher mortality due to lung cancer. The important fact is that in all studies, when other variables are held constant, cigarette smoking retains its high association with lung cancer.

The only factors that may show a higher correlation with lung cancer than heavy cigarette smoking are such occupations as those of the Schneeberg miners and manufacturers of chromate.[16] We are not acquainted with actual studies of these and related occupation groups in which cigarette and other tobacco consumption is also considered. Such studies, we suggest, would be useful additions to our knowledge of other etiologic agents and of the interplay between multiple causes in human pulmonary cancer.

III. Studies on Pathogenesis

Inhalation of Smoke

If cigarette smoking produces cancer of the lungs as a result of direct contact between tobacco smoke and the bronchial mucosa, smokers who inhale cigarette smoke should be exposed to higher concentrations of the carcinogens than noninhalers and therefore have a higher risk to the development of lung cancer. The retrospective study of Doll and Hill,[17] however, elicited no difference between patients with lung cancer and the controls in the proportion of smokers who stated that they inhaled. Fisher,[25] Hueper,[43] and Macdonald[54] have emphasized this point as contradictory to the smoking–lung-cancer relationship, and, of course, it is. Unfortunately, this particular finding was not reinvestigated in the prospective study of Doll and Hill.[18]

Three authors, Lickint,[50] Breslow *et al.*,[8] and Schwartz and Denoix,[68] however, *did* find the relative risk of lung cancer to be greater among inhalers than among noninhalers when age, type, and amount of smoking were held constant. It must be admitted that there is no clear explanation of the contradiction posed by the Doll-Hill[17] findings, though a number of plausible hypotheses could be advanced. More experimental work is required, including some objective definition and measurement of the depth and length of inhalation.

Hammond[37] has recently queried male smokers about their inhalation practices. He found that very few pipe and cigar smokers inhale; that most men inhale who smoke only cigarettes; and that there are proportionally fewer inhalers among men who smoke both cigars and cigarettes than among men who smoke only cigarettes. These findings are compatible with the view that differences in inhaling account for the fact that the lung-cancer death rate of cigar and pipe smokers is less than the lung-cancer death rate of cigarette smokers; and that the lung-cancer death rate of men who smoke both cigars and cigarettes is somewhat lower than the lung-cancer death rate of men who smoke only cigarettes.

Upper-Respiratory Cancer

Rosenblatt[67] has drawn attention to the fact that increased consumption of cigarettes has not been accompanied by an increase in upper-respiratory cancer similar to that noted in cancer of the lung and bronchus. Hueper[43] also has expressed doubts about the causative role of cigarette smoking on the basis that cigarette smoking is not associated with cancer of the oral cavity or of the fingers, which are often stained with tobacco tar.

The premise that a carcinogen should act equally on different tissues is not supported by experimental or clinical evidence.[70] Carcinogens, which produce liver tumors in animals, may be noncarcinogenic when applied to the skin. Coal soot, accepted as etiologically related to carcinoma of the scrotum in chimney sweeps, does not increase the risk to cancer of the penis. There is no *a priori* reason why a carcinogen that produces bronchogenic cancer in man should also produce neoplastic changes in the nasopharynx or in other sites. It is an intriguing fact, deserving further research, that carcinoma of the trachea is a rarity, whereas carcinoma of the bronchus is common among individuals exposed to chromates, as well as among chronic cigarette smokers.

Several studies have established the association of all types of tobacco smoking, including cigarettes, with cancer of the oral cavity.[81] However, the *relative* risk of developing cancer of the mouth is greater for cigar and pipe smokers than for cigarette smokers. The risk of laryngeal cancer is increased by smoking and an equal risk exists among cigarette, cigar, and pipe smokers.[80] The per capita consumption of cigars and pipe tobacco has decreased since 1920, while cigarette smoking has increased.[59]

These associations contrast sharply with the findings on lung cancer, which have consistently shown that cigarette smokers have much higher risks than either cigar or pipe smokers. Since 1920 the increase in tobacco consumption has been primarily due to the rise in cigarette consumption,[59] and the stabler rates for intra-oral and laryngeal cancer, while the lung-cancer rates have increased steeply, can be considered compatible with the causal role of cigarette smoking in lung cancer.

Effect of Tobacco Smoke on Bronchial Mucosa

Statements by Hartnett,[39] Macdonald,[54] and others[3,52] imply that the relationship of cigarette smoking and lung cancer is based exclusively on "statistics" and lacks "experimental" evidence. The differentiation between various methods of scientific inquiry escapes us as being a valid basis for the acceptance or the rejection of facts. Nevertheless it is true that historically the retrospective studies on lung cancer preceded the intensive interest in laboratory investigations stimulated by the statistical findings.

Hilding[40] has shown experimentally that exposure to cigarette smoke inhibited ciliary action in the isolated bronchial epithelium of cows. Kotin and Falk[45] obtained essentially the same results in experiments on rats and rabbits. Hilding[41] further showed that inhibition of ciliary action interfered with the mechanism whereby foreign material is ordinarily removed from the surface of bronchial epithelium. In addition he found that foreign material deposited on the surface tended to accumulate in any area where the cilia have been destroyed. Auerbach et al.[2] found that the small areas of the bronchial epithelium where ciliated columnar cells were absent appeared more frequently in smokers than in nonsmokers. Chang[12] found that cilia were shorter, on an average, in the bronchial epithelium of smokers than in that of nonsmokers.

These studies have demonstrated the existence of a mechanism whereby foreign material from any source (*e.g.*, tobacco smoke, industrial dusts, fumes from automobile exhausts, general air pollutants, and, perhaps, pathogenic organisms) is likely to remain in contact with the bronchial epithelium for a longer period in smokers than in nonsmokers.

Auerbach and his associates[2] studied the microscopic appearance of the bronchial epithelium of patients who died of lung cancer and patients who died of other diseases. Each of these two groups of patients was classified according to whether they were nonsmokers, light smokers, or heavy cigarette smokers. Among the cancer patients there were no nonsmokers. Approximately 208 sections from all parts of the tracheo-bronchial tree from each patient were examined. Many areas of basal-cell hyperplasia, squamous metaplasia, and marked atypism with loss of columnar epithelium were found in the tracheo-bronchial tree of men who had died of lung cancer. Almost as many such lesions were found in heavy cigarette smokers who had died of other diseases; somewhat less were found in light cigarette smokers; and much less in nonsmokers. Chang[12] has reported similar findings in the bronchial epithelium of smokers compared with nonsmokers.

The chief criticism of Auerbach's study has concerned terminology. Following the definition previously set forth by Black and Ackerman,[5] Auerbach *et al.* used the term "carcinoma-*in-situ*" to describe certain lesions with marked atypical changes and loss of columnar epithelium. Whether this is an appropriate term may be questioned, but it is not relevant to the validity of the findings. Certainly there are no data to indicate what proportion of these morphologically abnormal areas would progress to invasive carcinoma.

The recent findings of Auerbach *et al.* and Chang have been reproduced experimentally in animals. Rockey and his associates[66] applied tobacco "tar" directly to the bronchial mucosa of dogs. Within 3 to 6 weeks, the tar-treated surface became granular and later developed wartlike elevations. Upon microscopic examination, hyperplasia, transitional metaplasia, and squamous metaplasia were found in these areas. Leuchtenberger *et al.*[48] exposed mice to cigarette smoke for periods up to 200 days. The bronchial epithelium was then examined microscopically. Bronchitis, basal-cell hyperplasia, and atypical basal-cell hyperplasia were found in the majority of the animals, and squamous metaplasia in a few. Further work and longer periods of observation are necessary to establish whether some of these lesions would progress to frank neoplasia.

IV. Other Laboratory Investigations

Skin Cancer in Rodents

One of the links in the total evidence for the causal relationship of cigarette smoking and lung cancer is the demonstration that tobacco-smoke condensates (usually referred to as "tars") have the biologic property of evoking carcinoma in certain laboratory animals, particularly mice. The production of skin cancer in mice, following repeated, long-term applications of tobacco tar, has now been reported from at least six different laboratories.[7,23,28,61,63,83] It is undeniable that some investigators did not obtain positive results, perhaps because the dose and other experimental conditions were different, or because the complex tobacco tars probably varied widely in their composition. The negative results of Passey *et al.*[62] have been quoted by Hueper[43] and others, but a more recent experiment by Passey[63] with Swiss strain mice did lead to the appearance of at least two carcinomas after repeated applications of tobacco-smoke condensate.

Little[52] indicated that ". . . the extrapolation to the human lung of results obtained by painting of or injection into the skin of mice is decidedly questionable." Direct extrapolation from one species to another is, of course, not justified. Nevertheless, results in animals are fully consistent with the epidemiologic findings in man. A quotation from Kotin[44] is appropriate: "The chemical demonstration of carcinogenic agents in the environment and their successful use for the production of tumors in experimental animals do not prove or even especially strongly suggest a like relationship in the instance of man. When, however, a demonstrable parallelism exists between epidemiologic data and laboratory findings, greater significance accrues to both. Medical history is replete with examples in which laboratory findings have been proved ultimately to have their counterpart in the human experience. Exceptions have been very few."

Greene,[31] while discounting the significance of the induction of skin carcinoma in Swiss mice because of the constitutionally "high differential susceptibility" of the strain, believes that the failure to induce neoplasms in embryonic transplants exposed to tobacco tar is more important evidence. Greene's interesting technique does produce positive results when pure chemicals such as benzo[a]pyrene are used, and this chemical has been recovered from some samples of tobacco-smoke condensate. We are not acquainted with reports of neoplasms arising in embryonic tissue that has been exposed *in vitro* to coal tar, another crude mixture that contains carcinogens.

The high frequency of carcinoma induction reported by Wynder *et al.*[83] has not been achieved by other investigators, who reported that no more than 20 per cent of animals, and usually considerably less, developed carcinoma of the skin. The presence of cocarcinogenic materials in tobacco-smoke condensates has been demonstrated by Gellhorn[28] and by Bock and Moore.[7] To the mouse data are now added the data on the induction of skin cancer in some rabbits painted with tobacco-smoke condensate[30]; this condensate, when combined with a killed suspension of tubercle bacilli, and introduced into a bronchus, produced a carcinoma of the bronchus in one rat.[6]

Since malignant neoplasms have been obtained in several strains of mice, and a few neoplasms have been produced in rabbits and rats, the issue of strain or species limitation to the reaction is more difficult to maintain. It is, of course, a fact that many agents shown to be carcinogenic to the skin of mice have not been proved carcinogenic to man. In most instances there is simply no experience with such agents in man, so that lack of proof really represents lack of data, pro and con.

The Problem of Dosage

Little[52] has further questioned the applicability of animal data to man, as follows: "Tobacco smoke or smoke condensate has failed to produce cancer even on the skin of susceptible strains of mice when applied in the quantity and at an exposure rate that would simulate conditions of human smoking."

The differences in species, tissues, and conditions between the induction of neoplasms on the skin of mice and in the bronchi of man preclude fine comparisons of dose and time relationships.

Bronchogenic Cancer in Animals

The pulmonary adenomatous tumor in mice, rats, and guinea pigs cannot be compared with the bronchogenic carcinoma in man.[70] Until a few years ago, the experimental induction of epidermoid carcinoma had been achieved only in a few mice by passing strings impregnated with carcinogenic hydrocarbons through the lung. Epidermoid carcinoma of the lung was consistently produced in rats by beryllium,[78] by carcinogenic hydrocarbons introduced as fixed pellets into bronchi of rats,[47] and by inhalation of radioactive particles.[13]

Little[52] has noted that ". . . . prolonged exposure of the lungs of rodents to massive doses of cigarette smoke has failed to produce bronchogenic cancer." This remains true at the time of this report, although it can be questioned whether any animal receives as large a dose of cigarette smoke through indirect exposure as a human being does by voluntary deep inhalation. Therefore the failure may be a technical one, which may be solved by further experimentation. The early results of Leuchtenberger et al.[48] suggested that this may be achieved.

Carcinogens in Tobacco Smoke

The isolation and identification of specific chemical constituents in tobacco smoke, which are carcinogenic for the pulmonary tissue of man, is an important area for research.

It has been clear for some time that combustion or pyrolysis of most organic material, including tobacco, will form higher aromatic polycyclics of established carcinogenic activity.[85] A number of higher aromatic polycylics have been identified and isolated.[53,61,77,84] These materials include benzo[e]pyrene, benzo[a]-pyrene, dibenz[a,h]anthracene, chrysene, and, most recently, a newly established carcinogen, 3,4-benzfluoranthene. Whether these compounds are equally involved in human pulmonary carcinogenesis is, of course, conjectural.

Little[52] has implied that a specific constituent must be found to account for the biologic activity of tobacco smoke. This is not necessary. The situation is similar to the establishment of the carcinogenic activity of tar, which was accepted before the isolation of benzo[a]pyrene by Kennaway and his coworkers. In this instance, also, benzo[a]pyrene is most probably not the only carcinogen in the complex mixture called tar, and there are strong indications that some noncarcinogenic components in tar may have cocarcinogenic effects.

V. Interpretation

Three interpretations of the observed association of lung cancer and cigarette smoking are possible: (1) that cigarette smoking "causes" lung cancer, either (a) through the direct carcinogenic action of smoke on human bronchial epithelium or (b) by a more indirect mode of action such as making the individual susceptible to some other specific carcinogenic agent in the environment; (2) that lung cancer "causes" cigarette smoking, perhaps because a precancerous condition sets up a process which leads to a craving for tobacco; (3) that cigarette smoking and lung cancer both have a common cause, usually specified as a special constitutional make-up, perhaps genetic in origin, which predisposes certain individuals to lung cancer and also makes them cigarette smokers.

The second hypothesis was advanced by Fisher,[26] apparently for the sake of logical completeness, and it is not clear whether it is intended to be regarded as a serious possibility. Since we know of no evidence to support the view that the bronchogenic carcinoma diagnosed after age 50 began before age 18, the median age at which cigarette smokers begin smoking, we shall not discuss it further.

The Constitutional Hypothesis

The first hypothesis may be referred to as the *causal* hypothesis and the third as the *constitutional* hypothesis. Nothing short of a series of independently conducted, controlled, experiments on human subjects, continued for 30 to 60 years, could provide a clear-cut and unequivocal choice between them. We nevertheless argue that evidence, in addition to that associating an increased mortality from lung cancer with cigarette smoking, is entirely consistent with the causal hypothesis but inconsistent, in many respects, with the constitutional hypothesis, so that even in the absence of controlled experimentation on human beings the weight of the evidence is for the one and against the other.

The difficulties with the constitutional hypothesis include the following considerations: (a) changes in lung-cancer mortality over the last half century; (b) the carcinogenicity of tobacco tars for experimental animals; (c) the existence of a large effect from pipe and cigar tobacco on cancer of the buccal cavity and larynx but not on cancer of the lung; (d) the reduced lung-cancer mortality among discontinued cigarette smokers. No one of these considerations is perhaps sufficient by itself to counter the constitutional hypothesis *ad hoc* modification of which can accommodate each additional piece of evidence. A point is reached, however, when a continuously modified hypothesis becomes difficult to entertain seriously.

Changes in Mortality

Mortality from lung cancer has increased continuously in the last 50 years, and considerably more for males than females. Such an increase can be explained either as the result of an environmental change (to which males are more exposed or more sensitive than females, if both are equally exposed) or as the result of a sex-linked mutation. The constitutional hypothesis must be modified in the light of this increase, since an unchanging constitutional make-up cannot by itself explain an increase in mortality. Proponents of the constitutional hypothesis have not indicated the type of modification they would consider. Three suggest themselves to us: (1) differences in constitutional make-up are genetic in origin, but rather than predisposing one to lung cancer, they make one sensitive to some new environmental agent (other than tobacco), which does induce lung cancer; (2) differences in constitutional make-up are not genetic but are the result of differential exposure to some new environmental agent, which both predisposes to lung cancer and creates a craving for cigarette smoke; (3) the mutation has led to a greater susceptibility to lung cancer and a preference for cigarette smoke.

In the first two situations the effect of the postulated constitutional make-up would be mediated through an environmental agent. The modified hypothesis thus requires the existence of an environmental agent other than tobacco, exposure to which would be at least as highly correlated with lung-cancer mortality as exposure to cigarettes, and which also would be highly correlated with cigarette consumption. No such agent has yet been found or even suggested. In view of the magnitude of the increase in mortality from lung cancer, the third situation would require a mutation rate exceeding anything previously observed.

Experimental Carcinogenesis with Tobacco Tar

Condensed tobacco smoke contains substances that are carcinogenic for mouse and rabbit skin. It does not necessarily follow that these substances are also carcinogenic for human lungs nor does it follow that they are not. However, the constitutional hypothesis asserts they are not; and that it is simply a coincidence that these materials which are carcinogenic for experimental animals are also associated with a higher lung-cancer mortality in man.

Types of Tobacco and Cancer Site

A greatly increased lung-cancer risk is associated with increased cigarette consumption but not with increased consumption of pipe and cigar tobacco. Studies on cancer of the buccal cavity and larynx, however, have demonstrated a considerably higher risk among smokers, irrespective of the form of tobacco used. Only two ways of modifying the constitutional hypothesis to take account of this evidence occur to us: (1) There are two different constitutional make-ups, one of which predisposes to cigarettes but not to pipe and cigar consumption and to cancer of the lung, and the other predisposes to cancer of the buccal cavity and larynx but not of the lung and to tobacco consumption in any form. (2) Constitutional make-up predisposes to cigarette consumption and lung cancer only, but tobacco smoke, whether from cigarettes, cigars, or pipes, is carcinogenic for the mucosa of the buccal cavity and the larynx but not for the bronchial epithelium.

Mortality among Discontinued Smokers

Mortality from lung cancer among discontinued cigarette smokers is less than that among those continuing to smoke[18,38]; the magnitude of the reduction depending on amount previously smoked and the length of the discontinuance. The hypothetical constitutional factor which predisposes to lung cancer and cigarette smoking cannot therefore be a constant characteristic of an individual over his lifetime but must decrease in force at some time in life, thus resulting in the cessation of cigarette smoking and a concomitant, but not causally related, reduction in the lung-cancer risk. Furthermore, since cigarette smoking is rarely begun after age 35,[35] it must be inferred that the constitutional factor cannot increase in force with the passage of time, even though it may decrease.

In summary, the constitutional hypothesis does not provide a satisfactory explanation of all the evidence. It is natural, therefore, to inquire about the positive findings which support it. Even those who regard this hypothesis with favor would agree, we believe, that supporting evidence is quite scanty.

There are a number of characteristics in which cigarette smokers are known to differ from nonsmokers and presumably more will be discovered. Thus, cigarette smokers consume more alcohol, more black coffee, change jobs more often, engage more in athletics, and are more likely to have had at least one parent with hypertension or coronary artery disease.[34,51,56] Discontinued cigarette smokers are weaned at a later age than those continuing to smoke.[56] Recently, Fisher[27] reported that 51 monozygotic twins resembled each other more in their smoking habits than 33 dizygotic twins, thus suggesting a genetic determinant.

Two somewhat obvious, but necessary, comments on results of this type are in order: (1) The demonstration that a characteristic is related to smoking status does not by itself create a presumption that it is a common cause. It must also be shown to be related to the development of lung cancer among subgroups of individuals with the same smoking status. Alcohol and coffee fail to meet this test, while none of the other characteristics related to smoking status have been investigated from this point of view. (2) There is a quantitative question. Cigarette smokers have a ninefold greater risk of developing lung cancer than nonsmokers, while over-two-pack-a-day smokers have at least a 60-fold greater risk. Any characteristic proposed as a measure of the postulated cause common to both smoking status and lung-cancer risk must therefore be at least nine-fold more prevalent among cigarette smokers than among nonsmokers and at least 60-fold more prevalent among two-pack-a-day smokers. No such characteristic has yet been produced despite diligent search.

Measures of Differences

The comments in the last two paragraphs have utilized a relative measure of differences in lung-cancer risk. Since Berkson[4] has argued that a relative measure is inappropriate in the investigation of smoking and mortality, we now discuss the use of relative and absolute measures of differences in risk. When an agent has an apparent effect on several diseases, the ranking of the diseases by the magnitude of the effect will depend on whether an absolute or a relative measure is used. Thus in Dorn's study[20] of American veterans there were 187 lung-cancer deaths among cigarette smokers compared with an expectation of 20 deaths, based on the rates for nonsmokers. This yields a mortality ratio of 9.35 as a relative measure and an excess of 167 deaths as an absolute measure. For cardiovascular diseases there were 1,780 deaths among cigarette smokers compared to an expectation of 1,165. This gives a relative measure of 1.53 and an absolute measure of 615 deaths. Relatively, cigarettes have a much larger effect on lung cancer than on cardiovascular disease, while the reverse is true if an absolute measure is used.

Both the absolute and the relative measures serve a purpose. The relative measure is helpful in (1) appraising the possible noncausal nature of an agent having an apparent effect; (2) appraising the importance of an agent with respect to other possible agents inducing the same effect; and (3) properly reflecting the effects of disease misclassification or further refinement of classification. The absolute measure would be important in appraising the public health significance of an effect known to be causal.

The first justification for use of the relative measure can be stated more precisely, as follows:

> If an agent, A, with no causal effect upon the risk of a disease, nevertheless, because of a positive correlation with some other causal agent, B, shows an apparent risk, r, for those exposed to A, relative to those not so exposed, then the prevalence of B, among those exposed to A, relative to the prevalence among those not so exposed, must be greater than r.

Thus, if cigarette smokers have 9 times the risk of nonsmokers for developing lung cancer, and this is not because cigarette smoke is a causal agent, but only because cigarette smokers produce hormone X, then the proportion of hormone-X-producers among cigarette smokers must be at least 9 times greater than that of non-smokers. If the relative prevalence of hormone-X-producers is considerably less than ninefold, then hormone X cannot account for the magnitude of the apparent effect.

The second reason for using a relative measure may be phrased as follows:

> If two uncorrelated agents, A and B, each increase the risk of a disease, and if the risk of the disease in the absence of either agent is small (in a sense to be defined), then the apparent relative risk for A, r, is less than the risk for A in the absence of B.

The presence of other real causes thus reduces the apparent relative risk. If, for example, the relative risk of developing either disease I or disease II on exposure to A is the same in the absence of other causes, and if disease I, but not disease II, also has agent B present, then the apparent relative risk of developing disease I on exposure to A will be less than that for disease II.

The third reason for using a relative measure is:

> If a causal agent A increases the risk for disease I and has no effect on the risk for disease II, then the relative risk of developing disease I, alone, is greater than the relative risk of developing disease I and II combined, while the absolute measure is unaffected.

Thus, in the Hammond-Horn study, the association of cigarette smoking and lung cancer was higher when only patients with a well-substantiated diagnosis of lung cancer were considered, and was lower when the group included question-able diagnoses. Using the relative risk reveals the stronger association of ciga-rette smoking for epidermoid-undifferentiated carcinoma than for adenocarci-noma. The absolute measure would not differentiate between the risk for these subgroups.

The Causal Hypothesis

We turn now to a consideration of some of the contradictions in the causal hypothesis, alleged by various authors. Fisher[25] has stated:

> ■ When the sexes are compared it is found that lung cancer has been in-creasing more rapidly in men relatively to women. . . . But it is notorious, and conspicuous in the memory of the most of us, that over the last 50 years the increase of smoking among women has been great, and that among men (even if positive) certainly small. The theory that increasing smoking is 'the cause' of the change in apparent incidence of lung cancer is not even tenable in the face of this contrast. ■

The available statistics do not confirm Fisher's statement. According to the Tobacco Manufacturer's Standing Committee[76] male per capita consumption of cigarette tobacco in Great Britain increased from 1.9 pounds in 1906 to 8 pounds in 1956. Female per capita consumption increased from essentially zero, in 1906, to 3.1 pounds in 1956. Far from making the causal hypothesis untenable, these results are entirely consistent with it, and constitute, in fact, one of the links in the chain of evidence implicating cigarettes.

The fact that cigarette smoking was associated with a higher mortality not only from lung cancer but from many other causes of death was originally con-sidered as a contradiction by Arkin.[1] Commenting on the first Hammond-Horn report, he wrote:

> ■ It would thus appear that cigarette smoking is one of the causes of all ills and contributes to the over-all death rate, remembering that this rate includes such causes as accident, homicide, etc. It seems quite clear that cigarette smoking is. a symptom, not a cause. It is possible—even though this is a conjecture—that the type of person who is careful of his health is less likely to be a cigarette smoker and that the cigarette smoker is likely to be the person who generally takes greater health risks. ■

Both the later Hammond-Horn[38] report and the study of American veterans[20] show no difference between cigarette and noncigarette smokers in mortality from accidents, violence, and suicide. If nonsmokers are biologically self-pro-tective, it is only with respect to non-accidental causes of death.

Berkson[4] also has pointed to the multiple findings in both the Hammond-Horn and the Doll-Hill results and concluded that the observed associations may have some other explanation than a causal one. He suggests three: (1) "The observed associations are 'spurious'. . . . (2) The observed associations have a constitutional basis. Persons who are nonsmokers, or relatively light smokers, are the kind of people who are biologically self-protective, and biologically this is correlated with robustness in meeting mortal stress from disease generally. (3) Smoking increases the 'rate of living' (Pearl), and smokers at a given age are, biologically, at an age older than their chronologic age."

One might ask why the finding of an association with a number of diseases, rather than just one, is necessarily contradictory and must be regarded as supporting the constitutional hypothesis. Arkin[1] supplied no answer, while the relevant statements of Berkson[4] on this point were:

> ■ For myself, I find it quite incredible that smoking should cause all these diseases.
>
> When an investigation set up to test the theory, suggested by evidence previously obtained, that smoking causes lung cancer, turns out to indicate that smoking causes or provokes a whole gamut of diseases, inevitably it raises the suspicion that something is amiss.
>
> It is not logical to take such a set of results [e.g., an association of smoking with a 'wide variety of diseases'] as confirming the theory that tobacco smoke contains carcinogenic substances which, by contact with the pulmonary tissues, initiate cancerous changes at the site of contact. ■

We see nothing inherently contradictory nor inconsistent in the suggestion that one agent can be responsible for more than one disease, nor are we lacking in precedents. The Great Fog of London in 1952 increased the death rate for a number of causes, particularly respiratory and coronary disease, but no one has given this as a reason for doubting the causal role of the fog. Tobacco smoke, too, is a complex substance and consists of many different combustion products. It would be more "incredible" to find that these hundreds of chemical products all had the same effect than to find the contrary. A universe in which cause and effect always have a one-to-one correspondence with each other would be easier to understand, but it obviously is not the kind we inhabit.

The apparent multiple effects of tobacco do raise a question with respect to the mode of action, however, and since this question is related to another alleged contradiction—the apparent lack of an inhalation effect—we shall discuss them together. What mode of action, it has been asked, can one postulate to explain these diverse effects? Two remarks are in order: (1) The evidence that tobacco is a causal agent in the development of other diseases seems weaker than the evidence for lung cancer simply because the effects are smaller. While we would not exclude the possibility that cigarettes play a causal role in, for instance, the development of arteriosclerotic-coronary heart disease, the possibility that a common third factor will be discovered, which explains a 70 per cent elevation in risk from coronary heart disease among cigarette smokers, is less remote than the possibility that the ninefold risk for lung cancer will be so explained. (2) Accepting, for the sake of discussion, the causal role of cigarettes for any disease showing an elevated mortality ratio, no matter how small, the presence of other causes will be manifested in a lowered mortality ratio. Thus, even if cigarette consumption causes an elevation of 70 per cent in mortality from coronary heart disease, other causes of great importance must also be present, as is manifested by the high mortality from this disease among nonsmokers. The existence of a small number of nonsmokers who develop lung cancer is a definite indication, by the same token, that cigarettes are not an absolutely necessary condition and that there are other causes of lung cancer.

If tobacco smoke does have multiple effects, each of these effects must be studied separately because of the complex nature of the agent. To postulate in advance that a single mode of action will be found to characterize them all is an unwarranted oversimplification. It is generally accepted, for example, that tobacco smoke causes thromboangiitis obliterans in susceptible humans by interfering with the peripheral circulation, and that it causes tumors when painted on the backs of susceptible mice because of the presence of carcinogens in the tars. The *a priori* postulation of a single mode of action for these two effects is no substitute for detailed study of each.

As to the possible mode of action of tobacco smoke in inducing lung cancer, the evidence at this writing suggests direct action of substances in tobacco smoke on susceptible tissues with which they are in contact. Aside from background knowledge derived from experimental carcinogenesis which suggests this explanation, the following evidence favors it: (1) Cigarette smoke, which is usually drawn into the lungs, is associated with mortality from lung cancer, while smoke from pipes and cigars, which is usually not inhaled, is not. (2) For sites with which smoke is in direct contact, whether or not inhaled, particularly buccal cavity and larynx, the type of tobacco used makes less difference in incidence. (3) In experimental carcinogenesis, which uses tobacco tars, tumors have appeared at the site of application, and their incidence has not been seriously dependent on the type of tobacco used. (4) The relative risk of lung cancer is higher among cigarette smokers who inhale than among those smoking the same number of cigarettes per day, but who do not inhale.

Several critics[26,43,54] have stressed the failure of Doll and Hill,[17] in their preliminary report, to find a difference in risk between inhalers and noninhalers, but this finding was contradicted in three other studies.[8,50,68] Further work on this point is desirable, but would be more convincing if a more objective measure were found of the amount of smoke to which human bronchial epithelium is exposed in the course of smoking a cigarette.

Why, it is sometimes asked, do most heavy cigarette smokers fail to develop lung cancer if cigarettes are in fact a causal agent? We have no answer to this question. But neither can we say why most of the Lübeck babies who were exposed to massive doses of virulent tubercle bacilli failed to develop tuberculosis. This is not a reason, however, for doubting the causal role of the bacilli in the development of the disease.

One cannot discuss the mode of action of tobacco without becoming aware of the necessity of vastly expanded research in the field. The idea that the subject of tobacco and mortality is a closed one requiring no further study is not one we share. As in other fields of science, new findings lead to new questions, and new experimental techniques will continue to cast further light on old ones. This does not imply that judgment must be suspended until all the evidence is in, or that there are hierarchies of evidence, only some types of which are acceptable. The doctrine that one must never assess what has already been learned until the last possible piece of evidence would be a novel one for science.

It would be desirable to have a set of findings on the subject of smoking and lung cancer so clear-cut and unequivocal that they were self-interpreting. The findings now available on tobacco, as in most other fields of science, particularly biologic science, do not meet this ideal. Nevertheless, if the findings had been made on a new agent, to which hundreds of millions of adults were not already addicted, and on one which did not support a large industry, skilled in the arts of mass persuasion, the evidence for the hazardous nature of the agent would be generally regarded as beyond dispute. In the light of all the evidence on tobacco, and after careful consideration of all the criticisms of this evidence that have been made, we find ourselves unable to agree with the proposition that cigarette smoking is a harmless habit with no important effects on health or longevity. The concern shown by medical and public health authorities with the increasing diffusion to ever younger groups of an agent that is a health hazard seems to us to be well founded.

REFERENCES

1. Arkin, H.: Relationship between human smoking habits and death rates. Current Med. Digest 22: 37–44, 1955.
2. Auerbach, O., Gere, J. B., Forman, J. B., Petrick, T. G., Smolin, H. J., Muehsam, G. E., Kassouny, D. Y., and Stout, A. P.: Changes in the bronchial epithelium in relation to smoking and cancer of the lung; a report of progress. New England J. Med. 256: 97–104, 1957.
3. Berkson, J.: The statistical study of association between smoking and lung cancer. Proc. Staff Meet. Mayo Clin. 30: 319–348, 1955.
4. ———: Smoking and lung cancer: Some observations on two recent reports. J. Am. Stat. Assoc. 53: 28–38, 1958.
5. Black, H., and Ackerman, L. V.: The importance of epidermoid carcinoma in situ in the histogenesis of carcinoma of the lung. Ann. Surg. 136: 44–55, 1952.
6. Blacklock, J. W. S.: The production of lung tumours in rats by 3:4 benzpyrene, methylcholanthrene and the condensate from cigarette smoke. Brit. J. Cancer 11: 181–191, 1957.
7. Bock, F. G., and Moore, G. E.: Carcinogenic activity of cigarette-smoke condensate. I. Effect of trauma and remote X irradiation. J. Nat. Cancer Inst. In press, 1959.
8. Breslow, L., Hoaglin, L., Rasmussen, G., and Abrams, H. K.: Occupations and cigarette smoking as factors in lung cancer. Am. J. Pub. Health 44: 171–181, 1954.

9. Buckwalter, J. A., Wohlwend, E. B., Colter, D. C., Tidrick, R. T., and Knowler, L. A.: ABO blood groups and disease. J.A.M.A. 162: 1210–1214, 1956.

10. Case, R. A. M.: Smoking habits and mortality among workers in cigarette factories. Nature, London 181: 84–86, 1958.

11. Case, R. A. M., and Lea, A. J.: Mustard gas poisoning, chronic bronchitis and lung cancer. Brit. J. Prev. & Social Med. 9: 62–72, 1955.

12. Chang, S. C.: Microscopic properties of whole mounts and sections of human bronchial epithelium of smokers and nonsmokers. Cancer 10: 1246–1262, 1957.

13. Cember, H., and Watson, J. A.: Bronchogenic carcinoma from radioactive barium sulfate. A.M.A. Arch. Indust. Health 17: 230–235, 1958.

14. Clemmesen, J., Nielsen, A., and Jensen, E.: Mortality and incidence of cancer of the lung in Denmark and some other countries. Acta Unio internat. contra cancrum 9: 603–635, 1953.

15. Cohart, E. M.: Socioeconomic distribution of cancer of the lung in New Haven. Cancer 8: 1126–1129, 1955.

16. Doll, R.: Etiology of lung cancer. Advances Cancer Res. 3: 1–50, 1955.

17. Doll, R., and Hill, A. B.: A study of the aetiology of carcinoma of the lung. Brit. M. J. 2: 1271–1286, 1952.

18. ———: Lung cancer and other causes of death in relation to smoking; a second report on the mortality of British doctors. Brit. M. J. 2: 1071–1081, 1956.

19. Doll, R., Hill, A. B., and Kreyberg, L.: The significance of cell type in relation to the aetiology of lung cancer. Brit. J. Cancer 11: 43–48, 1957.

20. Dorn, H.: Tobacco consumption and mortality from cancer and other diseases. Acta Unio internat. contra cancrum. In press.

21. Dorn, H. F., and Cutler, S. J.: Morbidity from Cancer in the United States. Pub. Health Monogr. No. 29, Pub. Health Ser. Publ. No. 590. In press.

22. Dunn, H. L.: Lung cancer in the twentieth century. J. Internat. Coll. Surgeons 23: 326–342, 1955.

23. Engelbreth-Holm, J., and Ahlmann, J.: Production of carcinoma in ST/Eh mice with cigarette tar. Acta. path. ct microbiol. scandinav. 41: 267–272, 1957.

24. Finkner, A. L., Horvitz. D. G., Foradori, G. T., Fleischer, J., and Monroe, J.: An investigation on the measurement of current smoking by individuals. Univ. North Carolina Inst. Statistics, Mimeo Series No. 177, Chapel Hill, North Carolina, 1957.

25. Fisher, R. A.: Dangers of cigarette-smoking. Brit. M. J. 2: 297–298, 1957.

26. ———: Cigarettes, cancer and statistics. Centennial Rev. Arts and Sciences 2: 151, Michigan State University, 1958.

27. ———: Lung cancer and cigarettes? Nature, London 182: 108, 1958.

28. Gellhorn, A.: The cocarcinogenic activity of cigarette tobacco tar. Cancer Res. 18: 510–517, 1958.

29. Gilliam, A. G.: Trends of mortality attributed to carcinoma of the lung: possible effects of faulty certification of deaths due to other respiratory diseases. Cancer 8: 1130–1136, 1955.

30. Graham, E. A., Croninger, A. B., and Wynder, E. L.: Experimental production of carcinoma with cigarette tar. IV. Successful experiments with rabbits. Cancer Res. 17: 1058–1066, 1957.

31. Greene, H. S. N.: Hearings before a Subcommittee of the Committee on Government Operations, House of Representatives, 85th Congress, First Session. 204–224, 1957.

32. Haag, H. B., and Hanmer, H. R.: Smoking habits and mortality among workers in cigarette factories. Indust. Med. 26: 559–562, 1957.

33. Haenszel, W., and Shimkin, M. B.: Smoking patterns and epidemiology of lung cancer in the United States: are they compatible? J. Nat. Cancer Inst. 16: 1417–1441, 1956.

34. Haenszel, W., Shimkin, M., and Mantel, N.: A retrospective study of lung cancer in women. J. Nat. Cancer Inst. 21: 825–842, 1958.

35. Haenszel, W., Shimkin, M. B., and Miller, H. P.: Tobacco smoking patterns in the United States. Pub. Health Monogr. No. 45, Pub. Health Ser. Publ. No. 426. Washington, D.C., U.S. Gov't. Print. Office, 1956, 111 pp.

36. Hammond, E. C.: Smoking in relation to lung cancer. Connecticut M. J. 18: 3–9, 1954.

37. ——: Inhalation in relation to type and amount of smoking. In press.

38. Hammond, E. C., and Horn, D.: Smoking and death rates—report on forty-four months of follow-up of 187,783 men. J.A.M.A. 166: 1159–1172 and 1294–1308, 1958.

39. Hartnett, T.: Tobacco industry scoffs at survey. New York Times, p. 44, col. 3, July 6, 1958.

40. Hilding, A. C.: On cigarette smoking, bronchial carcinoma and ciliary action. II. Experimental study on the filtering action of cow's lungs, the deposition of tar in the bronchial tree and removal by ciliary action. New England J. Med. 254: 1115–1160, 1956.

41. ——: On cigarette smoking, bronchial carcinoma and ciliary action. III. Accumulation of cigarette tar upon artificially produced deciliated islands in the respiratory epithelium. Ann. Otol., Rhin. and Laryng. 65: 116–130, 1956.

42. Hearings before a Subcommittee of the Committee on Government Operations, House of Representatives, 85th Congress, First Session. 1957, 795 pp.

43. Hueper, W. C.: A Quest into the Environmental Causes of Cancer of the Lung. Pub. Health Monogr. No. 36, Pub. Health Ser. Publ. No. 452. Washington, D. C., U.S. Gov't. Print. Office, 1956, 54 pp.

44. Kotin, P.: The role of atmospheric pollution in the pathogenesis of pulmonary cancer, a review. Cancer Res. 16: 375–393, 1956.

45. Kotin, P., and Falk, H.: The deposition of carcinogen-bearing particulate matter in the tracheobronchial tree in relation to particle size and effect of air pollutants and tobacco smoke on ciliary activity and mucus secretion of the respiratory epithelium. (Abstract.) Proc. Am. Assoc. Cancer Res. 2: 127–128, 1956.

46. Kreyberg, L.: The significance of histological typing in the study of the epidemiology of primary epithelial lung tumours: a study of 466 cases. Brit. J. Cancer 8: 199–208, 1954.

47. Kuschner, M., Laskin, S., Cristofano, E., and Nelson, N.: Experimental carcinoma of the lung. In Proc. Third Nat. Cancer Conf. Philadelphia, J. B. Lippincott Co., 1956, pp. 485–495.

48. Leuchtenberger, C., Doolon, P. F., and Leuchtenberger, R.: A correlated histological, cytological, and cytochemical study of the tracheobronchial tree and lungs of mice exposed to cigarette smoke. I. Bronchitis with atypical epithelial changes in mice exposed to cigarette smoke. Cancer 2: 490–506, 1958.

49. Levin, M. L.: Etiology of lung cancer: present status. New York J. Med. 54: 769–777, 1954.

50. Lickint, F.: Atiologie und Prophylaxe des Lungenkrebses. Dresden, T. Steinkopff, 1953, 212 pp.
51. Lilienfeld, A. M.: A study of emotional and other selected characteristics of cigarette smokers and nonsmokers as related to epidemiological studies of lung cancer and other diseases. J. Nat. Cancer Inst. 22: 1959, in press.
52. Little, C. C.: Hearings before a Subcommittee of the Committee on Government Operations, House of Representatives, 85th Congress, First Session. 1957, pp. 34–61.
53. Lyons, M. J., and Johnston, H.: Chemical investigation of the neutral fraction of cigarette smoke tar. Brit. J. Cancer 11: 554–562, 1957.
54. Macdonald, I. G.: Hearings before a Subcommittee of the Committee on Government Operations, House of Representatives, 85th Congress, First Session. 1957, pp. 224–240.
55. Mainland, D., and Herrera, L.: The risk of biased selection in forward-going surveys with nonprofessional interviewers. J. Chron. Dis. 4: 240–244, 1956.
56. McArthur, C., Waldron, E., and Dickinson, J.: The psychology of smoking. J. Abnorm. & Social Psychol. 56: 267–275, 1958.
57. Medical Research Council: Tobacco smoking and cancer of the lung. Brit. M. J. 1: 1523–1524, 1957.
58. Mills, C. A., and Porter, M. M.: Tobacco smoking, motor exhaust fumes, and general air pollution in relation to lung cancer incidence. Cancer Res. 17: 981–990, 1957.
59. Milmore, B. K., and Conover, A. G.: Tobacco consumption in the United States, 1880–1955. Pub. Health Monogr. No. 45. Washington, D.C., U.S. Gov't. Print. Office, 1956, pp. 107–111.
60. Neyman, J.: Statistics—servant of all sciences. Science 122: 401–406, 1955.
61. Orris, L., Van Duuren, B. L., Kosak, A. I., Nelson, N., and Schmitt, F. L.: The carcinogenicity for mouse skin and the aromatic hydrocarbon content of cigarette-smoking condensate. J. Nat. Cancer Inst. 21: 557–561, 1958.
62. Passey, R. D., et al.: Cigarette smoking and cancer of the lung. Brit. Empire Cancer Campaign. Thirty-third Annual Report 1955, pp. 59–61.
63. Passey, R. D.: Carcinogenicity of cigarette tars. Brit. Empire Cancer Campaign. Thirty-fifth Annual Report 1957, pp. 65–66.
64. Rigdon, R. H.: Hearings before a Subcommittee of the Committee on Government Operations, House of Representatives, 85th Congress, First Session. 1957, pp. 114–131.
65. Rigdon, R. H., and Kirchoff, H.: Cancer of the lung from 1900 to 1930. Internat. Abstr. Surg. 107: 105–118, 1958.
66. Rockey, E. E., Kuschner, M., Kosak, A. I., and Mayer, E.: The effect of tobacco tar on the bronchial mucosa of dogs. Cancer 11: 466–472, 1958.
67. Rosenblatt, M. B.: Letter to Surgeon General, United States Public Health Service. Hearings before a Subcommittee of the Committee on Government Operations, House of Representatives, 85th Congress, First Session. 1957, pp. 753–754.
68. Schwartz, D. and Denoix, P.: L'enquette francaise sur l'etiologie du cancer broncho-pulmonaire: role due tabac. La Semaine des Hopitaux de Paris 33: 424–437, 1957.
69. Segi, M., Fukushima, I., Fugisaku, S., Kurihara, M., Saito, S., Asano, K., and Kamoi, M.: An epidemiological study on cancer in Japan. Gann 48: Supp. 1957, 63 pp.

70. Shimkin, M. B.: Pulmonary tumors in experimental animals. Advances Cancer Res. 3: 223–267, 1955.
71. Society of Actuaries, Transactions, vol. 8, meeting 20, 1955 Reports of Mortality and Morbidity Experience, April, 1956.
72. Steiner, P. E.: Symposium on endemiology of cancer of the lung; etiological implications of the geographical distribution of lung cancer. Acta Unio internat. contra cancrum 9: 450–475, 1953.
73. Stocks, P.: Report on cancer in North Wales and Liverpool region. Brit. Empire Cancer Campaign. Thirty-fifth Annual Report 1957, Supp. to Part II.
74. Stocks, P., and Campbell, J. M.: Lung cancer death rates among non-smokers and pipe and cigarette smokers. Brit. M. J. 2: 923–929, 1955.
75. Smoking and Health. Joint Report of the Study Group on Smoking and Health. Science 125: 1129–1133, 1957.
76. Statistics of Smoking, Tobacco Manufacturer's Standing Committee. Paper No. 1, London (Todd, G. F., ed.). 1958.
77. Van Duuren, B. L.: Identification of some polynuclear aromatic hydrocarbons in cigarette-smoke condensate. J. Nat. Cancer Inst. 21: 1–16, 1958.
78. Vorwald, A. J., Pratt, P. C., and Urban, E. J.: The production of pulmonary cancer in albino rats exposed by inhalation to an aerosol of beryllium sulfate. Acta Unio internat. contra cancrum 11: 735, 1955.
79. Wynder, E. L., Bross, I. J., Cornfield, J., and O'Donnell, W. E.: Lung cancer in women. New England J. Med. 225: 1111–1121, 1956.
80. Wynder, E. L., Bross, I. J., and Day, E.: A study of environmental factors in cancer of the larynx. Cancer 9: 86–110, 1956.
81. Wynder, E. L., Bross, I. J., and Feldman, R. M.: A study of the etiological factors in cancer of the mouth. Cancer 10: 1300–1323, 1957.
82. Wynder, E. L., and Cornfield, J.: Cancer of the lung in physicians. New England J. Med. 248: 441–444, 1953.
83. Wynder, E. L., Graham, E. A., and Croninger, A. B.: Experimental production of carcinoma with cigarette tar. Cancer Res. 13: 855–864, 1953.
84. Wynder, E. L., and Wright, G.: A study of tobacco carcinogenesis. I. The primary fractions. Cancer 10: 255–271, 1957.
85. Wynder, E. L., Wright, G., and Lam, J.: A study of tobacco carcinogenesis. V. The role of pyrolysis. Cancer. 11: 1140–1148, 1958.

STATISTICAL CRITICISM

IRWIN D. J. BROSS

In the great debate over smoking and lung cancer the quality of statistical criticism was, I think, rather poor (despite the eminence of the critics). The bitter lesson to be learned was this: *The "rules of the game" for statistical criticism need to be spelled out more clearly and completely.* These remarks represent a first step in this direction. While I will draw my examples from the lung cancer debate, similar instances can be found in most of the scientific areas in which statistical methods are employed. Much that nowadays passes as statistical criticism is superficial and sophomoric in character and serves to obscure a scientific discussion rather than to clarify it.

Let me emphasize at the start that the purpose of ground rules is to put the statistical critic on his mettle—not to muzzle him. The rules of the game for the *proponent* of scientific hypothesis, discussed in various texts on statistics and logic can help him to make the statements that are warranted by the data. If the proponent flagrantly violates these rules, they provide a basis for calling him to account.[4] In the same way, ground rules for a critic will help him to distinguish valid objections. Of course, they also provide a basis for calling a critic to account for irresponsible attacks on scientific study. If both proponents and critics have to watch their P's and Q's, we might hope that it would be easier to achieve broad agreement on scientific issues.

The Role of a Critic

As a first step toward the ground rules of statistical criticism, let us examine the roles of the critic and the proponent. In what follows, the critic will be considered as opposed to the proponent in the sense that he denies the proposed scientific hypothesis or at any rate denies that it has been demonstrated.

Although the critic's role appears purely negative, it has a positive side to it. Implicitly (and sometimes explicitly) he puts forth a counterhypothesis. This point may be clarified by a simple example. Let us say that a critic objects to the conclusions of a scientific study because the proponent has not used significance tests. This objection would be trivial if, for example, the value of the chi square was actually enormous. However, it would be a strong objection if a difference between two series (which was essential to the proponent's argument) was not

Reprinted by permission of the author and the publisher from *Cancer* 13 (1960), 394–400.

significant when the test was performed. But why is this objection strong? Because the critic can now frame a tenable counterhypothesis that explains the results in terms of sampling variation alone. Since the proponent cannot rule out this counterhypothesis, he cannot establish his own hypothesis.

In much the same way a critic who objects to a bias in the design or a failure to control some established factor is, in fact, raising a counterhypothesis (even though he may not state it). Since the counterhypothesis is essential in the logical structure of criticism, it facilitates debate when it is explicitly stated.[2] When the hypothesis is so stated, the basic question suggests itself: What is the responsibility of a critic with respect to his counterhypothesis?

A Criterion for Criticism

Consider the following tentative rule: The critic has the responsibility for showing that his counterhypothesis is tenable. In so doing, he operates under the *same* ground rules as a proponent.

This rule may appear to conflict with the principle that the *burden of proof* rests on a proponent, but this is not the case. Although both critic and proponent may operate under the same rules in establishing their respective hypotheses, there is a great difference in what happens next. When a critic has shown that his counterhypothesis is tenable, his job is done (while at this point the proponent's job is just beginning). A proponent's job is not finished as long as there is a tenable hypothesis that rivals the one he asserts.

Many critics seem to employ a rule that is much weaker than the tentative rule stated. They feel that a critic's responsibility ends when he merely *presents* a counterhypothesis without showing it to be tenable. This I regard as unrealistic because it imposes an impossible task on a proponent. He would be required to rule out every *conceivable* hypothesis. Since there are an unlimited number of such hypotheses, there would be no end to the proponent's labors. By restricting consideration to *tenable* hypotheses, the proponent's task becomes feasible (although onerous).

Tentative rule does not impose any impossible task upon the critic, since he can employ the usual scientific procedures to show that his counterhypothesis is tenable. For example, a minimal requirement would be that the effects predicted from the critic's hypothesis should be in line with the actual data, at least in direction and order of magnitude. The additional arguments needed to establish tenability depend on the nature of the hypothesis. For instance, if the hypothesis involves sampling variation alone, it would be tenable in any study employing samples. For hypotheses involving an artifact, the experience with this artifact in previous studies can be used to establish the direction and magnitude of the effect. It may even be possible to show the effect operating in the proponent's data. When a counterhypothesis involves a well known real factor, e.g., age or sex in an epidemiological study, it would be sufficient to mention the relationship, e.g., death rates from cancer tend to increase with age. However, when a counterhypothesis is novel or controversial, a critic (like a proponent in the same circumstances) will have to develop a strong argument.

For these reasons, the suggested rule for criticism seems to be both fair and feasible (and I will employ it in criticizing the critics).

Hit-and-Run Criticism

The bulk of statistical criticism is of the hit-and-run variety—the critic points out some real or fancied flaw and supposes that his job is done. Indeed, some critics appear to labor under the misconception that if some flaw can be found in a study, this automatically invalidates the author's conclusions. Since the critic makes no attempt to develop a tenable counterhypothesis, his performance is on a par with that of a proponent who glances at his data and then jumps to his conclusion.

Two examples should suffice to make this point plain. Quite a number of the critics of the Hammond and Horn study[9] (along with other prospective studies) have called attention to the possibility of misclassification of the cause of death on death certificates. Most of these critics dropped the matter at that point (apparently under the impression that they had scored a hit). However, if they had followed the usual scientific procedures in developing a tenable hypothesis—if they had looked at other studies or existing theory[3]—they would have found that misclassification tends to *diminish* observed differentials. If they had compared the Hammond and Horn tabulations of "purified" data, i.e., cases with confirmed diagnosis, with the "unpurified" data, they would have *seen* how misclassification operated to reduce differentials.

Another example is Berkson's model for a selection bias based on an item in the protocol of the Hammond and Horn study (initially sick individuals were excluded).[1] The model itself is a good example of constructive criticism, since it formulated the objection in a precise fashion that facilitated both theoretical and empirical investigation. However, I was amazed when, in talking with several statisticians, I encountered the opinion that this *model* seriously jeopardized the Hammond and Horn conclusions. Of course a model carries no weight in a scientific argument until it has been shown to be tenable. This particular model was untenable because it predicted that the differentials found in the study would *shrink* as time went by, whereas, if anything, the change with time was the *opposite* direction. What is more, even if the model had been tenable it would have been of little value in a counterhypothesis, since it could be shown mathematically that the bias could produce only slight differentials (the observed differentials had a different *order of magnitude*).[4]

We see, then, that it is not enough to spot flaws in a study; a responsible critic would go on to show how these flaws lead to a counterhypothesis that can explain the observations. If a critic fails to build a tenable hypothesis, he clearly fails in his duty.

Dogmatic Criticism

To show that his counterhypothesis is tenable, a critic may use arguments based on current statistical principles and practices. However, a critic has no license to make exaggerated claims, unfounded assumptions, or dogmatic assertions (even if the statements are quoted from statistical textbooks).

Consider the following quotation from Sir R. A. Fisher, which has been echoed by other eminent critics: "The evidence linking cigarette smoking with lung cancer, standing by itself, is inconclusive, *as it is apparently impossible to carry out properly controlled experiments with human material.*"[10] (The italics are mine.)

This blanket condemnation rests largely on one defect of the prospective studies as compared to controlled experiments. The exposure to cigarette smoke, i.e., smoking habits, is determined by the personal choice of each individual whereas ideally the exposure would be set by the experimenter (using a randomized allocation). Because of the lack of randomization, there is a *potential* "self-selection" bias (which suggests a counterhypothesis). If this counterhypothesis can be rendered tenable, then, indeed, the proponent's evidence is "inconclusive."

Instead of attempting to make the self-selection hypothesis tenable, Fisher simply dismissed the entire body of epidemiological data (involving carefully collected information on hundreds of thousands of individuals). He did so on the basis that the data do not meet certain theoretical standards for "properly controlled experimentation." This seems to me a gross violation of the empirical spirit of modern science *and* of modern statistics. It raises the theory of statistics, e.g., randomization, to the level of dogma.

Speculative Criticism

While I do not agree with those who say that there is no place for speculation in a scientific article, I do feel that there are definite restrictions on hypothetical excursions. For one thing, speculation should be clearly labeled as such; for another, speculations should not enter the conclusions. These restrictions apply equally to proponent and critic.

There is one type of counterhypothesis in which the temptation to speculate is very strong—hypotheses based on a new "real world" factor. A statistician should be especially careful with this type of substantive hypothesis because he is now in the domain of the subject matter field—he is functioning as an epidemiologist or sociologist or psychiatrist (depending on the nature of the new factor) rather than as a statistician.

The task of establishing the tenability of a substantive counterhypothesis is more difficult than that for a methodological counterhypothesis, since "local" ground rules, i.e., those of the particular scientific field, come into play. For example, in epidemiology a proposed new factor has to be consistent with the broad incidence patterns of the disease, e.g., geographic distribution, time trends, and sex ratios.

While numerous substantive counterhypotheses have been introduced in the lung cancer controversy, there has been practically no attempt to render such hypotheses tenable. Thus Berkson brought up Pearl's[12] "rate of living" hypothesis[2] but frankly admitted that: "Actually I do not know of any independent evidence for such an effect of smoking." He also cited the "constitution" hypothesis, noted one of its shortcomings, and remarked: "I do not profess to be able to track out the implications of the constitutional theory or to defend it. . . ." While it is to Berkson's credit that he clearly labeled these two counterhypotheses as speculative, they appear to play an important role in his subsequent rejection of the "carcinogen" hypothesis, i.e., speculations enter his conclusion.

It may be argued that it is too stringent to require a critic to show that his substantive counterhypothesis is tenable because he is not actually *asserting* it but merely *suggesting* it as a possible line for future research. However, I fail to see how a critic contributes to the scientific process if the suggested avenue for research is, in fact, a dead end road. Nor can I see how a critic can expect to point out a sensible direction for research unless he explores the tenability of his counterhypothesis—for example, by checking whether his notion jibes with the incidence pattern for lung cancer.

The most striking feature of lung cancer incidence is the drastic increase in the age specific male death rates over the past generation. This rapid increase is virtually *unique*—the female death rate shows much less change, other cancer rates are fairly stable, and the rates for other causes of death either show relatively minor changes or else are rapidly *decreasing*. The peculiar behavior of the male lung cancer rates poses some difficult questions for any substantive hypothesis. Why is lung cancer thus singled out? Why are male death rates affected and not female death rates? Why should this have happened in the last generation? I leave it to the reader to put these questions to some of the counterhypotheses raised, e.g., those based on "stress," "genetic factors," and "constitution."

In my opinion, even a cursory exploration would have shown most of the critics that their substantive counterhypotheses were untenable. Had this been done, much of the confusion in the lung cancer debate would have been avoided.

Tubular Criticism

Proponents of scientific hypotheses are often justly criticized for their "tubular vision"—a remarkable inability to "see" the evidence unfavorable to their hypothesis. Critics are equally subject to this type of defective vision. For example, Berkson[2] complained that "virtually all of the evidence" that cigarette smoke is carcinogenic comes from epidemiological-statistical studies. He was unable to "see" the evidence from vital statistics, combustion chemistry, animal experiments, lung tissue pathology, etc.

Tubular vision also occurs in the examination of actual data. Since Berkson is one of the few critics who (1) dealt with data, (2) stated his counterhypotheses, and (3) made a serious effort to establish their tenability, I will draw my examples from his work.[2] However, judging *over-all* performance, I would say Berkson far excels the other critics.

To appreciate the illustrations, we first must understand the *purpose* of Berkson's analysis of the Doll and Hill data.[5] His counterhypothesis was: "The observed associations are 'spurious' . . . the result of the interplay of various subtle and complicated 'biases.' " To establish tenability, Berkson first undertook to show that ". . . there can hardly be any doubt that association is shown for 'all or nearly all' causes of death. . . ." in prospective studies. Before examining Berkson's arguments for this crucial point, let us see how it is used to establish the counterhypothesis. Berkson said: "For myself, I find it quite incredible that smoking should cause all these diseases. . . . And if we are not crassly to violate the principle of Occam's razor, we should not attribute to each separate association a radically different explanation."

I would not interpret Berkson's remarks as a denial that an environmental factor, e.g., polluted milk, can be responsible for more than one disease. Hence tobacco smoke, which is chemically quite complex (containing nicotine, polycyclic hydrocarbons, etc.), *might* induce or aggravate several different diseases (e.g., lung cancer, coronary thrombosis, or chronic bronchitis) by radically different "specific" etiological mechanisms. We can, however, make a distinction between those diseases in which an etiological hypothesis based on chemical components in tobacco smoke can be supported by independent evidence (call these "specific" diseases) and the many other causes of death in which a corresponding hypothesis would be highly speculative (call these "nonspecific" diseases). Now *if* we find that many of the "nonspecific" diseases are associated with smoking, then I quite agree with Berkson that the "simple" hypothesis of a general bias running through the data is clearly preferable to the "complex" hypothesis requiring a large number of speculative hypotheses to account for the associations. Moreover, if we also find that the bias effect is similar in direction and magnitude to the effects found for the "specific" diseases, then we have a tenable counterhypothesis for the whole of the data and the proponents of "specific" hypotheses are in a hopeless position.

Of course, this argument hinges on a demonstration that there is "generalized association" in the "nonspecific" diseases. For this purpose, Berkson started with a Doll and Hill tabulation (Table 29)[2] that gave the death rates in 4 tobacco consumption categories for "lung cancer," "coronary thrombosis," "other respiratory diseases," "other cancers," and "other diseases."

For a significance test of "generalized association," Berkson suggested that: "Appropriate here is some form of permutation test. . . ." He went on to say that: "However it is figured, the probability of getting by chance . . . consistently higher death rates among the heavy smokers than among any of the 3 categories of less than heavy smokers, in each of 5 predesignated categories of cause of death, and in agreement with the independently obtained similar finding in the prospective study of Hammond and Horn,[9] must be considered negligible."

Here, I think, is an instance of "tubular vision." Two of the 5 categories represent "specific" diseases while a third, "other respiratory diseases," largely reflects the influence of chronic bronchitis—another "specific" disease. In other words, most of the evidence that Berkson used to *deny* "specific" effects came from these very effects! Indeed, *unless* these "specific" effects are included, there is little evidence for a "generalized association" in Table 29. Thus, while a permutation type test is significant at the 5 per cent level for the 2 "specific" diseases, the corresponding test for the 2 "nonspecific" causes is definitely *not* significant.

Tubular Criticism and Data

Berkson himself did not seem satisfied with his inferences from Table 29 for he proceeded to construct (from Doll and Hill tabulations), Table 34, which listed 15 causes of death (and hence permitted segregation of "specific" causes). This table is reproduced as Table 1 in this article.

Berkson clearly "sees" his "generalized association" operating in Table 1, but the only analytic evidence offered is: "The death rate for heavy smokers is higher than that for nonsmokers in 12 of the 15 categories, although in several instances the number of deaths, the differences of rates, or both, are small."

A "permutation" test that could be used on this evidence is the sign test. [Strictly speaking, the death rates in the different causes may not be independent because overenumeration in one cause might lead to underenumeration in a related cause.] Let I be the total number of "inversions" (i.e., cases in which the death rate was lower for the heavy smokers than for the nonsmokers). Let NI be the total number of "noninversions." Then using the sign test:

$$\frac{[|NI - I| - 1]^2}{NI + I} = \frac{[|12 - 3| - 1]^2}{12 + 3} = \frac{64}{15} = 4.27.$$

Since the 5 per cent level critical value is 3.84, the sign test is significant, and we would reject the null hypothesis that sampling variation alone can account for the result cited by Berkson. Unfortunately, a departure in the observed direction might be due to either "specific" or "generalized" association, and if we try to subdivide the causes the numbers will be so small that the sign test will have little power.

However, we can call on the big brother of the sign test, the sequence sign test, to do the job. As before, we count "inversions" but this time we consider all 6 of the pairwise comparisons that can be made between the 4 death rates for each cause. In Table 1 we count a pairwise comparison as an "inversion" if the death rate to the right of the other member of the pair is the smaller one. Thus, for cerebral hemorrhage the sequence of rates is 2.01, 1.94, 1.86, and 2.33. Starting with 2.01 as the "left hand" member of the pair, we have "inversions" quoted for 1.94 and 1.86 and a "noninversion" for 2.33. Moving on to 1.94 as

■ **Table 1.** Death rates for various smoking classes for individualized categories of disease (report of Doll and Hill[5])*

| | | Death rate, standardized/1,000 | | | |
| | | | Men smoking a daily average of: | | |
Category	Number deaths	Non-smokers	1–14 grams	15–24 grams	25 + grams
Cancer					
Lung	84	0.07	0.47	0.86	1.66
Upper respiratory and digestive tract	13	0.00	0.13	0.09	0.21
Stomach	32	0.41	0.36	0.10	0.31
Colon and rectum	57	0.44	0.54	0.37	0.74
Prostate	30	0.55	0.26	0.22	0.34
Other sites	88	0.64	0.72	0.76	1.02
Respiratory diseases					
Pulmonary tuberculosis	19	0.00	0.16	0.18	0.29
Chronic bronchitis	42	0.12	0.29	0.39	0.72
Other respiratory diseases	65	0.69	0.55	0.54	0.40
Coronary thrombosis	508	4.22	4.64	4.60	5.99
Other cardiovascular diseases	279	2.23	2.15	2.47	2.25
Cerebral hemorrhage	227	2.01	1.94	1.86	2.33
Peptic ulcer	18	0.00	0.14	0.16	0.22
Violence	77	0.42	0.82	0.45	0.90
Other diseases	183	1.45	1.81	1.47	1.57

* Data from Table 34 of Berkson.[2]

the "left hand" member of the pair, we have an "inversion" for 1.86 and a "non-inversion" for 2.33. Finally for the pair 1.86, 2.33 is a "noninversion." So for this cause we have 3 "inversions" and 3 "noninversions." Table 2 lists the results for the causes in Table 1.

For all causes, there are 27 inversions and 63 noninversions and the sequence sign test is:

$$K \frac{(|NI - I| - 1)^2}{NI + I} = \frac{9}{13} \frac{(|63 - 27| - 1)^2}{90} = 9.42$$

where

$$K = \frac{9}{2 \text{ (number factor categories)} + 5} = \frac{9}{2(4) + 5} = \frac{9}{13}$$

and represents an adjustment for the fact that the 6 pairwise comparisons in a cause are not independent. This test is significant at the 1 per cent level.

Since the sequence sign test is more powerful than the sign test, we are now able to segregate the "specific" and "nonspecific" causes (Table 2). I have also separated off 3 causes (subtotal B in Table 2) that are of questionable value for our purposes. There are less than 20 deaths in each of these series, and they were tabulated separately only because "specific" effects were suspected.

The "specific" causes (subtotal A in Table 2) show up as highly significant (8.65), although there are only 3 of them. The "nonspecific" causes in toto show 25 inversions and 29 noninversions, which is close to the expected values under the null hypothesis, i.e., 27 and 27, and is, of course, not significant (0.12). We might expect a "generalized association" to show most clearly in the "nonspecific" major causes since these 3 causes account for 40 per cent of all the deaths, but this is not the case (subtotal D in Table 2). Again in view of Berkson's demand for an ". . . explanation for the association shown with cancers . . . of such sites as the colon, stomach, and pancreas . . ."[2] we might expect a striking result for "nonspecific" cancers, but this was not found (subtotal C in Table 2). In short, a permutation type analysis fails to detect Berkson's "generalized associations" in the Doll and Hill data (although it picks up associations for the "specific" diseases easily enough).

No permutation analysis is presented in Berkson's article[2] and instead he simply cited 2 examples of nonspecific causes that he believed show evidence of association. Berkson had reservation about 1 of these causes, "violence," but the other ("cancer: other sites") is "notable": ". . . this group shows a graded increase of death rate with increased amount of smoking, from a rate of 0.64 for nonsmokers, to a rate of 1.02 for heavy smokers." However, as can be seen from Table 2, the cited example is the *only* "nonspecific" cause whose rates show a graded increase (I equals 0 and NI equals 6) with increased smoking. If this one cause is to be regarded as a strong argument for generalized association, what are we to make of the category "other respiratory diseases" that shows a very similar pattern but in the *opposite* direction (I equals 6 and NI equals 0)?

Summing Up

The lengthy illustration of "tubular vision" in the examination of data contains several important lessons for statisticians. First, it shows how dangerous it is—even for an experienced and competent statistician—to draw inferences by scanning data and picking out favorable cases. Second, it indicates how analytic tools can help to safeguard against the "tubular vision" to which we are all liable. Third, Berkson's approach[2]—while not successful for the Doll and Hill data—illustrates how an argument for the tenability of a counterhypothesis can be developed from a proponent's own data. Fourth, the example shows that the task of a responsible critic can be as difficult and exacting as that of a responsible proponent (whereas "hit-and-run" criticism is child's play).

■ **Table 2.** Inversion count for Table 1 (by cause)*

Group	Inversions	Noninversions
"Specific" causes		
Lung cancer	0	6
Chronic bronchitis	0	6
Coronary thrombosis	1	5
	—	—
Subtotal A	1	17
Questionable causes		
Pulmonary tuberculosis	0	6
Upper respiratory cancer	1	5
Peptic ulcer	0	6
	—	—
Subtotal B	1	17
Summary totals		
All "nonspecific"	25	29
All causes	27	63
"Nonspecific" cancers		
Stomach	5	1
Colon and rectum	2	4
Prostate	4	2
Other sites	0	6
	—	—
Subtotal C	11	13
"Nonspecific" major causes		
Cerebral hemorrhage	3	3
Other cardiovascular diseases	2	4
Other diseases	2	4
	—	—
Subtotal D	7	11
Other "nonspecific" causes		
Violence	1	5
Other respiratory diseases	6	0
	—	—
Subtotal E	7	5

* Table 1 is given as Table 34 by Berkson.[2]

In my discussion of the role and responsibility of the statistical critic, my theme has been: we should not have a "double standard" in science and statistics, one standard for proponents and another for critics. The same ground rules should apply to both. If a proponent should not jump to his conclusions or base them on dogma or speculation, neither should a critic. If a proponent should be wary of "tubular vision," so should a critic. In short, we might frame the following "golden rule" for critics: Do unto a proponent as you would have *him* do.

Technical Appendix

Derivation of the sequence sign test follows directly from a result given on page 241 of Feller's *An Introduction to Probability Theory and Its Applications*.[6] Feller proves that for a single sequence (under the null hypothesis) the number of inversions is asymptotically normally distributed with a mean

$$(E_1) = \frac{n(n-1)}{4} \quad \text{and variance}$$

$$(V_1) = \frac{(2n+5)(n)(n-1)}{72} \quad \text{or} \quad \frac{(2n+5)(E_1)}{18}.$$

Assuming independence for M causes, we find at once that the total number of inversions (I) is asymptotically normally distributed with

$$E = M(E_1), \text{ and } V = M(V_1).$$

Since

$$\frac{(I-E)^2}{V}$$

is asymptotically distributed as chi square with 1 degree of freedom, the sequence sign test (uncorrected) follows when the substitution $I + NI = 2E$ is made. I have included a correction for continuity analogous to the one used in the sign test.[11]

REFERENCES

1. Berkson, J.: Statistical study of association between smoking and lung cancer. *Proc Staff Meet. Mayo Clin.* 30: 319–348, 1955.
2. Berkson, J.: Smoking and lung cancer; some observations on 2 recent reports. *J. Am. Statist. A.* 53: 28–38, 1958.
3. Bross, I. [J.]: Misclassification in 2 × 2 tables. *Biometrics* 10: 478–486, 1954.
4. Brownlee, K. A.: Note on effects of nonresponse on surveys. *J. Am. Statist. A.* 52: 29–32, 1957.

5. Doll, R., and Hill, A. B.: Lung cancer and other causes of death in relation to smoking; second report on mortality of British doctors. *Brit. M.J.* 2: 1071–1081, 1956. Cited by Berkson, J.[2]

6. Feller, W.: An Introduction to Probability Theory and Its Applications, 2d ed., vol. 1. New York, N.Y. John Wiley & Sons, Inc. 1957.

7. Fisher, R. A.: Cancer and smoking. [Letter to the Editor.] *Nature, London* 182: 596, 1958.

8. Fisher, R. A.: Lung cancer and cigarettes? [Letter to the Editor.] *Nature, London* 182: 108, 1958.

9. Hammond, E. C., and Horn D.: Relationship between human smoking habits and death rates: follow-up study of 187,766 men. *J.A.M.A.* 155: 1316–1328, 1954. Cited by Berkson, J[2].

10. L[aurence], W. L.: Cigarette-cancer links disputed. *New York Times* 107: (sect. 4) 7, Dec. 29, 1957.

11. Mosteller, F.: Some statistical problems in measuring subjective response to drugs. *Biometrics* 8: 220–226, 1952.

12. Pearl, R.: The Rate of Living; Being an Account of Some Experimental Studies on the Biology of Life Duration. New York, N.Y. Albert A. Knopf, Inc. 1928. Cited by Berkson, J.[2]

13. Wynder, E. L., Bross, I. J., Cornfield, J., and O'Donnell, W. E.: Lung cancer in women; study of environmental factors. *New England J. Med.* 255: 1111–1121, 1956.

2 / EXPERIMENTAL AND QUASI-EXPERIMENTAL STUDIES

THE CONNECTICUT CRACKDOWN
ON SPEEDING: TIME SERIES DATA
IN QUASI-EXPERIMENTAL ANALYSIS*

DONALD T. CAMPBELL AND H. LAURENCE ROSS

Social research frequently encounters the task of evaluating change produced in nonrandomly selected groups by events which are beyond the researcher's control. The social scientist must verify that there has in fact been a change, and that the indicated event is its cause. Illustrations are manifold: a state terminates capital punishment, and proponents of this type of punishment predict an increase in the murder rate; a school is integrated, and supporters of the reform expect to find an increase in the positive self-evaluation of Negro pupils; a natural disaster occurs in a community, and altruistic behavior is expected to increase. Because in these situations the investigator has no control over the assignment of individuals or groups to "experimental" and "control" situations, the logic of the classical experiment must be reexamined in a search for optimal interpretative procedures.

This paper introduces, in the context of a problem in applied sociology and the sociology of law, a mode of analysis designed to deal with a common class of situations in which research must proceed without the benefit of experimental control. The general methodology expounded here is termed "quasi-experimental analysis." The specific mode of analysis is the "interrupted time-series design." Perhaps its fundamental credo is that lack of control and lack of randomization are damaging to inferences of cause and effect only to the extent that a systematic consideration of alternative explanations reveals some that are plausible. More complete explications of quasi-experimental analysis have appeared elsewhere;[1] this paper will merely illustrate its use in a situation where a series of observations has been recorded for periods of time both prior and subsequent to the experience of the specific event to be studied. Such data are quite commonly available, yet they are seldom fully utilized and investigators often confine themselves unnecessarily to much less satisfactory methodologies. The 1955 crackdown on speeding in the State of Connecticut furnishes an apt example of the potentialities of such quasi-experimental analysis.

A Program for Reducing Highway Fatalities

In 1955, 324 people were killed in automobile accidents on the highways of Connecticut. Deaths by motor vehicle accidents had reached a record high for

Reprinted by permission of the authors and the publisher from *Law & Society Review* **3** (August, 1968), 33–53.

the decade of the fifties as the usually hazardous Christmas holidays approached. Two days before Christmas, Governor Abraham Ribicoff of Connecticut initiated an unparalleled attempt to control traffic deaths by law enforcement, and announced his crackdown on speeders in that state.

Ribicoff believed, along with many safety specialists, that excess speed was the most common contributing factor in traffic deaths, and that control of speed would result in diminished fatalities. He believed that previous efforts to control speeding under the usual court procedures and by the existing "point system" had been inadequate. In a study of three months' records of the police court in Hartford, it was noted that no more than half the persons originally charged with speeding were so prosecuted, the charge often being diminished to a less serious one. Ribicoff wanted to initiate a program with reliable procedures and strong sanctions as a means to control speeding and thus to reduce traffic deaths.

On December 23, 1955, Governor Ribicoff announced that in the future all persons convicted of speeding would have their licenses suspended for thirty days on the first offense. A second violation was to mean a sixty-day suspension, and a third conviction for speeding would result in indefinite suspension of the driver's license, subject to a hearing after ninety days.

The decree was put into force through the Governor's power of appointment over local judges. Under Connecticut practice, the Motor Vehicle Department was suspending licenses on the recommendation of police court judges. The judges were appointed by the Governor, who threatened loss of reappointment in 1957 to judges who appeared lax in the conviction of speeders, or who did not recommend suspension of licenses to the Motor Vehicle Department.

In the first three months of 1956, license suspensions for speeding numbered 2,855, an increase of almost 2,700 over the corresponding period in 1955. There were ten fewer fatalities, and 765 fewer arrests for speeding. The Governor was reported "encouraged" by the drop in violations and in fatalities. The press quoted him as saying. "This is positive proof that operators are not only driving slower, but are driving better."

By late May, deaths had declined from 122 in 1955 to 107 in 1956. Suspensions for speeding numbered 4,559, as against 209 in 1955. Speeding arrests had dropped 53 per cent. The Governor received a telegram of commendation for the program from the National Safety Council.

At the end of June there were twenty-two fewer fatalities than in the first six months of 1955, representing a 15 per cent reduction. Suspensions for speeding in the first six months of the year had risen from 231 to 5,398, and arrests had declined from 4,377 to 2,735. Ribicoff announced:

■ Connecticut has succeeded in stopping the upward surge in highway deaths, and in the first six months of this year, contrary to the national trend, we have saved lives. Fewer people died on the highways this year than in the same period last year, in Connecticut. We did it by enforcing the law, something the safety experts said couldn't be done because the people wouldn't be behind it. ■

In July, a new State Police program, using unmarked police cars and making extensive use of radar, was inaugurated. The police issued a report stating that 2 per cent of the cars observed by radar on July 4 were found to be speeding; at a later date, it was claimed that no speeders were found among 53,000 cars similarly observed.

In the late summer, however, Connecticut experienced a very high number of traffic fatalities. By the beginning of September, 194 people had been killed, a number almost equal to the 195 of the comparable period in the previous year. The accident "epidemic" was embarrassing to the authorities, who retreated to defending the speeding crackdown on the grounds (a) that the fatality rate remained low in comparison with the national trend, which showed a 7 per cent increase; (b) that exposure to accidents in the state had increased by 100 million vehicle miles without an increase in deaths; and (c) that the total accident rate had risen, thereby lowering the proportion of fatal accidents to total accidents.

Fatalities were fewer in the fall of 1956, and by the end of the year Connecticut could count 284 deaths in traffic as against 324 in 1955. The Governor stated, "With the saving of forty lives in 1955, a reduction of 12.3 per cent from the 1955 motor vehicle death toll, we can say the program is definitely worthwhile."

The crackdown on speeding is still in effect in Connecticut, although it is no longer the subject of newsworthy comment. It was not entirely a political asset for the Democratic Governor. From the start, there were problems with neighboring states, which originate a substantial share of Connecticut traffic, and which at first refused to suspend licenses of drivers convicted of speeding in Connecticut. More important, many powerful individuals and groups within Connecticut resented the direct effects of the crackdown. Members of the Republican party wanted the program "tempered with justice." The Teamsters sponsored a bill to eliminate compulsory license suspension on a first offense, and other legislation granting restricted driving permits for "hardship" cases was introduced. These efforts were not successful in officially moderating the crackdown policy.

The people of Connecticut and their officials are paying what in many instances appears to be a high price for the continuation of the crackdown on speeding. Few will feel the price is too high if it can be shown that as many as forty lives per year are being saved. However, the question must be raised as to whether the results claimed for the program in 1956 are valid in the light of both formerly and more recently available statistics on highway fatalities.

Quasi-Experimental Analysis

Before-and-After Measures

Traffic fatalities in Connecticut for 1956, compared with 1955, are presented in Fig 1. These are the data upon which Governor Ribicoff relied in claiming success for the crackdown on speeding. Skillfully presented, such results can look impressive, but can also be fundamentally misleading.

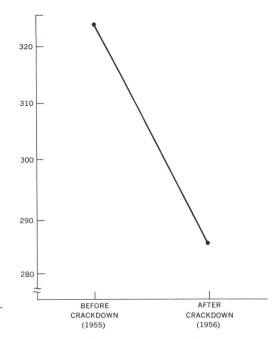

1 Connecticut traffic fatalities, 1955–
1956.

We can speak of the evidence presented in Figure 1 as a quasi-experiment: there is a "pretest" (the 1955 figures), an "experimental treatment" (the crackdown), and a "posttest" (the 1956 figures). A substantial change is noted which one would like to ascribe to the "experimental treatment." In quasi-experimental analysis this interpretation is held to be legitimate, provided consideration is given to plausible rival explanations of the differences, with supplementary analyses being added to eliminate these where possible. In the language of quasi-experimental analysis, the data of Figure 1 constitute a One-Group Pretest-Posttest Design. This design fails to control for the six common threats to the validity of experiments specified below:

1. *History.* This term denotes specific events, other than the experimental treatment, occurring between the pretest and posttest, which might account for the change. It furnishes a "rival hypothesis" to the experimental hypothesis, a competing explanation of the before-to-after change that must be eliminated as implausible, by one means or another, before full credence can be given to the experimental hypothesis. For instance, 1956 might have been a particularly dry year, with fewer accidents due to rain and snow, or there might have been a dramatic improvement of the safety features on the 1956-model cars. In fact, neither of these is a particularly plausible rival hypothesis in this instance, and we have not encountered more likely ones, so this potential weakness may not be crucial here.

2. *Maturation.* This term originates in studies of individuals, where it refers to regular changes correlated with the passage of time, such as growing older,

more tired, more sophisticated, etc. It is distinguished from history in referring to processes, rather than to discrete events. Thus, one could classify here the general long-term trend toward a reduction in automobile mileage death rates, presumably due to better roads, increased efficacy of medical care, etc. The better designs discussed below provide evidence concerning this trend in Connecticut in previous years, and in other states for the same year.

3.   *Testing.* A change may occur as a result of the pretest, even without the experimental treatment. In the present instance, the assessment of the traffic death rate for 1955 constitutes the pretest. In this case it is conceivable that the measurement and publicizing of the traffic death rate for 1955 could change driver caution in 1956.

4.   *Instrumentation.* This term refers to a shifting of the measuring instrument independent of any change in the phenomenon measured. In the use of public records for time-series data, a shift in the government agency recording the fatality statistics could account for such a shift. For example, suicide statistics increased a dramatic 20 per cent in Prussia between 1882 and 1883, when record keeping was transferred from the local police to the national civil service.[2] Similarly, Orlando Wilson's reforms of the police system in Chicago led to dramatic increases in rates for most crimes, due presumably to more complete reporting.[3] In earlier versions of the present study, the death rate per hundred million vehicle miles is computed by using the number of gallons of gasoline sold in the state to estimate the number of miles driven. The latter figure is obtained by multiplying the former by an empirically-derived constant. A decrease in the actual miles obtained per gallon, as through engines of larger horsepower or driving at higher speeds, could masquerade as a lower mileage death rate through inflating the estimate of miles driven. Conversely, if the crackdown actually reduced driving speeds, this would increase the miles-per-gallon actually obtained leading to an underestimate of mileage driven in the postcrackdown period, and consequently an overestimate of the fatality rate.

5.   *Instability.*[4] A ubiquitous plausible rival hypothesis is that the change observed is due to the instability of the measures involved. Were Figure 1 to show fatality rates for a single township, with the same 12.3 per cent drop, we would be totally unimpressed, so unstable would we expect such rates to be. In general, as is made explicit in the models for tests of significance, the smaller the population base, the greater the instability. In the uncontrolled field situation sample size is only one of many sources of instability. Much instability may be due to large numbers of change-producing events of the type which, taken individually, we have called history.

6.   *Regression.* Where a group has been selected for treatment just because of its extreme performance on the pretest, and if the pretest and posttest are imperfectly correlated, as they almost always are, it follows that on the average the posttest will be less extreme than the pretest. This regression is a tautological

restatement of the imperfect correlation between pretest and posttest, as it relates to pretest scores selected for their extremity. The *r* of the correlation coefficient actually stands for the percentage of regression toward the mean. An
analogous regression problem exists for time-series correlations.

Selection for extremity (and resultant retest regression) can be seen as
plausibly operating here in two ways: (a) of all states in 1955, this treatment was
most likely to be applied to one with an exceptionally high traffic casualty rate;
(b) for Connecticut, the most likely time in which a crackdown would be applied
would be following a year in which traffic fatalities were exceptionally high.

In the true experiment, the treatment is applied randomly, without relation
to the prior state of the dependent variable: the correlation between pretest
scores and exposure to treatment is zero. Likewise, in the most interpretable of
quasi-experiments, the treatment is applied without systematic relationship to
the prior status of the group. Thus, an analysis of the effects of a tornado or an
earthquake can be made with confidence that the pretreatment values did not
cause the tornado or the earthquake. Not so here: the high 1955 rates can plausibly be argued to have caused the treatment. That 1956 was less extreme would
then be expected because of regression.[5]

Interrupted Time-Series Analysis

Figure 2 plots traffic fatalities for five years before and four years after the
crackdown. This mode of quasi-experimental analysis has been labeled "Interrupted Time-Series" to distinguish it from the time-series analysis of economics.
In the latter, the exogenous variable to which cause is imputed is a continuously

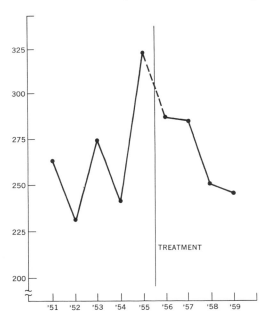

2 Connecticut traffic fatalities, 1951–
1959.

present variable, occurring in different degrees. In the Interrupted Time-Series, the "causal" variable is examined as an event or change occurring at a single time, specified independently of inspection of the data.

The Interrupted Time-Series design represents a use of the more extensive data which are often available even when only before-and-after measures are reported. Some potential outcomes of such a time-series analysis greatly reduce the plausibility of certain threats to validity. If the preexposure series shows but minor point-to-point fluctuations and no trend anticipating a big transtreatment shift, then maturation may not be plausible, for in most instances the plausible maturation hypothesis would have predicted shifts of the same order as the trans-treatment shift in each of the pretreatment stages. Reasonable models of the testing effect would have the same implications. (In our instance, this would be on condition that the annual fatality rates had been given equal publicity.) The outcome in Figure 2 is not of this readily interpretable sort, although the trend is perhaps generally upward prior to the treatment, and steadily downward subsequently.

Judgments of the plausibility of instrumentation effects must be based upon other than time-series data. However, notice should be taken here of a frequent unfortunate confounding: the administrative reform which is meant to produce a social change very frequently is accompanied by a coincident reform of the record keeping, ruling out valid inferences as to effects. The Chicago police re-form cited above is a case in point. In the present instance, we have found no evidence of a change in record keeping or index computing of the type that would produce a pseudo-effect.

The likelihood of regression, or of selection for "treatment" on a basis tend-ing to introduce regression, is supported by inspection of the time-series data. The largest change of any year is not the one after the crackdown, but is instead the upswing in the series occurring in 1954–55, just prior to the crackdown. In terms of crude fatality rates, 1955 is strikingly the highest point reached. It thus seems plausible that the high figure of 1955 caused the crackdown, and hence it seems much less likely that the crackdown caused the low figure of 1956, for such a drop would have been predicted on regression grounds in any case.

The graphic presentation of the precrackdown years provides evidence of the general instability of the accidental death rate measure, against which the 1955–56 shift can be compared. This instability makes the "treatment effect" of Figure 1 now look more trivial. Had the drop following the treatment been the largest shift in the time series, the hypothesis of effect would have been much more plausible. Instead, shifts that large are relatively frequent. The 1955–56 drop is less than half the magnitude of the 1954–55 gain, and the 1953 gain also exceeds it. It is the largest drop of the series, but it exceeds the drops of 1952, 1954, and 1958 by trivial amounts. Thus the unexplained instabilities of the series are of such a magnitude as to make the 1955–56 drop understandable as more of the same. On the other hand, it is noteworthy that after the crackdown, there are no year-to-year gains, and in this respect, the character of the time-series has changed. The plausibility of the hypothesis that instability accounts for the effect can be judged by visual inspection of the graphed figures, or by qualitative discussion, but in addition it is this one threat to validity which can be evaluated by tests of significance. These will be discussed later, and they do find some evidence of change exceeding that which the pretreatment instability would lead one to expect.

Multiple Time-Series

In many situations, time-series involving but a single experimental unit will be all that are available. In these situations, analyses on the above model are a great improvement over the usual before-and-after study. However, it is in the spirit of quasi-experimental analysis to make use of *all* available data that could help to rule out or confirm any plausible rival hypothesis. In a setting such as this, no randomly assigned control group is available. But in quasi-experimentation, even a non-equivalent control group is helpful. It provides the only control for history (for those extraneous change agents that would be expected to affect both the experimental and control group), and assists in controlling maturation, testing, and instrumentation. For Connecticut, it was judged that a pool of adjacent and similar states—New York, New Jersey, Rhode Island, and Massachusetts—provided a meaningful comparison. Figure 3 plots the death rates for the control states alongside Connecticut, all data being expressed on a per 100,000 population base to bring the figures into proximity. The control data are much smoother, due to the much larger base, *i.e.*, the canceling out of chance deviations in the annual figures for particular states.

While in general these data confirm the single time-series analysis, the differences between Connecticut and the control states show a pattern supporting the hypothesis that the crackdown made a difference. In the pretest years,

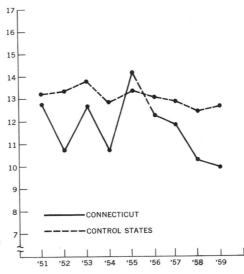

3   Connecticut and control states traffic fatalities, 1951–1959 (per 100,000 population).

Connecticut's rate is parallel or rising relative to the control, exceeding it in 1955. In the posttest years, Connecticut's rate drops faster than does the control, steadily increasing the gap. While the regression argument applies to the high point of 1955 and to the subsequent departure in 1956, it does not plausibly explain the steadily increasing gap in 1957, 1958, and 1959.

Figure 4 shows the comparison states individually. Note that four of the five show an upward swing in 1955, Connecticut having the largest. Note that all five show a downward trend in 1956. Rhode Island is most similar to Connecticut in both the 1955 upswing and 1956 downswing, actually exceeding Connecticut in the latter—in a striking argument against the hypothesis of a crackdown effect. However, the trend in 1957, 1958, and 1959 is steadily upward in Rhode Island, steadily downward in Connecticut, supporting the concept of effect.

The list of plausible rival hypotheses should include factors disguising experimental effects as well as factors producing pseudo-effects. Thus, to the list should be added *diffusion*, the tendency for the experimental effect to modify not only the experimental group, but also the control group. Thus the crackdown on speeding in Connecticut might well have reduced traffic speed and fatalities in neighboring states. Dodd reports such an effect in his classic experiment on community hygiene in Syria.[6] The comparison of posttreatment levels of Connecticut and the neighboring states might thus be invalid, or at least underestimate the effects. Conceivably one might for this reason prefer the single time-series analysis to the multiple time-series one. If highly similar remote states were available, these would make better controls, but for matters of either weather or culture adjacency and similarity are apt to be strongly associated.

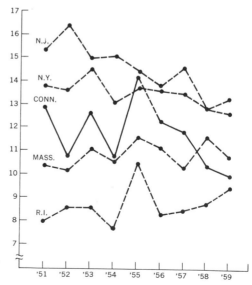

4   Traffic fatalities for Connecticut, New York, New Jersey, Rhode Island, and Massachusetts (per 100,000 persons).

Tests of Significance

Our position in regard to tests of significance is an intermediate one. On the one hand, we would agree that they are overly honored and are often useful in ruling out that one threat and should be used for that purpose. They are appropriate even where randomization has not been used because even there it is a relevant threat to validity to be able to argue that even had these data been assigned at random, differences this large would be frequent.[7]

The simplest tests conceptually are those testing for a difference in slope or intercept between pretreatment and posttreatment observations. As applied here these assume linearity and independence of error. It has been shown that the "proximally autocorrelated" error typical of natural situations (in which adjacent points in time share more error than non-adjacent ones) biases the usual tests in the direction of finding too many significant differences.[8] Unaffected by this bias is a t-test by Mood which compares a single posttreatment point with a value extrapolated from the pretreatment series.[9] None of these approached any interesting level of significance.

Glass[10] has introduced into the social sciences a more sophisticated statistical approach, based upon the work of Box and Tiao.[11] This has the advantages of realistically assuming the interdependence of adjacent points and estimating a weighting parameter thereof, of avoiding the assumption of linearity (at least in a simple or direct manner), and of weighting more heavily the observations closer to the point of treatment. A number of assumptions about the nature of the data must be made, such as the absence of cycles, but these can be examined from the data. Applying this test to monthly data, he finds a drop in fatalities not quite reaching the $P < .10$ level of significance. Using a monthly difference between Connecticut's rate and that of the pool of the four control states, still less of a significant effect is found. In what he regards as the most powerful analysis available, he computes an effect parameter for each of the four comparison states and compares the effect parameter of Connecticut with this. Connecticut shows more effect, with a significance level somewhere between $P < .05$ and $P < .07$, with a one-tailed test.

Thus on the graphic evidence of steadily dropping fatality rates, and on these marginal statistical grounds, there may be an effect. This effect, it must be restated, could be due to the crackdown, or could be due to the regression effect. (Regression effects can of course produce "statistically significant" results.)

Supplementary Analyses

In this section, we will present data that will further illustrate time-series analysis and, substantively, both indicate that the crackdown was put into effect and that it had some unanticipated and, to the policy-makers, probably undesired consequences.

Figure 5 presents evidence that the crackdown was put into effect, as indicated by a great increase in suspensions of licenses for speeding. Unfortunately,

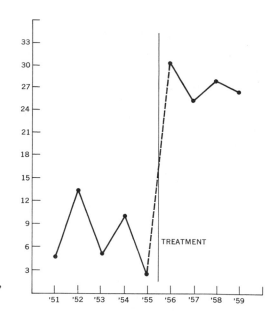

5   Suspensions of licenses for speeding,
as a per cent of all suspensions.

we have not been able to get control state data for this and the following variables,
but the single state time-series is quite convincing in itself. We regard it as con-
firming the appropriateness of the statistical tests that they indicate significant
differences. The single-point-extrapolation t is 4.33 with 4 degrees of freedom,
where 3.75 is significant at the $P < .02$ level.

Figure 6 plots the percentage which speeding violations constitute of all
traffic violations. This shows a decline, due presumably to greater conformity
to speed limits, although it is possible that policemen and prosecutors were more

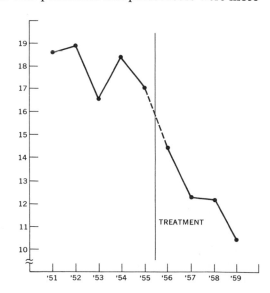

6   Speeding violations, as per cent of
all traffic violations.

willing, in the light of severe sanctions for speeding, to overlook minor infrac-
tions or to charge them as something else. While the graphic portrayal of declining speeding violations is convincing of a genuine effect, the statistical tests
are not so emphatic. The single-point-extrapolation t is 2.66 with 4 degrees of
freedom, not reaching the $P < .05$ level of 2.78.

From Figure 5 and the reports cited in the first section of this paper it is
clear that a real change in enforcement behavior resulted. It seems likely that
the proportion of drivers exceeding the speed limits on Connecticut highways
actually decreased. However, over and above these desired effects there are signs
of unforeseen and unwanted reactions. Figure 7 concerns persons whose licenses
were further suspended because they were convicted of driving with a suspended
license, expressed as a percentage of all suspensions. This jumps from an almost
consistent zero to some 4 to 6 per cent. Tests of significance confirm the effect.
The single-point-extrapolation t reaches an incredible 130.75, due to the very
small error term which the negligible variance of the pretest scores produces.
(While one feels uneasy with a practically zero variance, the consistent pretest zero
does genuinely make the later values unlikely.) Our interpretation of this phenomenon is that automobile transportation has become a virtual necessity for
many residents of the diffusely settled megalopolitan region that includes Connecticut, and these people are willing to risk very severe sanctions in order to
continue daily routines that involve driving. Since they are willing to drive with
a suspended license, suspension does not have the desired restrictive effect on
this group of drivers, which is probably much larger than the number appre-
hended and appearing in these statistics would indicate. Alternatively, of course,
the increase could result, in whole or part, from more vigorous efforts at

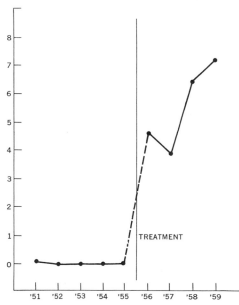

7   Arrested while driving with a suspended
license, as per cent of suspensions.

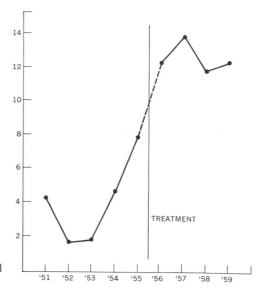

8   Per cent of speeding violations judged not guilty.

enforcement both in the crackdown itself and in special efforts at inspection comprising a followup of the crackdown effort.

Figure 8 shows a reaction on the part of the legal system. Even with fewer speeding violations reaching the courts (Figure 6), the courts were more lenient in their handling of these cases as expressed by the proportion of not guilty decisions. Tests of significance are borderline. The single-point-extrapolation t is 2.42, which with but 4 degrees of freedom fails to reach significance at the $P < .05$ level, for which 2.78 would be required. Larger proportions of not guilty judgments could be the result of more cases getting to court because of tightening of precourt standards, more generous handling by judges and prosecutors, or more vigorous defenses by the accused because more is at stake. The two effects shown in Figures 7 and 8 indicate a vitiation of the punitive effects of the crackdown in operation in a society where dependence on automobile transportation is acknowledged.

Conclusion

On the substantive side, the analysis has demonstrated that the Connecticut crackdown on speeding was a substantial enforcement effort, although some of its most punitive aspects were mitigated in practice. As to fatalities, we find a sustained trend toward reduction, but no unequivocal proof that they were due to the crackdown. The likelihood that the very high prior rate instigated the crackdown seriously complicates the inference.

We have, however, learned something about the response of the legal system to a reform bearing a harsh penal sanction. The courts, and probably also the police, are apparently unwilling to invoke penalties that might seem severe and unfamiliar in context. Moreover, the force of such penalties as are inflicted is vitiated by the willingness of the public to evade them. As in the case of white-collar crime, the effective punishment varies with the criminal.[12]

More important, we believe, than the specific findings of the study is the methodology here explored. While the social scientist cannot as a rule experiment on a societal scale, societal "experimentation" or abrupt focused social change is continually going on, initiated by government, business, natural forces, etc. The social scientist adds to his tools for understanding the social system when he attends to these events and documents their effects in as thorough a fashion as is possible. Insofar as correlational approaches differ from experimental analysis, it adds depth to the social scientist's work when he examines the fit of an experimental interpretation with full attention to the uncontrolled competing hypotheses.

The methodology for such quasi-experimental analysis has a long but unsystematic history, and offers much room for development. It should be remembered that not only are the raw materials shaped by the tools, but in the long run the tools are shaped by the materials upon which they work. We should not passively accept a methodology as a revealed truth, but rather should test it in use with our materials. Methodology has in fact an empirical history and its constituents have the status of empirical discoveries. The classical control group experiment is not typical of the physical sciences, but instead emerged from psychological laboratory research, and is peculiar to the social sciences and their problems.[13] Medical research has the placebo control group, and neurophysiology the sham operation control, as achievements of specific research traditions, not as logical dispensations from the philosophy of science or mathematical statistics. So too the methods for quasi-experimentation in settings like the present will emerge from an iteration of effort and criticism, in which many approaches will be rejected.

A final note on the treatment of uncontrolled variables is in order. On the one extreme there is that attitude often unwittingly inculcated in courses on experimental design, which looks askance at all efforts to make inferences where some variables have been left uncontrolled or where randomization has not taken place. In contrast, the quasi-experimental approach takes a radically different posture: any experiment is valid until proven invalid. The only invalidation comes from plausible rival explanations of the specific outcome. Regression effects and test-retest effects are such in many settings. An absence of randomization may in some specific way plausibly explain the obtained results. But unless one can specify such a hypothesis and the direction of its effects, it should not be regarded as invalidating. Subsequent consideration may uncover plausible rival hypotheses which have been overlooked, but such transitory validity is often the fate of laboratory experiments too.

At the other extreme is the naive attribution of cause which blithely fails to consider any explanations other than the author's favorite candidate. Such an orientation is likewise opposed. The quasi-experimentalist is obliged to search out and consider the available plausible rival hypotheses with all the vigilance at his command. While our coverage in this regard has been incomplete, we hope that we have at least illustrated such an approach.

NOTES

*   The preparation of this paper has been supported in part by the National Science Foundation (Grant GS 1309x), the U.S. Office of Education (Project C-998, Contract 3-20-001), the U.S. Bureau of Public Roads (CPR 11-5981), the National Institutes of Health, the U.S. Public Health Service (RG-5359), and the Automotive Safety Foundation (as an aspect of Experimental Case Studies of Traffic Accidents conducted at Northwestern University). A brief version of it appears as H. L. Ross and D. T. Campbell, "The Connecticut Speed Crackdown: A Study of the Effects of Legal Change," in *Perspectives on the Social Order: Readings in Sociology* 30–35 (H. L. Ross, ed.; 2nd ed., 1968).

1.   E.g., D. T. Campbell and J. S. Stanley, "Experimental and Quasi-Experimental Designs for Research on Teaching," in *Handbook of Research on Teaching* 171–246 (N. L. Gage, ed., 1963), reprinted as *Experimental and Quasi-Experimental Designs for Research* (1963); D. T. Campbell, "From Description to Experimentation: Interpreting Trends as Quasi-Experiments," in *Problems in Measuring Change* (C. W. Harris, ed., 1963); D. T. Campbell and K. N. Clayton, "Avoiding Regression Effects in Panel Studies of Communication Impact," in *Studies in Public Communication* 99–118 (Dept. of Sociology, University of Chicago, No. 3, 1961), reprinted in Bobbs-Merrill Reprints in Sociology as S-353. For an application of this type of analysis to legal impact see R. Lempert, "Strategies of Research Design in the Legal Impact Study," *Law & Society Review* 111 (1966).

2.   Cited in C. Selltiz, M. Jahoda, M. Deutsch, and S. W. Cook, *Research Methods in Social Relations* 323 (1959).

3.   J. Sween and D. T. Campbell, "A Study of the Effect of Proximally Autocorrelated Error on Tests of Significance for the Interrupted Time Series Quasi-Experimental Design" 31–32, Figs. 11 and 12 (mimeographed Research Report, Dept. of Psychology, Northwestern University, 1965). These figures also will appear in D. T. Campbell, "Reforms as Experiments," *American Psychologist* (to be submitted).

4.   Instability has not been singled out as a specific threat to validity in previous discussions of quasi-experimental design, although the discussion of tests of significance in such situations has implied it. Tests of significance obviously do not provide "proof" relevant to the many other sources of invalidity, but they are relevant to this one plausible rival hypothesis even where randomization has not been used.

5.   This issue is extremely complex. In ordinary correlation, the regression is technically toward the mean of the second variable, not to the mean of the selection variable if these means differ. In time-series, the regression is toward the general trend-line, which may of course be upward or downward or unchanging. A more expanded analysis of the regression problem in correlation across persons is contained in Campbell and Clayton (1961) and in Campbell and Stanley (1963), both cited in note 1 above.

6.   S. C. Dodd, "A Controlled Experiment on Rural Hygiene in Syria" (1934).

7.   D. T. Campbell, "Quasi-Experimental Design," in *International Encyclopedia of the Social Sciences*, Vol. 5, 259–263 (D. L. Sills, ed., 1968).

8.   Sween and Campbell, *op. cit.* The tests thus biased include tests of slope and intercept provided by H. M. Walker and J. Lev, *Statistical Inference* 390–395, 399–400 (1953). Note that this invalidates the discussion of tests of significance in Campbell (1963), *op. cit.*, 220–230. The "Clayton test" presented there was found in the Monte Carlo simulation by Sween and Campbell to have additional errors leading it to be too optimistic.

9.   A. M. Mood, *Introduction to the Theory of Statistics* 297–298 (1950).

10.   G. V. Glass, "Analysis of Data on the Connecticut Speeding Crackdown as a Time-Series Quasi-Experiment," *Law & Society Review* 3, 55–76 (1968); T. O. Maguire and G. V. Glass, "A Program for the Analysis of Certain Time-Series Quasi-Experiments," *Educational and Psychological Measurement* 27, 743–750 (1967); G. V. Glass, G. C. Tiao, and T. O. Maguire, "Analysis of Data on the 1900 Revision of German Divorce Laws as a Time-Series Quasi-Experiment," *Law & Society Review* (in press).

11.   G. E. P. Box and G. C. Tiao, "A Change in Level of a Non-stationary Time Series," *Biometrika* 52, 181–192 (1965); G. E. P. Box, "Bayesian Approaches to Some Bothersome Problems in Data Analysis," in *Improving Experimental Design and Statistical Analysis* (J. C. Stanley, ed., 1967).

12.   The classic reference is E. H. Sutherland, *White Collar Crime* (1959). See also H. L. Ross, "Traffic Law Violation: A Folk Crime," *Social Problems* 8, 231–241 (1961).

13.   E. G. Boring, "The Nature and History of Experimental Control," *American Journal of Psychology* 67, 573–589 (1954).

A CONTROLLED INVESTIGATION OF THE CHARACTERISTICS OF ADULT PEDESTRIANS FATALLY INJURED BY MOTOR VEHICLES IN MANHATTAN

WILLIAM HADDON, JR.
PRESTON VALIEN
JAMES R. McCARROLL
CHARLES J. UMBERGER

Accidents in which pedestrians are struck by motor vehicles account for a substantial fraction of the motor vehicle accident deaths occurring in the United States. For example, in 1959, of the 37,800 persons who died as the result of motor vehicle accidents in the United States, 7,750 were pedestrians.[1] Of these, 4,850 were struck in urban areas,[1] and press reports and the scanty information available suggest that most, if not all, of the world's major cities are endemic foci of such deaths.

New York City is a major such focus, one in which approximately 70 per cent (1955–1959) of those killed in motor vehicle accidents are pedestrians. In 1959 deaths of pedestrians accounted for 515 of the 737 killed as the result of accidents in the five boroughs of the city, and an unknown additional number occurred in the extensive surrounding urban area. During the same period, pedestrian deaths in New York City constituted 6.6 per cent of the pedestrian deaths in the nation and 62 per cent of those in New York State.

Despite the long history of this problem and its present magnitude, relatively little is known as to the characteristics of those killed, particularly in comparison with the characteristics of those who though similarly exposed are nonetheless not similarly involved. Although it has been known for many years that a large percentage of such fatally injured persons have been drinking heavily,[2,3,4] heretofore no one has determined the extent to which the population similarly at risk has been drinking. It has also been long known that the age-specific fatality rate distribution of those killed throughout the United States is J-shaped with a maximum in the grade school and preschool years and a minimum in the 15 to 34 year range, followed by large, progressive increases in the subsequent decades.[1,5,6] Again, however, it has not been known whether or not the age distribution of those similarly exposed is the same, or whether the age distribution of those killed results in part from an age-associated risk.

Despite this lack of scientifically gathered information large sums are spent annually throughout the United States in "pedestrian control" programs, public exhortations, and other measures which though often reasonable have not been

Reprinted by permission of William Haddon, Jr., and Pergamon Press, Inc., from *Journal of Chronic Diseases* 14 (December, 1961), 655–678.

the subject of adequately designed evaluations. To the contrary, much has been made of short-term fluctuations in incidence, both as evidence of the efficacy of such measures where the changes have been downward and, where the reverse has been the case, as evidence for their need.

The investigation described in this report emphasized the characteristics of accident-involved and non-accident-involved pedestrians rather than the characteristics of involved drivers and accident sites, although these are also undoubtedly of importance. The pedestrian characteristics chosen for study included age, sex, blood alcohol concentration, socioeconomic status, and others believed to be of more fundamental importance than the "pedestrian actions" (for example, disobeying given traffic regulations) around which most discussion of pedestrian accidents is centered. Since it was decided to study the pedestrian accident problem in adults rather than that in children, where somewhat different factors would be expected to be of importance, an "adult pedestrian" was defined for the purposes of this study as any pedestrian 18 years of age or older, a cutoff point which falls in the 15 to 34 years of age minimum in the fatality rate distribution. For practical reasons the investigation was limited to Manhattan.

Methods

Case series. With the exceptions to be noted, the case series consisted of 50 of the 52 pedestrians 18 years of age and older who died *as the result*, confirmed by autopsy and the weighing of the total of available information, of being struck by motor vehicles at known Manhattan sites and times between May 3 and November 7, 1959, and whose deaths occurred during the same period. The 52 deaths consisted of all such deaths known to the Accident Investigation Squad of the New York City Police Department and the Office of the Chief Medical Examiner. The 2 omitted cases were deleted through clerical errors.*

Postmortem examinations were performed in all cases, almost invariably on the morning following death. Whenever possible, blood from the heart or superior vena cava was obtained in cases in which survival had not exceeded 6 hours. Specimens of brain were also usually obtained. Since all of these specimens were negative for reducing substances other than ethanol, they were next analyzed with the use of a modified Widmark method.[8] The results were reported in milligrams of ethanol per 100 grams of specimen (milligrams per cent by

---

* A number of borderline cases were omitted as not meeting the above criteria. Included in this borderline group were: (1) two cases in which pedestrians, both elderly, died as the result of being hit by bicycles; (2) one case of homicide in which the pedestrian was pushed into the path of an oncoming car; (3) one case in which an injured 72-year-old woman who had stated that she had been knocked down by a car died without revealing the site or time of her accident; and (4) one case in which an 81-year-old man convalescing from a fractured pelvis and other injuries sustained when hit by an automobile died of coronary occlusion confirmed at postmortem examination by the finding of a fresh coronary thrombus.

weight), and each such analytical result was rounded off to the nearest 10 mg. per cent.

Data relative to the characteristics of the deceased and the circumstances of the accidents were obtained from the records of the Accident Investigation Squad, from the Office of the Chief Medical Examiner, and, in the case of motor vehicle operators' licenses, from the records of the New York State Bureau of Motor Vehicles. Additional data with respect to weather were obtained from the hourly observations of the New York Meteorological Observatory, Central Park.[9]

Control group. In brief, a control group was obtained by: (1) visiting each accident site on a *subsequent* date, but on the same day of the week and at a time as close as possible to the exact time of day of the accident; and (2) interviewing and obtaining breath specimens for alcohol analysis from the first 4 adult pedestrians of the same sex as the deceased reaching the site (see below). This resulted in a control or comparison group of 200 individuals comprising a sample of the universe defined by matching in each index case for sex, exact accident site, and time of day and day of week of accident.

As each death occurred, the case was added to the roster of cases for which controls were to be obtained during the next sampling period. These sampling periods were scheduled weeks in advance to fall at approximately 4 week intervals. Tuesdays and Wednesdays were treated as one day when convenient for scheduling purposes, but the 4 member control group for only one case of the 12 which had occurred on Tuesdays or Wednesdays was obtained on a different day from the day of week of accident occurrence. With this single exception, 48 of the 49 sites (one accident had resulted in 2 deaths) were visited on the same day of the week as that on which the accident had occurred. Under this sampling period procedure, 28 sites were visited within 4 weeks (i.e., ≤4 weeks) after the corresponding accidents, 38 within 5 weeks, and all but 8 within 6 weeks.

Two of the case accidents occurred on legal holidays, and 2 of the site visits also fell on legal holidays. As a result, no appreciable biases due to the inclusion or exclusion of such days are believed to have been present.

The site visits were made by a team of two or three of the authors and one to four medical students working at each location with one or two uniformed members of the Police Department Accident Investigation Squad (A.I.S.).

In visiting each site one of three basic approaches was used. In the first type, that used in many busy neighborhoods, for example, opposite Grand Central Station on a weekday at 6:10 p.m., the entire team arrived and immediately stopped the *first* 4 adult pedestrians of the same sex as the deceased. At such busy sites the group arrived and accomplished its purpose in 5 minutes or less from start to finish.

When the accident site was in a neighborhood in which it was suspected that the group might be seen and avoided, a second approach was used. Under such circumstances, for example, at sites in the Bowery, the group arrived and "swept the block" stopping successively the *first* 4 adult pedestrians of the required sex who were headed toward or away from the accident site. By pedestrian here and throughout this report is meant a person progressing by walking, not lounging stationary, sitting, or lying down.

In the third approach, used where pedestrian traffic was very light, for example at 108th Street and the East River (F.D.R.) Drive at 1:40 a.m., the group would lounge nearby or sit in a car at or near the site watching for approaching pedestrians, and as each of the *first* 4 of these came into view he, or, where appropriate, she, was quickly approached and stopped.

The site visited was the sidewalk point closest to the exact location of the accident as described on the police or medical examiner's report. For example, one report indicated that the deceased had been crossing the street 40 feet from a given corner. This was found to be directly in front of a "rathskeller," and it was at that point that the first 4 pedestrians were stopped.

Great care was taken to avoid any attempt at matching for the characteristics of the deceased, except in so far as sex and adulthood were concerned. In addition, for methodologic uniformity, at all sites the same investigator pointed out to the accompanying police each individual to be stopped. Although the exact details varied with the circumstances, the person was immediately approached and told by the policeman, "Please step over for a minute while the *doctors* ask you a few questions." A nearby member of the team immediately stepped up and began talking uninterruptedly: "I don't want to know your name; I merely want to ask you a few questions. Do you live in Manhattan?" The interview was usually easily begun in this manner, although 12 refusals occurred (see below).

To obtain the 4 pedestrians comprising the sample at each site, *all* pedestrians of the appropriate sex who appeared to be in their mid-teens or older were stopped until the requisite number of persons was obtained. Mid-teenagers were stopped in this manner to avoid biases which might otherwise have been introduced had the decision as to whether or not given individuals were or were not 18 or over been left to the investigator who was pointing out the persons to be stopped. In such borderline cases the interviewee was first asked his or her age, and if it fell below 18 the next pedestrian of the same sex was immediately stopped.

Where the individual stopped refused to cooperate, the pedestrian who followed immediately was stopped. For the purposes of this report a "refusal" is considered any case in which the individual met the sampling criteria, but from whom it was impossible to obtain *both* the complete interview *and* the breath specimen. Under this definition, there were *no* refusals at 39 of the 49 sites. There was one refusal at each of 10 sites, and at one site there were 2 refusals.

This investigation was carried out without publicity of any kind. With one exception it was invariably possible to stop the members of each pedestrian sample prior to the formation of the substantial group of watchers which sometimes formed thereafter. The exception, in a "tough" neighborhood at 2:30 a.m., involved the only site at which 2 persons had been fatally injured in the same accident. On arrival, it was possible to obtain quickly the first 7 but not the eighth interview and specimen of breath, a small, hostile crowd quickly forming from an adjacent bar. As a result, only the first 4 of the 7 interviews and specimens obtained at this site were used, being counted twice in the analyses of the data.

The interview included questions as to: place and length of residence; place of birth; age; present occupation; and marital status. Sex, apparent race, appearance and apparent sobriety, date, location, time of interview, and weather were also recorded.

Immediately on finishing the interview the interviewer stated approximately as follows, "I only have one more thing for you to do (and then you can go) and that is to blow up this bag for me." Simultaneously he removed a Saran bag (see below) from an envelope and showed the pedestrian how to place one of its two ends in his mouth and blow until told to stop. This finished, the pedestrian was thanked and told that the interview was over.

A large percentage of those interviewed were foreign born, and many of these admitted to no knowledge of English. Rather than weaken the investigation by omitting these pedestrians when no member of the team knew a common language, passersby were stopped and asked to serve as interpreters. Apparently because those walking in the same neighborhoods or, in some cases, accompanying those stopped (many of the latter being interviewed themselves) tended to know the same languages, this procedure proved very satisfactory. With its use no one failed to be interviewed because of a language barrier and interviews were completed in Armenian, German, Greek, Spanish, and other languages and dialects.

The average interview was recorded as beginning 1.5 minutes after the recorded time of the corresponding accident. One hundred and fifty-nine of the 200 paired time differences were within plus or minus 15 minutes (i.e., ≤ 15 minutes), and 179 were within 20 minutes. All interviews were obtained within 55 minutes of the corresponding accident times, and in only 7 instances did the difference exceed 30 minutes. These rare, longer intervals were considered preferable to obtaining variable numbers of controls at each site, a procedure which would have biased the control group toward the characteristics of the pedestrians at sites at which controls were more quickly obtainable.

Breath specimens. The Saran bag employed for the collection of the breath specimens was recently developed in the Department of Pharmacology, University of Toronto, for the collection of breath specimens from drivers suspected of drunken driving.[10] It represents a substantial methodologic advance since alcohol-containing breath specimens collected in it show only negligible losses in alcohol *concentration* with prolonged holding. This is in marked contrast with that obtained with other collection devices.[11] For example, the concentration of alcohol in rubber balloons falls by about one half in 15 minutes.[11] Alcohol-containing breath specimens collected in this manner prior to the transfer to the analytical apparatus (below) give results which are not significantly different from those obtained when the specimen is collected directly in that apparatus.[12]

The breath specimens were invariably analyzed within approximately 2 to 3 hours of collection. On returning to the laboratory, the breath-containing bags were placed for approximately one quarter hour or more in an incubator at approximately 40°C. in order to evaporate the condensate which had meanwhile formed inside, a precaution taken to avoid the possibility that changes in alcohol concentration in the gaseous phase might occur as the result of alcohol's differential solubility in the aqueous condensate. On removal from the incubator each specimen was very quickly transferred to the "Breathalyzer." The Breathalyzer is a commercially produced photoelectric device which, under standardized conditions, compares 2 ampules of potassium dichromate–sulfuric acid solution through one of which the breath specimen has been bubbled.[13] This results in an estimate, expressed to the nearest 0.01 per cent by weight (10 mg. per cent by weight), of the blood alcohol concentration at the time the breath specimen was collected. The reliability and accuracy of this device, when properly used, in estimating blood alcohol concentrations has been repeatedly documented.[13,14]

The Saran bags and the Breathalyzer subsequently used were not yet available at the time at which the site visits for the first 5 cases were made, and the 20 controls for these cases have been listed in the data as "no alcohol controls." However, at these sites breath specimens were collected, usually in toy balloons, as a part of the interviewing procedure, which was otherwise unchanged.

Cases employed for alcohol comparisons. Because of the relatively rapid rate at which alcohol is metabolized, the longer the interval between accident and death in any case, the greater was the probable postaccident lowering of the blood alcohol concentration.[15,16] Consequently, as a compromise between the necessity of having as large a case group as possible for the alcohol comparisons and the need to work with a group in which as little metabolic lowering as possible had occurred, only cases in which survival was less than 6 hours were used for such comparisons, with the exception that the 2 such short-survival cases among the first 5 cases referred to above were also not included in these comparisons since comparable controls were not obtained. To the extent to which such lowering occurred, this diminished the actual differences in this respect between the cases and the controls. In order to gain information as to the blood alcohol concentrations of those in the *total* control group, in addition to that portion of it derived from sites involving less than 6 hour survivals, specimens for analysis with the Breathalyzer were obtained from all of those successfully interviewed at all but the first 5 accident sites.

Comment on methodology. The obtaining of the accident site-matched controls on *subsequent* dates, rather than immediately following each accident, obviates three practical difficulties present when immediate site visits are attempted. First, it may be hours, days, or weeks before it is known whether or not a given case meets the criteria for admission to the series under study. Second, even when a decision to visit a site can be made immediately on notification of each successive accident's occurrence (and this requires that personnel be continuously on call), the time lags inherent in notification and travel to the site result in the controls always being obtained substantially later than the times of occurrence of the corresponding accidents. Third, since groups of onlookers often form immediately and remain for some time at such sites immediate sampling would probably result in sampling biases. These difficulties are not encountered with the experimental design employed in this investigation.

Such subsequent sampling, however, raises the possibility of pertinent intervening changes in the characteristics of pedestrians at the site. Changes of this type are believed greatly minimized by the matching for day of week, exact time of occurrence, sex, and adulthood, and these matchings were very successfully achieved. In addition, the weather (raining, or not raining) at 39 of the sites *at the times the interviews were obtained* (see below) was the same as at the times of the corresponding accidents, and it is likely that at least at these 39 sites the pedestrian and traffic *densities* were comparable to those at the times of the corresponding accidents. Also, the average accident site visit interval was quite short, less than 4 weeks, and the average temperature difference between the daily means for the accident dates and those of the visits was only $-4°F$. Finally (see footnote, Table V), it was established that there were no statistically significant shifts with time of year in the mean age of the fatally injured or in the mean age of the site-matched controls. These and the foregoing considerations lend additional confidence to the sampling method employed.

The fact that only 212 persons meeting the sampling criteria had to be stopped to obtain the 200 site-matched controls makes it very unlikely that any appreciable biases from this source were present. The majority of these 6 males and 6 females who refused were sober, well dressed, and often hurrying pedestrians. Six gave full interviews, 2 answered some questions, and 4 none. Three are known to have been drinking, 2 heavily, one of the latter being too intoxicated to blow up a bag. On the basis of the available evidence it is very unlikely that the exclusion of this small group resulted in any substantial biases.

Finally, it is pertinent that one previous investigation which found among accident-involved *drivers* a large, statistically significant excess of persons who had been drinking heavily used a somewhat similar design. In it "a year round checking of the breath of some accident and non-accident . . . operators in . . . Toronto . . . was made." "Each week from Monday until Saturday, 6:30–10:30 p.m. or later, . . . police accompanied by a research worker . . . attended as many traffic accidents . . . as possible. For each driver involved in an accident four or more non-accident drivers passing the scene . . . in cars of the same vintage at approximately the same time provided breath samples. . . ."[17] It was not known whether or not this method of study gave a representative sample of the universes of all accident and non-accident involved drivers.[18] However, this investigation, in which breath specimens were obtained from 2,015 *drivers*,[17] and that reported by Holcomb in which breath specimens were collected from

1,750 *drivers* passing certain traffic sampling points in Evanston, Illinois,[17,19] suggested the possible feasibility of the Manhattan pedestrian accident investigation reported here.

Results

Figure 1 shows the accident sites. Tables I and II give the day of week and time of day of occurrence, and Table III the distribution of the 50 postaccident survival intervals.

Table IV compares the weather (raining or not raining) at the accidents with the weather at the site visits. In making this comparison, the table gives first the weather at the time each site visit was first scheduled and includes the weather as found on first visit to the 4 sites which had to be revisited because on first arrival it was found that the police were absent because of higher priorities elsewhere. The last column includes the weather at these 4 sites at the time of the second, completed visits.

The experimental design was based upon obtaining site-, time-, and sex-matched controls for persons *fatally* injured. On this basis alone it would have been impossible to differentiate between age-associated accident involvement risks and age-associated risks of death, granted accident involvement.* Since it was considered quite possible that older persons had both higher risks of being hit than younger persons similarly exposed, *and* higher risks of death once hit, additional data as to the age of pedestrians involved in nonfatal motor vehicle accidents were obtained. This information was not available at the time the investigation was begun in May, but beginning October 1 the age and sex distributions of all pedestrians known to the police as injured but not killed in accidents in Manhattan became available. Table V summarizes these data in comparison with those obtained from the case series and the site-matched controls.

Because several of the characteristics of the cases and controls would be expected to be age-associated, where appropriate, each of the tables which follows gives both comparisons between the corresponding characteristic in the case group and in the total control group, and similar comparisons between the case group and an age-matched control group derived from the total site-matched control group. This matching was performed by matching each case with the one member of the control group of the same sex most nearly of the same age, and not more than 4 years different in age. Where more than one choice was possible a table of random digits was used to make the choice. It was thus possible to match 43 of the 50 cases, and these constitute the basis of the age-matched comparisons given in Tables VI, VII, IX, X, and XI.

---

* Accident causation research and statistics involving groups defined by given severities of injury have very consistently overlooked the possibility of pertinent associations between age and susceptibility to injury per se, as shown here and subsequently an important point. As a result such data are often of very limited value.

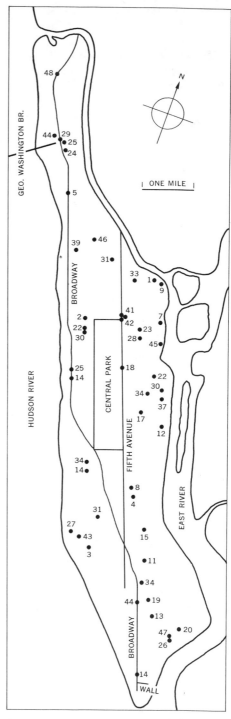

1   Locations at which 50 adult pedestrians were fatally injured, Manhattan, May-November, 1959.

The location numbers indicate the sequence of occurrence, The 12 females in the series were fatally injured at sites 2, 9, 10, 12, 22, 25, 30, 31, 32, 35, 44, and 49. Over longer periods than that studied there is a marked concentration of deaths in the Bowery area (sites 13, 19).

■ **Table I.** Day of week of accident

	Sun.	Mon.	Tues.	Wed.	Thurs.	Fri.	Sat.	Total
Number of accidents	5	6	4	8	8	8	10*	49*

* Includes one accident in which 2 persons were fatally injured.

■ **Table II.** Time of day of accident

	A.M.				P.M.				Total
	12–2	3–5	6–8	9–11	12–2	3–5	6–8	9–11	
Number of accidents	6*	3	2	3	5	5	11	14	49*

* Includes one accident in which 2 persons were fatally injured.

■ **Table III.** Postaccident survival of 50 adult pedestrians fatally injured by motor vehicles, Manhattan, May–November, 1959

Length of survival	Number of cases
< 1 hour and dead on arrival	13
1 < 2 hours	3
2 < 3 hours	4
3 < 4 hours	1
4 < 5 hours	—
5 < 6 hours	1
6–11 hours	1
12–23 hours	5
1 day	5
2 days	1
3 days	2
4 days	3
5– 7 days	5
8–14 days	4
15–30 days	—
> 30 days	2
Total	50

■ **Table IV.**   Weather at accidents and at subsequent site visits

	Number of accidents	Site visit as first scheduled*	Site visit as completed*
Raining	13†	7†	8
Not raining	37	43	42
Total	50	50	50

* See text.
† Probability of observing this difference (13/50 vs. 7/50) by chance: $P = 0.13$.

Tables VI, VII, and IX, respectively, give the comparisons for place of birth, place of residence, and marital status. Table VIII gives the distribution of distances between individuals' exact residences and their accident sites, and Table X gives the data with respect to socioeconomic status as judged by occupation.[20]

It is recalled that because of the rapidity of the metabolism of ethanol only those persons surviving less than 6 hours (and not among the first 5 cases, see above) are considered from the standpoint of their postmortem blood alcohol concentrations. Table XIA compares the alcohol concentrations of such persons

■ **Table V.**   Average age of fatally injured pedestrians, site-matched pedestrian controls, and nonfatally injured pedestrians

	Fatally injured	Site-matched controls	Nonfatally injured*
Mean age total†	58.8	41.6	48.4
Males	59.2‡	40.9‡	47.4‡
Females	61.7‡	43.7‡	50.3‡

* The injured-group means were derived from police records summarizing the age and sex distributions of the 209 pedestrians 18 years of age and over known to the police as having been nonfatally injured in Manhattan in the three periods: Oct. 1–7, Nov. 1–7, and Dec. 1–7, 1959. It is noted that the last 2 site visits fell on December 12.
† Because of the possibility of associations between time of year and age, the age distribution of the 18 cases and 104 controls entering their series on October 1 or later were tested for significance in comparison with the total case and control groups, respectively. Since neither of these showed significant differences ($P = 0.28$ and 0.52, respectively), the significance of the differences between the mean ages of the total members of each of the three groups were next tested and found highly significant (see text).
‡ Since the mean ages of the males and females in each column were found to be not significantly different, the comparisons between the three groups were based upon the mean ages of the total individuals of both sexes in each group.

■ **Table VI.** Place of birth

	A*				B†			
	Cases		Site-matched controls		Age and sex-matched cases		Age and sex-matched controls	
	No.	%	No.	%	No.	%	No.	%
Continental United States	15	30.0	113	56.5	15	34.9	21	48.8
Outside continental United States	26	52.0	87	43.5	21	48.8	22	51.2
Unknown	9	18.0	—	0.0	7	16.3	—	0.0
Total	50		200		43		43	

* In A, $P = 0.02$ (χ^2 omitting unknown).
† In B, $P = 0.52$.

■ **Table VII.** Place of residence

	A*				B†			
	Cases		Site-matched controls		Age and sex-matched cases		Age and sex-matched controls	
	No.	%	No.	%	No.	%	No.	%
Manhattan	42	84.0	142	71.0	35	81.4	31	72.1
Other New York City	2	4.0	30	15.0	2	4.7	5	11.6
Other New York State	2	4.0	9	4.5	2	4.7	4	9.3
Other	—	0.0	19	9.5	—	0.0	3	7.0
Unknown	4	8.0	—	0.0	4	9.3	—	0.0
Total	50		200		43		43	

* In A, $P = 0.004$ (χ^2, Manhattan vs. total of other, unknown omitted).
† In B, $P = 0.04$.

■ **Table VIII.** Distance between place of residence and site of fatal accident*

Distance	Number
0– 499 feet	12
500– 999 feet	9
1,000–1,499 feet	3
1,500–1,999 feet	3
2,000–2,499 feet	5
2,500–3,499 feet	4
3,500–1 mile	2
1–2 miles	1
2–3 miles	2
3–8 miles	0
8–9 miles	1
Unknown	4
Nonresident	4
Total	50

* These data were obtained by locating each accident site and the residence of the corresponding fatally injured person as precisely as possible on a large map of Manhattan and measuring their straight line separation.

■ **Table IX.** Marital status

	A*				B†			
	Cases		Site-matched controls		Age and sex-matched cases		Age and sex-matched controls	
	No.	%	No.	%	No.	%	No.	%
Married	15	30.0	114‡	57.0	14	32.6	25§	58.1
Widowed	10	20.0	15	7.5	9	20.9	6	14.0
Divorced	2	4.0	11	5.5	2	4.7	3	7.0
Never married (single)	14	28.0	60	30.0	12	27.9	9	20.9
Unknown	9	18.0	—	0.0	6	14.0	—	0.0
Total	50		200		43		43	

* In A, $P = 0.01$ (χ^2 combining widowed and divorced and omitting unknown).
† In B, $P = 0.19$.
‡ Includes 8 "separated."
§ Includes one "separated."

■ **Table X.** Socioeconomic status

	A*				B†			
	Cases		Site-matched controls		Age and sex-matched cases		Age and sex-matched controls	
	No.	%	No.	%	No.	%	No.	%
Upper third‡	7	14.0	59	29.5	5	11.6	11	25.6
Middle third§	12	24.0	74	37.0	12	27.9	15	34.9
Lower third‖	18	36.0	37	18.5	16	37.2	8	18.6
Housewives and unknowns	13	26.0	30	15.0	10	23.3	9	20.9
Total	50		200		43		43	

* In A, $P = 0.003$ (χ^2 omitting housewives and unknowns).
† In B, $P = 0.07$.
‡ 000–399 in U.S. Bureau of Census classification of occupations.
§ 400–699.
‖ 700–999.

with those in the *entire* control group (omitting the 20 controls for the first 5 cases). Table XIB compares the alcohol concentrations of the same individuals with those of the controls obtained at the same accident sites, and Table XIC compares the 17 such persons with less than 6 hour survival included in the 43 cases successfully matched for age and sex with the members of the control group with which they were matched.

Discussion

The design and methods employed in this investigation represent the development of a theoretically and practically clean and efficient approach to the controlled study of certain aspects of accident phenomena. Although only a small number of the details of design and methodology are new, taken together they represent a unique contribution. Their application, in addition, has resulted in one of the very few well-controlled accident investigations completed to date.

The accidents studied tended to occur, as previously reported for other cities,[21] outside of the major business and shopping areas (Fig. 1). They fell predominantly in the evening, late evening, and very early morning hours (Table II), as often previously reported. Seventy-three per cent (36/49) of the accidents occurred in the 12 hour period beginning at 3 p.m., and 51 per (cent 25/49) in

■ **Table XI*A*.** Blood alcohol concentrations

Blood alcohol concentration	Surviving less than 6 hours*		Total Site-matched controls†		
	No.	%	No.	%	
00 (none)	5	25.0	118	65.6	Employing partial x^2, $P < 0.10$,
10–40	5	25.0	30	16.7	> 0.05, comparing the 00 and 10–
50–90	1	5.0	14	7.8	40 groups in the case and control
100–140	2	10.0	5	2.8	groups. $P > 0.20$, comparing simi-
150–190	5	25.0	3	1.7	larly the number in the 00–40 and
200–240	1	5.0	6	3.3	50–140 groups. $P < 0.001$, com-
250–290	—	0.0	1	0.6	paring the 00–140 and 150+
Laboratory loss	1	5.0	3	1.7	groups. The total x^2 yielded
					$P < 0.001$.
Total	20‡		180		

* Includes all of the less than 6 hour survival cases except for the 2 among the first 5 cases. See text. The 00, 50–90, and 100–140 groups each contain one value based upon analysis of brain rather than blood. It is noted that brain alcohol concentrations tend to be lower than the corresponding blood concentrations.[15]
† No alcohol controls were obtained from Cases 1–5. See text.
‡ Of the 20 persons who died within 6 hours 7 were women, 3 of whom were in the 00 group. Three were in the 10–140 group and one was in the 150–190 group.

the 6 hours immediately preceding midnight. In the 3 hour period ending at 9 a.m., a period when the city's motor vehicle and pedestrian traffic increases sharply, only 2 such fatal accidents occurred, the smallest number in any 3 hour period. This, by itself, should suggest that gross exposure per se is not the major determinant of the occurrence of such accidents, and that the factors of importance are more active at other times of day. These findings are consistent with what might be expected in view of the overrepresentation in the case group (see below) of the elderly, of persons with high blood alcohol concentrations, and of Manhattan residents.

The predominantly evening and nighttime occurrence of these adult pedestrian accidents (Table II) and the frequently short survival (Table III) underscore the need for emphasizing the evening, nighttime, and early morning in the organization of emergency medical care, a point of general relevance in the motor vehicle accident picture. It is well known, for example, that the majority of other types of fatal motor vehicle accidents also tend to occur at such times of day,[1,22] and that rapid death is common.[22]

■ Table XI*B*. Blood alcohol concentrations

Blood alcohol concentration	Surviving less than 6 hours		Site-matched controls from same sites		
	No.	%	No.	%	
00 (none)	5	26.3	55	72.4	Employing partial x^2, $P < 0.02$,
10–40	5	26.3	8	10.5	comparing the numbers in the 00
50–90	1	5.3	7	9.2	and 10–40 groups in the case and
100–140	2	10.5	1	1.3	control groups. $P > 0.20$, compar-
150–190	5	26.3	—	0.0	ing similarly the numbers in the
200–240	1	5.3	3	3.9	00–40 and 50–140 groups. $P <$
250–290	—	0.0	1	1.3	0.001, comparing the 00–140 and
Laboratory loss	*	0.0	1	1.3	150 + groups. The total x^2 yielded
					$P < 0.001$.
Total	19		76		

* One case in which laboratory-lost specimen is omitted, as are its 4 site-matched controls (all of which were in the 00 group).

■ Table XI*C*. Blood alcohol concentrations

Blood alcohol concentration	Age and sex matched cases with less than 6 hours survival		Corresponding age and sex-matched controls		
	No.	%	No.	%	
00 (none)	3	17.6	13	76.5	Because of the small numbers
10–40	5	29.4	1	5.9	here, the data were combined
50–90	1	5.9	1	5.9	into concentrations: (1) less
100–140	2	11.8	1	5.9	than 50 mg. per cent, and (2)
150–190	5	29.4	—	0.0	50 mg. per cent and higher.
200–240	1	5.9	—	0.0	$P = 0.02$ (exact test).
Laboratory loss	—	0.0	1	5.9	
Total	17		17		

Table IV shows that weather (raining vs. not raining) was *not* significantly associated with the occurrence of the accidents studied. However, since pedestrian *density* may be lower in the rain, the risk per unit of exposure *may* nonetheless be higher in the rain than in its absence, a point outside of the experimental design employed.

One of the most striking findings is that those killed averaged some 17 years older than those who though similarly exposed were not similarly involved (Table V), a very highly significant difference ($P < 0.001$). As noted previously, without additional information it would not have been possible to determine whether this difference was the result of: (1) greater risk of accident involvement with age; (2) greater susceptibility to fatal injury once involved; or (3) a combination of both. With the use of the additional data relative to the injured, it was found that the mean age of the nonfatally injured was intermediate between the mean age of those killed and the mean age of those similarly exposed at the fatal accident sites. Each of these differences (viz., fatally injured vs. site-matched controls; fatally injured vs. nonfatally injured; and site-matched controls vs. nonfatally injured) was also very highly significant ($P < 0.001$). The most reasonable interpretation is that there is an increased risk of accident involvement with increased age, and that in addition there is with age an increased risk of fatal outcome, once involved. The former has often been suggested, but not previously documented; the latter is consistent with much clinical evidence relative to shifts with age in the results of trauma. Both indicate that the pedestrian's chances of surviving his mechanized environment decrease with increased age.* Many factors, however, other than age are undoubtedly of importance in individual cases, as is suggested by the fact that the youngest of those fatally injured was in his twenties, that 6 were in their thirties, and that 8 were in their forties.

Tables VI, IX, and X show that those fatally involved were, in comparison with those not involved, significantly more often foreign born, less often married, and more often of lower socioeconomic status. However, none of these differences remained significant when the older age of the persons was taken into account (Tables VI, IX, and X). Neither Negroes nor persons born in Puerto Rico, two major Manhattan population groups, were found significantly more or less often in the case group than among the controls, and no geographically definable

---

*   Haddon and McFarland, in discussing (1958) knowledge of the physical thresholds of human head injury and the importance of such information for the purposes of automotive crash design, emphasized that there appeared to be no threshold data available with regard to either the young or the old. They stated further: "In view of the marked anatomic differences such as the open fontanelles exhibited by infants and the differences in proportion, structure and mass shown by the immature, one would expect discontinuities or at least changes in thresholds during the first two decades. Similarly, the clinically common changes with age, including alterations in tissue elasticity, bone density, superficial soft tissues, and cerebral blood supply seen in those passing middle age suggest that these groups also undergo shifts, probably downward, in their abilities to successfully resist abrupt changes in velocity. . . ."[23] The present results are consistent with the latter expectation.

foreign-born group was significantly overrepresented in the data summarized in Table VI.

Table VII shows: (1) that visitors and commuters were not to any substantial extent represented in the case group; and (2) that Manhattan residents were significantly more often found in the case group than in the control group, even when the older age of the former was taken into consideration. It is of interest in this context that many of those killed were hit very close to their residences (Table VIII). This cannot be attributed entirely to a corresponding localization of exposure since, as just noted, Manhattan residents had a higher risk than nonresidents similarly exposed *at the same sites.*

Table XI shows that the presence of ethyl alcohol in the blood, particularly in high concentration, was highly associated with such accident involvement, that only a minority of those killed who died within 6 hours had not been drinking, and that the findings were similar whether the comparison was made with the total control group, with the controls from the same sites, or with the age- and sex-matched controls. These findings are similar to and consistent with those relative to *drivers* obtained by other workers using laboratory, field trial, and epidemiologic methods.[16,17,24-28]

The smallness of the series precludes the estimation of relative risk as a function of blood alcohol concentration, but it is seen (Table XI*B*) that persons with blood alcohol concentrations in the low, 10–40 mg. per cent range (0.01–0.04 per cent by weight) were found significantly ($P < 0.02$) more often among the cases than among the noninvolved controls obtained from the same accident sites. Although the disproportion is seen to become much greater at the higher alcohol concentrations, it is pertinent that Smith and Popham,[25] on the basis of a comparison of accident-involved *driver's* blood alcohol concentrations in relation to their estimated responsibilities for their accidents, found that accident-responsible drivers were statistically first overrepresented in the 30 to 50 mg. per cent blood alcohol range. Similarly, a number of very well-designed laboratory and field studies have shown that some *drivers* with concentrations below 50 mg. per cent show decreases in pertinent skilled performance directly attributable to the pharmacologic effects of ethyl alcohol.[16,24,26-28] The present findings suggest that the ability of at least some *pedestrians* to negotiate city traffic without fatal mishap begins to deteriorate significantly in the 10–40 mg. per cent blood alcohol range, although other factors associated with the use of alcoholic beverages might also contribute.

To place these concentrations in perspective, on the basis of competent research, it has been demonstrated, for example, that a 155 pound man drinking in one hour or less and one to two hours after an average meal would probably reach a blood alcohol concentration of 50 mg. per cent by consuming a minimum of approximately 5 ounces of U.S. 80 proof liquor,* a concentration of 100 mg.

---

* U.S. "80 proof" equals "70 proof" under the definition employed in Canada and Great Britain. The difference between the British ounce (28.4 ml.) and the U.S. ounce (29.6 ml.) is negligible in this context.[15]

per cent by consuming a minimum of approximately $7\frac{1}{2}$ ounces, and a concentration of 150 mg. per cent by consuming a minimum of approximately 10 ounces, all under the same conditions.[16] In the *case* series the percentages of those killed whose blood alcohol concentrations were at or above these three values were 47 per cent (9/19), 42 per cent (8/19) and 32 per cent (6/19), respectively. These percentages are somewhat similar, for example, to those obtained in adjacent Westchester County and in the City of Baltimore. In the former during the 10 years 1950–1959, of the 69 pedestrians 18 years of age or older fatally injured and dying within 4 hours 64 were tested postmortem for alcohol. In this group the corresponding percentages were 42 per cent (27/64), 38 per cent (24/64), and 25 per cent (16/64).[29] In Baltimore from January, 1951, through April, 1956, 200 pedestrians 20 years of age and older were killed. Among these the percentages at or above 50 and 150 mg. per cent were, respectively, 45 per cent (90/200) and 32 per cent (64/200).[4] These data show that the appreciable prior consumption of beverage alcohol by adult pedestrians fatally injured by motor vehicles is a phenomenon by no means unique to Manhattan, and that the frequencies with which given blood alcohol concentrations are observed are remarkably similar elsewhere.

The high percentages of fatally injured Manhattan pedestrians showing high blood alcohol concentrations should not, however, be taken as typical of all adult Manhattan pedestrians. The control series represents the adult pedestrian traffic of the same sex composition as a case series derived largely in the evening and nighttime from accident sites at many of which elevated blood alcohol concentrations would be expected to be commonly found. Despite this it is noteworthy that 67 per cent (118/177) (Table XI) of the controls' breath specimens did not have measurable concentrations of alcohol (00), and that an additional 17 per cent (30/177) represented blood concentrations (10-40) in which many social drinkers would be expected to fall. It is of interest that the percentages of the control group with given concentrations were considerably higher than those obtained by Holcomb[17,19] and Lucas and associates[17] in their large series of drivers (see above, "Methods"). In the first of these, in which drivers were stopped in Evanston, Illinois, throughout the 24 hours, those having concentrations at or above 70 (sic), 110 (sic), and 150 mg. per cent, respectively, were 4.5 per cent (79/1,750), 1.3 per cent (23/1,750), and 0.4 per cent (7/1,750).[17,19] In the second investigation, in Toronto, Canada, in which drivers were stopped in the evening at accident sites, the percentages above 50, 100, and 150 mg. per cent were 8.7 per cent (176/2,015), 3.3 per cent (67/2,015), and 1.4 per cent (28/2,015), respectively.[17] These differences suggest that the frequencies of given blood alcohol elevations may be higher in pedestrian than in driving populations, but this cannot be resolved until parallel studies of both such populations have been completed in the same geographic area. Such work is now under way in New York City.

It is pertinent in view of the age-associated risks of involvement and of fatal outcome, once involved, that *in the control group* those whose blood was estimated not to contain measurable quantities of alcohol (00) were significantly ($P < 0.05$) *younger* than those with measurable concentrations (10+ mg. per cent). The difference (40.3 vs. 41.9 years), however, was small. Further, those with low concentrations (10-40) in the control group (mean age 42.2) were not significantly ($P > 0.05$) different in age from those with higher concentrations (50+) (mean age 41.6).*

In the case group, in marked contrast, although the numbers were much smaller, those in the 00 group were significantly ($P < 0.05$) *older* (mean age 70.8 years) both than those in the 10-40 group (mean age 51.6 years) and than those in the entire 10+ group (mean age 46.2). The difference between the mean ages of the 5 members of the 10-40 group (see above) and the 9 members of the 50+ group (mean age 43.2), though suggestive, was not significant ($P > 0.05$).

As noted in connection with Table V, the members of the total case group were very significantly older than the members of the total control group. When comparisons were made between those cases and controls with given blood alcohol concentrations, the cases in the 00 and in the 10-40 mg. per cent groups, respectively, were both significantly older ($P < 0.05$) than the corresponding controls, but the difference between the mean ages in the case (43.2) and control (41.6) groups in the 50+ range was not significant ($P > 0.05$). These and the foregoing data show that in the series studied increased age was significantly associated with fatal pedestrian accident involvement, both in the absence of measurable prior ingestion of alcohol and in the case of those whose blood alcohol concentrations were relatively low (10-40). Similarly, relatively high blood alcohol concentrations were found to be significantly associated with such fatal accident involvement in the absence of significant differences in age (see above), a result also obtained when age (and sex) were controlled (Table XIC). These findings and inspection of the data suggest that the case series was comprised of two substantially discrete groups each of which had an increased risk of fatal involvement, namely, a group of the elderly whose blood either contained no measurable amounts of alcohol, or relatively little, and a group of the middle-aged who had been drinking heavily. Consequently, the design of control measures should take these characteristics into consideration. For example, as Schmidt and Smart[31] have appropriately pointed out, "highway education slogans" would not be expected to be efficacious in the case of accidents associated with alcoholism.

It would be of interest if it had been possible to determine the extent to which chronic alcoholics were overrepresented in the case series. Unfortunately, although at least a few of those killed are believed to have been alcoholic derelicts, it was not possible to investigate this point further. In addition, liver specimens were not retained, and it was consequently not possible to describe the presence

---

* The significance of the differences given in this and the following two paragraphs were calculated by the method of Scheffé for judging all contrasts in the analysis of variance.[30]

of fatty degeneration and cirrhosis among those killed, and, if found, to determine whether, as might be anticipated, blood alcohol concentration at death
would have correlated with the presence of such hepatic disease. That such
questions are of pertinence was demonstrated by excellent research in Sweden
which showed that chronic alcoholics and other alcohol abusers were many
times more often found among a consecutive series of male traffic accident victims than would have been expected on the basis of their numbers in the general
population.[32] Similarly, Schmidt and Smart, studying an alcoholism clinic population in Toronto, have found that male chronic alcoholics who were drivers had
motor vehicle accident rates per mile of exposure very significantly higher than
expected in the general population. In the Swedish and Canadian series there
was no over-representation of such heavy alcohol users in accidents in which
alcohol was not a factor, and Schmidt and Smart have concluded with respect
to such drivers "that the reported differences in accident involvement between
alcoholics and the general driving population is closely related to the driving
behavior only after the consumption of alcohol."[31] Whether this results exclusively from the pharmacologic effects of alcohol per se or whether other factors
intimately associated with its use also contribute remains to be determined. This
area will require much more work before these points can be entirely decided.
On the basis of the evidence available from these other investigations and the
present, descriptive evidence, it is reasonable to regard the chronic alcoholic as
contributing both as a driver and as a pedestrian to the motor vehicle accident
picture, but to an extent which requires further documentation. There can be
no question, however, that motor vehicle accidents in general represent in part
one source of the morbidity and mortality derivative from the excessive use of
alcoholic beverages. Similarly, the accidents involving the elderly group showing
little or no alcohol at death may be regarded as representing one source of the
morbidity and mortality associated with advanced age, and as such should concern those in geriatric medicine.

The point has been made by others that few fatally injured pedestrians are
the holders of licenses to drive motor vehicles.[21] This, however, is to be expected
from the age distribution of those involved. On the basis of age- and sex-specific
license-holding rates for New York City residents calculated from data available
to the authors, only 11.9 license holders would have been expected in a 44 member group with the age and sex composition of the 44 known New York City
residents in the case series (Table VII). Low percentages of license holders in
such groups are, as a result, hardly surprising even though they may be of importance in choosing the emphasis of education and other control measures.
Further, license-holding rates of pedestrians would be expected, because of the
presumably disproportionate inclusion of nondrivers, to be lower than those of
the general public of the same age and sex composition. In the present case it
was possible to check this expectation by having the New York State motor
vehicle license files manually checked for the 44 city residents of known name and

address in the index case series. Three of these were found to have held licenses at death, and an additional 3 whose names, ages, and addresses were in part similar to those on record in the files *may* have held licenses. The probability of observing this difference (6 vs. 11.9) by chance is < 0.05 (χ^2). However, because of the shortcomings of the state records as collected and maintained, this latter finding should be accepted with reservation pending confirmation.

Although the data available relative to the involved vehicles and drivers do not justify precise statistical analysis, it is pertinent that some of the pedestrians killed are known to have been *not* substantially responsible for the accidents in which they were involved. As examples: In one accident a motor scooter first involved in a nearby collision with a truck, threw its rider to his death and then approached and fatally injured a pedestrian. In another, one of the small number which occurred in the major business areas of the city, the operator of a sports car lost control of his vehicle and struck and fatally injured a pedestrian. Additional accidents, in which the pedestrians may not have been completely responsible, involved intoxicated drivers, and 4 accidents were "hit and run." In such cases the characteristics of the pedestrians killed would be expected to be more nearly those of the noninvolved pedestrians than would be the case among those presumably responsible in larger part for their own accident involvements. Consequently, since the case series includes some such cases, the associations found may be considered as conservative estimates of the magnitude of the associations which would probably have been found had it been possible to study only those totally responsible for their own deaths.

Similarly, the fatally injured group probably contained some individuals who were killed by forces of such great magnitude that anyone, regardless of age, would have been killed. The characteristics of such fatally injured individuals, granted their accident involvement, would not be influenced by an increased susceptibility to fatal outcome of pertinence in the case of lesser impacts, and as a result their characteristics would be expected to approach those of the relatively much larger nonfatally injured accident-involved group. Since those hit by such great forces would tend to be killed outright or, if not, to have relatively short survival, the effect of the inclusion of this group in the total case series would be expected to have most greatly influenced the characteristics of the subgroup comprised of those dead on arrival or dying within one hour.

Consistent with this expectation is the fact that the mean age of the dead on arrival and < 1 hour group, 48.2 years, was not significantly different from that, 48.4, of the nonfatally injured controls (see Tables III and V). In addition, this dead on arrival and < 1 hour group was significantly ($P < 0.05$) younger than the remainder of the fatally injured group. There was no significant age difference ($P > 0.05$), however, between those in the 1 to 3 hour and 4 to 71 hour groups; whereas those surviving 72 hours or longer were significantly ($P < 0.05$) older (mean age 70.4) than those dying between 1 and 71 hours (mean age 56.6) after their accidents. The latter finding is consistent with much clinical evidence as to the poorer course and increased occurrence of fatal, late complications among older patients.*

Finally, as in any investigation concerned with the pathology derivative from a given population, questions must arise as to the extent to which the sequences of events leading to that pathology are qualitatively and quantitatively similar to those operative in other populations. Although, as Russell[33] has pointed out, any event or group of events must be totally unique if described completely in all parameters, findings based upon one population tend to have relevance elsewhere to the extent to which the pertinent characteristics of the one are elsewhere present. Since the subpopulations constituting the Manhattan community are in many respects unique, the question must arise as to the extent to which the results reported here would be duplicated if other populations were studied. Unfortunately, since this is the first investigation of its kind, it is at present not possible to compare its findings definitively with those from other areas. It is possible, however, to point out certain similarities between the Manhattan situation and that obtaining elsewhere.

First, as noted in the introduction, the distribution of the age-specific death rates of pedestrians killed nationally in the United States is J-shaped with a maximum in the grade school and preschool years; a minimum in the late second, third, and early fourth decades; and a progressively increasing rate thereafter. From data available to the authors it has been found that the distribution of the age-specific pedestrian death rates of Manhattan residents of all ages is similarly J-shaped and that the rates in corresponding age groups are of similar magnitude. Second, it has been noted, as reported for other cities, that the accidents studied tended to occur outside of the major business areas. Third, the time-of-day distribution is similar to that seen elsewhere. And, fourth, as elsewhere, a substantial fraction of those fatally injured had been drinking heavily. These similarities between the Manhattan situation and that in other areas suggest that the factors shown here to be of importance in Manhattan are not completely without relevance in other areas.

Summary

1. The present investigation, the first of its kind, was designed to compare the characteristics of pedestrians 18 years of age and older fatally injured in Manhattan with those who though similarly exposed were not similarly involved. The case series consisted of 50 of the 52 such pedestrians fatally injured at known sites and times in Manhattan between May 3 and Nov. 7, 1959, and whose deaths occurred during the same period. Autopsies were performed in all cases and appropriate specimens obtained. Data with respect to those nonfatally injured were also secured.

---

*   The significance of the differences in this paragraph were calculated by the method of Scheffé for judging all contrasts in the analysis of variance.[30]

2.   The control group was obtained by visiting each accident site on a subsequent date, but on the same day of the week and at exactly the same time of day, and stopping, interviewing, and obtaining breath specimens (for alcohol) from the first 4 pedestrians of the same sex as the deceased, and 18 years of age or older. Of 212 so stopped, only 12 failed to cooperate fully.

3.   The results obtained included both purely descriptive and controlled observations. Among the former: The accidents tended to occur outside of major shopping and business areas. Fifty-one per cent occurred in the 6 hours preceding midnight, 73 per cent in the 12 hours beginning at 3 p.m., and the smallest number in the 3 hours ending at 9 a.m. Forty-four per cent of those killed survived less than 6 hours. This together with the common evening and nighttime occurrence underscores the need for emphasizing the same period in the organization of emergency medical care.

4.   Weather, raining vs. not raining, was not significantly associated with the occurrence of such accidents, although increased risk with rain may have been obscured by associated decreases in pedestrian density.

5.   The mean age of those killed was 58.8 years; of those nonfatally injured 48.4 years; and of those interviewed at the fatal accident sites 41.6 years. The most reasonable interpretation of these findings is that there is, first, an age-associated risk of involvement per se, and, second, an age-associated risk of fatal outcome, once involved. Because of these differences and the probability that others of the characteristics studied would show associations with age, comparisons between the case and control groups included comparisons between age- and sex-matched members of both groups.

6.   The members of the case group were significantly more often foreign born, less often married, and more often of lower socioeconomic status than were those in the control group. However, when these comparisons were made between cases and controls of the same age and sex, no significant differences remained. It was also found that neither Negroes nor those born in Puerto Rico, two major population groups, were significantly more or less commonly found in the case than in the control groups.

7.   Only 4 of the 46 persons in the case group of known residence lived outside of Manhattan. Consequently, neither commuters nor visitors contributed substantially to the deaths studied. In addition, many of those killed were hit within relatively short distances of their residences. This can *not* be attributed entirely to a corresponding localization of exposure since Manhattan residents were found significantly more often in the case series than among those similarly exposed *at the same sites*, even when the difference in age between the two groups was taken into consideration.

8.   Because postmortem specimens for alcohol analysis were employed, comparisons involving the blood alcohol concentrations of members of the case series

were limited to those who had survived less than 6 hours. In this group 26 per cent showed no alcohol, 47 per cent had concentrations of 50 mg. per cent or higher, 42 per cent, 100 mg. per cent or higher, and 32 per cent, 150 mg. per cent or higher. The corresponding percentages in the much larger control group were 67 per cent (none), 16 per cent ($\leq$ 50), 8 per cent ($\leq$ 100), 6 per cent ($\leq$ 150 mg. per cent), respectively. Significant differences were found whether the cases were compared with the members of the total control group, with the site-matched controls from the same accident sites, or with age- and sex-matched members of the control group. The data suggest that the risk first becomes significantly increased in the low, 10-40 mg. per cent range.

9. The members of the case group found to have either low blood alcohol concentrations or no measurable amount were significantly older than the corresponding members of the control group. In contrast, the members of the case group with high blood alcohol concentrations were not significantly older than the corresponding members of the control group. The data suggest that the case series was composed of two substantially discrete groups, each with increased risk, namely, a group of the elderly who had been drinking little or not at all, and a group of the middle aged who had been drinking heavily.

10. The importance of determining the extent to which the chronic alcoholic is overrepresented in such accidents is discussed. It is believed that such individuals were present in the case series, but controlled observations appropriate to this point were not possible. It is emphasized that fatal adult pedestrian accidents must be regarded as contributing portions of the morbidity and mortality associated with alcoholism and with advanced age.

REFERENCES

1. Accident Facts, 1960 Edition, National Safety Council, Chicago.
2. Heise, H. A.: Alcohol and Automobile Accidents, J.A.M.A. **103**: 739, 1934.
3. Gonzales, T. A., and Gettler, A. O.: Alcohol and the Pedestrian in Traffic Accidents, J.A.M.A. **117**: 1523, 1941.
4. Freimuth, H. C., Spencer, R. W., and Fisher, R. S.: Alcohol and Highway Fatalities, J. Foren. Sc. 3: 65, 1958.
5. Accident Facts, 1959 and previous editions, National Safety Council, Chicago.
6. National Office of Vital Statistics: Personal communication, 1959.
7. Gonzales, T. A., Vance, M., Helpern, M., and Umberger, C. J.: Legal Medicine, Pathology and Toxicology, ed. 2, New York, 1954, Appleton-Century-Crofts, Inc., p. 1085.
8. Gonzales, T. A., Vance, M., Helpern, M., and Umberger, C. J.: Legal Medicine, Pathology and Toxicology, ed. 2, New York, 1954, Appleton-Century-Crofts, Inc., pp. 1090–1091.

9. Local Climatological Data, Immediate U.S. Weather Reports. New York Meteoro-
    logical Observatory, Central Park, U.S. Department of Commerce, Weather
    Bureau, May–December, 1959.

10. Salem, H., Lucas, G. H. W., and Lucas, D. M.: Saran Plastic Bags as Containers
    for Breath Samples, Canad. M.A.J. **82**: 682, 1960.

11. Kalow, W., Lucas, G. H. W., and McColl, J. D.: Containers for Breath Samples
    for Alcohol Analysis, Proc. Second Internat. Conference on Alcohol and Road
    Traffic, Toronto, 1953, pp. 137–138.

12. Lucas, G. H. W.: Personal communications, 1959 and 1960.

13. Friedmann, T. E., and Dubowski, K. M.: Chemical Testing Procedures for the
    Determination of Ethyl Alcohol, J.A.M.A. **170**: 47, 1959. Also published in Chemi-
    cal Tests for Intoxication Manual, Committee on Medicolegal Problems, A.M.A.,
    Chicago, 1959.

14. Monnier, D., and Ruedi, W.: Étude critique du "Breathalyser" appareil de dosage
    de l'alcool dans l'haleine, Rev. internat. de criminol. et de police technique **12**:
    61, 1958.

15. Harger, R. N., and Hulpieu, H. R.: Pharmacology of Alcohol, *in* Thompson, G.
    N., editor: Alcoholism, Springfield, Ill., 1956, Charles C. Thomas, Publisher.

16. Coldwell, B. B., editor: Report on Impaired Driving Tests, Crime Detection Labo-
    ratory, Royal Canadian Mounted Police, Queen's Printer, Ottawa, 1957.

17. Lucas, G. H. W., Kalow, W., McColl, J. D., Griffith, B. A., and Smith, H. W.:
    Quantitative Studies of the Relationship Between Alcohol Levels and Motor
    Vehicle Accidents. Proc. Second Internat. Conference on Alcohol and Road
    Traffic, Toronto, 1953, pp. 139–142.

18. Smith, H. W.: Personal communication, 1960.

19. Holcomb, R. L.: Alcohol in Relation to Traffic Accidents, J.A.M.A. **111**: 1076,
    1938.

20. U.S. Bureau of the Census: 1950 Census of Population, Alphabetical Index of
    Occupation and Industries (Revised Edition), Washington, D.C., 1950.

21. Planned Pedestrian Program. The AAA Foundation for Traffic Safety, Washington,
    D.C., 1958.

22. Haddon, W., Jr., and Bradess, V. A.: Alcohol in the Single Vehicle Fatal Accident:
    Experience of Westchester County, New York, J.A.M.A. **169**: 1587, 1959. Re-
    printed in Traffic Safety Research Review 3: 4, 1959.

23. Haddon, W., Jr., and McFarland, R. A.: A Survey of Present Knowledge of the
    Physical Thresholds of Human Head Injury From an Engineering Standpoint,
    Annual Report 1957–1958, Commission on Accidental Trauma, Armed Forces
    Epidemiological Board, Department of Defense, 1958.

24. Bjerver, K., and Goldberg, L.: Effect of Alcohol Ingestion on Driving Ability:
    Results of Practical Road Tests and Laboratory Experiments, Quart. J. Stud.
    Alcohol. **11**: 1, 1950.

25. Smith, H. W., and Popham, R. E.: Blood Alcohol Levels in Relation to Driving,
    Canad. M.A.J. **65**: 325, 1951.

26. Loomis, T. A., and West, T. C.: Influence of Alcohol on Automobile Driving Ability: Experimental Study for Evaluation of Certain Medicolegal Aspects, Quart. J. Stud. Alcohol. **19**: 30, 1958.

27. Cohen, J., Dearnaley, F. J., and Hansel, C. E. M.: The Risk Taken in Driving Under the Influence of Alcohol, Brit. M. J. June 21, 1958.

28. Drew, G. C., Colquhoun, W. P., and Long, H. A.: Effect of Small Doses of Alcohol on a Skill Resembling Driving, Brit. M. J. Oct. 25, 1958, pp. 993–999. Reprinted in Traffic Safety Research Rev. **3**: 4, 1959.

29. Haddon, W., Jr., and Bradess, V. A.: Unpublished observations, 1960.

30. Scheffé, H.: A Method for Judging All Contrasts in the Analysis of Variance, Biometrika **40**: 87, 1953.

31. Schmidt, W. S., and Smart, R. G.: Alcoholics, Drinking and Traffic Accidents, Quart. J. Stud. Alcohol. **20**: 631, 1959.

32. Bjerver, K. B., Goldberg, L., and Linda, P.: Blood Alcohol Levels in Hospitalized Victims of Traffic Accidents, Proc. Second Internat. Conference on Alcohol and Road Traffic, Toronto, 1953, pp. 92–102.

33. Russell, B.: On the Notion of Cause, *Proceedings* of the Aristotelian Society, 1912–1913 (reference as given in Russell, B.: Mysticism and Logic, Garden City, New York, 1957, Doubleday and Company).

THE SOCIAL PSYCHOLOGY OF THE BEHAVIORAL SCIENTIST: ON SELF-FULFILLING PROPHECIES IN BEHAVIORAL RESEARCH AND EVERYDAY LIFE*

ROBERT ROSENTHAL

Behavioral scientists are said to be such a scientifically self-conscious group that there may one day be a psychology of those psychologists who study psychologists. That, for the most part, is in the future but in the present there is a clearly developing science of the behavioral scientist as he conducts his research with human and animal subjects.

The social situation which comes into being when a behavioral scientist encounters his research subject is a situation of both general and unique importance to the behavioral sciences. Its general importance derives from the fact that the interaction of experimenter and subject, like other two-person interactions, may be investigated empirically with a view to teaching us more about dyadic interaction in general. Its unique importance derives from the fact that the interaction of experimenter and subject, *un*like other dyadic interactions, is a major source of our knowledge in the behavioral sciences.

To the extent that we hope for dependable knowledge in the behavioral sciences, we must have dependable knowledge about the experimenter-subject interaction specifically. We can no more hope to acquire accurate information for our disciplines without an understanding of the data collection situation than astronomers and zoologists could hope to acquire accurate information for their disciplines without their understanding the effects of their telescopes and microscopes. It is for these reasons that increasing interest has been shown in the investigation of the experimenter-subject interaction system. And the outlook is anything but bleak. It does seem that we can profitably learn of those effects which the behavioral scientist unwittingly may have on the results of his research.

Unprogrammed Effects of the Behavioral Scientist

It is useful to think of two major types of effects which the behavioral scientist can have upon the results of his research. The first type operates, so to speak,

Paper prepared for New Directions in Social Science Research, Fourth Annual Research Conference, North Dakota State University, November 11, 1967. Reproduced with the author's permission.

* The research described in this paper has been supported by research grants (G-17685, G-24826, GS-177, GS-714, GS-1741) from the Division of Social Sciences of the National Science Foundation. An earlier version of this paper entitled "The Psychology of the Psychologist" appeared in F. L. Ruch, *Psychology and Life*, 7th ed., Chicago: Scott, Foresman, 1967. Pp. 645–652.

in the mind, in the eye, or in the hand of the investigator. It operates without affecting the actual response of the human or animal subjects of the research; it is not interactional. The second type of experimenter effect is interactional; it operates by affecting the actual response of the subject of the experiment. It is a sub-type of this latter type of effect, the effects of the investigator's expectancy or hypothesis on the results of his research, which will occupy most of the discussion. First, however, some examples of other effects of the investigator on his research will be mentioned.

Observer effects. In any science, the experimenter must make provision for the careful observation and recording of the events under study. It is not always so easy to be sure that one has, in fact, made an accurate observation. That lesson was learned by the psychologists, who needed to know it, but it was not the psychologists who focussed our attention on it originally. It was the astronomers.

Just near the end of the 18th century, the royal astronomer at the Greenwich Observatory, a man called Maskelyne, discovered that his assistant, Kinnebrook, was consistently "too slow" in his observations of the movement of stars across the sky. Maskelyne cautioned Kinnebrook about his "errors" but the errors continued for months. Kinnebrook was fired.

The man who might have saved that job was Bessel, the astronomer at Königsberg, but he was 20 years too late. It was not until then that he arrived at the conclusion that Kinnebrook's "error" was probably not willful. Bessel studied the observations of stellar transits made by a number of senior astronomers. Differences in observation, he discovered, were the rule, not the exception (Boring, 1950).

That early observation of the effects of the scientist on the observations of science made Bessel perhaps the first student of the psychology of scientists. More contemporary research on the psychology of scientists has shown that while observer errors are not necessarily serious they tend to occur in a biased manner. By that is meant that, more often than we would expect by chance, when errors of observation do occur they tend to give results more in the direction of the psychologist's hypothesis (Rosenthal, 1966).

Interpreter effects. The interpretation of the data collected is part of the research process and a glance at any of the technical journals of contemporary behavioral science will suggest strongly that while we only rarely debate the observations made by one another, we often debate the interpretation of those observations. It is as difficult to state the rules for accurate interpretation of data as it is to state the rules for accurate observation of data, but the variety of interpretations offered in explanation of the same data implies that many of us must turn out to be wrong. The history of science generally, and the history of psychology more specifically, suggest that more of us are wrong longer than we need to be because we hold our theories not quite lightly enough. The common practice of theory monogamy has its advantages, however. It does keep us motivated to make more crucial observations. In any case, interpreter effects seem less serious than observer effects. The reason is that the former are public while the latter are private. Given a set of observations, their interpretations become generally available to the scientific community. We are free to agree or disagree with any specific interpretation. Not so with the case of the observations themselves. Often these are made by a single investigator so that we are not free to agree or disagree. We can only hope that no observer errors occurred and we can, and should, repeat the observations.

Intentional effects. It happens sometimes in undergraduate laboratory science courses that students "collect" and report data too beautiful to be true. (That probably happens most often when students are taught to be scientists by being told what results they must get to do well in the course, rather than being taught the logic of scientific inquiry and the value of being quite open-eyed and open-minded.) Unfortunately, the history of science tells us that not only undergraduates have been dishonest in science, but fortunately, such instances are rare. Nevertheless, intentional effects must be regarded as part of the inventory of the effects of the investigator himself.

Intentional effects, interpreter effects, and observer effects all operate without the investigator's affecting his subject's response to the experimental task. In those effects of the experimenter himself to be described next, we shall see that the subject's response to the experimental task is affected.

Biosocial effects. The sex, age, and race of the investigator have all been found to affect the results of his research. What we do not know and what we need to learn is whether subjects respond differently simply to the presence of experimenters varying in these biosocial attributes or whether experimenters varying in these attributes behave differently toward their subjects and, therefore, obtain different responses from them because they have, in effect, altered the experimental situation for their subjects. So far, the evidence suggests that male and female experimenters conduct the "same" experiment quite differently, so that the different results they obtain may well be due to the fact that they unintentionally conducted different experiments. Male experimenters, for example, were found in two experiments to be more friendly to their subjects (Rosenthal, 1967).

Biosocial attributes of the subject can also affect the experimenter's behavior, which in turn affects the subject's responses. In one study, for example, the interactions between experimenters and their subjects were recorded on sound films. In that study it was found that only 12 per cent of the experimenters ever smiled at their male subjects while 70 per cent of the experimenters smiled at their female subjects. Smiling by the experimenters, it was found, affected the results of the experiment. From this evidence and from some more detailed analyses which suggest that female subjects may be more protectively treated by their experimenters (Rosenthal, 1966), it might be suggested that in the psychological experiment, chivalry is not dead. This news may be heartening socially, and it is interesting social-psychologically, but it is very disconcerting methodologically.

Sex differences are well established for many kinds of behavior. But a question must now be raised as to whether sex differences which emerge from psychological experiments are due to the subject's genes, morphology, enculturation, or simply to the fact that the experimenter treated his male and female subjects differently so that, in a sense, they were not really in the same experiment at all.

So far we have seen that both the sex of the experimenter and the sex of the subject can serve as significant determinants of the way in which the investigator conducts his research. In addition, however, we find that when the sex of the experimenter and the sex of the subject are considered simultaneously, certain interaction effects emerge. Thus male experimenters contacting female subjects and female experimenters contacting male subjects tend to require more time to collect portions of their data than do male or female experimenters contacting subjects of the same sex. This tendency for opposite-sex dyads to prolong their data-collection interactions has also been found by others (Rosenthal, 1967).

Psychosocial effects.   The personality of the experimenter has also been found to affect the results of his research. Experimenters who differ in anxiety, need for approval, hostility, authoritarianism, status, and warmth tend to obtain different responses from their experimental subjects. Experimenters higher in status, for example, tend to obtain more conforming responses from their subjects, and experimenters who are warmer in their interaction with their subjects tend to obtain more pleasant responses from their subjects.

Situational effects.   Experimenters who are more experienced at conducting a given experiment obtain different responses from their subjects than do their less experienced colleagues. Experimenters who are acquainted with their subjects obtain different responses than do their colleagues who have never met their subjects before. The things that happen to the experimenter during the course of his experiment, including the responses he obtains from his first few subjects, can all influence his behavior and changes in his behavior can lead to changes in subjects' responses. When the first few subjects of his experiment tend to respond as they are expected to respond, the behavior of the experimenter changes in such a way as to influence his subsequent subjects to respond too often in the direction of his hypothesis (Rosenthal, 1966).

Modeling effects.   It sometimes happens that before an experimenter conducts his study he tries out the task he will later have his research subjects perform. Though the evidence on this point is not all that clear, it would seem that at least sometimes, the investigator's own performance becomes a factor in his subjects' performance. When the experimental stimuli are ambiguous, for example, subjects' interpretations of their meaning may too often agree with the investigator's own interpretations of the stimuli.

Expectancy effects.   Some expectation of how the research will turn out is virtually a constant in science. In the behavioral sciences the hypothesis held by the investigator can lead him unintentionally to alter his behavior towards his subjects in such a way as to increase the likelihood that his subjects will respond so as to confirm his hypothesis or expectation. We are speaking, then, of the investigator's hypothesis as a self-fulfilling prophecy. One prophesies an event and the expectation of the event then changes the behavior of the prophet in such a way as to make the prophesied event more likely. The history of science documents the occurrences of this phenomenon with the case of Clever Hans as prime example (Pfungst, 1911, 1965).

Hans was the horse of Mr. von Osten, a German mathematics instructor. By tapping his foot, Hans was able to perform difficult mathematical calculations and he could spell, read, and solve problems of musical harmony. A distinguished panel of scientists and experts on animals ruled that no fraud was involved. There were no cues given to Hans to tell him when to start and when to stop the tapping of his foot. But of course there were such cues, though it remained for Oskar Pfungst to demonstrate that fact. Pfungst, in a series of brilliant experiments, showed that Hans could answer questions only when the questioner or experimenter himself knew the answer and was within Hans' view. Finally, Pfungst learned that a tiny forward movement of the experimenter's head was the signal for Hans to start tapping. A tiny upward movement of the head of the questioner or a raising of the eyebrow was the signal to Hans to stop his tapping. Hans' questioners expected Hans to give correct answers, and this expectation was reflected in their unwitting signal to Hans that the time had come for him to stop his tapping. Thus the questioner's expectation became the reason for Hans' amazing abilities. We turn now to a consideration of more recent experiments which show that an investigator's expectation can come to serve as self-fulfilling prophecy.

Self-Fulfilling Prophecies in Behavioral Research

To demonstrate the effects of the investigator's expectancy on the results of his research, at least two groups of experimenters are needed, each group with a different hypothesis or expectancy as to the outcome of its research. One approach might be to do a kind of census or poll of actual or potential experimenters in a given area of research in which opinions as to relationships between variables were divided. Some experimenters expecting one type of result and some experimenters expecting the opposite type of result might then be asked to conduct a standard experiment. If each group of experimenters obtained the results expected, results opposite to those expected by the other group of experimenters, we could conclude that the expectation of the experimenter does indeed affect the results of his research. Or could we? Perhaps not. The problem would be that experimenters who differ in their theories, hypotheses, or expectations might very well differ in a number of important related ways as well. The differences in the data they obtained from their subjects might be due, then, not to the differences in expectations about the results but to other variables correlated with expectancies.

A better strategy, therefore, than trying to find two groups of experimenters differing in their hypotheses would be to "create" two groups of experimenters differing only in the hypotheses or expectations they held about the results of a particular experiment. That was the plan employed in the following research.

Ten advanced undergraduates and graduate students of psychology served as the experimenters. All were enrolled in an advanced course in experimental psychology and were, therefore, already involved in conducting research. Each student-experimenter was assigned as his subjects a group of about 20 students of introductory psychology. The experimental procedure was for the experimenter to show a series of ten photographs of people's faces to each of his subjects individually. The subject was to rate the degree of success or failure shown in the face of each person pictured in the photos. Each face could be rated as any value from -10 to $+10$ with -10 meaning extreme failure and $+10$ meaning extreme success. The 10 photos had been selected so that, on the average, they would be seen as neither successful nor unsuccessful, but quite neutral, with an average numerical score of zero.

All 10 experimenters were given identical instructions on how to show the photographs to their subjects and were given identical instructions to read to their subjects. They were cautioned not to deviate from these instructions. The purpose of their participation, it was explained to all experimenters, was to see how well they could duplicate experimental results which were already well-established. Half the experimenters were told that the "well-established" finding was that people generally rated the photos as of successful people (rating of $+5$) and half the experimenters were told that people generally rated the photos as being of unsuccessful people (ratings of -5). Then the experimenters conducted their research.

The results were clear. Every experimenter who had been led to expect ratings of people as successful obtained a higher average rating of success than did any experimenter expecting ratings of people as less successful. Such clear-cut results are not common in behavioral research, so two replications were conducted. Both these subsequent experiments gave the same results; experimenters tended to obtain the data they expected to obtain. Other workers in other laboratories have also shown that the experimenter's expectation may affect the results of his research though the details cannot be given here (Rosenthal, 1966). The combined probability that the results of all the relevant experiments might have occurred by chance is less than one in a million million.

Subsequent experiments in the program of research described here were designed not so much to demonstrate the effects of the investigator's expectancy as to learn something about the conditions which increase, decrease, or otherwise modify these effects. It was learned, for example, that the subjects' expectations about what would constitute behavior appropriate to the role of "experimental subject" could alter the extent to which they were influenced by the effects of the experimenter's hypothesis.

Through the employment of accomplices, serving as the first few subjects, it was learned that when the responses of the first few subjects confirmed the experimenter's hypothesis, his behavior toward his subsequent subjects was affected in such a way that these subjects tended to confirm further the experimenter's hypothesis. When accomplices, serving as the first few subjects, intentionally disconfirmed the expectation of the experimenter, the real subjects subsequently contacted were affected by a change in the experimenter's behavior to also disconfirm his experimental hypothesis. It seems possible, then, that the results of behavioral research can, by virtue of the early data returns, be determined by the performance of just the first few subjects.

In some of the experiments conducted, it was found that when experimenters were offered a too-large and a too-obvious incentive to affect the results of their research, the effects of expectancy tended to diminish. It speaks well for the integrity of our student-experimenters that when they felt bribed to get the data we led them to expect, they seemed actively to oppose us. There was a tendency for those experimenters to "bend over backward" to avoid the biasing effects of their expectation, but with the bending so far backward that the results of their experiments tended to be significantly opposite to the results they had been led to expect.

Individual differences among experimenters in the degree to which they obtain results consistent with their hypothesis have been discovered. The evidence comes both from additional experiments and from the analysis of sound motion pictures of experimenters interacting with their experimental subjects. Those experimenters who show greater expectancy effects tend to be of higher status in the eyes of their subjects and they seem to conduct their experiments in a more professional, more competent manner. They are judged more likable and more relaxed, particularly in their movement patterns, while avoiding an overly personal tone of voice that might interfere with the business at hand. It is interesting to note that, although the influence of an experimenter's expectancy is quite unintentional, the characteristics of the more successful influencer are very much the same ones associated with more effective influencers when the influence is intentional. The more successful agent of social influence may be the same person whether the influence be as overt and intentional as in the case of outright persuasion attempts, or as covert and unintentional as in the case of the experimenter's subtly communicating his expectancy to his research subject.

We know that the process whereby the experimenter communicates his expectancy to his subject is a subtle one. We know that it is subtle because for five years we have tried to find in sound films the unintended cues the experimenter gives the subject—and for five years we have failed, at least partly. But there are some things about the unintentional communication of expectancies that have been learned.

We know that if a screen is placed between experimenter and subject there will be a reduction of the expectancy effect, so visual cues from the experimenter are probably important. But the interposed screen does not eliminate expectancy effects completely, so auditory cues also seem to be important. Just how important auditory cues may be has been dramatically demonstrated by the work of Adair and Epstein (1967). They first conducted a study which was essentially a replication of the basic experiment on the self-fulfilling effects of experimenters' prophecies. Results showed that, just as in the original studies, experimenters who prophesied the perception of success by their subjects fulfilled their prophecies as did the experimenters who had prophesied the perception of failure by their subjects.

During the conduct of this replication experiment, Adair and Epstein tape-recorded the experimenters' instructions to their subjects. The second experiment was then conducted not by experimenters at all, but by tape-recordings of experimenters' voices reading standard instructions to their subjects. When the tape-recorded instructions had originally been read by experimenters expecting success perception by their subjects, the tape-recordings evoked greater success perceptions from their subjects. When the tape-recorded instructions had originally been read by experimenters expecting failure perception by their subjects, the tape-recordings evoked greater failure perceptions from their subjects. Self-fulfilling prophecies, it seems, can come about as a result of the prophet's voice alone. Since, in the experiment described, all prophets read standard instructions, self-fulfillment of prophecies may be brought about by the tone in which the prophet prophesies.

Early in the history of the research program on self-sulfilling prophecies in the behavioral sciences, it had been thought that a process of operant conditioning might be responsible for their operation (Rosenthal, 1966). It was thought that perhaps every time the subject gave a response consistent with the experimenter's expectancy, the experimenter might look more pleasant, or smile, or glance at the subject approvingly, even without the experimenter's being aware of his own reinforcing responses. The experimenter, in other words, might unwittingly have taught the subject what responses were the desired ones. Several experiments were analyzed to see whether this hypothesis of operant conditioning might apply. If it did apply, we would expect that the subjects' responses gradually would become more like those prophesied by the experimenter—that there would be a learning curve for subjects; but no learning curve was found. On the contrary, it turned out that the subjects' very first responses were about as much affected by their experimenters' expectancies as were their very last responses. Since the very first response, by definition, cannot follow any unwitting reinforcement by the experimenter, the mechanism of operant conditioning can be ruled out as necessary to the communication of experimenters' expectancies.

True, there was no learning curve for subjects, but there seemed to be a learning curve for experimenters. Several studies showed that expected results became more likely as more subjects were contacted by each experimenter (Rosenthal, 1966). In fact, there was very little expectancy effect in evidence for just the very first-seen subjects. If the experimenter were indeed learning to increase the unintended influence of his prophecy, who would be the teacher? Probably the subject. It seems reasonable to think of a subject's responding in the direction of the experimenter's hypothesis as a reinforcing event. Therefore, whatever the covert communicative behavior of the experimenter that preceded the subject's reinforcement, it will be more likely to recur. Subjects, then, may quite unintentionally shape the experimenter's unintended communicative behavior. Not only does the experimenter influence his subjects to respond in the expected manner, but his subjects may well evoke just that unintended behavior that will lead them to respond increasingly as prophesied. Probably neither subject nor experimenter "knows" just exactly what the unintended communication behavior is—and neither do we.

Some Methodological Implications

The implications of the research concerning the effects of the experimenter's expectancy on the results of his research are of two general kinds: those that are primarily methodological and those that are more substantive. Our focus here will be more on some of the substantive implications but brief mention may be made of some implications for how we conduct research in the behavioral sciences.

To the extent that the results of behavioral research are affected by the expectation of the experimenter, we can only place a lessened confidence in these results. But to say that our confidence is weakened in the results of many experiments as they are actually conducted is not to say that our confidence is weakened in the basic logic of the experimental method. We must simply take those, only sometimes inconvenient, extra precautions required to prevent or reduce expectancy effects or those procedures designed to permit us to assess whether they have or have not affected the results of our research.

It is possible for research investigators to employ, as data collectors, research assistants who have not been told the purpose of the research. As long as the investigator's expectation can be kept from these data collectors, there should be no effects attributable to the investigator's expectation. There are some experiments in which the experimenter need have no direct contact with the subjects and, in such studies, automated data collection systems should be employed to reduce any possibility of the unintended influence of the experimenter's expectation. When a human data collector is required, and that is often the case, the amount of contact between experimenter and subject can at least be reduced in order to minimize any opportunity for unintended communication.

Not only because of the danger of expectancy effects but also because of the general nature of other experimenter effects, it would be desirable to employ larger numbers of experimenters for each study than are now routinely employed. That would permit the assessment of the extent to which different experimenters obtained different results, and, in any area of psychological research, that is a fact worth knowing.

Only one final technique for the control of expectancy effects can be mentioned here and that is the employment of special control groups known as "expectancy controls." In any experiment employing an experimental (treatment) and a control (no treatment) condition, two extra groups are added. In one of these added groups, the data collector is led to believe that no treatment has been administered when, in fact, it has. In the other added group, the data collector is led to believe that the treatment has been administered when, in fact, it has not. Such a research design permits the assessment of the effects in which the investigator is primarily interested as well as the assessment of the magnitude or complicating effect of the experimenter's expectancy (Rosenthal, 1966).

Self-Fulfilling Prophecies beyond the Laboratory

Perhaps the most compelling and the most general substantive implication of the research described here is that human beings can engage in highly effective and influential unintended communication with one another. More specifically, if we may generalize from experimenters to people more generally, it appears that one person's expectancy for the behavior of another may come to serve as a self-fulfilling prophecy. These implications invite further research. We will want to know how people communicate with one another nonverbally and un-intentionally. We will want to know whether in everyday life, predictions become realities by the very act of prediction. When an experienced physician or psycho-therapist tells the neophyte therapist that the neophyte's patient has a good or a poor prognosis, is the experienced clinician only assessing, or is he actually creating the poor or good prognosis? When the employer tells the employee that a task cannot be accomplished, does the accomplishment therefore become less likely? When a respected source suggests to a teacher that a child's intellec-tual ability will show marked gains, will that prophecy be self-fulfilled? So far there are few answers to most of these research questions, except to the last, but before we describe that research from beyond the laboratory, let us return briefly to the lab for some background data.

In the course of the research program on expectancy effects, it seemed im-portant to learn whether these effects occurred only when the experimental subjects were humans. Accordingly, 12 experimenters were each given five rats who were to be taught to run a maze with the aid of visual cues. Half the experi-menters were told that their rats had been specially bred for maze-brightness; half the experimenters were told that their rats had been bred for maze-dullness. Actually, of course, there were no differences between the rats assigned to each of the two groups. At the end of the experiment, the results were clear. Rats who had been run by experimenters expecting brighter behavior showed significantly superior learning compared to rats run by experimenters expecting dull be-havior (Rosenthal and Fode, 1963). The experiment was repeated, this time em-ploying a series of learning experiments each conducted in Skinner boxes. Half the experimenters were led to believe that their rats were "Skinner box bright" and half were led to believe that their animals were "Skinner box dull". Once again there were not really any differences in the two groups of rats, at least not until the end of the experiment. Then the allegedly brighter animals really were brighter; the alleged dullards really duller (Rosenthal and Lawson, 1964).

If rats became more bright when expected to by their experimenter, it seemed possible that children might become more bright when expected to by their teacher. Educational theorists had, after all, been saying for a long time that culturally disadvantaged children were unable to learn because their teachers expected them to be unable to learn. True, there was no experimental evidence for that theory but the two studies employing rats suggested that these theorists might be correct. The following experiment was therefore conducted (Rosenthal and Jacobson, 1966; in press).

All of the children in an elementary school serving a lower socioeconomic status neighborhood were administered a nonverbal test of intelligence. The test was disguised as one that would predict intellectual "blooming." There were 18 classrooms in the school, three at each of the six grade levels. Within each grade level the three classrooms were composed of children with above average ability, average ability, and below average ability, respectively. Within each of the 18 classrooms approximately 20 per cent of the children were chosen at random to form the experimental group. Each teacher was given the names of the children from her class who were in the experimental condition. The teacher was told that these children had scored on the "test for intellectual blooming" such that they would show remarkable gains in intellectual competence during the next eight months of school. The only difference between the experimental group and the control group children, then, was in the mind of the teacher.

At the end of the school year, eight months later, all the children were re-tested with the same IQ test. This intelligence test, while relatively nonverbal in the sense of requiring no speaking, reading, or writing, was not entirely non-verbal. Actually there were two subtests, one requiring a greater comprehension of English—a kind of picture vocabulary test. The other subtest required less ability to understand any spoken language but more ability to reason abstractly. For shorthand purposes we refer to the former as a "verbal" subtest and to the latter as a "reasoning" subtest. The pretest correlation between these subtests was $+.42$.

For the school as a whole, the children of the experimental groups showed only slightly greater gain in verbal IQ (2 points) than did the control group children. However, in total IQ (4 points) and especially in reasoning IQ (7 points), the experimental group children gained appreciably more than did the control group children.

When educational theorists have discussed the possible effects of teachers' expectations, they have usually referred to the children at lower levels of scholastic achievement. It was interesting, therefore, to find that in the present study, children of the highest level of achievement showed as great a benefit as did the children of the lowest level of achievement of having their teachers expect intellectual gains.

At the end of the school year of this study, all teachers were asked to describe the classroom behavior of their pupils. Those children from whom intellectual growth was expected were described as having a significantly better chance of becoming successful in the future, as significantly more interesting, curious, and happy. There was a tendency, too, for these children to be seen as more appealing, adjusted, and affectionate and as lower in the need for social approval. In short, the children from whom intellectual growth was expected became more intellectually alive and autonomous or at least were so perceived by their teachers.

We have already seen that the children of the experimental group gained more intellectually, so the possibility existed that it was the fact of such gaining that accounted for the more favorable ratings of these children's behavior and aptitude. But a great many of the control group children also gained in *IQ* during the course of the year. Perhaps those who gained more intellectually among these undesignated children would also be rated more favorably by their teachers. Such was not the case. The more the control group children gained in *IQ*, the more they were regarded as *less* well-adjusted, as *less* interesting, and as *less* affectionate. From these results it would seem that when children who are expected to grow intellectually do so, they are considerably benefited in other ways as well. When children who are not especially expected to develop intellectually do so, they seem either to show accompanying undesirable behavior or at least are perceived by their teachers as showing such undesirable behavior. If a child is to show intellectual gain it seems to be better for his real or perceived intellectual vitality and for his real or perceived mental health if his teacher has been expecting him to grow intellectually. It appears that there may be hazards to unpredicted intellectual growth.

A closer analysis of these data, broken down by whether the children were in the high, medium, or low ability tracks or groups, showed that these hazards of unpredicted intellectual growth were due primarily to the children of the low ability group. When these slow-track children were in the control group, where no intellectual gains were expected of them, they were rated more unfavorably by their teachers if they did show gains in *IQ*. The greater their *IQ* gains, the more unfavorably were they rated, both as to mental health and as to intellectual vitality. Even when the slow-track children were in the experimental group, where *IQ* gains were expected of them, they were not rated as favorably relative to their control group peers as were the children of the high or medium track, despite the fact that they gained as much in *IQ* relative to the control group children as did the experimental group children of the high group. It may be difficult for a slow-track child, even one whose *IQ* is rising, to be seen by his teacher as a well-adjusted child, and as a potentially successful child, intellectually.

The effects of teacher expectations had been most dramatic when measured in terms of pupils' gains in reasoning *IQ*. These effects on reasoning *IQ*, however, were not uniform for boys and girls. Although all the children of this lower socioeconomic status school gained dramatically in *IQ*, it was only among the girls that greater gains were shown by those who were expected to bloom compared to the children of the control group. Among the boys, those who were expected to bloom gained less than did the children of the control group (interaction $F = 9.27, p = .003$). In part to check this finding, the experiment originally conducted on the West Coast was repeated in a small Midwestern town. In this study, conducted with Judy Evans, the children were from substantial middle-class backgrounds. This time the results were completely reversed. Now it was the boys who showed the benefits of favorable teacher expectations. Among the girls, those who were expected to bloom intellectually gained less in reasoning IQ than did the girls of the control group (interaction $F = 9.10, p = .003$). Just as in the West Coast experiment, however, all the children showed substantial gains in IQ. These results, while they suggest the nontrivial effects of teacher expectations, also indicate the probable complexity of the effects of teacher expectations as a function of pupils' sex, social class, and very likely, other variables as well.

In both the experiments described, IQ gains were assessed after a full academic year had elapsed. However, the preliminary results of an experiment conducted with Don Anderson suggest that teacher expectations can significantly affect students' intellectual performance in a period as short as two months. In this small experiment, the 25 children were mentally retarded boys with an average pretest IQ of 46. Expectancy effects were significant only for reasoning IQ and only in interaction with membership in a group receiving special remedial reading instruction in addition to participating in the school's summer day camp program ($p \leq .03$, two-tail). Among these specially tutored boys those who were expected to bloom showed an expectancy disadvantage of nearly 12 IQ points; among the untutored boys who were participating only in the school's summer day camp program, those who were expected to bloom showed an expectancy advantage of just over three IQ points. (For verbal IQ, in contrast, the expectancy disadvantage of the tutored boys was less than one IQ point, while the expectancy advantage for the untutored boys was over two points.)

Another study, this time conducted in an East Coast school with upper middle-class pupils, again showed the largest effect of teachers' expectancies to occur when the measure was of reasoning IQ (Conn, Edwards, Rosenthal, and Crowne, 1967). In this study, both the boys and girls who were expected to bloom intellectually showed greater gains in reasoning IQ than did the boys and girls of the control group, and the magnitude of the expectancy effect favored the girls very slightly. Also in this study, we had available a measure of the children's accuracy in judging the vocal expressions of emotion of adult speakers. It was of considerable theoretical interest to find that greater benefits of favorable teacher expectations accrued to those children who were more accurate in judging the emotional tone expressed in an adult female's voice. These findings, taken together with the research of Adair and Epstein (1967) described earlier, give a strong suggestion that vocal cues may be quite important in the covert communication of interpersonal expectations.

We may conclude now with a brief description of just one more experiment, this one conducted by W. Victor Beez (1967), who kindly made his data available for the analyses to follow. This time the pupils were 60 pre-schoolers from a summer Headstart program. Each child was taught the meaning of a series of symbols by one teacher. Half the 60 teachers had been led to expect good symbol-learning and half had been led to expect poor symbol-learning. Most (77 per cent) of the children alleged to have better intellectual prospects learned five or more symbols but only 13 per cent of the children alleged to have poorer intellectual prospects learned five or more symbols ($p < 2$ in a million). In this study the children's actual performance was assessed by an experimenter who did not know what the child's teacher had been told about the child's intellectual prospects. Teachers who had been given favorable expectations about their pupils tried to teach more symbols to their pupils than did the teachers given unfavorable expectations about their pupils. The difference in teaching effort was dramatic. Eight or more symbols were taught by 87 per cent of the teachers expecting better performance, but only 13 per cent of the teachers expecting poorer performance tried to teach that many symbols to their pupils ($p < 1$ in 10 million).

These results suggest that a teacher's expectation about a pupil's performance may sometimes be translated not into subtle vocal nuances but rather into overt and even dramatic alterations in teaching style. The magnitude of the effect of teacher expectations found by Beez is also worthy of comment. In all the earlier studies described, one group of children had been singled out for favorable expectations while nothing was said of the remaining children of the control group. In Beez' short-term experiment it seemed more justified to give negative as well as positive expectations about some of the children. Perhaps the very large effects of teacher expectancy obtained by Beez were due to the creation of strong equal but opposite expectations in the minds of the different teachers. Since strong negative expectations doubtless exist in the real world of classrooms, Beez' procedure may give the better estimate of the effects of teacher expectations as they occur in everyday life.

REFERENCES

Adair, J. G., and Epstein, J. Verbal cues in the mediation of experimenter bias. Paper read at Midwestern Psychological Association, Chicago, May, 1967.

Beez, W. V. Influence of biased psychological reports on teacher behavior. Unpublished manuscript, Indiana University, 1967.

Boring, E. G. *A History of experimental psychology* (2nd ed.). New York: Appleton-Century-Crofts, 1950.

Conn, L. K., Edwards, C. N., Rosenthal, R., and Crowne, D. Emotion perception and response to teacher expectancy in elementary school children. Unpublished manuscript, Harvard University, 1967.

Pfungst, O. *Clever Hans.* Translated by Rahn, C. L. New York: Holt, 1911; Holt, Rinehart and Winston, 1965.

Rosenthal, R. *Experimenter effects in behavioral research.* New York: Appleton-Century-Crofts, 1966.

Rosenthal, R. Covert communication in the psychological experiment. *Psychological Bulletin* **67** (1967), 356–367.

Rosenthal, R., and Fode, K. L. The effect of experimenter bias on the performance of the albino rat. *Behavioral Science* **8** (1963), 183–189.

Rosenthal, R., and Jacobson, Lenore. Teachers' expectancies: determinants of pupils' *IQ* gains. *Psychological Reports* **19** (1966), 115–118.

Rosenthal, R., and Jacobson, Lenore. *Pygmalion in the classroom: teacher expectation and pupils' intellectual development.* New York: Holt, Rinehart and Winston [published in 1968—Ed.].

Rosenthal, R., and Lawson, R. A longitudinal study of the effects of experimenter bias on the operant learning of laboratory rats. *Journal of Psychiatric Research* **2** (1964), 61–72.

ATTITUDES AND NON-ATTITUDES:
CONTINUATION OF A DIALOGUE

PHILIP E. CONVERSE

Some years ago Carl Hovland (1959) undertook a systematic comparison of conclusions which had been reached concerning the modification of attitudes through communication within two broad research traditions: the *experiment* and the *sample survey*. Despite common substantive interests, these two traditions had remained rather insulated from one another, and as Hovland noted, their separate efforts had produced results easily taken as contradictory. The purpose of Hovland's essay was twofold. First, he wished to point out that these apparently divergent views about the ease of persuading to attitude change could be readily reconciled by proper understanding of the differences in the two types of research designs and the backgrounds of the investigators involved in each. To the best of our knowledge, members of both traditions felt that the reconciliation was well handled. Secondly, however, Hovland seemed concerned in a more general sense with a need to bridge the gap between experiment and survey, and in effect called for a more vigorous dialogue between the two traditions.

This paper is written in an effort to continue the dialogue. It is not our intention here to retrace Hovland's steps in any detail, although a number of things to be said have relevance for his argument. Nor, for that matter, do we wish to rehearse the differential powers and shortcomings of the two methods, for we would subscribe with little amendment to most of the conclusions long since reached by parties interested in the subject. It seems that divergences in outlook are likely to arise between the two traditions if for no other reason than the fact that the experimentalist is able to study what *can* happen in situational configurations which he creates and controls, while survey analysts pay a more passive attention to what *does* happen in an actuarial sense, as a matter of relative empirical frequency. Thus, in the case Hovland discussed, it appears true that when audiences are exposed to certain persuasive communications on certain kinds of issues under certain further experimental conditions, considerable attitude change can be demonstrated. From an actuarial point of view, however, these conditions occur in nature infrequently: few people expose themselves to potentially contrary messages even though a torrent of such messages may be sent, and various other aspects of the experimental condition go unfulfilled as well.

Revised version of a paper read at the Seventeenth International Congress of Psychology in Washington, D.C., August, 1963. Reproduced by permission of the author.

Perhaps the clearest function which sample survey results may fulfill in any dialogue, then, is to remind the experimentalist of the actuarial mainstream, pointing out sources of critical variation in "natural" attitude-change processes to which he may have become insensitive. It is in this spirit that our remarks are made. We will begin by a presentation of results from one analysis of sample-survey data on attitude change. We choose this analysis because it seems to have implications not only for some of the methodological practices common in experimental work on attitude change, but also for the way in which the attitude continuum is to be conceptualized. Carried a step or two further, the results suggest hypotheses which might be worthy of experimental test within the areas described by balance, congruity or dissonance theories of attitude change.

Statistical Properties of Certain "Naturalistic" Attitude Changes

The data to be reported are drawn from a sequence of panel studies conducted on a national cross-section of the adult population of the United States over a four-year period from 1956 to 1960. The immediate occasions for the surveys were the three national elections of 1956, 1958 and 1960. In principle, respondents were interviewed at five different points in time over this period: before and after the election in 1956; after the election in 1958; and once again, before and after the 1960 election. In practice, slightly less than 70 per cent of the original 1956 pool of respondents who were still alive and in possession of their faculties were successfully reinterviewed in the 1960 waves of the panel. However, analyses across a wide variety of social and attitudinal characteristics suggested that the 1960 survivors were a remarkably unbiased subset of the original pool of respondents.

The panel aspects of the study sequence were fully utilized, in the sense that the interview schedules applied at the various points in time contained direct repetitions of a wide array of items bearing on attitudes and social situations. Here we shall focus on some of the time-change aspects of the attitudinal data.

The simplest property to assess from these attitude measurements has to do with the correlation of measurements of the same items over time. Empirically, the range in variation of such test-retest correlations on attitude measurements computed after a two-year interval was very wide, covering a space in the correlation continuum from roughly .10 to .80.[1] Furthermore, the data made clear that these turnover correlations were quite stable for specific items over comparable periods of time: if the correlation of item A between t_1 and t_2 turned out to be .4, for example, it was demonstrable that the same correlation computed for the same item between the interval t_2 and t_3 would rarely be much more than .03 or .04 from .40 as well. In short, then, varying items had very differential but very stable rates of attitude turnover associated with them over the two-year test-retest span.

Cursory inspection of differences in turnover rates attached to varying items was sufficient in many cases to indicate why the turnover rate fell in the levels where it was found. Thus, for example, items which showed test-retest correlations of less than .20 typically had to do with the particular election as an object of estimation. Since three elections were covered, it is quite obvious that while the questionnaire items were identical, the objects of reference—the different elections—were in many respects different objects, so that almost complete turnover of opinion could hardly be taken as surprising. At the very high end of the turnover range, measures of generalized affect toward the major political parties approached a two-year test-retest correlation of .80. Here, of course, the objects are familiar ones evoking strong affect from many people, and are characterized by a reasonable amount of temporal stability in their attributes as perceived by the public.

Included among the attitude items, however, was a battery of eight questions directed at the principal issues of public policy which were being debated during the period of the study. These included attitudinal items of a familiar Likert type on matters of civil rights, social welfare legislation, the relation of government to free enterprise, and problems of foreign policy such as aid to neutral countries and the like.

We shall focus our attention on this set of attitudinal items for two reasons. First, they resemble closely the type of item to which the experimentalist often gravitates in his attitude studies. Secondly, the empirical properties of the items were quite striking. For while the meaning-substance of the items seemed to have changed very little during the period of the study, and while the items were chosen specifically to capture the cleavages in basic psychological commitments in public politics of the period, the test-retest correlations were all within the lower half of the empirical range, running roughly from .23 to .46 within both of the two-year time spans available for inspection.

There are at least two possible reactions to such low coefficients. One is to imagine that public opinion on these items must have been in a high state of flux during this period, with a very considerable evolution of attitudes in the wake of changing national events. There were, however, several empirical problems which such an interpretation would encounter. In the first place, the marginal attitude distributions for the various time points were remarkably similar despite high rates of turnover within the tables.[2] It would seem that if national events were exerting systematic forces on opinion in a manner which would produce meaningful evolution of public attitudes, the distributions of opinion should progress in one direction or another over time, rather than remain relatively stable, with almost all of the individual change in one direction being counterbalanced by an equal amount of individual attitude change in the opposing direction. Secondly, the items had been chosen to avoid superficial attitudes toward short-term events, in an attempt to plumb more basic and stable dispositions toward questions of public policy. Hence no very large measure of meaningful change was to be expected. Indeed, examination of the differential rates of turnover within the battery of issue items suggested that the more basic and ideological the issue dimension was, and the more remote its referents were from day-to-day change in national events, the higher the turnover of opinion. Thus, for example, the most unstable issue of all was one having to do with whether or not the federal government should "leave things like electric power and housing for private businessmen to handle." Somehow it seemed implausible that large proportions of the American population between 1956 and 1958, or between 1958 and 1960, had shifted their beliefs from support of creeping socialism to a defense of free enterprise, and that a correspondingly large proportion had moved in the opposite direction, forsaking free enterprise for advocacy of further federal incursions into the private sector.

This being so, the more reasonable reaction to the low coefficients is simply that we were doing a very poor job of tapping the attitudinal dimensions at which we originally aimed, and that our results, viewed now as test-retest correlations in the strict sense, give witness to an incredible degree of measurement unreliability. Hence we should not talk of results at all until we go back and develop better measuring instruments.

There is somewhat more internal evidence supporting this view than was the case for the evolution-of-opinion interpretation. One of these items of evidence is particularly relevant to our argument. Originally we had assumed that some of these items, vis-à-vis some people in the population, would have very little meaning. Hence we had taken elaborate precautions to remove such people from any sense of obligation to respond to items which generated no affect for them. Thus, for example, the battery of issue items was prefaced by a statement which pointed out, among other things, that "different things are important to different people, so we don't expect everyone to have an opinion about all of these (things)." Furthermore, as each item in the battery was read, the respondent was explicitly asked whether or not he had an opinion on the matter and only if he said that he did was he further asked what his opinion was. These precautions may be fruitfully compared with many common attitude-measurement situations in which experimental instructions entreat the subject to express some kind of attitude other than the indifference point even though he may find it hard to do so. After all, "don't know's," equivocations and other forms of missing data are exasperating in analysis and are to be avoided at all cost. However, we felt that it was more important to deal with missing data than with measures laden with "noise."

Our screening procedures were successful enough that variously across the set of attitude items, anywhere from a handful to 35 per cent of the sample confessed that it had no genuine opinion on the matter under consideration. Ironically, however, the low test-retest correlations which we have cited for these items were computed for the subset of people who did lay claim to some opinion; the many no-opinion people were set aside. Furthermore, it was readily discovered that there was almost a perfect correlation between the issue items ordered according to proportions of people who said they had no opinion, and the ordering produced across the same items in terms of response stability.

These pieces of evidence, of course, lead toward a strong suspicion of item unreliability, although it is rather distressing to learn that such unreliability remains after all of our precautions to avoid the measurement of non-existent attitudes. However, let us not be too hasty in our judgment, for the heart of the analysis which we wish to report turns out to throw an odd and unexpected light on the whole question of reliability.

The most revealing statistical property of these attitude-change data emerges when we consider not simply the correlations between the same attitudes over two-year spans, but also the correlation for each attitude between the initial and terminal interviews, a span of four years. For we discover that these t_1-to-t_3 correlations tend to be just about the same magnitude as the t_1-to-t_2 correlations, or the t_2-to-t_3 correlations. That is, surprising though it may be, one could predict 1960 attitudes on most of these issue items fully as well with a knowledge of individual attitudes in 1956 alone as one could with a knowledge of the more proximal 1958 responses. Furthermore, the tendency toward parity of the three correlations is clearest among the issue items with greatest turnover; among the more nearly stable items, the four-year correlation tends to be slightly lower than the two-year correlations, a pattern which is of course much closer to our intuitive expectations.

At this point we will find it useful to shift some of our weight from the vocabulary of correlation to the vocabulary of Markov chains, a body of mathematical theory useful in treating stochastic change processes. Within this vocabulary, the tables representing attitudes at different points in time can be converted into proportions by rows, and considered as empirical matrices of transition probabilities. The similarity of the pair of two-year tables for most of these issue items provides some presumptive evidence for the assumption that whatever else may be said, these matrices as reckoned in summary fashion over the population can usually be considered constant in their probabilities over time.

Proceeding with this assumption, it can readily be demonstrated that the empirical parity of the three time-correlations could not occur if it were true that the issue responses of the total population were properly describable by a single constant matrix of transition probabilities through the two steps from t_1 to t_3. For if such a condition held, then the four-year time-correlations would necessarily take values substantially below those of the two-year correlations, the differences ranging upward from .10 to .20 or more under common conditions.

Hence it is clear that no single transition matrix constant over the two-year stages can account for the observed response behaviors. In other words, if we maintain the assumption of constant matrices over time, then we are forced to conclude that the time paths of response can only be treated as arising from some mixture of two or more transition matrices, and not one alone.

Let us imagine what these matrices might be. At first glance it is apparent that there is a whole range of matrices which, while mathematically possible, are entirely implausible in the empirical situation at hand, and which we can therefore rule out of serious consideration as describing the behavior of *any* member of the population. These are the subset of possible matrices which, if cast as second-order determinants, have negative values, or which in any form would generate negative time-correlations. In content terms, a genuine negative time-correlation would mean that respondents who had agreed with an item in 1956 must have gone out of their way to disagree with that item in 1958, and then remember to agree with it again in 1960. This would seem to be highly unlikely behavior, even if it were conceivable that respondents could remember specific responses they had made to an interview two years earlier; and since this seems quite inconceivable in itself, it seems fair to rule out such matrices as impossible.

Once this constraint is added to the picture, however, we begin to have some strong leverage on our data. In particular, we can now say that if the total population were to be described in terms of a mixture of *two* transition matrices, then there are only two which in combination would generate our phenomenon of three equal time-correlations. These two matrices are (1) the identity matrix, with probabilities of 1.0 in the major diagonals; and (2) what we might call a "random" matrix, of equiprobable responses. And quite naturally, the magnitude of the three equal time-correlations would be a simple function of the relative prevalence of these two matrices in the population.

This model for response behavior we might call a "black-and-white" model, for it posits a very stringent division of the population into two sharply contrasting subsets. In content terms, one portion of the population would be perfectly stable in its responses over time, while the other portion would be given to response time-paths which in a strict statistical sense were random. On the face of it, this would seem to be an unlikely descriptive model. Furthermore, while most of the assumptions we have made about the nature of the data which have led us to this model seem quite palatable, our final assumption was that only two transition matrices were necessary to describe the behavior of the population. This constraint seems somewhat gratuitous: we would much sooner suppose that a continuous shading of different matrices were represented in the population.

Happily, in this instance, the data permit a test of the goodness of fit of the simple black-and-white model. There are several statistical manipulations which would accomplish the same general end. We will describe one which is as simple to follow intuitively as any of them.

Let us assume that the black-and-white model comprises an accurate and exhaustive account of the attitude responses generated over time. Then it follows that any individuals who change from one side of an attitude scale (say, the "agree" side) to the other ("disagree") between t_1 and t_2 must of necessity belong to that portion of the population whose responses are random. They are a "pure" random group. However, they do not exhaust the total set of subjects following random response paths. For between t_1 and t_2 certain subjects following random response paths would give two consecutive responses on the same side of the issue by chance alone. Fortunately, the proportion of such subjects in the cells of stable t_1-t_2 attitudes is calculable, given the numbers of subjects who fall in the minor diagonals, or change cells. This does not mean, of course, that we can isolate the "random" subjects from those whose response paths are stable in a meaningful sense. But we can tell in considerable precision how "polluted" with such people the set of apparently stable people is.

Therefore, we can define two sets of people on the basis of the pattern of t_1 and t_2 responses. One is the pure random set. The other is a mixture, in known proportions, of the perfectly stable and the perfectly random respondents.

If the black-and-white model is a proper description of response behavior in the population, then, we can predict with similar precision the nature of the relationship between t_2 and t_3 responses for each subset. The purely random people should show a t_2-t_3 correlation between responses of .00. The polluted subset should show a t_2-t_3 correlation greater than the total-population time-correlations, but falling well short of unity because of the remaining admixture of random respondents. Just how far short of unity this second correlation would fall can of course be readily calculated on the basis of knowledge of relative proportions of random and stable respondents.

As an initial test of the model we chose data arising from the item for which the black-and-white model seemed on a priori grounds to be least inconceivable. That is, we sought the item from our battery for which it seemed likely that *genuine* attitudes would be most deeply ingrained and hence immutable over time, and yet one which would be basically "ideological" enough that the issues posed might be truly beyond the ken of substantial numbers of people in a cross-section population. The item described above concerning the relative roles of government and private business matched these specifications in excellent fashion. It was not entirely coincidental that this was the item on which the largest proportion of respondents had indicated that they had no opinion, and the item which had shown the highest response instability of any in the battery among those who did claim opinions.

Respondents were then sorted into two groups in the manner described above, on the basis of the pattern of t_1 and t_2 responses. The predictions were that the pure random group would show a t_2-t_3 correlation of .00, and that the second group would show a correlation of .47, if the black-and-white model were indeed an appropriate description of the underlying response process. The results of the primary test showed t_2-t_3 correlation values of .004 for the first group, and of .489 for the second group. In other words, the time data generated by this issue item fit the predictions of the black-and-white model with remarkable precision.[3]

We then proceeded to test the same model for a number of the other issue items, although in varying degree they had face content and zero-order time-correlations which suggested in advance that they could be expected to depart from the model somewhat. The test showed that indeed they did, although the bifurcation of t_2-t_3 correlations between the two test groups remains quite extreme. Thus, for example, the key correlation for the putative "random" subset departs from .00, but rarely rises above a figure of about +.09. Hence we might conclude that there remains a "near-fit" for the other items as well.

This fact of "near-fit" may be conceptually more important than meets the eye at first glance. For there are widespread assumptions about processes of attitude measurement, as well as a few formal models, which presuppose some underlying continuum of latent response probabilities vis-à-vis any single attitude item. Thus, for example, in a heterogeneous population, one might expect that ideally one could isolate individuals for whom response probabilities towards taking one of two positions on a given item range continuously between .5 and 1.0. What is intriguing about the black-and-white model, along with the "real" data which fit it, is the demonstration of an absence of such continuity, with two maximally discontinuous classes (or three classes, if one distinguishes between the perfectly stable "pro" class and the equally stable "anti" class).

Once data depart significantly from this simple model, the number and variety of models which could conceivably account for the data become large indeed, and the discriminatory power of our mathematical deductions evaporates accordingly. In these instances it is very easy to fall back on vaguer notions of latent-response probability continua. Perhaps this is appropriate. However, the fact that one set of these data fits the black-and-white model very well, and the other sets of conceptually comparable items only miss a fit with the model in modest degree, suggests that we should not abandon the black-and-white model completely in imagining the processes which underlie the responses to other items in the battery. In other words, it would seem likely that were the truth of the matter isolable, we would discover that a very large proportion of the responses to the other items in the battery could best be understood in terms of two sharply discontinuous classes of respondents, the stable and the random. What is new in these other items, and what leads further data to diverge somewhat from the black-and-white model, is the presence of some few people who are undergoing a meaningful evolution of attitudes on the issue in question. The crucial fact, from the point of view of our argument, is the strong likelihood that even the attitude items straying somewhat from the expectations of the black-and-white model are clouded by large numbers of purely random responses.

What psychological interpretation is to be placed on such random responses? It seems to us most simple to imagine that they came from people with no real attitudes on the matter in question, but who for some reason felt obliged to try a response to the item despite our generous and repeated invitation to disavow any opinion where none was felt. In this vein, it may be useful to analyze exactly what the objects were which we were asking our respondents to evaluate. For example, the key black-and-white item on government and private enterprise posed as an object of potential attitude not just the federal government or private business, but rather a *type of relation* between the two. Furthermore, the manifest content failed to make clear which of the two parties to this relation would feel helped or hurt by it. This means that respondents who may have had some prior feeling of generalized affect toward private business or toward the federal government (or both) could not respond stably, for lack of this further information which the question presupposes. The experimentalist may find this an incredible observation, for the information presupposed—that private business does not generally want further governmental expansions into its economic sector—seems almost a ubiquitous piece of the "common culture." However, the survey analyst rapidly comes to recognize that presupposition of any information about objects which lie beyond the daily ken of the subjects tested will miss the mark for substantial numbers of people in a heterogeneous population. Indeed, in the case of the attitude item fitting the black-and-white model, it can be calculated from the data that something less than 20 per cent of the total sample fell into the category of real and stable attitudes on the item. The remaining 80 per cent represented confessions of "no opinion" or statistically random responses. Unfortunately, it was a *minority* within this 80 per cent which took advantage of our invitation not to bother fabricating an opinion. When attitudes are asked for in such a setting, people are remarkably obliging.

Relevance of Findings for Experimental Studies

At this point the experimentalist may well ask, "Of what interest is all this to me? I want to understand the implications of attitudes once people have psychological states worthy of the name. I am a student of attitudes, and not a student of non-attitudes." This is, of course, an impeccable position. It presumes, however, that what he typically studies are indeed attitudes, and not non-attitudes concealed with hastily-fabricated affective judgments, as was the case with a full plurality of our test population. A reading of the experimental literature over the years suggests to me, however, a remarkable insensitivity to this possibility. And when I keep this possibility in mind in reading any given study, I often end up with an interpretation of results that is quite oblique to the interpretation offered by the investigator. In other words, there seems to be food for thought here even for investigators who wish to limit their efforts to the study of genuinely-formed attitudes, but who do little to protect themselves against the measurement of non-attitudes by mistake. Therefore it is appropriate to explore the implications of these survey data several steps farther.

The most obvious implication has to do with instrument reliability. Once we granted that the low-time correlations for these items were not likely to be accounted for by "true" attitude change, but rather should be seen as test-retest coefficients of reliability, we were prepared to send the whole instrument back to the shop for repairs, since a reliability coefficient of .3 is disastrously low. Yet the fit with the black-and-white model suggests that where people actually *had* attitudes, the single item could scarcely be further perfected, for on a trial as stringent as a two-year test-retest, the reliability coefficient was indistinguishable from perfection. From this point of view, what needs repair is not the item but the population. Less facetiously, the moral is clear: where measurement reliability is at issue, the measurement of non-existent states is very unrewarding. And while the classical view of these matters took "reliability" to be a property (or number) attached to the measuring instrument, we could not have a more dramatic example of the fact that reliability in our field of inquiry is instead a joint property of the instrument *and* the object being measured.

Other aspects of psychological measurement may deserve review in this light. Speaking from personal experience, I would hypothesize that such a phenomenon as *test fatigue* is itself a direct consequence of pressures, felt by the subject to search for faint or non-existent bits of affect to fulfill the requirements of the attitude questionnaire. In those rare cases where an attitude item or battery dovetails nicely with thoughts or feelings I have experienced on my own with any strength or clarity before, even such an impersonal process as marking a questionnaire offers the reward of pleasant catharsis. Such pleasure seems somewhat infrequent, however, and the hunt-and-fabricate feeling is fully as familiar.[4] One outcome of such harassment is fatigue; another is a more or less conscious recourse to some response set touched off more by question form than question content.

Underlying the overestimate of who has attitudes about what, perhaps, is the common view held by many social psychologists of the individual as a vibrant bundle of attitudes. Nothing we have said need call this view into question in the least respect: it is certainly an heuristic viewpoint and undoubtedly a faithful one as well. However, it is all too easy to assume from such a view that mere selection of a "familiar" object or controversy as a point of attitude measurement must evoke true attitudes in all or almost all of a test population. There is, of course, a very wide logical leap from the first of these propositions to the second. Possible objects of attitudes are infinite, and a person can be seen as a vibrant bundle of attitudes without any assurance that his attitudes extend to more than a very tiny subset of such objects. Phenomenological differences in information and attention almost ensure the contrary: it may well be difficult to find objects in most domains which will not be matters of non-attitude for many members of the test population.

In sum, then, there is a very real sense in which *attitudes take practice*—practice which is genuine in the sense of having been powered by own psychic energy aside from the kind of transient situation created by the experimentalist or the survey interviewer. Where such practice has not occurred, the state to be measured is non-existent. The measurement of non-existent states gives maximally unreliable results. If the subject himself were helpful to the investigator in refusing to report very *ad hoc* feelings as "attitudes," then the problems would be greatly diminished. This does not occur, however. Hartley (1946) years ago collected a full set of ethnic attitudes toward groups that did not exist. We made a great effort to encourage holders of non-attitudes to bypass such items. Some accepted the invitation, but the majority did not. Whatever our intentions, the attitude questionnaire is approached as though it were an intelligence test, with the "don't know" and "can't decide" confessions of mental incapacity.

It is true that on many grounds the survey analyst is more exposed to the dangers of studying non-attitudes than is the experimentalist. That is, despite great variety in experimental procedures, there are some rather typical aspects of attitude-change studies which intentionally or accidentally provide protection. One example of accidental protection is the use of college students as subjects. Non-attitudes on a wide range of matters which seem "common culture" to the investigator are an inevitable consequence of information impoverishment among the less well-educated strata of heterogeneous populations. While the professor is likely to be impressed that college sophomores are not very well-informed either, they remain, relative to the total population, a fairly alert group. Hence, if a specific attitude item were to show an 80 per cent non-attitude rate in a hetero- geneous population, the nature of the population the experimentalist uses might well reduce the rate on the same item to something like 30–50 per cent, among college sophomores.

More intentional steps for protection include such things as the multiple- item battery and the choice of attitude-objects which are "close to home" for all of the subjects, and hence far more likely to have become the object of genuine affect for any population member. Certainly one need not worry greatly about non-attitudes in the sense in which we use the term here when the object of evalu- ation is "mother" and the dimensions of evaluation so common (as in the more typical uses of the semantic differential) that they are part of anybody's common judgmental vocabulary.

However, in attitude-change experiments *per se* there are pressures away from the havens of protection which either multiple-item batteries or the choice of very homely objects can afford. In the classic format of the "before" measure- ment, the persuasive message and the "after" measurement, the message itself must be of some limited content scope, and there are in turn only a limited num- ber of attitude items which can be imagined within such a scope. Hence the item base of very many attitude-change measures is extremely limited, if indeed it exceeds one item. Similarly, the necessity of dealing with some "common" object of orientation to which the persuasive message can effectively pertain makes the use of objects which are phenotypically knit into the lives of test subjects ("mother," "my work," "my professor," etc.) rather awkward. Add to these difficulties the need to deal in objects which are controversial, along with an understandable desire to treat "socially significant" attitudes, and the com- mon result is not only the use of a narrow item base, but attitude-objects of political, intellectual or social interest which tend to lie beyond what is very salient for many of the test subjects. It is, of course, in such areas that non-attitudes abound, even for college sophomores.

If it can be granted that many attitude studies have measured an abundant number of non-attitudes on the supposition that they were attitudes, what differ- ence has it really made? Do not the holders of non-attitudes, particularly with multiple-item measures, tend to gravitate toward the zero point of "indifference," where they belong? And even though they may abound, do they do anything more than add "noise" to the results, attenuating them rather than biasing them?

First, let us take the question of the meaning of the attitude continuum, for this is what is at stake when we say that non-attitudes should fall at the "zero-point." It might be mentioned in passing that a frightening number of our random respondents were capable of giving "strong agree" or "strong disagree" responses, probably under pressure to introduce some variety into their strengths as well as to give some attitude. With multiple items, however, it is indeed likely that inconsistencies (which will be frequent in the expression of non-attitudes) will drive the respondent toward the middle of any summary attitude measure. The question becomes, then, whether or not that is really where we want him.

Now there are several ways of imputing meaning to zones on this basic attitude continuum. It is generally assumed that an extreme location has something to do with either an intense or at least a univocal attitude. One way of visualizing the matter is to reduce the molar concept of a generalized attitude toward a complex attitude-object into its molecular parts—the set of affective reactions which the individual holds toward all of the component properties of the object which he perceives. In such a reading, the proper location of the individual on the attitude continuum with respect to the molar object is some algebraic summation of ratio of component valences, weighted in one fashion or another.

While we know remarkably little about what combining rules may pertain, we do know that we can expect some generalization of affect or "strain toward symmetry" (Newcomb, 1953) among these molecular valences, such that the molar attitude toward the object tends to be somewhat more univocal than the same affective components might be if the properties of reference resided in a scatter of dissociated objects. However, we also know that this is no more than a trend, and one which reality very often forestalls. People do maintain mixed attitudes toward very many objects, especially those not lending themselves to any easy dissociation. Indeed, the instance of the perfectly-mixed reaction occurs often enough that it has attracted a term of its own, which is ambivalence, an uncomfortable state but not a non-existent one.

Where should ambivalent people be located on the attitude continuum? Most certainly, it would seem, they deserve a position on the middle, at the zero-point. However, we now see that things are becoming somewhat crowded here, for we have already created something like Sherif's zone of indifference, and located our non-attitudes in the middle of this zone. In some instances, perhaps, the consequences of this overcrowding are few. But there are many instances of experimental treatment of attitude change in which it may matter a great deal.

Take as a concrete example the implication of the Osgood congruity model (Osgood et al., 1955 and 1957) that attitudes near the zero point are moved greater distances by persuasive information than are attitudes initially located towards the extremes of the continuum, a matter which has received experimental confirmation in the typical format of the attitude change study. Perhaps such wider movement under the experimental conditions would be equally true of intense but ambivalent attitudes as well as of non-attitudes. Intuitively, however, we would expect that there would be rather drastic differences among holders of the two types of "zero-attitudes." It is easy to see that people bringing actual "non-attitudes" to the experimental situation (whatever affective answers they may have given initially) would be strongly affected by the information in the persuasive message, since the experimental situation may be one of the first times they have ever paid attention to any kind of information about the item in controversy. However, if we assume that people can become intensely ambivalent only through an appreciation of the pros and cons of a controversy, it does not seem likely that a brief reiteration of some of the pro arguments will create the same kind of striking attitude change.

If initial non-attitudes are present in such experiments, and if the bulk of the systematic change in measurement is attributable to these people, would we not be more accurate in speaking of "attitude-formation" studies rather than studies of attitude change? Even the term "formation" may be unduly strong, for the non-attitude-holders by definition have little interest in the proposed attitude-object, and save in the case where enforced attention sparks some further self-starting interest in the object, it would seem likely that the nascent attitude expressed in the "after" measurement might decay from memory rather readily.

We would argue that holders of non-attitudes, in the measure that they can be detected at all, deserve no location at the zero-point of the attitude scale, but rather should be located "off the continuum" entirely, in proper recognition of a non-existent state. If they were disposed of in this manner, then the truly ambivalent would be left as a relatively pure group in the center of the continuum. In view of a postulated strain toward symmetry among valences of attitude-object properties, this would mean that more of our attitude distributions would show a U-shaped form when properly measured, and fewer would show the heavy concentrations of responses near the scale midpoint noted by Lorge (1937). In this respect, while the nature of his scales were somewhat different, we heartily applaud the suggestion by Brim (1955) that more intermediate or equivocal responses are likely to be associated with impoverished information about the object in question.

Non-Attitudes and Broader Theories of Attitude Change

Up to this point we have limited ourselves to a consideration of the implications of non-attitudes for certain methodological practices and the interpretation of some experimental findings. We believe that there are a number of implications here which are positive as well, in the sense that they suggest extensions of experimental work within the terms of several current approaches to attitude change.

However, we must first broaden our notion of the significance of the non-attitude, and we shall do so by localizing it as one polar zone on a dimension describing a relationship between the subject and the potential attitude-object. This dimension is intended to be conceptually independent of the primary, positive-negative continuum indicating direction of affect toward the object.

For convenience we shall call this dimension one of centrality of the attitude-object to the subject.[5] Objects of non-attitudes lie at the extreme of low centrality. At the opposite pole, objects which are extremely central to the subject might well be called, in accord with the Sherif-Cantril (1947) usage, "ego-involved."[6]

Some such dimension has received only moderate lip service and remarkably slight experimental attention. Perhaps its most notable experimental use has come in the tradition carried on by Sherif, Hovland, Harvey and others, with particular note due to their efforts to influence attitudes toward alcohol and prohibition held by individuals with deep convictions on the subject in "real life" (Hovland, Harvey, and Sherif, 1957), and the discovery of a marked contrast in susceptibility to influence as a function of the amount of ego-involvement on the issue. Similarly, Rosenberg (1960) has used "issue interest" as an explicit variable in his experimental design.

These are, however, among a small group of exceptions. Hovland (1959), despite his own appreciation of the importance of such a dimension in determining the course of attitude change, remarked with some rue that "the whole concept of ego-involvement is a fuzzy one," and called for further theoretical work on the matter. Or again, Festinger's primary statement of dissonance theory features as a crucial variable the "importance" of relevant cognitive elements to the subject, or what we would call the centrality of their referents for him. Yet as Festinger's discussion moves toward experiment, "importance" becomes not a manipulated property of cognitive elements *per se*, but rather an attribute of a more global decision-event. Even in this second sense relatively little has been done with the variable experimentally, as Brehm and Cohen (1962) have pointed out; and we find the relationship between the second sense and the first quite obscure.[7]

It does seem true as Hovland implied that notions of ego-involvement *per se* do not hold out easy empirical "handles" for the experimentalist, and perhaps this is why there has been no greater spate of experimental activity commissioning such a dimension as an explicit variable. But one of the reasons why we wish to suggest the conceptual dimension of *object-centrality* is that we believe that there are numerous handles for treatment which have been overlooked in the past.

The dimension of centrality has two faces, as we shall deal with it. The first face is the more familiar one: centrality in a purely motivational sense. This is the flavour carried by the term "ego-involvement," and summarizes also the stabilizing characteristic of attitude structures stressed by the "functional" approach to the dynamics of attitude change by Katz and others (e.g., Sarnoff and Katz, 1954; Katz, 1960). In this latter context, the motivational centrality of a potential attitude-object has to do with the degree to which the object gears into the primary goal or need-structures of the individual. Actually, the functionalists are less likely to speak in terms of "degree" than in terms of the "*way*" in which attitude-objects are linked to diverse underlying needs. While the modes whereby similar attitudes gear into different needs for different people

is without question a critical specification in understanding case studies of attitude change, there remains hope that less particularistic statements about
attitude change can rest on the more streamlined variable of "degree." However,
any good operational work with such a "degree" variable would seem to require
a capacity to identify, measure and reliably equate intensities of very disparate
needs from person to person, as well as to establish some estimate of the tightness of linkage between the potential attitude-objects and such needs. There is
little here that seems within clear operational reach, however accurate we may
feel the underlying suppositions about reality to be. Too frequently, thinking
in this vein is thrown into a reverse logic: since we cannot move this person's
attitude, it must be anchored in some deep underlying need, although we are
at a loss to know just what that need may be; or we begin to engage in rather
free-floating imagination to "explain" what the need is. Difficulties of this sort
are what we have referrred to above as a dearth of empirical "handles" in
dealing with the motivational face of the centrality dimension.

The second, or cognitive, face of the centrality dimension has received less
attention, although sample-survey data recommend it to our attention. The
subject has, however, been adumbrated in a number of comments made by the
authors of *Attitude Organization and Change* (Hovland and Rosenberg, 1960),
where the assumption is noted on several occasions that sheer "amount of thinking" about particular objects of attitudes has the effect of increasing consistency
among attitude components, and some demonstration of the phenomenon seems
to occur as a by-product of an experiment by McGuire. Of course, the absence
of any significant amount of prior thinking about a potential attitude-object is
one of the hallmarks of what we have styled as the "non-attitude," and attempts
to measure investigator-shaped components of such psychological states should
produce data of maximal inconsistency. In any event, cognitive centrality may
ideally be taken to refer to the proportion of "mental time" which is occupied
by attention to the attitude-object over substantial periods. In its dependence
upon notions of "thinking" or "the forefront of consciousness," it is very close
to what is often referred to as the salience of an object, although we avoid this
word because of its customary short-term connotations of stimulus-bound and
transient arousal. It is only the set of objects which are persistently salient for
the actor over substantial periods of time, within or outside of the physical
presence of the object itself, which are defined as cognitively central.

Given this "ideal" definition of cognitive centrality, measurement may seem
fully as difficult as it was in the case of motivational centrality. Unlike the
motivational case, however, some of the reliable concomitants of cognitive
centrality (excluding the tautological concomitant of attitude stability) are very
easy to measure. That is, we see as reliable concomitants of cognitive centrality
at least the following:

1) heightened attention to the object, leading to alertness in singling out information about the object from the total flow of information with which the
individual is bombarded in the environment;

2) an increased probability of successful storage or retention of information about the object, leading to increased differentiation of cognitions about the object and the sheer volume of relevant information stored;

3) an increase in the number of "active" associative bonds which tie this object with other cognized objects through various types of "linking" information.

Among these concomitants, perhaps the sheer amount of ancillary information held by the subject with respect to the object (beyond information conveyed by the attitude item itself) lends itself most readily to rapid measurement. Indeed, although there are implicit sampling problems in the choice of items, survey studies suggest that the natural "range of talent" in stored information about the kind of "external" attitude-object under discussion here is likely to be extreme even within populations which are relatively homogeneous on other grounds. This means in turn that measurement of level of information about the object is likely to be far easier and more reliable than the measurement of the attitude itself.

Given this ease of measurement and the seeming importance of centrality in attitude change, it is remarkable indeed how far one can look in the experimental literature for such an explicit variable. It is true that quite recently Rosenberg and Abelson (in Hovland and Rosenberg, 1960), in an excellent discussion of the microprocesses of attitude change, referred to the crucial role played by the "cognitive files" of information relevant to the attitude-object that the subject possesses, and there is of course a perfect identity between the volume of these files and what we are calling the amount of information stored about an object. However, even in this sequence of experiments it does not appear that this variable, or anything much like it, has actually been studied.

It seems a shame to leave the matter here. Somehow when we read an experimental study involving the manipulation of attitudes toward some object of controversy—say, abstract art—we have a great thirst to know which of the experimental subjects were art majors and knew a good deal about the properties of abstract art, as opposed to the experimental subjects who were rather vague as to just what abstract art was, and certainly innocent of the details of the controversy as it may rage in aesthetic circles. Our frustration is compounded by the reflection that an information scale of one, two or three items could make such a discrimination with deadly accuracy.

Ideally, of course, we would want to know not only how *much* information the individual holds, but more precisely *what* that information is in the specific case, for this in a functionalist vein not only gives a better picture of the phenotypic attitude structure, but also would suggest the kinds of information which would be most effective in changing it (see Rosenberg, 1956). However, this approach leads to the same complexities and phenomenological particularities which make notions of motivational centrality difficult to deal with in any clean operational way. Furthermore, it is our belief that attention paid even to such an elemental and simply-measured variable as gross differences in amount of stored information with respect to the object would lead to a large number of important and experimentally verifiable generalizations in the area of attitude change. While all of these generalizations would revolve around the core proposition that attitudes toward objects of high centrality are harder to change, *ceteris paribus*, than are attitudes toward objects of low centrality, many sub-propositions could be tested which would advance our understanding of the mediating processes.

Take, for example, the notion of incredulity, with which all students of the persuasion process have been obliged to deal in one way or another, at least as an appended correction function. While it is undoubtedly true, as many have observed, that the location of a point of incredulity in any given case depends in some degree on the distance between the individual's own attitude position and that represented by the message, it seems likely that the location of such a point must depend as heavily upon the amount of information held by the subject with respect to the attitude-object prior to the receipt of the message. Thus the impact of the message should be greater if it contains information new to the subject, rather than old and incorporated (or subjectively discredited) information. And of course the probability that *any* given message will contain arguments new to the subject is logically the perfect inverse of the amount of information he already holds relative to the object. Similarly, the subject's implicit estimate as to the reliability of the sender as a source of information would seem likely to vary widely according to the ratio of own stored information to the apparent amount of information which the sender possesses on the subject. Even an opinionated amateur may feel obliged to credit the contrary information of an expert; an expert may discredit new information transmitted by an obvious amateur even though it implies support for some of his predispositions. In short, then, the amount of information the individual has stored about the object prior to the persuasion attempt should profoundly modify the course of such a process, and the introduction of such a factor in experimental studies would help illuminate the phenomenon of incredulity as well as the more general aspects of susceptibility to attitude change.

The Rosenberg-Abelson discussion (in Hovland and Rosenberg, 1960) of microprocesses underlying the redress of cognitive imbalance, resting as it does upon a procedure of "search" through the "cognitive files," can yield a variety of other propositions worth experimental test with amount of information as a measured variable. And even earlier in the process, it is likely that the individual who is well-informed about an object of controversy can screen out channels of potential incoming information more effectively from "afar" than the more poorly-informed bystander. The well-informed person *knows* which newspaper columnists are so wrong they are not worth reading; the poorly informed person, while less likely to read any columnists, perhaps, will be unable to exercise such knowledgeable selection on the occasions when he does.

Much more generally, the whole notion of centrality, cognitive or motivational, would seem crucial for balance theories in predictions of *which* attitude will change (or will change *more*) when the familiar triangle of valences (such as between self-other-object or self-source-message) becomes imbalanced. When attitudes toward one or the other external object must change to restore balance, the less central of the two should undergo the primary adjustment. To some degree, the precise predictions of the Osgood congruity model can be taken as implying this very thing. However, this implication follows only if it be true that objects which are extremely central for any individual (e.g., "mother," "self") cannot be the object of ambivalent feelings, but are necessarily the objects of extreme, univocal attitudes. As indicated above, however, we are reluctant to accept this assumption, and would enjoy seeing what difference might occur in experimental results if there were greater assurance that the center of the Osgood scales relative to the remote objects used in attitude-change studies were restricted to the ambivalent, with non-attitudes discarded. However, the basic generalization about centrality and balance would seem an important one.

Without too many additional assumptions, it can be deduced from balance theory itself that when the attitude toward one of two objects must change, the object which is the less central (as we have defined the matter) is more likely to undergo change. This can be seen by taking account of the fact that objects involved in the balance triangle are also involved in cognitive associations with other objects as well. Festinger (1957) has suggested that a cognitive element which is dissonant with some other may resist change toward consonance because such change would create other dissonances. Since the more central the object, the more numerous and active are its associative bonds with other cognitive objects, it follows directly that change in attitude toward the less central of two objects will result in fewer new imbalances with further associated cognitive systems. Imbalance being unpleasant, such change will be preferred if any occurs at all.

In addition to the possibility of changing own attitudes toward one or another of two objects, such as a source and a message or another person and an object of mutual attention, a further mode of redressing imbalance involves some dissociation of the external objects or refusal to accept the immediate evidence which associates them in a way creating imbalance. The role which object centrality plays in this broader scheme of possibilities might well be the following:

Relative centrality of attitude objects *A* and *B*	Outcome of imbalance
1) *A* more central than *B*	Attitude toward *B* changes
2) *A* and *B* of equal *low* centrality	Imbalance not noticed or, if noticed, readily tolerated
3) *A* and *B* of equal *high* centrality	Some form of dissociation or denial of external evidence concerning *A–B* bond

The assumptions underlying this scheme are not particularly new, and indeed are at least implicit in most discussions of the subject. Dissonance theory posits quite directly that the subjective importance (or centrality) of the objects involved in the dissonant relationship not only guides the outcome of the attitude change, but also is a key determinant of the intensity of the discomfort which the dissonance occasions. Similarly, discussions of pressures toward the restoration of balance through attitude change often append the observation that these pressures presuppose that the objects are of some concern to the individual (item 2). It might be observed as well that most treatments of dynamic conflict which involve notable reality distortions are concerned principally with attitude-objects which are extremely central for the individual (the self, intimate associates, crucially valued objects), and hence operate almost exclusively in the domain defined by item 3.[8]

What we wish to stress, then, is less the novelty of the scheme than the gross discrepancy between the widespread common-sense assumption in discursive and theoretical work that some such dimension plays a prime modifying role in situations of incongruity or imbalance, and the scanty experimental attention paid to it.[9] We know very little in a systematic way about the truth of this bit of common sense. We know little as well about the sources of variation in centrality of the same objects for different people.

Nor, we may note in closing, do we know how flagrantly we have "cut corners" on reality in the foregoing discussion by dealing with cognitive and motivational centrality as though they represented a unitary dimension. The short-term defense for this tactic is a simple one: across the universe of possible attitude-objects for any given individual, the empirical correlation by object between the two types of centrality is certain to be very high. That is, experimental results, survey results and common sense join in suggesting that objects which are motivationally central to a person are likely to be cognitively central to him as well; and objects that are not central in one sense are not likely to be central in the other. Hence our blurring of the difference between the two types of centrality can suffice as a first approximation. But in the degree of fit between the two lie issues which seem of fundamental theoretical importance, yet which the survey analyst is ill-equipped to illuminate. Perhaps a resumption of our dialogue at a later date can include commentary on this score as well.

NOTES

1. All correlation coefficients cited in this paper are Kendall tau-betas (see Kendall, 1955) computed on square ($k \times k$) tables. For the benefit of the reader more accustomed to the Pearson product-moment coefficients, we might note that with non-pathological bivariate distributions, the Pearson coefficient computed on the same tables with linear scoring tends to give consistently liberal (high) estimates of the degree of association, relative to the tau-beta. The difference between the two estimates is slight (.02) in the low ranges (correlations of .1 or .2) but increases

considerably in the higher ranges, so that a tau-beta coefficient of .75 might be interpreted as a Pearson coefficient of .85 or .90.

2.   This rather reliable property has deeply impressed other survey analysts dealing with panel data. See, for example, Wiggins (1955).

3.   It should be noted that the initial test was carried out in a preconceived format with little attention to the fact that the test might have been carried out in alternative formats. The alternatives depend primarily on the way in which the data may be collapsed to carry out the critical test. That is, the attitude turnover tables for t_1–t_2 must inevitably be reduced from their "raw" format (5 × 5 matrices) to a 2 × 2 format, with the tiny handful of "undecideds" dropping out of the middle row and column of the table, if one is to define the two subsets of the population necessary to make the test. The question arises as to what size tables should be employed in computing the t_2–t_3 rank-order correlations. Initially we computed these critical correlations for the two test groups on the basis of 4 × 4 tables, utilizing the maximal remaining information. The results of this test are the ones cited in the text. Later we ran the computations a second time, evaluating the t_2–t_3 correlations on the basis of collapsed 2 × 2 tables, rather than the 4 × 4 form. The results of this test are slightly less pretty, as the t_2–t_3 correlation for the random group slips somewhat farther off the "dead center" of .000 into the negative correlation region, although the departure is not great ($-.05$). Another version of the test, suggested by Wiggins (1955), also utilizes only the dichotomous responsibility over the three time points. Here one posits a three-class response model:

	Probability of a "plus" response
Class I	$.5 + a$
Class II	$.5$
Class III	$.5 - a$

Then one uses the configuration of three-stage data to solve for a. The issue item under discussion yields an estimate of .52 for a, which once again is essentially indistinguishable from our black-and-white model.

4.   These felt difficulties are true not only of items requiring attitude locations, but also of measurements of a perceptual or personality type, which require a location of oneself, others, or other objects on some judgmental dimension. Once again, where the investigator's dimension is some very customary item in my own evaluative toolkit, such locations are easy to make, and I would feel that I could reproduce them at a later date quite accurately. If, however, the dimension involved is not one in terms of which I customarily locate objects, even though I may understand its meaning, the search process is more tedious, and I have less faith that I could reproduce my responses short of rote memory of the response marked before.

5.   The usage here departs notably from that developed for the same term by Rokeach (1960).

6. Of course it is scarcely coincidental that the concept of ego-involved attitudes came to be emphasized in an earlier moment of collaboration between the sample-survey and experimental traditions. The fact that we have come upon the matter from the opposing pole—that of non-attitudes—should not conceal the fact that sample surveys were proffering the same indications about attitude change twenty years ago that we wish to develop in more detail here.

7. Brehm and Cohen discuss Zimbardo's (1960) experimental manipulation of "issue importance" as one of the infrequent examples. This manipulation clearly operationalizes decision-importance (second sense) and not element-importance. Indeed, in explicating the experiment, Brehm and Cohen are forced to rely on *unmanipulated* differences in amount of "prior commitment" to various presumed cognitive elements in the decision. And here momentarily their "prior commitment" means precisely what we mean by centrality, and probably Festinger's "importance" (first sense). (See Brehm and Cohen, 1962, especially pp. 58–59.)

8. We exclude from consideration here the apparent reality distortions demonstrable with objects of slight centrality which represent casual guesses in the absence of objective information rather than a more dynamic defense against a clear and present reality.

9. One of the few clear exceptions is Pilisuk (1962). Although the centrality dimension is not used as an experimental variable, the experimental hypothesis has to do with resistance to change of attitudes toward highly central objects after induction of some imbalance. Hence the experimental design lies within the class of situations defined by item (3) in the schema above. The results—that attitudes toward the key objects do not change, but that the subjects doubt the genuineness of the situation or rationalize in a variety of ways to "decouple" the imbalanced terms—fall generally within our expectations.

REFERENCES

Brehm, J., and A. R. Cohen, *Explorations in Cognitive Dissonance*, New York: Wiley, 1962.

Brim, O. G., "Attitude Content-Intensity," *American Sociological Review* 20 (1955), 68–76.

Festinger, L., *A Theory of Cognitive Dissonance*, Stanford: Stanford U. Press, 1957.

Hartley, E. L., *Problems in Prejudice*, New York: King's Crown Press, 1946.

Hovland, C. I., "Reconciling Conflicting Results Derived from Experimental and Survey Studies of Attitude Change," *American Psychologist* 14 (1959), 8–17.

Hovland, C. I., O. J. Harvey, and M. Sherif, "Assimilation and Contrast Effects in Reactions to Communication and Attitude Change," *Journal of Abnormal and Social Psychology* 55 (1957), 244–252.

Hovland, C. I., and M. Rosenberg, Eds., *Attitude Organization and Change*, New Haven, Conn.: Yale U. Press, 1960.

Katz, D., "The Functional Approach to the Study of Attitudes," *Public Opinion Quarterly* 24 (1960), 163–204.

Kendall, M., *Rank Correlation Methods*, New York: Hafner, 1955.

Lorge, I., "Gen-like: Halo or Reality," *Psychological Bulletin* **34** (1937), 545–546.

Newcomb, T. M., "An Approach to the Study of Communicative Acts," *Psychological Review* **60** (1953), 393–404.

Osgood, C. E., and P. H. Tannenbaum, "The Principle of Congruity in the Prediction of Attitude Change," *Psychological Review* **62** (1955), 42–55.

Osgood, C. E., G. J. Suci, and P. H. Tannenbaum, *The Measurement of Meaning*, Urbana: Univ. of Illinois Press, 1957.

Pilisuk, M., "Cognitive Balance and Self-Relevant Attitudes," *Journal of Abnormal and Social Psychology* **65** (1962), 95–103.

Rokeach, M., *The Open and Closed Mind*, New York: Basic Books, 1960.

Rosenberg, M. J., "Cognitive Structure and Attitudinal Affect," *Journal of Abnormal and Social Psychology* **53** (1956) 367–372.

Rosenberg, M. J., "Cognitive Reorganization in Response to the Hypnotic Reversal of Attitudinal Affect," *Journal of Personality* **28** (1960), 39–63.

Sarnoff, I., and D. Katz, "The Motivational Bases of Attitude Change," *Journal of Abnormal and Social Psychology* **49** (1954), 115–124.

Sherif, M., and H. Cantril, *The Psychology of Ego Involvements*, New York: Wiley, 1947.

Wiggins, L. M., "Mathematical Models for the Interpretation of Attitudes and Behavior Change: The Analysis of Multi-Wave Panels," unpublished doctoral dissertation, Columbia University, 1955.

Zimbardo, P. G., "Involvement and Communication Discrepancy as Determinants of Opinion Change," *Journal of Abnormal and Social Psychology* **60** (1960), 86–94.

3 / ECONOMIC
    AND
    AGGREGATE
    ANALYSIS

MEASURING INEQUALITY

HAYWARD R. ALKER, JR.

Diluting the weight of votes because of place of residence impairs basic constitutional rights under the 14th Amendment, just as much as invidious discrimination based upon factors such as race . . . or economic status. . . .

EARL WARREN, *former Chief Justice of the Supreme Court*

Political philosophers have always tried to describe the goals of political communities. Modern political analysis has translated this quest into the problems of clarifying goals and evaluating policy alternatives. These goals are in turn described as differing value distributions, such as the various ways in which wealth, political power, and educational opportunities might be shared in our society.

Those primarily concerned with describing and explaining political behavior are faced with problems similar to those of political philosophers. Empirical researchers need to conceptualize and describe actual value outcomes in different political associations.

Both normative philosophers and empirical theorists must solve similar measurement problems—one group of scholars must carefully evaluate the alternatives they envision while the other needs accurately to assess the situations at hand. Practicing politicians, who are not always able to divide themselves so nicely into philosophic and hardheaded parts, are faced with both problems at once—they have frequently to compare the world as it is with the world as they would like it to be.

Because mathematical concepts may be defined independently of any particular content, they may be applied to a wide range of actual or potential value distributions. After defining and relating several mathematical ways of measuring the degree to which values are shared, in this chapter we shall apply them to politically relevant experience: legislative malapportionment, American income distributions before and after taxes, and racial imbalance in the public schools of New Haven, Connecticut. These situations all reveal inequalities— unequally shared values such as votes, wealth, and white classmates. In each case, actual situations will be evaluated in terms of various policy goals and alternatives.

A. Mathematical Definitions of Inequality

Examples from the literature of politics. Ways in which value inequalities can be measured have frequently been mentioned in the literature of politics. A brief review of a few of these suggestions will help to bring some of their central aspects into focus.

We may recall how justice was defined by Pythagoras, Plato, and Aristotle in mathematical terms. Injustice was considered to be the lack of justice, or the violation of the various mathematical equalities with which justice was associated. Aristotle mentioned several norms against which actual injustice might be compared. One of them was the idea of democratic equality:

■ The democratic conception of justice is the enjoyment of arithmetical equality, and not the enjoyment of proportionate equality on the basis of desert [i.e., merit, as Aristotle himself would have preferred]. On this arithmetical conception of justice the masses must necessarily be sovereign . . . ■

In ideal agricultural democracies:

■ Equality *might* be taken to mean that the poorer class should exercise no greater authority than the rich, or in other words, that sovereignty . . . [should be] equally vested in all the citizens on a numerical basis. [Then] the upholders of democracy could afford to believe that equality—and liberty—was really achieved by their constitution. ■

Assuming that there are two classes which compose the state—the wealthy class and the poor, and that both classes should obey the will of the "major part" of the entire state, Aristotle suggests how justice would be secured:

■ [In the case when the majorities of each class disagree] we may attribute sovereignty to the will of a majority of persons *who are also the owners of a majority of property.* . . . Suppose that 6 of the 10 [members of the wealthy class] have arrived at a decision conflicting with that of 15 of the 20 [poor]. This means that the minority of 4 in the wealthy class agrees with the majority in the poorer class. . . . In that case sovereignty should rest with the will of that side [be it the side of the 6 + 5 or of the 15 + 4] whose members on both of its elements being added together, have property in excess of that belonging to the members of the other.[1] ■

Jean Jacques Rousseau distinguished between "natural inequality" and "moral or political inequality" arising out of the conventions of human society. The latter he defined as consisting of

■ the different privileges, which some men enjoy to the prejudice of others; such as that of being more rich, more honoured, more powerful or even in a position to exact obedience.[2] ■

Finally, recall Lasswell's definition of an elite.

■ The influential are those who get the most of what there is to get. Available values may be classified as *deference, income, safety*. Those who get the most are *elite;* the rest are *mass.*[3] ■

Several conclusions emerge from a reading of these and other authors.

1. *Inequalities relevant to politics include those in several different value categories.* Rousseau's list mentions power, wealth, and honor (social respect), which will be studied below. Lasswell's multivalued scheme of analysis would also include skill, intellectual enlightenment, affection (family and friendship), physical and mental well-being, and moral rectitude.

2. *Political worth, or value, can at least in theory be measured with the accuracy of a ratio or an interval scale.* In his theory of proportionate equality, Aristotle implies that merit or "desert" can be measured on a ratio scale. Otherwise political representation or other rewards could not be rationed out in proportion to individual worth. The example of democratic sovereignty defined in terms of "a majority of property" also requires quantitative measurement, for if citizens' properties could only be ranked in their value, adding and subtracting these values would not be allowed by the logical rules of ordinal measurement. Aristotle could not meaningfully add the wealth of rich or poor property owners unless their worth (i.e., property) was measured on at least an interval scale.[4]

3. *Equality and inequality can be ascribed to either individuals or collectivities.* Rousseau, for example, focuses on those individuals with more "privileges" than others. For Aristotle injustice can mean inequality between two classes in society.

4. *Individual values may be absolutely or contextually defined.* Political worth may accrue equally to every individual citizen, or it might be defined proportionately with respect to some average share of privilege or merit.

5. In studying inequality, *it is useful to cumulate both values and individuals.* Both Aristotle and Lasswell suggest adding values so that the compared populations or values constitute a majority of citizens or a major part of the values concerned.

A mathematical formalization. Mathematically all of the above injunctions are easy to follow. Because pure mathematics is content-free, a set of mathematical formulas for describing equality and measuring departures from it may easily be applied to different kinds of values. Both actual and desired value positions of symbolically identified individuals and groups will be defined on interval or ratio scales. If these values have these measurement properties, subtracting from them or dividing them by average or proportionate value shares should not raise any difficulty. Finally, as will be illustrated below, cumulating values held by certain proportions of the population is a key idea in the assessment of the overall inequality of a particular value distribution. Geometrically and alge-braically, cumulative value distributions suggest a great variety of politically relevant measures of inequality.

Let us imagine a universe U consisting of values and individuals. Let us label each individual out of a total population of N members by an integer i (where i may equal $1, 2, \ldots$, or N). The values held by each individual will be denoted v_i and *assumed* to have the properties of either interval or ratio scales. We shall also assume that the total values in the universe (symbolized by V) equals the sum of the values held by its individual members. Using the capital form of the Greek letter *sigma* (Σ) as a summation sign, this assumption can be stated as a symbolic equation:

$$\sum_{i=1}^{N} v_i = v_1 + v_2 + \ldots + v_N = V \tag{1}$$

This equation may be read: "the sum of all v_i (from $i = 1$ all the way up to $i = N$) is equal to V."

We shall complicate our imaginary universe by also assuming that it can be completely divided up into NG distinct groups of individuals. Individuals in each group will be assumed to have equal value shares. These additional assumptions can be symbolically stated; letting j be an integer identifying any particular group ($j = 1, 2, \ldots$, or NG), we shall denote the equal values held by each member of group j as v_j. The number or frequency of members in group j will be symbolized by f_j. Equation (2) below indicates that total group membership adds up to the total population N. The next equation shows that multiplying each group's size by the typical value belonging to any of its members, and then summing these results for all groups, gives the value total of the universe, i.e., V.

$$\sum_{j=1}^{NG} f_j = N \tag{2}$$

$$\sum_{j=1}^{NG} f_j v_j = V \tag{3}$$

Each of these summations is for all groups ($j = 1, 2, \ldots$, and NG).

A final definition in translating the analysis of value distributions into mathe-matical symbols will be some way of identifying the norms or standards that are theoretically expected of an individual or group. Both moral philosophers and factual observers must compare actual distributions with those they normatively or empirically expect. For any individual i (or group j), let these expectations be symbolized by a subscripted (e_i or e_j). Mathematically, *equality means that for each individual or group the value held corresponds to the value he is expected to have:*

$$v_i = e_i \quad (i = 1, 2, \ldots, \text{and } N) \tag{4}$$

For simplicity this and subsequent concepts and their symbolic definitions will be given only for individuals, although similar statements about v_j and e_j will usually apply.

Democratic equality and proportionate equality each suggest different formulas for calculating an individual's expected value position (his e_i). Letting a v with a bar over it symbolize the *average value held* $[\bar{v} = (1/N) \sum\limits_{i=1}^{N} v_i]$, the norm of democratic equality requires each individual to have the same average amount of values:

$$e_i = \bar{v} \quad (i = 1, 2, \ldots, \text{and } N) \tag{5}$$

Proportionate equality, on the other hand, requires that values be distributed in a presumably unequal fashion according to other individual characteristics, such as merit, property, knowledge, etc. (No end of debate is in sight, to be sure, on which other characteristics are appropriate, but this is not the immediate mathematical problem.) If individual merit is symbolically denoted m_i, Aristotle would expect values (like political power) to be distributed according to a constant proportion of merit:

$$e_i = k \times m_i \quad (i = 1, 2, \ldots, \text{and } N) \tag{6}$$

In Equation (6) k is a constant of proportion relating units of normatively expected value to units of merit.

As we shall see below, *the basic element in all mathematical definitions of inequality is some measure of the extent to which v_i does not equal e_i*. In measuring inequality we should look for the extent to which Equation (3.4) is not in fact true, using either Equation (5) or Equation (6) or some other formula to define the norm of equality.

A point of considerable importance is that, even when someone does not morally accept the goal of democratic equality, he might be willing to describe degrees of inequality in terms of deviations from the egalitarian ideal. A similar remark holds for the operationally more difficult concept of proportionate equality, a norm that will not be fully explored in the discussions below. Thus either kind of norm may serve as a theoretically useful standard for either moral or factual comparisons.

Measures of individual inequality. What does it mean to say that someone is more powerful? Or enjoying more than proportionate equality in public rewards? These questions can be answered in several ways.

1. *Value differences and ratios.* We know that for interval measures of power, comparisons can be made according to interval differences. Values measured on ratio scales can even be divided or multiplied by other values in a meaningful way. Consider two individuals, Tom and Dick. Inequalities between them could be expressed as differences or ratios, that is, by

$$v_{\text{Tom}} - v_{\text{Dick}} \quad \text{or} \quad v_{\text{Tom}}/v_{\text{Dick}}$$

Tom, for example, might be 10 units more powerful, or two times more powerful than Dick.

If Tom and Dick were, respectively, the *most powerful* and *least powerful* individuals, their value difference (called a *range*) or their value ratio (called the *ratio of largest to smallest* values) would indicate the extremes of the entire population.[5]

2. *Differences from the average.* Using the definition of democratic equality in Equation (5), individual inequality can be defined by subtracting from actual values held the expected, i.e. the average, level of values held in the population. Those with above average value positions could be considered "privileged," while those below average are clearly "discriminated against." Because for universes different from U the average value $(\bar{v})$ may be of a different level, $v_i - \bar{v}$ may take on different values in different universes. In other words, the meaning of privilege and discrimination depends on the context for which they are defined.

3. *Ratios of advantage.* Values defined according to ratio scales can meaningfully be divided by value standards. Ratios of advantage $(v_i/\bar{v})$ can also be thought of as contextually defined indices of individual privilege or discrimination.

An interesting comparison between interval and ratio scales of measurement arises at this point. Interval scales with arbitrary zero points cannot meaningfully be divided or multiplied by other interval scales. What about intervally measured differences from an average? The answer is yes, *if* the mean (i.e., average) value in a particular distribution is considered a non-arbitrary zero point. Measuring inequality against an egalitarian ideal means does just this. Value positions are redefined as above or below average, i.e., as privileged or discriminatory. The expression $v_i - \bar{v}$ now has a meaningful zero point (perfect equality) even if the original value scale of the v_i did not.

If we want to compare these differences in two different universes, we could standardize them, dividing them by their respective $\bar{v}$'s. Symbolically, such an expression would be

$$\frac{v_i - \bar{v}}{\bar{v}} = \frac{v_i}{\bar{v}} - 1 \tag{7}$$

It turns out from the algebraic manipulation indicated in Equation (7) that expressing *differences* as fractions of an overall standard gives results very similar to *ratios* of advantage. In fact, subtracting 1 from a ratio of advantage gives a standardized difference from a mean. We need not know whether v_i is really twice as big as $\bar{v}$ in order to say that the differences from a mean are an exact proportion of the mean. This result will be very helpful in comparing different ways of measuring inequality in entire value distributions.

Cumulative measures of inequality. Cumulative measures enable the observer to measure the fraction of total values held by various proportions of the population. When presented geometrically, they suggest a great variety of individual and collective measures of inequality.

1.   *The Lorenz curve.* Cumulative value distributions start by ranking all individuals according to their ratios of advantage. Ratios for groups of individuals can be calculated by an equivalent procedure, dividing the percentage of values they hold by the percentage of population they represent. Starting with those most discriminated against, a line is drawn representing the total percentage of values held by increasingly larger percentages of the population. A hypothetical curve of this sort, called a Lorenz curve, is shown in Figure 1.

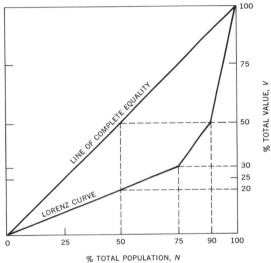

1   A Lorenz Curve of values held by cumulative proportions of a population.

In the picture as drawn the Σv_i for the poorest half of the population is only 20 per cent of V, while on the other hand, the wealthiest 10 per cent of the population has 50 per cent of obtainable values. Going along the Lorenz curve in this fashion indicates in a comprehensive way the extent to which various groups have more or less than their proportionate share of values.

The 45-degree line in Figure 1 represents a norm of complete, democratic equality. It indicates how values *should* be distributed if all v_i were actually equal to $\bar{v}$. As shown in the figure, complete equality means that both the poorest and wealthiest halves of the population have equal shares of the universe's total values. Other moral or factual expectations could be represented in a similar manner. Some other Lorenz curve, perhaps even the one drawn in Figure 1, could be used as a standard for evaluating the overall pattern of inequality. In fact, if the curved line in Figure 1 resulted from a distribution of values according to Aristotle's calculations of merit and Equation (6), then he could say that an *actual* cumulative distribution looking like the line of equality was far too egalitarian!

2.   *The slopes curve.* Both ratios of advantage and differences from the average can be measured on a Lorenz curve. To show why this is true, it will only be necessary to talk about ratios of advantage [because of the equivalence between

these two kinds of measures established in Equation (7) above]. *The basic result is that ratios of advantage are slopes of a Lorenz curve.* It is easy to explain why this is so. A slope of a line is obtained by dividing a vertical rise by the corresponding horizontal distance. For a particular individual this ratio is the percentage of the total values he holds divided by the percentage of the total population he represents, i.e.,

$$\frac{100\left(v_i \bigg/ \sum_{i=1}^{N} v_i\right)}{100(1/N)}$$

Reducing this expression to simplest terms gives the ratio of advantage $v_i/\bar{v}$. Slopes of the Lorenz curve may be approximated visually or plotted separately, as shown in Figure 2.

3.   *The equal share coefficient.* An important change in the Lorenz curve occurs when its slope, the ratio of advantage, equals and begins to exceed one. People to the right of this point of the curve get more than an equal share in the allocation of values. People to the left get less than their (equal) share. It is thus possible to define an *equal share coefficient* as equal to the percentage of the population getting something less than an equal share of values. In Figure 1, this would be 75 per cent of the population. Bruce Russett and the present author have suggested interpreting the remaining population percentage (in this case 25 per cent) as the size of the middle and upper classes. *In egalitarian terms, the equal share coefficient measures the percentage size of the underprivileged population.*[6] Certainly, where a society is polarized into two classes such an interpretation would be appropriate. In other, more complicated universes, *double-share* or *triple-share coefficients* might also be useful.

4.   *The minimal majority.* Lasswell's definition of an elite identifies those who get the *most*, not those who get more than an equal share. If our value units were legislative votes, it would be equivalent to refer to a *minimal majority*, the smallest number of individuals controlling a majority of the legislature. For the Lorenz curve in Figure 1, the minimal majority is 10 per cent of the population. In a similar fashion one could measure the size of the population holding the top 10 per cent of values, and so on.

5.   *Summing differences and ratios.* Measures using more information regarding a cumulative value distribution are likely to be more reliable in characterizing entire distributions. Summing value differences or ratios of advantages give more comprehensive measures of inequality than indices like the range or the largest/smallest ratio defined above.

What differences and ratios might we sum? Three possibilities suggested by the Lorenz curve come to mind, each of which leads to a famous measure of inequality. First, for interval level measurements, why not sum differences from value standards—as defined in Equation (4)? In the case where the e_i's equal $\bar{v}$ however, summing for all i is of no avail:

$$\sum_{i=1}^{N} (v_i - \bar{v}) = \sum_{i=1}^{N} v_i - \sum_{i=1}^{N} \bar{v} = N \cdot \frac{\Sigma v_i}{N} - N \cdot \bar{v} = 0 \tag{8}$$

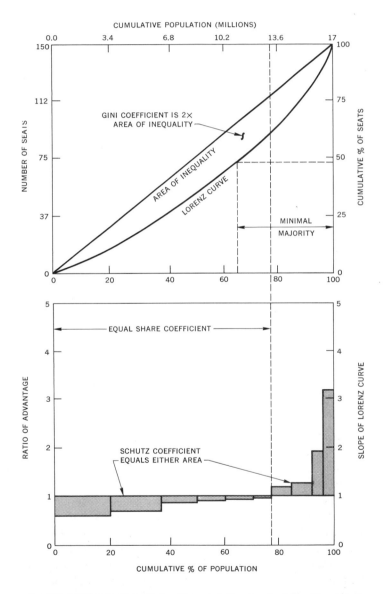

2   A Lorenz Curve and related "Slopes Curve" for the apportionment of the New York State Assembly 1960. (*Source: See note* 10)

Equation (8) shows that the mean value $\bar{v}$ has the property that summing deviations on both sides of the mean will always give 0! On the average, the negative deviations cancel out the positive ones. A more meaningful approach would be to sum deviations, *ignoring their signs*. The mean deviation measure of inequality has been defined in just this way, dividing by the number of cases:

$$\text{Mean deviation} = \frac{1}{N} \cdot \sum_{i=1}^{N} |v_i - \bar{v}| \tag{9}$$

The vertical bars in this expression refer to the absolute (positive) value of the difference $v_i - \bar{v}$, regardless of whether it is positive or negative.

If the v_i varied widely, so would their mean deviation. To facilitate comparison of value distributions, expressions like the above are often normalized or standardized so as to range between 0 and 1. A *normalized mean deviation* can be defined in this manner as

$$\text{Normalized mean deviation} = \frac{\sum_{i=1}^{N} |v_i - \bar{v}|}{\sum_{i=1}^{N} v_i} \tag{10}$$

Because of the identity between a normalized $(v_i - \bar{v})/\bar{v}$ and $(v_i/\bar{v}) - 1$, it is not surprising that summing ratios of advantage, i.e. adding the slopes of different segments of a Lorenz curve, will give a coefficient essentially the same as the normalized mean *deviation*. To avoid the problem of summing to zero, it is necessary to sum the ratio $v_i/\bar{v}$ only where it is greater than or less than one, but not both. *R. R. Schutz's coefficient of inequality*, a second type of summing measure, sums ratios of advantage above *or* below the equal share point (at which $v_i = \bar{v}$):

$$\text{Schutz coefficient} = \sum_{v_i \geq \bar{v}} \left(\frac{v_i}{\bar{v}} - 1\right) \Delta X_i = \sum_{v_i \leq \bar{v}} \left(1 - \frac{v_i}{\bar{v}}\right) \Delta X_i \tag{11}$$

In Equation (11) the summations are above or below the equal share point of the population. For individuals, ΔX_i, read "delta-X sub i," is either the percentage $100 \cdot \frac{1}{N}$ or the simple fraction $\frac{1}{N}$. The equivalence between the two expressions in Equation (11) can be easily derived from Equation (8).[7]

As an indication of the degree of inequality evidenced by the cumulative distribution, it is geometrically appealing to calculate the area between the Lorenz curve and the line of equality. Dividing this *"area of inequality" by its maximum size* gives a third measure, *Gini's coefficient of inequality*. Said another way, the Gini index sums, for each individual in the population, the difference between where he is on the Lorenz curve and where he would be expected to be in the case of democratic equality. This sum is divided by its maximum possible value so that the Gini coefficient ranges between 0 and 1.

Mathematically, the formula for the Gini index can most easily be expressed in terms of two fractional variables X_i and Y_i, corresponding respectively, to coordinates of the horizontal and vertical axes of a Lorenz diagram (as in Figure 1):

$$X_i = \frac{i}{N} \quad \text{and} \quad Y_i = \sum_{k \leq i} v_k / V \tag{12}$$

To compute the area between the actual cumulative distribution and the standard 45-degree line of equality, one can sum the areas of rectangles representing cumulatively the inequality of each individual or group. Let the height of the line of equality corresponding to the location of an individual i, be E_i. It will in fact equal the sum of all democratically expected values of individuals to the left of i, expressed as a fraction of the value total V. Using k as a convenient index of summation for these people [as in Equation (12)], thus

$$E_i = \sum_{k \leq i} e_k / V \tag{13}$$

Finally, for each individual, we need to know the width of his vertical segment of the area of inequality. This answer—let us again call it ΔX_i—is just that fraction of the X axis where he belongs:

$$\Delta X_i = X_i - X_{i-1} \quad (i = 1, \ldots, N) \tag{14}$$

When $i - 1 = 0$, X is of course 0.

With these conventions, adopted so that both axes range from 0 to 1, it is possible to give three equivalent definitions of the Gini index. The maximum value of the area above the cumulative Lorenz curve is that of the triangle beneath the line of equality: one-half its base times its height. If percentages along the axes are used, this amounts to 5,000; in fractional terms, a simpler value of $\frac{1}{2}$ can be employed. Normalizing (dividing) the actual area of inequality by $\frac{1}{2}$ we have

$$\text{Gini index} = 2 \cdot \text{area of inequality} \tag{15a}$$

Expressing this area approximately as the sum of rectangles with heights $E_i - Y_i$ and widths ΔX_i,

$$\text{Gini index} = 2 \sum_{i=1}^{N} (E_i - Y_i) \Delta X_i \tag{15b}$$

Since we are assuming here that the E_i forms a straight line, the line of complete equality with a slope of 1, the E_i will, for our purposes, equal $1 \cdot X_i$. Therefore, we have

$$\text{Gini index} = 2 \sum_{i=1}^{N} (X_i - Y_i) \Delta X_i \tag{15c}$$

B. Unequal Votes, Taxes, and Schools

The *abstractness* of the mathematical ideas like those in the above hypo-thetical exercise accounts for the wide range of their applicability. As ways of describing and evaluating various policy alternatives several of the measures defined above will now be applied to a variety of political situations. We have already seen how the Lorenz curve presentation of cumulative distributions allows explicit, visual comparisons between *actual* and empirically or normatively *expected* value distributions. This feature of Lorenz curves (and of the corres-ponding slopes curves) strongly recommend their use in political analysis. In the example below, a Lorenz curve for legislative malapportionment, a slopes curve for alternative public tax laws, and a Lorenz curve comparing actual racial imbalance with a proposed solution illustrate the value of this approach.[8]

Legislative malapportionment in New York.   In their epic 1964 decision on legislative apportionment (*Reynolds* v. *Sims*, etc.) the Supreme Court majority declared that "the fundamental principle of representative government in this country is one of equal representation for equal numbers of people, without regard to race, sex, economic status, or place of residence within a state."[9] Both houses of state legislature were required to meet this test, and as a result appor-tionments in Alabama, New York, Maryland, Virginia, Delaware, and Colorado were held unconstitutional. Many of the arguments by the majority of the Court used some of the measures of inequality that have already been discussed. We shall illustrate them and several alternatives by reference to a Lorenz curve and the corresponding slopes curve for the New York State Assembly in 1960. (See Figure 2.)[10] This geometric way of describing and evaluating malapportionment is especially appropriate because the Court has accepted the norm of democratic equality, which in the Lorenz curve of Figure 2 is again indicated by a 45-degree line of equality.

One additional comment about the validity of this approach may be helpful. Justice Stewart, in dissent, asserted that "nobody's right to vote has been denied . . . nobody has been deprived of the right to have his vote counted." The major-ity, on the other hand, joined Justice Warren in saying that "diluting the weight of votes because of place of residence impairs basic rights under the 14th Amend-ment. . . ." What is the difference between these two views? One of them clearly thinks of the "right to vote" as "present" or "absent," a qualitative attribute; the other sees it as something *more* or *less* enjoyed in a quantitative fashion. If the representation of an individual from one county cannot be compared with that of another, then the following analysis would not apply. We must therefore assume that operational definitions like the fraction of seats per population fraction, or the fraction of a representative held by a voting individual, are valid measures on a ratio scale of the right to vote.

The Court asks rhetorically, "can one person be given twice or ten times the voting power of another. . . .?" In Figure 2 we see that the top 3 per cent of the population has ratios of advantage greater than 3.0. Their votes count three times as much as those of the average citizen! As shown by the slopes curve in the lower half of the figure, the next highest 5 per cent of the population is about twice as powerful as the average. Looking again at the Lorenz curve, we see that this top 8 per cent of the population (in absolute terms, about 1.2 million voters) has 20 per cent of the representative strength in the Assembly.

The Court is unable to "sanction minority control of state legislative bodies." Compared with other states, New York's Assembly is not atypically unequal. [11] Yet the (grouped) data in Figure 2 indicate that 35 per cent of the state's population, all from the *most* overrepresented counties, have potential majority control of the Assembly. The equal share coefficient further tells us that 77 per cent of the population is underrepresented in the legislature, although until we get down to the "poorest" or "weakest" 38 per cent, they all have approximately 90 per cent of their "right to vote" or better.[12]

What about cumulative measures of malapportionment? The minimal majority measure (which is partly cumulative) was used by the Court, and so in fact were average ratios of advantage for population subgroups. Regarding the New York Senate, the Warren opinion refers to the average population of the senatorial districts in the "populous counties" and in the "less populous counties." It goes on to say that "a citizen in a less populous county had under the 1953 apportionment, over 1.5 times the representation, on the average, of a citizen in a populous county. . . ." *The Court is thus averaging ratios of advantages, very much in the manner of a standardized mean deviation or a Schutz coefficient.* If "the less populous" counties are those below the equal share point, the correspondence would be exact, if only a denominator term were used to normalize the result. Such normalization would in fact facilitate comparisons with other states in attempting to see which suffered from a greater degree of malapportionment. The Schutz coefficient for the example is very easily obtained if we sum ratios of advantage above unity for those percentages of the population at the right end of the slopes curve: approximately it equals

$$3(3.4 - 1) + 5(2.0 - 1) + 8(1.25 - 1) + 7(1.20 - 1) = 15.6$$

The Court also refers to points on the Lorenz curve, or a rough approximation to it. They are hampered by the particulars of the case because they can only refer to the share of seats held by the counties where the appellants reside: "According to 1960 census figures, the six counties [where they reside] had a citizen population of 9,192,180, or 56.2 per cent of the . . . total. . . . They [the appellants] are currently represented by 72 Assemblymen . . . 48 per cent of the Assembly. . . ." Looking at the Lorenz curve in Figure 2, we find that the *most* underrepresentative 56 per cent of the citizen population has about 41 per cent of the Assembly seats, a more unequal situation than cumulating for the plaintives alone (our data, however, may not be strictly comparable with the Court's).

A comprehensive way of stating the *overall* inequality indicated by the Lorenz curve would be to find what proportion the actual area of inequality is of the entire possible area of inequality. The approximate value for the Gini coefficient of 0.22, indicates that New York's Assembly is 22/100 of the way to-ward complete inequality in this particular geometric sense. Other Assemblies, we suspect, would be worse.[13] Again, the Court could facilitate such comparisons by using measures (like the minimal majority, the Schutz coefficient, or the Gini coefficient) that are independent of the particular population and legislative sizes being measured.

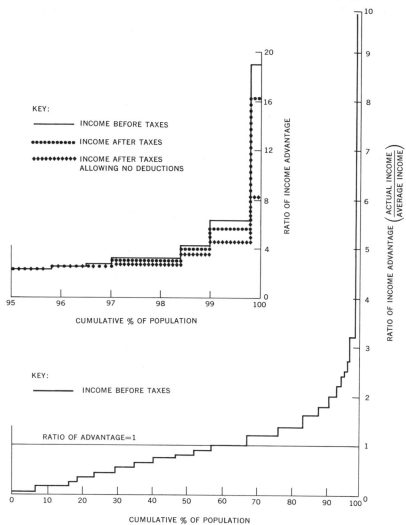

3   Ratios of income advantage before and after taxes. (*Source: See note* 15)

Income equality, before and after taxes. There is a good deal of emotional argument surrounding the extremes of wealth and poverty in any country. How burdensome the inequality of wealth is depends, of course, on the social and human costs of low incomes and the other opportunities forgone as a result of an unequal distribution of wealth. Those favoring the inequality of wealth cite its supposed stimulant effect on the poor and other favorable economic consequences, such as the excellence made possible in private and public life.

Even more emotions are energized on the subject of taxation. Poor and middle income groups complain of their burdens, asking for more "progressive" tax burdens placed on the wealthy. The defenders of the poor call for at least a partial redistribution of wealth. As a result a tax structure existed in 1960 which, after all deductions, exemptions, and capital gains and losses had been taken into account, theoretically, taxed million dollar incomes between 80 and 90 per cent. Subsequent legislation has in theory reduced these rates.

The measures we have already used to study malapportionment can also be used to study the distribution of income in American society, and the effects of our supposedly progressive tax structure.

First, it is possible to compare American income distributions with those of other countries using comprehensive indices like the Gini coefficient. Unfortunately, comparable data are not always available for this purpose. Nonetheless, in a recent careful examination of income distributions before taxes in 20 mostly developed countries, it was found that the American Gini index for 1956 was about 0.40, ranking 13th.[14] Compared with other nations, the United States does not appear atypically unequal. [Note, in passing, the interesting possibility that, if New York is typical, formal political power (representation) in a democracy may be more equally shared than income and wealth. Cumulative indices of value concentration allow provocative comparisons of value distributions in different contexts.]

What effect do taxes have on the inequality of incomes? In other words, how progressive is the tax structure—to what extent does it place heavier burdens on the rich and reduce overall income inequality? Answers to this kind of question depend heavily on the data available. Fortunately, the National Committee on Governmental Finance has recently provided more accurate answers to this kind of questions than heretofore were possible.[15] *The result of a comparison of the degree of inequality in income before and after taxes is that there was remarkably little change as a result of the then effective tax structure. To be specific, in 1960 the Gini index before taxes was 0.45, while after taxes it was 0.43!*

Plotting Lorenz curves for incomes before and after taxes (as reported to the government) reveals almost no change in the slope of the curve except for a small increase in equality at the upper end of the income distribution. To get a better idea of the overall pattern involved, the slopes curve for income before taxes has been plotted in Figure 3, with an enlarged insert for the top 5 per cent of the tax returns. The average income per tax return was about $6,000. With this information we see, for example, that about 35 per cent of the tax returns showed incomes of less than half the average and that about 65 per cent of the returns showed less than this amount (this latter percentage is the size of the equal share coefficient). At the other end about 10 per cent of the returns were more than twice the average, while less than 1 per cent of the tax returns reported incomes over $60,000.

What about the effects of tax structure? Looking carefully at the insert we see that only the top 1 per cent of income receivers were noticeably diminished in their share of the wealth. Before taxes most of them had about 6 times more than average; afterwards the figure was close to 5. Among the top tenth of a per cent of the population, on the average, the decrease was also slight, from a ratio of income advantage near 19 to one close to 16. It should be clear why the Gini coefficients before and after taxes were so remarkably similar. Only the very upper end of the Lorenz curve was noticeably affected.

This remarkable stability in the income distribution, which we might expect still to hold today, suggests further explorations. First, consider the line in the insert in Figure 3 corresponding to the statement "after assumed taxes." As an interesting policy alternative incomes after taxes, *allowing no deductions of any kind*, were approximated in a computer analysis of 100,000 tax returns. The result in Figure 3 shows that incomes reported by the richest 0.10 per cent would then be cut from ratios of advantage averaging about 16 down to ratios of around 8. For the other members of the population, however, changes in the tax laws of this sort would not have had a very substantial effect. Because only about 10 per cent of the tax returns were over $12,000, steeper tax rates for those earning more than this amount were not likely to change anything but the very upper end of the Lorenz curve.

A related question concerns the actual degree of progressiveness present in the tax structure. Tax progressivism means higher percentage rates for higher income groups. It is predicated on the not unreasonable assumption (which someday may be a proposition that can be tested) that taking 50 per cent of his wealth away from a millionaire does not "hurt" as much as doing the same to someone earning 4,000 dollars. The opposite situation, where the rich pay their taxes at lower percentages than the poor, is called "regressive."

In Figure 4 effective taxes, in percentages of income given to the Federal government, are plotted on what is known as a semilog graph. (The horizontal axis increases logarithmically, not simply additively, giving a better look at the upper end of the income distribution.) Three alternative curves have been plotted: the "no deductions" hypothetical rate; the rate that would result if exemptions, deductions, and sick pay were allowed; and, finally, actual tax rates allowing all deductions, including capital gains credits. Progressive tax rates occur in those ranges where the height of a rate curve increases with increasing income level. The *degree of progressiveness* can be measured by the *slope* of the rates curve, which gives the percentage of tax rate increase per $100,000 income increase. It should be clear to the reader that non-logarithmic graph paper would give the same numerical measure of progressiveness, but would not give the same overall visual impression of the steepness of the slope.

As mentioned earlier, tax returns below $10,000–$12,000 seem to have similar slopes before and after exemptions, etc. For these 90 per cent of all

individuals or families, capital gains do not appreciably affect their effective
tax rates. To the right of the $10,000 gross income level, however, we see that
effective tax rates under a "no deductions" tax structure and a rate structure
with "no capital gains deductions" rise quite steeply to rates between 70 and 90
per cent. *Capital gains credits, however, reduce the effective tax rates for people
earning over $100,000 by something like 50 per cent*! Compared to those below
$10,000, all higher income returns pay higher tax rates, but the remarkable
nature of the 1960 American tax structure was that for incomes between $10,000
and $50,000 it was quite steeply progressive, while for incomes between $100,000
and $1,000,000 the effective rates were actually regressive. Then they began to
go up again. Those making around $100,000 paid (on the average) about 32
per cent of their income in taxes. Those making between $500,000 and $1,000,000,
most of which was probably non-salaried income from capital gains, paid
24 per cent, while those that did better than that owed only slightly more, about
29 per cent. Senator Douglas claimed, in fact, that no one paid the hypothetical
maximum which in 1960 was a 90 per cent rate.

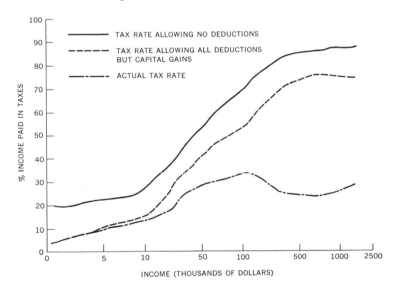

4   The effects of various deductions on the American tax structure in 1960. (*Source: See
note* 15)

Ethical judgments about Figures 3 and 4 are left to the reader. The several
hypothetical policy alternatives indicated in these figures would not appreciably
change the overall pattern of income inequality, only the very upper end. We
have found that the number of people in these ranges is very small; it appears
that tax incomes resulting from changes in current capital gains tax provisions
for individuals would not greatly alter either total government revenue or the
overall inequality of income in the United States.

Racial imbalance in New Haven's junior high schools. Racial imbalance in public education results from more than outright intimidation; in the North, as well as the South, patterns of residential segregation and the tendency to go to nearby schools are partially responsible. Other problems, like poor classroom facilities and the effect on morale of being put into a "second-class" school, are also definitely involved.

For these reasons, it is operationally difficult to define the degree of segregation present in any school in a valid and reliable way. The approach taken here will concentrate on the degree of racial imbalance in the classroom, a variable that is likely to be closely associated with many of the other aspects of educational segregation, and which often seems to be the most visible point of contention in many Northern debates over the redistricting of public schools. Operationally, the percentage of white classmates is thus assumed to be valued good, in exactly the same way that income and voting representation were in the previous illustrations.

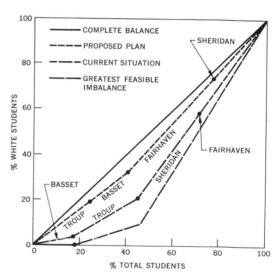

5 Four alternative patterns of racial imbalance in New Haven junior high schools.

Relevant data for four different junior high schools in New Haven, Connecticut, are given in Table 1. The numbers of whites, non-whites, and total students in each school are first presented. With these data, cumulative percentages for the entire junior high school population of New Haven can be calculated. These percentages and their ratio are given in the last three columns of the table.

It may be recalled from the previous discussion of the slopes curve that the ratio of the percentage of white students to the percentage of all students is a ratio of advantage. These ratios show that Bassett has proportionally less than one-fifth as many whites as do all the schools on the average, while Sheridan and Fair Haven have about 40 per cent more than is typical.

In Figure 5, we can consider both the cumulative extent of racial imbalance in these schools and the effects of a proposed plan for improving racial balance. Visually, unlike the tax reform alternatives mentioned previously, it is clear that the school board's proposal goes a long way toward removing racial imbalance. Whereas in June 1964 only 9 per cent of Bassett's students were white (they amounted to 3 per cent of the entire population of white students), the proposal suggests changing this proportion to 50 per cent. The proposed change is so significant that the Bassett school will no longer have the highest degree of racial imbalance. Perfect racial equality would have all four schools with whites in a 3 : 2 majority (see the totals in Table 1); the proposed plan, by hitting heavily at the worst area of inequality, would move the Lorenz curve quite close to democratic equality.

■ **Table 1.** The actual racial breakdown of students in New Haven's four junior high schools, June, 1964*

	Number of students			Cumulative percentages		
	Whites	Nonwhites	Total	% of all whites	% of all students	% whites/ % students
Bassett	55	555	610	3	17	0.18
Troup	419	415	933	19	27	0.70
Sheridan	741	148	889	34	25	1.36
Fair Haven	968	140	1,108	44	31	1.42
Total	2,183	1,357	3,540	100	100	1.0 (weighted average)

*   These data are taken from a frank and commendably courageous document issued by the New Haven Public Schools, Dr. Laurence G. Paquin, Superintendent, June 8, 1964, entitled *Proposals for Promoting Equality of Educational Opportunity and Dealing with the Problems of Racial Imbalance*, pp. 10–11. A plan similar in most respects to the proposals discussed below was eventually voted into effect by the school board.

The actual degree of improvement of racial balance can best be indicated by measures like the Gini or Schutz coefficients. After performing the calculations required by Equation (15a), we find that the current situation corresponds to a Gini index of 0.25, while the proposal as sketched in Figure 5 would mean a much smaller Gini index of 0.09. These numbers indicate that the proposal is certainly more than a "token reform": it would cut racial imbalance by more than half.

An additional way of evaluating the proposed change is with respect to the worst possible situation. The hypothetical Lorenz curve resulting from "moving" as many Negroes as possible into Bassett and Troup is also given in Figure 5.

It indicates the maximum feasible racial imbalance when school sizes are kept the same and the non-whites are kept in the non-white schools as much as possible. The Gini coefficient for this curve is about 0.40. Dividing 0.09 and 0.25 by this figure gives 0.23 and 0.63, respectively. In words, the policy alternative proposed to the New Haven School Board would decrease racial imbalance in New Haven junior high schools from 63 to 23 per cent; it would bring the school system three-quarters of the way towards the egalitarian democratic goal of complete racial balance.

NOTES

1. Ernest Barker, *The Politics of Aristotle* (New York: Oxford University Press, 1958), pp. 258–261. Italics in the original translation.

2. J. J. Rousseau, *A Dissertation on the Origin and Foundation of the Inequality of Mankind.*

3. H. D. Lasswell, *Politics: Who Gets What, When, How* (Cleveland: World Publishing Company, 1958), p. 13.

4. Operational definitions of other kinds of values of all kinds are sometimes also possible on an interval scale. Von Neuman and Morgenstern's *Theory of Games and Economic Behavior* (Princeton: Princeton University Press, 1944) gives a rigorous way of defining and measuring on an interval scale the value of events or objects to competing actors in risk-taking situations (see Chapter 7). S. S. Stevens in "Measurement, Psychophysics and Utility," in C. West Churchman and Philburn Ratoosh, *Measurement: Definitions and Theories* (New York: Wiley, 1959), suggests how values might be measured on ratio scales using an experimental approach.

5. As applied to different electoral districts, the *ratio of largest to smallest* voting representations has frequently been used to measure legislative malapportionment See, for example, Andrew Hacker, *Congressional Districting: The Issue of Equal Representation* (Washington, D.C.: The Brookings Institution, 1963), p. 23, and the sources he cites.

6. This coefficient (actually its percentage complement) was first suggested in H. R. Alker, Jr., and B. M. Russett, "On Measuring Inequality," *Behavioral Science*, 9, 3 (July 1964), pp. 207–18. Most of the remaining coefficients of inequality discussed in this chapter, and original sources, are given in this article.

7. I have also shown in Alker and Russett, *op. cit.*, that, when values and populations are expressed in percentage terms, the Schutz coefficient equals fifty times the normalized mean deviation.

8. Other measures, like the largest/smallest values ratio, lose a good deal of relevant information about the overall shape of a distribution. Even the minimal majority measure talks about a single point on a curve, but it at least appears to reflect the overall shape of a Lorenz curve more accurately than do measures based on the highest and/or lowest units alone. (See Alker and Russett, *op. cit.*, for details.) Glendon Schubert and Charles Press, "Measuring Malapportionment," *American*

Political Science Review, LVIII, 2 (June 1964), pp. 302–27, have impressively analyzed all American state legislatures using varieties of the mean deviation (involving squared, cubed and fourth-power deviations). Although their approach is commendably comprehensive, it does not lend itself so easily to graphic or verbal statements of policy alternatives defined in a cumulative fashion.

9. All quotations from this decision have been taken from *The New York Times*, June 16, 1964, pp. 28–31.

10. Data have been taken from Ruth Silva, "Apportionment of the New York State Legislature," *American Political Science Review*, LV, 4 (December 1961), pp. 870–881, Table XIV. They have been grouped into ten approximately equal categories of 15 seats each.

11. *Compendium on Apportionment* (Washington, D.C.: National Municipal League, 1962), actually indicates that 30 out of 48 state lower houses had smaller minimal majorities than did the New York Assembly.

12. Applying a rule suggested by a committee of the American Political Science Association, that all legislative districts should not depart from the average level of representation by more than 10 per cent, the slopes curve in Figure 3.2 indicates that all 23 per cent of the population above the equal share point would have to be redistricted, as would the most underrepresented 38 per cent. Other policy alternatives could of course be indicated by horizontal lines of various heights cutting across the slopes curve.

13. Alker and Russett, *op. cit.*, found 18 out of 27 *state senates* to have higher Gini coefficients of inequality.

14. Russett and Alker, Deutsch, Lasswell, *World Handbook of Political and Social Indicators* (New Haven: Yale University Press, 1964), p. 174.

15 The data reported here were made available to the author by Mr. George Sadowsky of Yale, Dr. Joseph Pechman of The Brookings Institution, and the National Committee on Government Finance, which supervises Brookings' Studies of Government Finance. They result from a computer analysis of approximately 100,000 tax returns made up of a sample of adjusted gross incomes below $100,000 combined with a complete enumeration for those incomes in the higher tax brackets. Exact correspondence with the earlier Gini coefficient for income before taxes should not be expected because (1) income may not have the same meaning in both examples; (2) the earlier data may have been grouped differently and less accurately; (3) the earlier data are for 1956, not 1960; and (4) the present results are for a population of tax returns (whether individually or jointly filed), not individuals. A curve similar to Figure 4, but only for taxable returns, has been published in Richard Goode, *The Individual Income Tax*, The Brookings Institution, Washington, D.C., 1964, p. 236.

TRICKLING DOWN: THE RELATIONSHIP BETWEEN ECONOMIC GROWTH AND THE EXTENT OF POVERTY AMONG AMERICAN FAMILIES

W. H. LOCKE ANDERSON*

Introduction

The growth of the American economy has proceeded sufficiently far that severe poverty has become a problem of a minority of its citizens, no longer a problem common to most men in most places. It is this fact, as Galbraith has pointed out,[1] that makes it possible to contemplate a redistribution program for the elimination of poverty. As long as the income of the average family was below a decent minimum, redistribution could not possibly succeed in eliminating poverty, although it has always been possible to alleviate its most distressing instances by redistribution. However, if it were deemed socially desirable to do so, it would now be possible to eliminate extreme poverty through a redistribution involving less than 2 per cent of the gross national product.[2]

The long-run impact of the President's attack on poverty is not redistributive in the ordinary tax and transfer sense. One of its chief aims is to build up the earning power of today's poor and tomorrow's potential poor. The only sense in which this is redistributive is that it is deliberately designed to raise the productivity of those at the lower end of the income distribution more rapidly than the average productivity rises. This will change the shape of the income distribution, of course, but in the process it will raise the nation's productive potential. Hence it will help some citizens without hurting others. However, in the short run it is almost exclusively redistributive, taking from the current earnings of the productive to build up the human and physical capital of the less productive.

Critics of this program may well argue that the problem of poverty will speedily be eliminated by economic growth within the framework of our existing system of income distribution. Such arguments deserve careful examination, for if they are by and large correct, the case for a national poverty program would be weakened somewhat.

Both Galbraith[3] and Michael Harrington[4] have denied the validity of this argument, pointing out that today's poor live largely outside the mainstream of American life—they are the victims of "case poverty" in Galbraith's words—

Reprinted by permission of the author and Harvard University Press from *The Quarterly Journal of Economics* **78** (November, 1964), 511–524. Copyright © 1964 by the President and Fellows of Harvard College.

they inhabit the "other America," to use Harrington's particularly apt description. This paper presents statistical evidence showing that their contention is basically correct. It shows that the elimination of poverty through "trickling down" is likely to be slower and more uncertain in the future than it has been in the past. It further points out some of those groups in the society who are relatively untouched by changes in the general level of income.

The analysis is confined exclusively to the income of families. This omits consideration of the over 10 million "unattached individuals." An analysis of poverty among these people could be made along essentially the same lines as for families.

The paper relies heavily on the statistics contained in the Census Bureau publication, *Trends in the Income of Families and Persons in the United States: 1947 to 1960*.[5] While these statistics are perhaps not so rich as the imagination of Mr. Galbraith or the experience of Mr. Harrington, they have considerable appeal to the admirer of "hard facts."

Income Growth and Distribution

The income distribution stretches as average income grows; if this were not true, poverty would long since have ceased to be a problem. In colonial times, the income gap between the very poor and all but the very rich must have been at most a few hundred dollars. Since the median income in the United States now is well above any upper bound of poverty, if the dispersion of income had remained constant as its central tendency grew, no one would now be poor.

But the dispersion of income expands along with its central tendency. The quintile boundaries of the income distribution rise approximately by the same percentages, thus bringing widening absolute differentials—the "stretching." (See Figure 1.) This accords with our retributive standards of justice; people are rewarded in proportion to their relative degrees of social worth or productivity. It incidentally guarantees the persistence of poverty without public policies designed to redistribute income or earning power.

The Incidence of Poverty and its Changes

In subsequent discussion, we shall consider a family to be poor if its total money income from all sources is less than $3,000 in 1959 prices.[6] The shortcomings of this single standard are too well known to require comment here;[7] it has the overriding virtue of simplicity.

The stretchability of the income distribution largely disappears with a log transformation. If we visualize the process of income growth as the rightward movement of a roughly symmetrical distribution of the log of income with a roughly constant dispersion, it is apparent that the proportion of families receiving less than $3,000 will decline very slowly for a while, then quite rapidly, then slowly again, giving steady growth in the median values of income. This is illustrated in Figure 2. When the great mass of the people are poor (Phase 1), only a few people "spill over" into affluence as income grows. As time passes and the median of income approaches the poverty boundary, people spill over quite fast (Phase 2). However, as the masses become affluent, further income growth pulls fewer and fewer over the boundary (Phase 3). The situation shown in Figure 2 can be transformed into the "Poverty Curve" of Figure 3, showing the "incidence of poverty" (proportion of families with incomes below $3,000) as a function of the log of median income. If income grows steadily, the log of the median income is a proportional transformation of time, so the poverty curve becomes an inverted "Pearl-Reed" curve of the incidence of poverty.

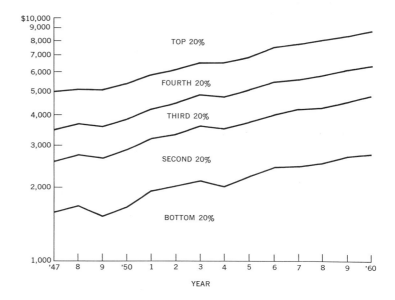

1   Quintile limits of the income distribution of all families, 1947–60, in 1959 dollars.

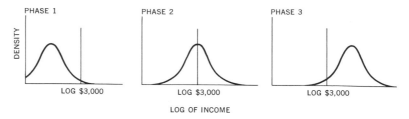

2   Income distribution at various stages of economic growth.

There are, of course, no discontinuities which separate the three phases. A distinction among the three situations shown in Figure 2 is convenient for discussion, however.

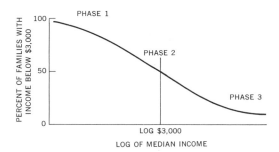

Figure 3

Measuring the Poverty Curve

If there were income distribution data over a sufficiently long period of time, it would be possible to plot straightforwardly the progress of the population along the poverty curve. Since all of the available data are confined to a period in which the income distribution was fairly dense in the vicinity of $3,000, it is necessary to use cross-section data in an attempt to measure the shape of the curve during Phases 1 and 3.

The total of families in the nation may be broken down into six separate "subnations" of widely differing degrees of affluence, each of which has a wide internal dispersion of income. In Table 1 these groups are listed along with their numbers of families, median incomes, and interquintile income ranges[8] in 1959.

In Figure 4 the income-poverty experiences of these subgroups are plotted for the period 1947–60. This combines the time series on the subgroups with a cross-section comparison of the positions of the groups.

These trace out an S-shaped curve of the kind hypothesized in the discussion of Figures 2 and 3. Group 1 (rural nonwhite farm) is clearly in Phase 1. The

■ **Table 1.** Family subgroups, 1959

Subgroup	Number of families (thousand)	Median income (dollars)	Interquintile income range (dollars)
White			
Urban	24,587	5,754	3,145–8,865
Rural nonfarm	12,899	5,513	3,034–8,302
Rural farm	3,342	3,153	1,418–5,861
Nonwhite			
Urban	3,033	3,527	1,709–5,970
Rural nonfarm	743	1,908	914–4,160
Rural farm	458	1,138	548–2,234
Total	45,062	5,417	2,715–8,466

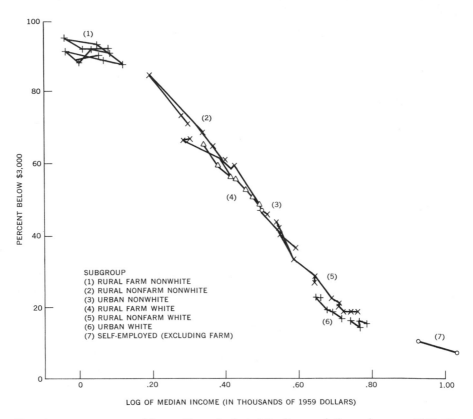

4   Poverty curve as measured by position of selected family population subgroups, 1947–60.

nonfarm white majority groups (5 and 6) show the expected curvature in their progress. The point at which the curvature becomes noticeable, which could be taken as the boundary between Phases 2 and 3, seems to be at about a 20 per cent incidence of poverty, corresponding to a $5,000 median income. The boundary between Phases 1 and 2 may be symmetrically placed at an 80 per cent incidence, corresponding to a median income of $1,800. The 50 per cent incidence point is, of course, $3,000, the geometric mean of the two boundary points.

Unfortunately none of the exhaustive subgroups lies firmly within Phase 3 for the entire data period, so it is impossible to get an accurate reading on the shape of the poverty curve in Phase 3 from these data. However, there is a group of the population—families whose head is self-employed—which is quite wealthy on the average but which cuts across occupational lines sufficiently to have a fairly typical internal variety of income experience. In 1959 this group numbered 622 thousand, had a median income of $11,194, and had an interquintile income range from $6,242 to $22,558.

This is quite a small subgroup which has a highly variable median income, has a small fraction of poor, and presents severe income measurement problems.

Hence it is necessary to do some averaging to get a picture of the relationship between income and poverty among the self-employed. The two points plotted for the self-employed (group 7) in Figure 4 are averages for 1948–54 and 1955–60. Their position and the slope of the line joining them supports the expectation that the poverty curve should flatten out beyond some median income level, which is apparently about $5,000.

A great deal of caution should be attached to this piece of evidence, however. The self-employed group by its definition excludes those families in which the head is not employed; it also excludes farmers. Hence its data probably understate the incidence of poverty which would exist if the entire population of families were to have a median income equal to that of the self-employed. They establish a lower bound to the range of the curve.

None of these data can rigorously be shown to describe the income-poverty relationship in the whole population at various stages in its progress. Nonetheless, it is comforting to find that the subgroup data conform to expectations, and the observed curvature in the path of the urban white group has considerable significance for future developments.

Subgroup Poverty Curves

The data on relationships between median incomes and the incidence of poverty in various population subgroups are interesting for the light they can shed on the shape of the poverty curve for the whole population at income levels outside the range of documented experience. They are also useful for the less aggregative approach to the relationship between income growth and poverty reduction which will be followed in the remainder of this paper. For this purpose, it is useful to think of each of the various subgroups as having its own median income, poverty incidence curve. If, for instance, economic growth could be expected to affect principally the incomes of groups in Phase 2 of their own poverty curves, poverty would decline much more rapidly than if it were to affect primarily groups in either Phase 1 or Phase 3.

The fundamental thesis of this paper is that the nonfarm white majority of the country has entered Phase 3 and that most of the Phases 1 and 2 groups in the country are isolated from general economic growth; their incomes do not increase in proportion to aggregate income. This implies that a poverty program will be required for further rapid reduction in the extent of poverty. The principal exception to this position is the case of Negro families (in the North), who are not isolated and who are still in Phase 2.

Poverty Status of Population Subgroups, 1959

The 1960 Census data[9] provide considerably more cross-classification detail on the income status of families than the *Current Population Survey*. Table II, and the associated Figure 5 show the family population cross-classified

■ **Table 2.** Income status of selected family population subgroups, 1959

Subgroup	Number of families	Per cent of all families	Number of poor families	Per cent of poor families	Incidence (per cent)	Median income	Group code in Figure 5
Male Head							
65 and over							
White							
Farm	491.2	1.1	303.7	3.1	61.8	2,341	1
Nonfarm	4,267.5	9.5	1,938.3	20.1	45.4	3,390	2
Nonwhite							
Farm	42.0	0.1	36.3	0.4	86.4	1,338	3
Nonfarm	329.3	0.7	221.9	2.3	67.4	1,935	4
Under 65							
White							
Farm	2,348.8	5.4	965.5	10.0	39.6	3,755	5
Nonfarm	30,383.2	67.3	2,982.4	30.9	9.8	6,582	6
Nonwhite							
Farm	208.2	0.5	171.6	1.8	82.4	1,448	7
Nonfarm	2,791.9	6.2	935.2	9.9	34.1	3,999	8
Female Head							
65 and over							
White							
Farm	58.5	0.1	34.3	0.4	58.6	2,405	9
Nonfarm	791.0	1.8	325.8	3.4	41.2	3,799	10
Nonwhite							
Farm	7.9	0.0	7.0	0.1	88.6	1,264	11
Nonfarm	115.8	0.3	85.3	0.9	73.7	1,690	12
Under 65							
White							
Farm	74.3	0.2	44.4	0.5	59.8	2,280	13
Nonfarm	2,382.3	5.3	1,021.9	10.6	42.9	3,522	14
Nonwhite							
Farm	22.3	0.0	20.0	0.2	89.7	1,251	15
Nonfarm	744.3	1.6	538.7	5.6	72.4	1,798	16
Total	45,148.5	100.0	9,650.3	100.0	21.4	5,663	

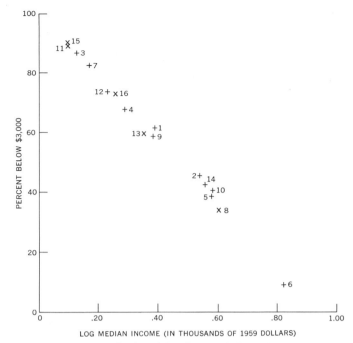

5   Income-poverty status of selected family population subgroups, 1959.

by various demographic characteristics of the family head which have a strong impact on income.

As these data show, the dominant majority of white, nonfarm families headed by a male under 65 years of age had incomes in 1959 which were much higher than those of any other subgroup, and an incidence of poverty which was much lower. Much of the poverty in this group (which contained about 30 per cent of the poor) must be attributed either to disability, unemployment, or residence in a chronically depressed area. Since this group was selected for its relative lack of handicaps, it surely had an incidence of poverty below that which the whole population would have at the same median income, but it must certainly have been well into Phase 3 of its own poverty curve. Further income growth for this group could be expected to erode its poverty quite slowly.

The second wealthiest group of families studied, whose only disqualifying defect was race, was still in Phase 2, and contained about 10 per cent of the poor.

The remaining groups, containing about 60 per cent of the poor families, were strung out over the lower portion of the income distribution. Nonwhite farmers were the most desperate; these groups, comprising about $\frac{1}{2}$ per cent of all families, had $2\frac{1}{2}$ per cent of the poor. All the nonwhite farm groups were in Phase 1.

Table 2 suggests in almost all cases that, given all other characteristics, it is worse for the family head to be nonwhite rather than white, a farmer rather than a nonfarmer, over 65 rather than under 65, and a woman rather than a man, although there are a few interesting exceptions evident in Table 2.

The many interactions involved in Table 2 would provide material enough in themselves for a separate article. In Table 3 the data of Table 2 have been reorganized to reveal some of these. The most striking are that:

1) age is a disadvantage for families headed by males but not for those headed by females;
2) among the aged, it is not additionally disadvantageous for the head to be a female; it is among the young that this matters;
3) the age and sex of the family head make more of a difference off the farm than on;
4) the largest differences among families headed by a male under 65 are found between white and nonwhite farmers, and between farm and nonfarm non-whites.

The data contained in Table 3 will repay careful study. However, a thorough examination of these interactions and their causes would stray too far from the main theme of the present discussion.

The Elasticity of Subgroup Incomes with Respect to Economic Growth

These Census data have shown that in 1959 about one-third of the family population, containing over 65 per cent of the poor families, were in groups which were in Phase 2 of the poverty curve. That is, they were living in subgroups whose median incomes were neither far beyond nor hopelessly far below the poverty boundary. If the incomes of these groups were to grow steadily, their poverty could be expected to decline steadily. For any of these groups, an increase in median income of about $2\frac{1}{2}$ per cent would reduce the incidence of poverty by 1 percentage point, judging from the slope of the central portion of Figure 4.

The data of the annual *Current Population Survey* do not provide sufficient cross classification to trace the income experience of the sixteen subgroups across time, but they do permit a trace of the marginal classes (male head, female head; white, nonwhite; nonfarm, farm; head under 65, head over 65) from 1947 to 1960 in constant (1959) dollars. To study the degree to which the incomes of these marginal groups respond to movements in aggregate income, a series of regressions has been fitted relating the percentage change in each groups' median income to the percentage change in deflated personal income per capita (per member of the noninstitutional population 14 years and over). The results of these regressions are presented in Table 4.[10]

For two of the poor minority categories—families with a female head and families with a head over 65—the regression is insignificant. The median incomes of these groups are insensitive to movements in per capita personal income, and grow very slowly. For the farm families, the relationship is of questionable

■ Table 3. Median incomes of selected family population subgroups classified by sex, age, race and residence of family head

Subgroup	Non-farm	Farm	Per cent difference	Subgroup	White	Non-white	Per cent difference
Male head				**Male head**			
65 and over				*65 and over*			
White	3,390	2,341	+ 44.8	Farm	2,341	1,338	+ 75.0
Nonwhite	1,935	1,338	+ 44.6	Nonfarm	3,390	1,935	+ 75.2
Under 65				*Under 65*			
White	6,582	3,755	+ 75.3	Farm	3,755	1,448	+159.3
Nonwhite	3,999	1,448	+176.2	Nonfarm	6,582	3,999	+ 64.6
Female head				**Female head**			
65 and over				*65 and over*			
White	3,799	2,405	+ 58.0	Farm	2,405	1,264	+ 90.3
Nonwhite	1,690	1,264	+ 33.7	Nonfarm	3,799	1,690	+124.8
Under 65				*Under 65*			
White	3,522	2,280	+ 54.4	Farm	2,280	1,251	+ 82.3
Nonwhite	1,798	1,251	+ 43.7	Nonfarm	3,522	1,798	+ 95.9

Subgroup	Under 65	65 and over	Per cent	Subgroup	Male head	Female head	Per cent difference
Male head				**Head 65 and over**			
Farm				*Farm*			
White	3,755	2,341	+ 60.4	White	2,341	2,405	− 2.7
Nonwhite	1,448	1,338	+ 8.2	Nonwhite	1,338	1,264	+ 5.9
Nonfarm				*Nonfarm*			
White	6,582	3,390	+ 94.2	White	3,390	3,799	− 10.8
Nonwhite	3,999	1,935	+106.7	Nonwhite	1,935	1,690	+ 14.5
Female head				**Head under 65**			
Farm				*Farm*			
White	2,280	2,405	− 5.2	White	3,755	2,280	+ 64.7
Nonwhite	1,251	1,264	− 1.0	Nonwhite	1,448	1,251	+ 15.7
Nonfarm				*Nonfarm*			
White	3,522	3,799	− 7.3	White	6,582	3,522	+ 86.9
Nonwhite	1,798	1,690	+ 6.4	Nonwhite	3,999	1,798	+122.4

■ **Table 4.** Regressions relating group median incomes to per capita personal income (percentage changes)

Subgroup	Number 1960 (thousand)	Median income 1947 (1959 $)	Median income 1960 (1959 $)	Per cent change	Poverty incidence 1960	Intercept	Slope	Adjusted R^2
All families	45,435	3,957	5,547	40.4	22.1	0	1.078	.618‡
Male head	40,826	4,056	5,779	42.5	18.9	0	1.118	.793‡
Female head	4,609	2,849	2,928	2.8	51.1	0.5	—	*
White	41,104	4,127	5,761	39.6	19.4	0	1.084	.670‡
Nonwhite	4,331	2,110	3,190	51.2	47.1	−0.5	1.551	.520‡
Nonfarm	41,945	4,204	5,724	36.2	19.6	0	.982	.679‡
Farm	3,490	2,585	2,838	9.8	52.6	−5.0	2.489	.418†
Head under 65	39,235	4,110	5,784	40.7	18.2	0	1.097	.693‡
Head 65 or over	6,200	2,398	2,862	19.3	52.5	1.5	—	—

* Adjusted R^2 negative or virtually zero.
† Significant at 5 per cent level.
‡ Significant at 1 per cent level.

reliability (significant at the 5 per cent level but not at the 1 per cent level), but shows quite a high elasticity. However, there is a negative intercept which implies that the total population per capita income must grow at 2 per cent a year for farm income to remain constant.[11] For the nonwhite families, the elasticity is quite high, the intercept is negligible, and the regression is highly significant.[12]

These regressions suggest that changes in the rate of income growth do not directly affect families with an aged or female head to any appreciable extent, and that the farm families are fighting an uphill battle if they remain on the farm. Among the poor groups singled out in this analysis, only the nonwhites directly benefit from general economic growth. By contrast, in each of the divisions studied, the median income of the majority group responded reliably to growth in the aggregate with an elasticity of one or slightly more.

Conclusions

The above analysis has singled out a dominant subgroup of families—white, nonfarm, headed by a man under 65 years of age—whose median income follows the movements of aggregate income quite closely. In this group poverty is confined to a small minority, less than 10 per cent, which, however, constitutes about 30 per cent of all poor families. Aggregate income growth seems likely to reduce poverty in this group more slowly in the future than it has in the past, for only a thin tail of its income distribution now lies below the poverty boundary. This is so even though the median income of the group grows reliably in proportion to the per capita income of the whole population.

It has singled out a second group—the nonwhite, nonfarm families headed by a man under 65 years of age—whose group median income has a high elasticity with respect to aggregate income. This group still has a moderately high incidence of poverty. Hence its poverty can be expected to decline rather rapidly in the future in response to general economic growth.

The remaining groups of families—the farm families and the families headed by a woman or an aged person—are to a great degree isolated from economic growth. Their median incomes are not reliably responsive to aggregate income. Although they constitute only about 25 per cent of the families in the population, they have 60 per cent of the nation's poor families. For these, income simply does not "trickle down" directly enough to be counted upon to reduce poverty.

This does not imply that economic growth does not help these groups at all. Higher earnings for the working-age population raise their savings accumulated for retirement. The higher the incomes of families headed by males, the more likely it is that widows will be well provided for. Higher nonfarm incomes raise the demand for farm products somewhat, and they ease the process of migration from farm to city employment. However, all these processes are slow, indirect, and uncertain compared with the process by which economic growth affects the nonfarm population of families headed by a working-age male.

Strongly rising aggregate income will clearly help the economically mobile urban nonwhite group to a considerable extent, particularly outside the South. It will also be of some help to the poor minority of the dominant white group. Within each of these groups, however, there are some families whose poverty will be alleviated only by special programs, and for the families whose head is an aged person, a woman, or a farmer, such programs are mandatory if poverty is to be markedly reduced.

This analysis suggests that movements along the poverty curve corresponding to the existing income distribution will imply a declining rate of reduction of poverty. The poverty program is designed to change the shape of the poverty curve, to reduce the incidence of poverty corresponding to any given median population income. Without such a change, the poor will be with us in large numbers for many years to come.

NOTES

*   The author was on the staff of the Council of Economic Advisers at the time this paper was written. He would like to thank William Capron, Robert Lampman, and Burton Weisbrod for their helpful comments on earlier drafts.

1.   J. K. Galbraith, *The Affluent Society* (Boston: Houghton Mifflin, 1958), p. 329.

2.   The 1964 *Annual Report of the Council of Economic Advisers* (Washington: U.S. Government Printing Oflffice, 1964), p. 77.

3.   Galbraith, *op. cit.*, Chap. XXII.

4.   Michael Harrington, *The Other America* (Baltimore: Penguin Books, 1963).

5.   The U.S. Bureau of the Census, *Trends in the Income of Families and Persons in the United States: 1947 to 1960*, Technical Paper No. 8 (Washington, 1963). This document contains an extensive compilation of income distribution data from the *Current Population Reports*, Series P-60, converted to a constant (1959) dollar basis by deflation with the consumer price index. It was prepared by Herman P. Miller.

6.   This differs somewhat from the standard used in the Council of Economic Advisers *Report*, in which the boundary was placed at $3,000 in 1962 prices. The use of a 1959 dollar standard was solely dictated by convenience in using the Census data. The 1959 standard is only $115 higher than the 1962 standard.

7.   See, for instance, the C.E.A. *Report*, pp. 57–59.

8.   This is the range between the boundaries which divide the middle three-fifths of the income distribution from the two extreme fifths.

9.   U.S. Bureau of the Census, *U.S. Census of Population: 1960. Subject Reports. Families.* Final Report PC (2)—44 (Washington, 1963).

10.   An attempt was made to measure separate coefficients for changes in undeflated per capita income, the consumer price index, and the unemployment rate. However, a shortage of data points and high intercorrelation among these predictors led to useless results.

11. The Census data understate the rise in incomes of families who have once lived on farms, since migrants from low-income farms to higher-income nonfarm areas are classed with the nonfarm areas after they have moved.

12. This high elasticity is not observable among Southern nonwhite families. The median real income of this group increased by only 4.9 per cent from 1953 to 1960 (1953 is the first year for which such data are available). During the same period the median income of all nonwhites rose 17.5 per cent. Part of the rapid growth of nonwhite incomes must be attributed to migration from the low-income South to the higher-income North and West.

THE COSTS OF AUTOMOBILE
MODEL CHANGES SINCE 1949

FRANKLIN M. FISHER
ZVI GRILICHES
CARL KAYSEN

I. Introduction: Aims of the Study

This paper reports estimates of the costs to the consumer of the changes in private automobile specifications that took place during the 1950's. Throughout we concentrate on the costs that would not have been expended if cars with the 1949[1] model lengths, weights, horsepowers, transmissions, and other specifications had been produced in every year. As there was technological change in the industry, we are thus assessing not the expenditure that would have been saved had the 1949 models themselves been continued; but rather the expenditure that would have been saved had such cars been continued but been built with the developing technology.

We count as costs not only the costs to the automobile manufacturers themselves of special retooling for new models, but also the direct costs of producing larger, heavier, and more powerful cars, plus the costs of automatic transmissions, power brakes, and the like. Finally, we include the secondary costs not paid out by the automobile companies but paid nevertheless by the consuming public in the form of increased expenditures for gasoline necessitated by the "horsepower race."

This procedure clearly counts as "changes" *all* changes in those specifications which directly relate to the appearance or performance of the automobile. We do not count alterations in design of the car that do not *directly* change the package the consumer thinks he is buying. Thus, we assume that horsepower is a dimension of the car that enters directly into the utility function of the car-buyer, but that engine displacement is not. This is not to say that changes in engine displacement are not relevant; it is to say that such changes are relevant only insofar as they influence one of the performance or appearance variables under consideration.

We have mentioned a consumer's utility function. The use of this concept carries with it the clear implication that the changes we consider may all have been desired by the car-buying public.[2] The question thus naturally arises: why not cost only those changes which were essentially "frills"? Why include in the

Reprinted by permission of the authors and The University of Chicago Press from *Journal of Political Economy* **70** (October, 1962), 433–451. Copyright © 1962 by The University of Chicago.

estimates such things as automatic transmissions that were quite arguably improvements? The answer is that there is always a presumption of consumer sovereignty in the market economy and that it would be wholly arbitrary for us to say "this change was an improvement, and this was unnecessary" without detailed information on the utility functions of consumers. If tailfins were a frill, what about increased horsepowers? What about *extremely* increased horsepowers? Where there are costs, there are likely to be benefits as well, and, while the automobile market is not perfectly competitive, it seems likely to us that for most of the period in question the car manufacturers were giving the public what it wanted, save perhaps for overshooting in some respects.

We thus wish to avoid having this study taken as an indictment of the automobile companies. We are rather in the position of one who observes another man drinking various liquors. We do not blame the bartender for anything save that he occasionally gives the man more than he asks for of some expensive drink; nor do we question the man's right to drink; nor do we distinguish between "good" liquors and "bad." We do, however, present the bar bill. Since the argument is sometimes advanced that the resources spent on automobile model changes could be put to better use in the public sector,[3] it is clearly worth investigating the order of magnitude of the resources involved.

Section II considers the direct costs of model changes as well as the effect on advertising expenditures. Section III discusses retooling expenditures, and Section IV gasoline consumption. The results are combined and summarized in the final section, where we return to the question whether the estimated costs were worth incurring.

II. Direct Costs and Advertising Expenditures[4]

In this section we present estimates of the increases in consumer expenditures on automobiles associated with the changes in size and horsepower that have occurred since 1949. We discuss here how much more it costs to produce the, say, average 1958 car, given the 1958 levels of costs and technology, than it would have cost (at 1958 prices and with 1958 retooling expenditures) to produce a car of 1949 average specifications with the average 1949 level of "attachments." We shall treat the additional cost of the 1958 technology (above the 1949 level) —and the cost of retooling—in Section III. The "cost" estimates in this section consist of estimates of the increase in price due to increases in size and horsepower; the increase in expenditure due to the wider use of automatic transmissions, power steering, and power brakes; and the increase in price due to the increase in advertising expenditures above the 1949 levels.[5]

Only the effects of changes in size and horsepower present a difficult estimation problem, and hence only the solution to this particular problem will be discussed in some detail here. Ideally a group of engineers and cost accountants could produce the appropriate estimates of what it would cost to produce an average 1949-specifications car in each of the subsequent years. Unfortunately,

■ **Table 1.** Coefficients of single-year cross-sectional regressions relating logarithm of new United States passenger-car prices to various specifications, annually 1950–61

Model year	No.	Con-stant	Coefficients* of				R^2
			H	W	L	V	
1950	72	1.2709	.158	.484	.832	−.024	.892
			(.048)	(.0285)	(.115)	(.014)	
1951	55	1.4329	.117	.017	.818	.012	.909
			(.054)	(.031)	(.116)	(.013)	
1952	51	1.7174	.097	.105	.578	−.020	.927
			(.042)	(.030)	(.127)	(.015)	
1953	54	1.9328	.113	.103	.471	−.034	.891
			(.044)	(.038)	(.136)	(.020)	
1954	65	2.3766	.202	−.026	.398	−.024	.857
			(.037)	(.042)	(.106)	(.014)	
1955	55	2.4570	.118	.095	.202	−.050	.871
			(.059)	(.050)	(.128)	−(.026)	
1956	87	2.3359	.065	.163	.192	−.052	.907
			(.027)	(.027)	(.079)	(.016)	
1957	95	2.7370	.051	.059	.171	−.011 plus significant	.967
			(.013)	(.017)	(.057)	(.010) coefficients	
						for T, A, P, B	
1958	103	3.0389	.007	.142	−.073	.005 plus T, A, P, B	.906
			(.018)	(.026)	(.092)	(.021)	
1959	87	3.1077	.052	.103	−.068	−.031 plus T, A, P	.939
			(.013)	(.017)	(.065)	(.016)	
1960	78	2.9723	.052	.059	.065	−.017 plus T, A, P, C	.951
			(.009)	(.020)	(.073)	(.011)	
1961	99	2.2530	.026	.132	.309	.011 plus T, P, C	.940
			(.011)	(.017)	(.080)	(.012)	

*   Dependent variable—logarithm of "list" (advertised delivered) price. Logarithms to the base 10. To convert the results to natural logarithms multiply all coefficients by 2.3. The resulting coefficient, if multiplied by 100, would measure the *percentage* impact on price of a *unit* change in a particular specification or "quality," holding the other specifications constant.

H, advertised brake horsepower, in 100's.
W, shipping weight in 1,000 pounds.
L, over-all length, in hundreds of inches.
V, 1 if the car has a V-8 engine; 0 if it has a 6-cylinder or less engine.
T, 1 if the car is a hardtop; 0 if not.
A, 1 if automatic transmission is "standard" equipment (included in price); 0 if not.
P, 1 if power steering is "standard"; 0 if not.
B, 1 if power brakes are "standard"; 0 if not.
C, 1 if the car is designated as a "compact"; 0 if not.

(Footnote continued on p. 229)

we lack both the specialized knowledge and the resources required for such calculations. Instead, we make use of the apparent close relation between selected dimensions (specifications) of an automobile and its price at a point in time to estimate what the price would have been, at the same point of time, for a car with a different set of specifications.[6]

Table 1 presents the results of annual regressions of the logarithm of car prices (list) for different makes and models on the horsepower, weight, and length of these cars, and on a set of classificatory ("dummy") variables for other "qualities" such as whether a car has a V-8 engine, whether an automatic transmission is included in the list price (is "standard" equipment), and so forth. As can be seen from these results, the use of three numerical variables (horsepower, weight, and length) and several dummy variables explains, on the average, 90 per cent or more of the cross-sectional variance in the logarithm of list prices at a point of time. While the coefficients of particular dimensions are not very stable, the direction of their change over time (for example, the fall in the relative "price" of horsepower[7] and length) is consistent with other evidence and what we know about the industry.[8]

The regressions presented in Table 1 are used to estimate what would have been the list price of a car with the specifications of the average 1949 car each year since 1949.[9] This series and that of the average list prices of the cars actually produced move closely together until about 1954 when they begin to diverge, the difference (shown in col. [1] of Table 2) reaching its maximum in 1959 and

Source: *Specifications and prices, 1949, 1951–53:* Annual statistical issues (March 15) of *Automotive Industries* and annual issues of *Automotive News Almanac, 1954–60:* Various issues of National Automobile Dealers Association's *Used Car Guide*, Washington. *1955–58:* Data are from the February issue of the corresponding year. For 1954 models, figures are taken from July, 1959, issue; for 1959 models, from January, 1959, issue: and for 1960, from December, 1959, issue. *1950 and 1961: Red Book: Official Used Car Appraisals* (Chicago: National Market Reports, Inc.). November 14, 1956, and January 1–February 14, 1961. Some 1961 data are also based on *Car Fax* (Vol. VI, No. 1, 1961 ed., New York). Power brakes data for some years are taken from various issues of *Ward's Automotive Yearbook*. Prices of automatic transmissions, power steering, and power brakes are taken from various issues of *Automotive News Almanac* and from October 1–November 14, 1958, issue of the *Red Book*.

Production Data: 1956–60 by model years by makes is taken from *Automotive Industries*, March 15, 1961. 1961 model-year data are from *Automotive News*, August 7, 1961. For 1955 it was assumed that the model year began in November of the previous year; for 1954 that the model year was January–October; model-year production by makes was computed from monthly production figures by make given in the 1955 and 1956 March 15 issues of *Automotive Industries*. For 1949-53 it was assumed that the model year coincided approximately with the calendar year; calendar-year production data by makes were taken from *ibid*. Data on models within makes and on V-8 engine, automatic transmissions, and power steering and brakes installations were available only for calendar years based on registration data (*Ward's Automotive Yearbook*, various issues). These data were transformed into percentages of a particular make, and these calendar-year within-make percentages were used to break down the model year production figures by makes to arrive at model-year production figures by makes *and* models. For 1961 we used 1960 calendar-year data on models within makes to break down the 1961 model-year production data by makes.

then declining slightly. During the 1956–61 period the difference between the average list price of the cars actually produced and the predicted price for the average 1949 car averaged approximately $450 per car, or about 17 per cent of the actual average list price.

The calculated price differences shown in column (1) of Table 2 are subject to several reservations. First of all they are based on list prices and may not represent the trend of actual prices adequately. In particular, if actual prices paid fell relative to list prices, the actual difference in price will be overestimated by our procedure. If, for example, discounts from list price increased from zero in 1949 to an average of about 15 per cent in 1960, then the average figure given for 1956–61 should be about $380 per car rather than the estimated $450.[10]

■ **Table 2.** Total "direct" costs of automobile change since 1949

Model year	Per car cost of increase in						Total passenger car pro- duction (000's) (7)	Total "direct" cost of model change† ($ millions) (8)
	Size and horse- power* (1)	Use of optional equipment			Adver- tising expense (5)	Total (6)		
		Auto matic trans- mission (2)	Power steer- ing (3)	Power brakes (4)				
1950	$ − 13	$12	—	—	$ − 3	$ − 4	6,659	− 27
1951	17	33	$ 2	—	− 2	50	5,331	267
1952	58	38	9	$ 1	0	106	4,337	460
1953	11	35	22	3	0	71	6,135	436
1954	160	55	21	7	3	246	4,359	1,072
1955	279	70	23	9	10	391	6,201	2,425
1956	377	72	14	6	14	483	6,295	3,040
1957	518	86	25	9	13	651	6,218	4,048
1958	410	86	31	10	16	553	4,256	2,354
1959	520	87	30	9	14	660	5,568	3,675
1960	447	75	31	9	13	575	6,011	3,456
1956–60 average							584	3,315

Source: See Table 1.
*   The regressions presented in Table 1 were used to predict the price of a car with average 1949 specifications. The specifications of the average 1949 car used in these predictions were: horsepower—104.24, weight—3,289.5 pounds, length—200.84 inches and fraction with V-8 engines—0.4067.
†   Col. (6) × col. (7).

On the other hand, we have priced *all* cars at their four-door sedan prices, not taking into account the faster growth in the number of higher priced station wagons, convertibles, and other car models. Since our equations make percentage changes in price depend on changes in absolute specification levels, a higher "true" average price would lead also to a higher estimate of the difference.

Third, these and later calculations are based on "predictions" from statistically estimated equations that do not fit the data perfectly and hence are subject to error. The probable magnitude of this error can be calculated, however. The standard error of the regression line (the "standard" prediction error at the mean levels of the independent variables) is quite high for any one year. It averaged about $170 in the 1956–61 regressions. Thus, there is some doubt whether any *one* particular annual difference is statistically significantly different from zero. The consistency in the sign of these differences leaves little doubt, however, about their significance for the 1956–61 period as a whole. The quoted figures should thus provide a good estimate of the orders of magnitude that are involved here, since in no case were the average 1949 specifications outside the range of the observed variation in the specifications of later model-year cars. We are always interpolating rather than extrapolating to get at our "predictions."

The next set of "cost" estimates is very simple. Columns (2)–(4) of Table 2 present the estimated cost (per car) of the increased use of automatic transmissions, power steering, and power brakes. In each case we took a time series of list prices, a time series on the increase in the percentage use of these items (since 1949) as optional equipment (not already included in the price as "standard" equipment), and computed the "cost" per car as the product of these two series. Again, these "costs" reach their peak in 1958 or 1959.

Column (5) of Table 2 presents the estimated increases in advertising expenditures associated with the above described model changes. We took a time series of advertising expenditures per car (for calendar years) from *Advertising Age*. These data are of doubtful quality but are used for lack of a better source. The main difficulty here is to devise a measure of the 1949 *quantity* of advertising per car in subsequent prices. We attempt to approximate such a measure by inflating the 1949 average advertising expenditures per car by the implicit GNP deflator. This deflator probably rises less than advertising *rates*, but the real cost of reaching and informing a particular consumer must have fallen somewhat during this period. Television rates, for example, have clearly not risen in proportion to the increase in the number of viewers. If anything, these calculations probably underestimate the "real" increase in the *quantity* of advertising per car. We estimated the "cost" of increased advertising as the difference between current advertising expenditures per car and the 1949 advertising expenditure level in current prices. Again these "costs" reach their peak in 1958.

The total direct cost of model changes (col. [8]) is estimated for each year by totaling the above described estimates (col. [6]) and multiplying them by the annual passenger-car production figures (col. [7]). For 1956–60 these costs average about $3.3 billion annually. This is probably an underestimate since we have left out of our calculations such other changes as the optional purchase of higher horsepower engines, power seats, power windows, various optional "trim" items, and so forth. On the other hand, allowing for the growth of discounting would reduce this figure to about $2.8 billion annually. In addition, the "prediction error" (two standard deviations) associated with these figures could lead them to be too high *or* too low by about $1.0 billion.

III. Retooling Expenditures[11]

The most obvious cost of automobile model changes is the expenditure by the automobile manufacturers for the new tools, jigs, and dies needed to produce new models. Were models to remain unchanged, such expenditures would clearly be reduced to the level necessary to replace existing equipment as it wears out.

Of course, such expenditures on the physical equipment of production are not the only ones directly associated with model changes. There are, in addition, the costs of research and development and of design of the new models. Unlike the expenditures for retooling, however, the latter costs are not available, and we shall thus not be able to include them in our estimates. The exclusion of these costs, however, is not *wholly* undesirable. In the preceding section and in the following one we charge as "costs" expenditures that could have been avoided by producing cars with 1949 specifications *with the current technology*. It would clearly be inconsistent to charge also the costs of securing that technology. Since the development in which we are interested has been largely in engine design (see the next section), taking the form of reducing the "cost" of horsepower, it seems likely that the costs of securing that technology are a much larger part of research and development and design costs than of retooling expenditures. It follows that we are largely avoiding double counting here.[12]

It may appear, however, that we are double counting by including retooling expenditures as well as the direct costs discussed in the last section. Retooling expenditures are costs to the automobile companies and are presumably reflected in the prices of new cars which we already used in the regressions and computations of the previous section. It seems to follow that we have already included retooling expenditures (and research and development and design costs) implicitly in our estimates of direct costs. This is not the case, however. We used the regressions of the last section to estimate the direct costs of producing cars with 1949 specifications with current technology. But the costs of retooling (which are reflected in our regressions) are also reflected in such estimates. Hence our estimated direct costs for 1949 specification cars are *overestimates* of the costs that would have been incurred had no model changes taken place, since in the latter event the prices of all cars would have been lower because of the elimination of retooling costs. It is thus not double counting to add retooling expenditures at this point.[13]

As our estimates of retooling expenditures, we took the expenditures for special tools included in additions to plant and property reported by the automobile firms to the Securities and Exchange Commission[14] and charged by them to current costs. The relevant figures are available by calendar year; for the most part we have interpreted them as applicable to the model year following that calendar year.[15] The figures are available for the full period we consider, save that the Ford figures are only available beginning with the 1953 model year, and figures for Studebaker are not available before the merger with Packard. These problems were handled as follows:[16]

Ford. In 1953, Ford retooling expenditures were 10 per cent of the total. We have added 10 per cent to the totals for the preceding years.

Studebaker. In 1954, expenditures by Packard were 1.3 per cent of the total (adjusted to include Ford). In 1955, expenditures by Studebaker-Packard were 3.7 per cent. We therefore added 2.4 per cent to the total for each year before 1955.

Clearly, the first adjustment is the only one of any importance; it seems conservative in view of higher Ford expenditures in later years.

To allow for normal replacement of worn-out equipment, we ignored the fact that 1949 was a year of substantial model change and assumed that all expenditure for that model year was for replacement of worn-out equipment; this yielded an upper limit of $190 billion for normal replacement expenditures. Taking into account model changes in 1949, $150 billion seems more than ample as an estimate of normal replacement expenditures (especially in view of the expenditure of only $175 million on retooling in 1950) and we use this figure adjusted for changes in the wholesale price index for metalworking machinery. The resulting costs and costs per car (including 8 per cent for taxes that would have been saved) are presented in Table 3.

IV. Gasoline Consumption[17]

A. The Data

This section deals with the saving in gasoline consumption that would have been effected had the "horsepower race" not occurred—had 1949 specifications been continued. To estimate this saving requires detailed data by model on miles per gallon performance of automobiles. The only such data available are the figures on miles per gallon during the period of ownership reported by Consumers Union and Consumer Research (principally the former) for 185 different models tested over the period 1948—July, 1961.[18]

B. Fuel Economy and Engine Size

There has been considerable technological progress in engine design over the last fifteen years. In particular, as the automobile manufacturers moved toward higher and higher horsepower cars in the middle and late fifties, they also redesigned engines to secure higher horsepower for a given engine size. This had

■ Table 3. Retooling costs of model changes since 1949

| Model year | Millions of current dollars | | Cost per car* (current dollars) (3) |
	Total expenditures for special tools (1)	Retooling costs attributable to model changes (2)	
1950	175.3	19.6	2.9
1951	208.5	45.2	8.5
1952	262.8	81.7	18.8
1953	419.5	246.5	40.2
1954	439.1	263.5	60.5
1955	632.7	469.2	75.7
1956	523.3	336.2	53.4
1957	947.3	771.7	124.1
1958	827.8	625.7	147.0
1959	745.8	532.1	95.6
1960	756.5	536.6	89.3
1961	896.5	678.9	125.6
1956–60 average	760.1	560.5	98.9

*   Production data 1950–60 from Table 2; 1961 estimated production from *Automotive News*, August 7, 1961.

the dual effect of reducing the extra gasoline consumption attendant on horse-power increases and (as noted in Sec. II) of reducing the direct cost of horsepower. Accordingly, we had to find some way of measuring such progress in engine design in order to estimate the gasoline consumption that would have occurred had cars with 1949 horsepowers been built in each successive year *with the developing technology.*

Since the available test statistics for any given year are too scanty to allow us to analyze each year's models wholly separately (as in Sec. II), our solution was a compromise between the need for enough data to perform any analysis and the impossibility of pooling the test data in any simple way because automobiles with different types of transmission cannot be simply lumped together for such purposes. We proceeded to break the problem into two parts: the relation of engine size to gasoline consumption and the effect of horsepower on engine size. The former relation was studied by pooling all test data for cars with a given transmission; the latter effect was studied by analyzing engine data for each successive year separately. This procedure involved the assumption that tech-nological change was largely restricted to changes in engine design or in the type of transmission employed (we were able to use a moderately fine breakdown by transmission types) rather than acting to alter the effects of existing transmissions without changing their type.[19]

Consumer Reports each year presents a statistic which they term "Fuel Economy Factor" and which we shall denote by F. This statistic is "the cubic feet of cylinder volume swept by the pistons on their suction strokes while the car travels one mile in high gear."[20] If engine displacement (D) is measured in cubic inches and the number of engine revolutions per mile in top gear is denoted by R, then:

$$F = \frac{R}{2}\left(\frac{D}{1728}\right). \tag{1}$$

R, in turn, is dependent on wheel size and axle ratio, while D, as we shall see, is highly correlated with horsepower for a given engine type. Statements in *Consumer Reports* clearly imply that, if these data are segregated by type of transmission, they should be related to F.[21] This indeed turns out to be the case.

As already stated, F is defined for the performance of the car in its top gear. It would be possible to construct similar variables which measure performance in lower gears, but these would of course be almost perfectly correlated with F, for either manual or automatic transmissions, given the limited number of forward gears. However, even if we were to use such similar variables for lower gears, it would still be incorrect to regress gasoline consumption on them, pooling observations for cars with a different number of forward gears; the distribution of mileage over the different forward gears will not be the same for a car with four such gears as for a car with three or two. It follows that the coefficients in such regressions will be different for cars with a different number of forward gears. This being so, our data must be segregated by the number of forward gears before F can be used as the only "displacement-type" variable in the regression.[22] Accordingly, we segregated the data into 2-speed automatics, 3-speed automatics, 4-speed automatics, manuals without overdrive, and manuals with overdrive. Fortunately, the test data are sufficiently numerous to support the ensuing analysis.[23] We therefore regressed gallons per 10,000 miles of car travel (denoted by G) on F for each of the five transmission categories.

As already remarked, the true relationship we are seeking is one between G and variables similar to F reflecting performance in various gears as well as during idling periods. Given our segregation by transmission type, such variables are almost perfectly correlated with F, and we thus use F alone. However, the goodness of fit of the true relationship—and, therefore, of our estimated one as well—clearly depends on the stability of the distribution of mileage over the various forward speeds or gears (and, less importantly, of the distribution of time between idling and motion) over the tests reported. Since this distribution is not very stable, we expect to find somewhat low (though statistically significant) correlations.[24] On the other hand, the relative stability of this distribution will depend on how much choice is left to the driver as to when to shift gears. We should, therefore, expect to find higher correlations for automatic-transmission cars than for manual-transmission cars, other things being equal. A similar argument leads us to expect higher correlation for 2-speed automatics than for 3-speed ones, for 3-speed automatics than for 4-speed ones, and for cars with manual transmissions than for those with overdrive.[25]

All these predictions as to the relative size of the R^2's are borne out by the results (Table 4). Their agreement with our predictions gives us some confidence in their relevance.

■ **Table 4.** Regressions of gasoline consumption (G) on *Consumer Reports'* Fuel Economy Factor (F)

Transmission type	Regression equation	R^2	No.
2-speed automatic	$G = 214 + 2.38*F$ (0.287)	.748	27
3-speed automatic	$G = 248 + 2.18*F$ (0.179)	.693	68
4-speed automatic	$G = 380 + 1.54*F$ (0.359)	.368	35
Manual without overdrive	$G = 240 + 1.79*F$ (0.388)	.422	31
Manual with overdrive	$G = 308 + 1.68†F$ (0.648)	.233	24

*   Significant at 0.1 per cent level.
†   Significant at 2 per cent level.

C. Engine Size and Horsepower[26]

The present section is concerned with the effects of horsepower on F, our measure of engine size. These effects are assumed to operate only on engine displacement, D, the principal determinant of F, an innocuous assumption as the number of engine revolutions per mile, R, the other variable in equation (1), does not vary greatly from model to model.

As our measure of horsepower, we take "maximum advertised horsepower" (as in Sec. II), despite the fact that this variable is based on stripped engine performance rather than on actual power delivered to the rear wheels.[27] We considered the effects of transmission characteristics in the previous section. Moreover, if advertised horsepower is what the car-buyer thinks he is buying, it is advertised horsepower whose cost we wish to ascertain.

For a given type of engine and given engine efficiency, engine displacement (D) and horsepower (H) are theoretically proportional. Actual engines, however, were redesigned during the 1950's to permit the construction of high-horsepower engines at relatively lower displacements.[28] Accordingly, we did not pool observations from different years but estimated instead the relationship separately for each year.[29]

The fact that, for a given engine type, horsepower and displacement are roughly proportional implies that technological change takes the form of shifting a ray through the origin. Not all developments in engine design, however, can be applied to all horsepowers. Hence, while the points for a given engine type lie on a ray through the origin, not all points on that ray can represent actual engines. Successive technological changes which are aimed at higher horsepower engines become applicable at successively higher horsepower levels. Thus our regressions, save for the early years, are estimates not primarily of the relationship between displacement and horsepower for a given engine type but of the relationship between engine design and horsepower.[30] We are estimating the effect of higher horsepower on the availability of displacement-horsepower ratio reducing techniques. The fact that we obtain such a good fit leads us to accept a linear form for that relationship, and our faith in it is further bolstered by the fact that in every year the range of horsepowers covered in the data is extremely wide. Further, the 1949 horsepowers are all inside that range, so that we shall be interpolating between actual figures in applying our results to them.

It is important to realize that the relationship between D and H is exactly what we want. To take a given engine type and extend the line for high-horsepower cars backward toward the origin would give a most misleading overestimate of the extent to which the developing technology could have been used to effect gasoline economies at 1949 horsepowers. The engine redesigns for high-horsepower cars simply could not have been applied to these lower levels. Our estimates, however, provide precisely the required information: the extent to which advances in engine design are applicable at *given* horsepowers.

The results of these regressions are presented in Table 5.[31] We report standard errors for the constant terms, as the question of whether the regression line passes through the origin is obviously of interest. These results show a clear pattern. Starting with the expected ray through the origin in 1948, there is a slight decline in the slope to 1950–51, without much change in intercept. From 1952 to 1955, the slope diminishes rapidly and the intercept rises substantially.[32] From 1955 through 1961 the coefficients remain roughly constant.[33]

This pattern is to be expected from the preceding discussion. Starting with the ray through the origin which represents the displacement-horsepower relation for a given engine type, minor improvements took at first the form of lowering the slope of that ray slightly (making horsepower cheaper in terms of displacement). With the start of the horsepower race, this effect was accompanied by the introduction of new rays, with lower slopes, attainable only at higher and higher horsepowers. The result in regression terms is depicted schematically in Figure 1, with R_1, R_2, and R_3 representing three engine types, representative of a whole spectrum of techniques (largely higher compression-ratios and efficient use of high octane gasoline) available at higher horsepowers. The dashed portion

■ **Table 5.** Regressions of displacement (D) on maximum advertised horsepower (H)

Model year	Regression equation	R^2	No.
1948	$D = 0.738 + 2.30*H$ (17.0) (0.155)	.880	32
1949	$D = 6.24 + 2.17*H$ (12.0) (0.106)	.938	30
1950	$D = 6.29 + 2.14*H$ (13.8) (0.120)	.908	34
1951	$D = 11.4 + 2.04*H$ (11.1) (0.0963)	.930	36
1952	$D = 30.0† + 1.80*H$ (11.1) (0.0900)	.917	38
1953	$D = 70.3* + 1.42*H$ (12.2) (0.0946)	.851	41
1954	$D = 82.2* + 1.26*H$ (14.1) (0.0987)	.798	43
1955	$D = 112* + 0.938*H$ (10.8) (0.0595)	.883	35
1956	$D = 103* + 0.950*H$ (10.4) (0.0505)	.912	36
1957	$D = 108* + 0.860*H$ (11.1) (0.0472)	.910	35
1958	$D = 109* + 0.856*H$ (11.6) (0.0444)	.921	34
1959	$D = 101* + 0.914*H$ (10.4) (0.0390)	.945	34
1960	$D = 109* + 0.851*H$ (19.2) (0.0783)	.797	32
1961	$D = 73.4* + 1.07*H$ (12.2) (0.0564)	.914	36

*   Significant at 0.1 per cent level.
†   Significant at 1 per cent level.

of each ray represents that part of the ray which is unavailable, while the dotted circle shows the range of observations on the ray. BC is the resulting estimated regression line. As the horsepower race progressed, new rays became available to the right of R_3 at higher horsepowers, while existing techniques were used to produce higher horsepower engines at given displacements. The effect of all this was to shift BC upward and lower its slope. Finally, with the slackening of the horsepower race and the introduction of the compact cars, existing techniques were used to produce the required lower horsepower engines, thus sliding the dotted circles back toward the origin, shifting the regression line BC downward and raising its slope slightly.

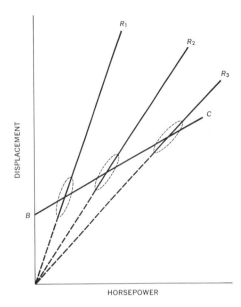

1   Illustration of technological change in the horsepower-displacement relationship.

The magnitude of these effects is of some interest. Our results indicate that a car in the 80–90 horsepower range (slightly below the range encountered for most low-priced cars) would have had a roughly constant displacement up until 1961 when a very moderate decline in displacement would have occurred. At 100 horsepower, displacement fell from about 230 cubic inches in 1948 to 194 cubic inches in 1960 and 180 in 1961. At 200 horsepower, however, displacement fell from about 460 cubic inches in 1948 to about 280 in 1960 and 1961. At higher horsepowers, the fall was, of course, greater. In all cases, most of the reduction occurred in the 1951–55 period.

D. Gasoline Costs of Model Changes

The relations summarized in Tables 4 and 5 were used to estimate the saving in gasoline consumption that would have been expected had 1949 specifications been continued. First, we estimated the gasoline consumption per 10,000 miles of each actually produced automobile model. Where Consumer Union test data were unavailable, we estimated ("predicted") it from the appropriate equation in Table 4, using "fuel economy factors" computed from published engine displacement and rpm data. These "predictions," together with the actual test data, where available, were then aggregated to produce comparable figures for company brand names such as Chevrolet, Ford and Dodge, using (as in Sec. II) weights constructed from model-year production data where available and from calendar-year registration data otherwise.[34] These figures were in turn averaged to secure average figures for the industry for each model year, 1949–60, using as weights actual production data by brand name, where available, or registrations as of July 1 of the year following the close of the model year.

To estimate the gasoline consumption that would have been incurred by cars with 1949 specifications, we took first each 1949 model's horsepower and used the results of Part C of this section to estimate what the model's displacement would have been in each successive year. From these estimates we selected as the displacement figure for each year the minimum of the displacements estimated for that model from 1950 to the year in question and the actual displacement for 1949. These displacements were then transformed into fuel economy factors using equation (1) from Part B and assuming that engine revolutions per mile in high gear would have been the same as in 1949. The resulting values of F were then transformed into gasoline consumption per 10,000 miles by use of the results of Part B of this section.

These estimated gasoline consumption figures were aggregated into brand-name figures using the 1949 weights. The results were then aggregated in turn into industry figures using registrations of 1949 cars as of July 1, 1950.[35] The resulting estimates of miles per gallon performance for both the actual and the constant 1949 specification cars are given in Table 6 for model years 1949 through 1960.

Table 6 shows that, while gasoline mileage was declining from 16.4 miles per gallon in 1949 to 14.3 miles per gallon in 1959, it could have been rising to 18.0 miles per gallon had 1949 specifications been continued. Even the rise to

■ **Table 6.** Miles per gallon performance of new actual and constant 1949 specification cars

Model year	Miles per gallon, new actual cars	Miles per gallon, new 1949 specification cars	Extra cost of new actual cars per 10,000 miles* (current dollars)
1949	16.4	—	—
1950	16.4	16.7	3.1
1951	15.7	16.9	12.5
1952	16.0	17.1	11.4
1953	16.1	17.2	11.7
1954	15.6	17.3	18.4
1955	15.1	17.4	26.8
1956	14.8	17.7	34.6
1957	14.5	17.9	42.4
1958	14.4	17.9	43.2
1959	14.3	18.0	44.3
1960	15.3	18.0	30.6
1961	15.2†	18.5	37.2‡

*   Valued at prices in Table 7 (below).
†   1960 weights used.
‡   At 1960 prices.

15.3 miles per gallon that occurred with the introduction of the compacts of 1960 fell far short of the actual 1949 level, let alone the level that could have been achieved. In money terms, the average owner of a 1959 car (the most gasoline-consuming model year) was paying about $44 per 10,000 miles more for gasoline than would have been the case with 1949 specifications—about 20 per cent of his total gasoline expenditures. For high-price high-horsepower cars, the additional cost was even greater.

Unlike the costs discussed in the last two sections, the costs of extra gasoline consumption do not terminate with the building and sale of the car; they continue over the life of the automobile. We must therefore estimate the total gasoline consumption of that part of the car *stock* consisting of cars built after 1949 that would have been avoided in each year with constant 1949 specification.[36]

■ **Table 7.** Gasoline consumption costs of model changes since 1949

Year	Extra Gasoline con-sumption by post-1949 cars (million gals.)	Average per post-1949 car (gals.)	Per cent of actual gasoline con-sumption by such cars	Average retail price of gas including tax (current dollars per gal.)*	Gasoline costs of model changes	
					Per post-1949 car (current dollars)	Millions of total current dollars
1950	45.4	14.7	2.6	.2776	4.1	12.6
1951	126.1	15.1	2.7	.2815	4.3	35.5
1952	362.4	27.2	4.7	.2856	7.8	102.0
1953	542.7	29.8	5.2	.2969	8.8	161.1
1954	797.4	33.7	5.8	.3004	10.1	239.5
1955	1,237.7	42.1	7.2	.3007	12.7	372.2
1956	1,906.7	53.6	9.1	.3093	16.6	589.7
1957	2,523.6	62.7	10.5	.3196	20.0	806.5
1958	3,025.4	69.3	11.5	.3138	21.7	949.4
1959	3,642.0	77.0	12.7	.3149	24.2	1,146.9
1960	4,189.0	83.3	12.6	.3213	26.8	1,345.9
1956–60 average						967.7

*   One cent per gallon added (see text) to figures for 1950–58 in American Petroleum Institute, *Petroleum Facts and Figures, 1959*, p. 379; 1959–60 *Platt's Oilgram Price Service.*

To construct estimates of gasoline consumption by actual post-1949 cars for each year, we took the average gasoline consumption by brand name and model year derived above and multiplied them by the registration figure for that brand name and model year as of July 1 of the year in question. The basic assumption used in the construction of estimates of the gasoline consumption of the constant 1949 specification car stock was that the history of these cars would have duplicated the actual history of the 1949 models, so far as the distribution in any year *l* of such cars over brand names is concerned.[37]

The resulting estimates of gasoline consumption by post-1950 cars for both the actual and the 1949 specifications car stock assume that cars were driven 10,000 miles per year, on the average. However, the Bureau of Public Roads and the American Petroleum Institute estimate the actual average mileage of passenger cars at somewhat less than this, their estimates ranging between about 9,000 and 9,500 miles per year.[38] There is no need for great precision here, and we took 9,250 miles as the relevant figure for every year.

■ **Table 8.** Total estimated costs of model changes since 1949 (Millions of current dollars)

Year*	Total direct costs (1)	Retooling costs (2)	Gasoline costs (3)	Total costs† (4)
1950	− 27	20	13	6
1951	267	45	36	348
1952	460	82	102	644
1953	436	246	161	844
1954	1,072	264	240	1,576
1955	2,425	469	372	3,266
1956	3,040	336	590	3,966
1957	4,048	772	806	5,626
1958	2,354	626	949	3,924
1959	3,675	532	1,147	5,354
1960	3,456	537	1,346	5,339
1956–60 average				4,843
Present value in 1961 of future gasoline costs already committed‡				7,110

* We have combined model-year and calendar-year figures. The actual timing of the various elements of the total is slightly different.

† Total may not equal sum of components due to rounding.

‡ Due to lack of data at time of writing, we do not present complete estimates for 1961. Preliminary estimates using 1961 figures presented in earlier sections indicate that costs in that year (including gasoline costs) continue well above $5 billion.

We valued gasoline consumption at the current retail prices for regular gasoline, including tax,[39] adding one cent per gallon as an adjustment for the higher price of premium grade gasoline.

The resulting estimates are given in Table 7. However, they do not tell the whole story. As mentioned earlier, gasoline consumption costs of model changes last throughout the life of the car. Thus, even if the 1962 and all later model years were to see a return to 1949 specifications, the additional gasoline expenditures due to the 1950–61 model changes would continue for the next decade at least. Assuming an average car life of ten years, and discounting the future at 10 per cent (surely an ample rate), the present value in 1961 of such expenditures (at 1960 prices) is about $7,109.5 million.

V. Total Costs and Conclusions

The various components of costs estimated in previous sections are brought together in Table 8 and graphed in Figure 2.

What can we say about these figures?

First, let us ask whether our estimates are likely to overstate or understate the costs to the economy of model changes since 1949. The answer seems to be that our estimates understate the cost. Aside from items previously discussed, we have not attempted to estimate such possibly important secondary costs as the added traffic and parking problems due to greater car length, or the costs in human life and property damage that may have resulted from higher horse-powers.[40] Further, new model cars (especially as automatic transmissions became more and more widespread) tended to have higher repair costs than would presumably have been the case with 1949 specifications. None of these items has been included in our estimates.

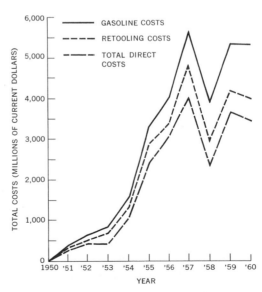

2   Total estimated costs of model changes since 1949.

Moreover, while we argued in Section III that the exclusion of design and research and development costs was in part an avoidance of double counting, it is clear that large elements of such design and research and development costs hardly contributed to the technological change involved in our estimates. One need only mention the expenditures that Ford must have incurred in the introduction of the short-lived Edsel to realize that we have failed to include some sizable items in our analysis.

Next, we have assumed throughout that the number of cars would have been unchanged had 1949 specifications been continued. This may or may not be a good assumption, but it is difficult to argue that *more* cars would have been sold. It follows that, if anything, our results fail to cost the extra cars that were in fact produced.

Finally, in choosing the 1949 model year as a standard for specifications, and in resting our analyses on the actual costs and gasoline consumption of domestically produced cars, we have not asked whether a more stringent standard could not be derived from the experience of various European car producers. Our cost estimates rest on the historical experience of the domestic industry. Had we chosen a European small-car standard, estimated costs clearly would have been higher.

For all these reasons, it seems to us that our estimates must err considerably on the low side, even after the greatest benefit of the doubt is given to the stochastic nature of our estimates. The order of magnitude of the cost of model changes is clearly greater than that indicated in our figures. On the other hand, we have not attempted to assess monetary benefits. For example, the increases in horsepower and in the use of power steering and automatic transmissions may have led to an increase in the average speed of automobile travel of about 10 per cent.[41] Assuming that in the base period the average speed was about 30 miles per hour, that approximately 9,000 miles were traveled by a car per year, and that on the average there were about 1.5 passengers per car, we get an estimate of 45 man-hours saved per new car year. Valuing these hours at $1.00 per hour[42] leads us to a guess of $45 as the annual per car benefit from the time saving aspects of higher speeds. This is a large figure, of the same order of magnitude as our estimate of the costs of increased gasoline consumption per car, and would similarly persist throughout the life of the car. It is hard to think of many additional "benefits" of this sort. Their existence, however, is indicated by the apparent willingness of consumers to pay for at least some of these changes.

The costs of model changes since 1949 were thus a substantial part of expenditures on automobiles, especially in the last half of the 1950's, our estimates running about $5 billion a year.[43] Were such costs worthwhile? It is difficult to say. There is a presumption that consumer purchases are worth the money paid, yet one might argue that the fact that our figures for the late 1950's (about $700 in the purchase price per car, or more than 25 per cent, and $40 per year in gasoline expenses) will probably seem surprisingly high to consumers[44] is an indication that the costs in question were not fully understood by the consuming public.

On the other hand, one must not press such an argument too far. We have repeatedly stated that, in every model year considered, the *average* 1949 specifications lay inside the actual range of specifications encountered. The clear implication is that consumers could have bought such cars had they wished. Moreover, such items as automatic transmissions, power brakes, and power steering were separately available and had prices of their own. It is thus extremely hard to claim that at least some of the costs of model changes were not explicitly reflected in the prices set before consumers. Indeed, the only elements of such costs that were obviously not explicitly stated were the costs of retooling and advertising and (possibly) gasoline costs. Thus consumers knowingly purchased more costly cars than those with 1949 specifications, even in the presence of *some* explicit cost differential in favor of the latter.

All in all, save for the understatement of costs involved and the possibility that such costs were not fully understood by car-buyers, the model changes of the last decade seem to have been largely those desired by the consuming public, at least until the last years of the horsepower race. There are thus grounds for believing that car owners (at the time of purchase) thought model changes worth most of the cost. The general presumption of consumer sovereignty thus implies that these model changes *were* worth their cost.[45] How heavily that presumption is to be weighted in all the presence of some cost understatement or in the presence of advertising directed at the formation or changing of tastes[46] is not a question that can be readily decided. Nor, indeed, is it obvious in retrospect that a referendum among the same car owners on the desirability of model changes would now reveal (or would have revealed in 1949) the same preferences for model change that seem to have been revealed in the historical market place.

It is thus not easy to decide whether the costs reported in this paper were worth incurring. Unlike some other examples of product change, the issue seems difficult enough to be worth raising. No one would deny that the shift from the horse and buggy to the automobile and the change from the kerosene lamp to the electric light were worth their respective costs.[47] Such improvements were so large and obvious that the issue is easy to decide. Whether this is true of some or all of the changes from the 1949 automobile specifications seems to us to be at least an open question.[48]

NOTES

1. 1949 is the earliest year for which all necessary data are available. It will be evident from the data that choice of 1950, 1951, or 1952 as the base year would not substantially alter the results.
2. We say "may," not "must," for the market in question is far from perfect.
3. See, for example, J. K. Galbraith. *The Affluent Society* (Boston: Houghton Mifflin Co., 1958), p. 352 and elsewhere.

4. We are indebted to G. S. Maddala for research assistance with this section. Some of the computations reported in this section, originally designed for other purposes, were supported by a grant from the National Science Foundation to the University of Chicago to allow Griliches to engage in econometric studies of technological change.

5. The last item belongs more properly in the section dealing with the cost of a given "technology" but is discussed in this section for reasons of convenience.

6. For a more detailed discussion of the problems associated with relating cross-sectional differences in the price of a commodity to differences in "quality," dimensions, or specifications see Z. Griliches, "Hedonic Price Indexes for Automobiles: An Econometric Analysis of Quality Change" (Bureau of the Budget-NBER Price Statistics Review Committee Staff Report No. 3, printed in United States Congress, Joint Economic Committee, *Government Price Statistics*, Hearings . . . January 24, 1961, [Washington, Government Printing Office, 1961], pp. 173–96), and the literature cited there.

7. In particular, the fall in the relative "price" of horsepower clearly stems from the technological change in horsepower-engine size relation studied explicitly in Sec. IV below.

8. Similar regressions were also run in linear form (rather than the semi-log form reported here) and using "piston displacement in cubic inches" as an additional variable without any improvement over the reported results. The "insignificance" of the displacement variable is due to its extremely high correlation with horsepower. Since we are primarily interested in costing horsepower, we introduce it here directly rather than going through a circuitous procedure such as that necessary in Sec. IV.

    Estimates were also made using several cross-sections at a time, imposing the condition that the various slope coefficients be the same for different years, but allowing the level of average prices ("technology") to shift "neutrally" over time, by assigning a separate constant term for each cross-section. The results were similar to those reported here and, since they do not lead to substantially different estimates or interpretations, are not reproduced here. Some of these estimates have been presented in Z. Griliches, "Hedonic Price Indexes . . . ," *op. cit.*

9. In view of the form of our regressions, if profit margins and wholesale-retail mark-ups are roughly constant in percentage terms, or at least uncorrelated with the various specification variables, this is also an estimate of "costs."

10. For data on discounts see A. F. Jung, "Price Policy and Discounts in the Medium- and High-priced Car Market," *Journal of Business*, October 1960, pp. 342–47.

11. We are grateful to Lloyd Dollett, of the Securities and Exchange Commission, for his courtesy and assistance. The computations in this section were performed by Felicity Skidmore. We are indebted to members of the Harvard Research Seminar in Quantitative Economics for suggestions.

12. Since we are not estimating "secondary" costs other than gasoline consumption, we feel safe in saying that the inclusion of retooling expenditures leaves our estimates on the low side.

13. One qualification is necessary. If the recoupment of retooling costs in car prices is correlated with specifications, we have already counted some of it. In view of the

semi-logarithmic form of our regressions, however, this effect will cancel out if it is roughly proportional to car price. This seems likely, since retooling expenditures per car are probably greater for high-priced models. In any case, such a bias in our results cannot be large, for despite the huge increase in retooling expenditures over the period, our regressions show declining "prices" for specifications even after technological change in engine design practically ceased (as evidenced by our results of the next section). Moreover, the double counting engendered by this effect applies only to a part of the full retooling expenditure. We therefore feel fairly safe in neglecting it.

14. Form 10K, Schedule V.

15. The only exceptions are Willys-Overland and Nash and later American Motors, which report for the year ended September 30. (Neither of these is a large part of the total, and the first is clearly negligible.) We have still assumed that such expenditures took place at the *end* of the reporting year and were for the *following* model year. This seems clearly to have been the case since about 1955 but is less certain before that time. Readjustment to account for this (if needed) would be only one of timing and would make very little difference in the industry totals in any case.

16. Figures for Hudson in 1953 and Kaiser in 1950 are also missing. We did not bother to adjust the totals for this, because the first figure was clearly only about 1 per cent of the total at the most, and the second was much less.

17. We should like to thank our research assistants, Stephen A. Resnick and David Shapiro, who secured most of the data here discussed; George Delehanty, who computed the weights for the relative importance of makers' models within automobile makes; and Felicity Skidmore and Cynthia M. Travis, who performed most of the computations directly relevant to gasoline consumption. The materials in this section of the study are based on work done for other purposes under a grant from Resources for the Future, Inc., to Massachusetts Institute of Technology to allow Fisher to study quantitative aspects of the economics of supply and demand in the petroleum industry.

18. Other reported data are generally either for constant-speed tests, or highly aggregated.

19. Visual inspection of the residuals from our regressions seems to bear this out, as there does not seem to be any tendency for the scatter in the relation of gasoline consumption to engine size, given transmission type, to change over time.

20. "U.S. Autos 1961," *Consumer Reports*, XXVI, No. 4 (April, 1961), 176.

21. *Ibid.*

22. *F* can be used also as the sole explanatory variable in the regressions, because such other variables as automobile weight enter principally into the determination of the characteristics and especially the size of the engine.

23. For the period 1949–61, there are almost no tests of semi-automatic transmissions but the number of cars with such transmissions is negligible.

24. Cf. comments on the test statistics in "Road-test Report on the Full-size 'Low-priced' V-8's," *Consumer Reports*, XXVI, No. 2 (February, 1961), 107.

25. Since the variability of the distribution of mileage over forward speeds can be expected to be relatively high (*ceteris paribus*) when the number of forward speeds is large and the amount of shifting among them consequently great.

26. We are indebted to A. R. Rogowski, of the Department of Mechanical Engineering at M.I.T., for preliminary discussion of some of the technical matters covered in this section. He is emphatically not to be held responsible for our opinions, conclusions, results, or especially errors, nor for the evidently rudimentary state of our information on automotive mechanics.

27. Cf. "U.S. Autos 1961," *op. cit.*, p. 176.

28. This redesign took the form largely of raising compression ratios and of shifting the torque-rpm curve. The rising octane content of gasoline also helped.

29. The observations in these computations were on engines rather than on cars. We eliminated observations on other models produced by a given company that had the same engine.

30. Since the correlation between horsepower and displacement is so high for each year, and this is the relationship of interest, there is no need to introduce the effect on compression ratios as an explicit step.

31. We present the results for the model years 1948–61 inclusive since the pattern seems of interest.

32. Note that this change in the slope coefficients reflects itself (roughly) as a change in the direct cost of horsepower already reported in Sec. II.

33. This pattern is not simply the result of sampling fluctuations. The hypothesis that all the regressions are from the same true relationship is emphatically rejected by covariance analysis, the relevant F statistic being 28.9, whereas the probability of observing an F even as high as about 2.1 if the hypothesis were true would be .001 (with 26 and 468 degrees of freedom). Moreover, such significant inhomogeneity is not merely due to the behavior of the intercepts. A further test of slope equality only yields an F statistic of 29.1, whereas the probability of observing an F even as high as about 2.7 if the slopes were all the same would be .001 (with 13 and 468 degrees of freedom). It is thus apparent that our results reflect real changes in structure for the period as a whole (similar tests would doubtless fail to reject the null hypothesis of no structural change for 1955–60).

34. The basic assumption in the latter case was that the *internal* distribution of each brand name over the various maker's models it included was the same for the calendar year as for the model year. This involved a host of minor problems of comparability between successive years' models too numerous to discuss in detail. The registration data are collected by R. L. Polk & Co., and reported in several trade journals.

35. We assume here and below that the distribution of 1949 cars by brand names would have been preserved had 1949 specification been continued. Since brand market shares have not changed very much, this is not an important assumption.

36. We must make here some assumption about the change in gasoline consumption over the life of a car. Since we are primarily interested in the *difference* between the gasoline consumption of the actual car stock and of one made up of 1949 specification cars, we have only to assume that the effect of age on gasoline consumption

is linear and the same in both cases, so that with the same age distribution of cars in the car stock, the difference in gasoline consumption will be unaffected.

37. Other assumptions as to the composition of the car stock over brand names would have been more difficult to apply in practice and would make little difference to the totals. To assume that the total number of cars would have been less than actually was the case would have given a higher estimate of costs.

38. American Petroleum Institute, *Petroleum Facts and Figures, 1959* (New York, 1960), pp. 252–53.

39. We include taxes here as elsewhere as we are measuring expenditure by car owners. Taxes were about 7–10 cents per gallon during the period.

40. Potentially at least, these costs could be estimated. Some parking garages charge a higher fee for longer cars, and insurance claims paid presumably could be analyzed for variation with specifications, other things being equal. This would be a full-scale undertaking, however.

41. This and the following figures are purely illustrative. We have been unable to find a consistent set of national data on this topic. The following calculation is only intended to indicate the possible magnitude of such benefits. These estimates are probably on the high side.

42. This relatively low figure is used, since a substantial fraction of these passengers are women and children who are not in the labor force.

43. These figures include tax and are thus measures of expenditures by consumers. At factor costs they would still be over $4 billion a year.

44. The Automobile Manufacturers Association clearly regards them as extremely high (see letter of Harry A. Williams [its managing director] in *The Nation*, February 17, 1962, p. 128).

45. Indeed, one of the authors has used some of the same calculations to measure the improvement in the *quality* of automobiles since 1949 (see Griliches, "Hedonic Price Indexes . . . ," *op. cit.*).

46. Or in the presence of external diseconomies of consumption in the case of some of the non-costed items mentioned earlier in this section.

47. Cf. Williams, *op. cit.*, and *Barron's Weekly*, January 11, 1962, p. 7.

48. "The 1949 car . . . was pretty advanced transportation for its day" (Williams, *op. cit.*).

REGISTRATION AND VOTING:
PUTTING FIRST THINGS FIRST

STANLEY KELLEY, Jr.
RICHARD E. AYRES
WILLIAM G. BOWEN

In their book *Non-Voting*, published in 1924, Charles E. Merriam and Harold F. Gosnell reported that many persons otherwise eligible to vote had been disfranchised by Chicago's registration requirements. Their data showed that "there were three times as many adult citizens who could not vote because they had failed to register as there were registered voters who had failed to vote in the particular election"[2] and that "entirely different reasons [for not voting] were emphasized by those who were not registered than by those who were registered but did not vote . . ."[3] Their observation can hardly be said to have been influential. Until very recently most students of voting have paid little attention to the temporally prior act of registration.[4]

Failure to do so has had important consequences. It has made it easy to discount unduly the significance of *political* influences on the size and composition of electorates; easy to argue unrealistically about the value of efforts to increase the turnout of voters; and easy to be puzzled about some aspects of the behavior of voters.

I. The Design of the Study

The study out of which this article grows was undertaken in an effort to find answers to two questions: To what extent can differences from place to place in the turnout of voters in elections be accounted for by differences in the number of those registered to vote? What factors are most strongly associated with variations in the percentage of those of voting age who do register to vote in different localities? We tried to find answers to these questions by analyzing registration and voting in 1960 in 104 of the nation's largest cities.[5]

Our analysis was guided by Anthony Downs' discussion of voting in his *An Economic Theory of Democracy*. Downs assumes that "every rational man decides to vote just as he makes all other decisions: if the returns outweigh the costs, he votes; if not, he abstains";[6] and that assumption enables him to make a number of interesting deductions about which voters are likely to vote and which are not. We decided to assume that both the voter's decision to register and decisions made by party organizations about efforts to induce citizens to register are made after a similar rational calculation of benefits and costs. If

Reprinted by permission of the authors and the American Political Science Association from *The American Political Science Review* **61** (June, 1967), 359–379.

one makes that assumption, it follows that variations in rates of registration among cities are the consequence of differences among them in the way voters assess the value of registering, in the interest politicians have in adding new names to the registration rolls, in costs voters perceive to be associated with the act of registering, and in costs of mounting registration drives. About such assessments, interests, and perceptions we had no direct information, but they could reasonably be supposed to be affected by several factors about which information was available.

The value that voters attach to the act of registering and that politicians put on registration drives should vary, for instance, with the competitiveness of a state's party politics and with the offices that are at stake in an election. As the probable division of the vote for the major parties in a state approaches 50–50, presidential candidates and all candidates for state-wide office have an increasingly strong incentive to induce their partisans to register, and the voter has an increasingly large (if still very small) chance to cast a ballot that will decide the outcome of a contest. As the number of officials to be elected in any given election rises, or, perhaps more accurately, as the scope of governmental power at stake in any election increases, so should the voter's estimate of the importance of the election. We therefore decided to examine the relationship of registration to both these variables.

There are three rather different sorts of costs that voters may see as involved in the act of registering to vote. In the first instance there are *monetary* costs. In 1960 some southern cities literally charged a fee, the poll tax, for putting one's name on the list of eligible voters; but in other places registering might also mean a loss of income through loss of time on the job or time away from a business.[7] Perhaps a more important cost is simple *inconvenience*. To get their names on a registration roll almost all voters must go out of their way to a greater or lesser extent and in some places the bother involved is very considerable indeed. Finally, there are costs of *obtaining information* about registering to vote. A voter must find out where and when he can register and if he is eligible to do so, and acquiring this information may take an appreciable amount of time and effort. We postulated that the magnitude of one or more of these sorts of costs would be greater, and would be seen as greater, in cities where citizens must take a literacy test;[8] where all voters must re-register at frequent intervals; where it is necessary to register considerably in advance of election day; and where the hours during which, and places at which, one can register are restricted.

The findings of the major studies of voting were a second important influence on our early speculation about factors that might account for differences among cities in rates of registration. Registration is hardly ever represented as anything but a purely instrumental act: one registers in order to vote. One would suppose, therefore, that most of the factors that encourage or discourage voting also encourage or discourage registering to vote. Proceeding on that supposition, we posited a strong relationship between registration and those socio-economic and psychological factors that have figured prominently in explanations of the turnout of voters in elections.[9] We could not, of course, hope to discover whether a relationship actually existed between registration and each such factor; no data were available to us on the psychological states or personal traits of persons of voting age in the cities we studied.[10] We could and did, however, try to find out if the proportion of citizens of voting age who were registered to vote in a city was associated with the median income and average educational attainment of the city's residents and with the numbers of recent migrants, young people, males, and Negroes in its population.

There has been less agreement on why various socio-economic factors are related to turnout in elections than on the fact that they are related, but such is the present state of the literature on voting. Downs attributes differences in the turnout rates of various classes of citizens to their varying abilities to bear the costs of voting or variations in what voting costs them. Thus, to make sense of the choices an election offers him, the educated man needs less additional information than someone who is poorly educated, and higher income groups are in a better position to pay the costs of finding out how their interests are affected by alternatives (and to pay other costs of voting) than are low income groups.[11] S. M. Lipset offers very similar explanations for the relationship of income and education to turnout, and both Downs and Lipset note also that the turnout rates of low-income groups may be lowered by confusion resulting from exposure to a largely conservative press.[12] Campbell and his colleagues argue that "The educated person is distinct from the less educated not only in the number of facts about politics at his command, but also in the sophistication of the concepts he employs to maintain a sense of order and meaning amid the flood of information";[13] the educated man is therefore less likely to abstain from voting out of a feeling that politics is too complicated to understand. Low rates of participation in elections among young voters have been explained by reference to their fluid occupational interests, greater mobility, lack of firm attachments to political parties, and absence of clear positions in the social life of their communities.[14] The low turnout of women relative to men is usually attributed to the cultural definition of politics as the concern of men, and that of Negroes relative to whites is attributed to deliberate efforts to discourage Negro voting and to the status of Negroes as a low-income group. It has been argued that newcomers to a community are less likely to vote than old residents because they have less contact with locally dominant groups, because their mobility is likely to have exposed them to politically relevant cross-pressures, and because they are likely to be disqualified for voting by local residence requirements.[15]

Certain common sense considerations were a third influence on our guesses about the factors that might make for higher or lower levels of registration. States require varying periods of residence in the state, and in the county and voting district, before a person is eligible to register even if he is otherwise qualified to do so. All states also require voters to be citizens of the United States. One would therefore expect that variations from place to place in residence requirements and any local variations in numbers of resident aliens would make a difference in the proportion of persons of voting age who are registered to vote in different cities. Further, rates of registration are known to vary regionally. This relationship might reflect differences in the culture of regions rather than regional differences in the values of the variables so far discussed. Finally, those cities having systems of permanent registration employ methods of differing efficiency to remove from registration rolls the names of voters who have died, moved away, or failed to vote for a specified period, a fact which could also account for some of the variation in registration rates from city to city.

It should be apparent that testing some of the hypotheses of interest to us entailed formidable problems in gathering data. We chose to study registration in 1960 because we were able to secure data on registration for a number of jurisdictions from the national committees of the two major parties; moreover, the presidential election of 1960 coincided with a decennial census year. We chose the nation's large cities as units of observation because there were a sufficient number of them to make statistical analysis fruitful and because we could secure data for them that was unavailable either for states or counties. Several of the states, for instance, collect no information on the numbers of their citizens registered to vote. Registration, voting, and census data are reported by counties, but the hours, days of the week, and kinds of places where citizens can register are frequently determined at lower levels of government, and so may vary considerably within counties.

Cities are units of observation well suited to examining the effects on registration of differences among localities in the extent of inter-party competition, residence requirements, closing dates for registration, and the availability of places to register. Inter-city analysis is less appropriate for an examination of the effects on registration of individual characteristics such as sex, age, education, and income, which can be better studied by treating the individual as the unit of observation. For instance, it is obviously better to draw inferences about the effects of sex on registration from a direct comparison of registration rates between males and females (after allowing for the effects of other variables) than from a comparison of inter-city differences in registration associated with inter-city differences in sex-ratios. The main reason for including variables which measure individual characteristics in our inter-city analysis was to guard against the possibility that substantial differences among cities in, for example, the proportion of men in the population, might obscure the true effects on registration of variations in such factors as the degree of inter-party competition, residence requirements, and so on. It was also of interest of course, to see if the variables which measure individual characteristics were sufficiently powerful to cause differences among cities in registration rates.

In analyzing differences among cities in the percentage of the voting-age population registered to vote, we used ordinary multiple-regression techniques, and we assumed that linear fits could be used to approximate the true relationships among our variables. Other aspects of our procedures can be explained most conveniently as we present our findings.

II. Findings

Registration related to turnout. Our findings with respect to the first of the two major questions in which we were interested—that concerning the relationship of registration to the turnout of voters in elections—can be reported in a few sentences. In the full sample of cities, 78 per cent of the variation in the percentage of the population of voting age that voted could be accounted for by variations in the percentage of the population of voting age that was registered to vote.[16] As one would expect, the relationship was almost one-to-one; that is, if the percentage of the population of voting age registered to vote in city A was one per cent higher than in city B, then the percentage of the population of voting age actually voting in city A was, on the average, almost exactly one per cent higher than in city B.[17] Moreover, it seems clear that registration requirements are a more effective deterrent to voting than anything that normally operates to deter citizens from voting once they have registered, at least in presidential elections. The mean percentage of *those of voting age who were registered to vote* in the full sample of cities was 73.3 per cent and the standard deviation was 14.3 per cent. In contrast, the mean percentage of *those registered to vote who voted* was 81.6 per cent with a standard deviation of 11.7 per cent. Thus the latter was not only higher but also varied within a narrower range.

Variations in proportion registered. What factors account for the wide range of differences among cities in the proportion of the population of voting age that is registered to vote? Discussion of our findings with respect to this second question must be considerably more extensive. To begin with, we will report what we found to be the most important influences on rates of registration in our full sample of cities. We will then present additional information obtained by examining registration only in those cities with systems of permanent registration (the reason for this separate analysis of cities with systems of permanent registration will be apparent later), by controlling for regional influences, and by analyzing the pattern of residual variance.

Findings with Respect to the Full Sample of Cities

Table 1 summarizes the results of our analysis of the registration of voters in the full sample of cities.[18] It seems clear that we included among our explanatory factors a number of highly significant ones: Together, the twelve independent variables in Regression I.1 "explain" (in the sense usual when interpreting multiple regression equations) nearly 80 per cent of the variation among cities in percentages of the population of voting age registered to vote. Only one of these twelve variables (the percentage of males in the population of voting age) failed to have the expected sign, and six had "t" values large enough to imply that their regression coefficients were significantly different from zero at a level of confidence of 95 per cent or better. In a second regression (I.2 in Table 1) that included only these six variables, the value of R^2 fell just three percentage points, and all six continued to show statistically significant relationships to the dependent variable.[19]

Socio-economic factors. Regression I.1 included six socio-economic variables—age, race, education, income, sex, and length of residence.[20] Only three—age, education, and race—were significantly related to variations among cities in rates of registration. The implications of the regression coefficients of these variables may be stated as follows:

A. If the number of persons in the age-group 20 to 34 relative to the number of persons of voting age in a city was larger than the average of all cities in the sample by one per cent, the city's rate of registration tended to be one-half of one per cent below the average of all cities in the sample.
B. If the residents over 25 years of age in a city had a median educational attainment one year above the average of all cities in the sample, the city tended to have a rate of registration that was two to three per cent above the average of all cities in the sample.
C. If the percentage of non-whites in a city's population was greater by one per cent than the average in all cities of the sample, the city tended to have a rate of registration that was a little less than one-fifth of one per cent below the average of all cities in the sample.

The relationship described in (C) is of particular interest, since it held even when allowances had been made for the use of literacy tests in some cities and even when our race variable was included in the same regression with variables that reflected differences between whites and non-whites in average income, average educational attainment, and ratios of younger to older persons of voting age.

That we did not find variations in the median income of the populations of cities to be significantly related to rates of registration is also of some interest. Although higher median incomes for the populations of the cities of our sample were associated with higher rates of registration in our multiple regression, the regression coefficient for the income variable was not quite significant at the 90 per cent level of confidence. We did find that we could easily push the "t" value for the income variable high enough to indicate a relationship significant at the 99 per cent level of confidence if we dropped our race and education variables from the analysis, since both of these had fairly high correlations with the income variable.[21] But various experiments of this kind showed that the income variable, by itself, had less explanatory power than either of the other two. Where intercorrelations of this kind exist, it is impossible on the basis of the statistical techniques we used to sort out the "independent" effect of any of the variables in a precise way. Nevertheless, our results do give some further support to the conclusion of the authors of *The American Voter* that a voter's education has more directly important consequences for his participation in elections than does his income.[22]

■ **Table 1.** Regression analysis of differences among cities in percentage of the population of voting age registered to vote (104 cities, 1960)

Variables[a]	Ex-pected sign	Regression I.1[b]			Regression I.2[c]		
		b	*(s)*	*t*	*b*	*(s)*	*t*
Independent Variables							
Socio-economic factors							
Age (per cent 20–34)	–	−0.47	(0.20)	2.33*	−0.50	(0.18)	2.79**
Sex (per cent male)	+	−0.18	(0.63)	0.28			
Race (per cent non-white)	–	−0.14	(0.07)	2.05*	−0.17	(0.07)	2.46*
Education (median yrs. completed)	+	2.13	(0.99)	2.16*	2.88	(0.72)	4.02*
Income ($100/yr.)	+	0.23	(0.16)	1.43			
Length of residence (per cent from out of state)	–	−0.20	(0.15)	1.33			
Factors affecting the value of the vote							
Inter-party competition (per cent)	–	−0.30	(0.10)	3.02**	−0.41	(0.07)	5.60**
Factors affecting the costs of registration[d]							
Provisions regarding literacy tests	+	0.09	(0.04)	2.17*	0.12	(0.04)	3.29**
Closing date for registration	+	0.13	(0.04)	3.45**	0.15	(0.03)	4.28**
Times and places of registration	+	2.20	(2.00)	1.10			
Registration system (permanent or periodic)	+	0.06	(0.04)	1.52			
Other factors[d]							
Residence requirements	+	0.04	(0.04)	0.96			
Dependent Variable: Percentage of population of voting age registered to vote							
Mean			73.3			73.3	
Standard deviation			(14.3)			(14.3)	
F-ratio			28.05			52.20	
Standard error of estimate			7.0			7.2	
Number of cities			104			104	
R^2			.79**			.76**	

(Footnote on page 257)

We found that differences in the relative numbers of men and women of voting age in the populations of the cities of our sample had no observable effect on rates of registration in our cities. There were, we think, several reasons for this result. In the first place, differences in the ratios of men to women in the population of voting age in the cities of our sample were relatively slight: The standard deviation of the variable was only 1.49 per cent around the mean percentage of males in the population of voting age. Secondly, our data concerned registration in large cities, and the differences between men and women in turnout in elections have been found to be smaller in metropolitan areas than elsewhere.[23] Finally, collinearity of our sex variable with other variables tended to obscure any relationship it might otherwise have shown to rates of registration; those cities in the sample with the largest percentages of males in their population of voting age, it turned out, also tended to have unusually large concentrations of young voters and recent migrants from out of state.

The last of the socio-economic variables included in Regression I.1, length of residence, was positively related to rates of registration, but the relationship was not statistically significant. The authority of this finding is compromised somewhat, however, by our reliance on a rather imprecise measure of length of residence, and it is entirely possible that we would have obtained a significant result if we had been able to use a better one.

Factors affecting the value of the vote. From our efforts to detect any effects on rates of registration of factors affecting the value of the vote, we can report two findings. The first, made at an early point in our study, is that differences from city to city in the offices that were at stake in the election of 1960 had very little, if any, impact on registration; the correlation between rates of registration and an index we constructed to reflect such differences was small and not significant. What this result suggests is what the marked differences in turnout for presidential or other elections would also seem to indicate: That the interest of voters in presidential races in the United States is so great that few additional voters are attracted to the polls by an interest in the outcome of other contests.

Rates of registration in our sample of cities were, however, very strongly related to another factor affecting the value of the vote: The normal degree of competitiveness of partisan politics in statewide contests. As Table 1 indicates, the regression coefficient of our index of inter-party competition was easily

---

Notation: b = net (partial) regression coefficient; (s) = standard error of regression coefficient; t = t-value of regression coefficient (t-values may differ from $b/(s)$ ratios in table because of rounding); ** = significant at 99 per cent; * = significant at 95 per cent.
[a] Defined in Appendix I.
[b] Includes all variables.
[c] Includes only variables significant at 95 per cent level in Regression I.1.
[d] As we indicate in Appendix I, these sets of variables are measured by indices whose scales are arbitrary. Thus, no units of measurement are shown in parentheses, and no meaning can be attached to the absolute values of the regression coefficients of these variables without bearing in mind how each index was scaled. The "t" values can, however, be interpreted in the usual way as indicators of statistical significance.

significant at the 99 per cent level of confidence in both regressions.[24] This result is consistent with evidence bearing on the relationship of turnout in elections to party competition that has been presented by a number of students of voting[25] and with our own expectation that a high level of competition between parties would increase the incentive for people to register and for politicians to get them to register. It is somewhat at variance, however, with conclusions that Robert Lane and that Angus Campbell and his associates have reached about the relationship between turnout and party competition.

Lane has argued that "although closeness of contest tends to enlist certain politicizing motives and, where habitual, to create stronger parties, the relationship between closeness of contest and turnout in the United States and Britain is small."[26] His conclusion with respect to Great Britain is hardly compelling, since Gosnell has offered equally good evidence for the contrary view.[27] With respect to the United States, Lane acknowledges the closeness of elections in states to be related to turnout but makes much of the fact that variations among *counties* in rates of non-voting did not appear to be associated with variations among *counties* in the Democratic percentage of the two-party vote in the 1952 presidential election.[28] That fact is quite consistent with our own hypothesis about the relationship of party competition to participation in elections, however, since we expected the relative closeness of contests to affect rates of participation only when the former had relevance to the value of voting; and the level of partisan competition in counties has no meaning for the value of voting in presidential elections.[29]

Angus Campbell and his colleagues found that voters in the election of 1956 with only a weak preference for one party or the other were no more likely to go to the polls whether they saw the election to be one-sided or close. Voters with strong partisan preferences were more likely to vote if they expected the election to be close, but, according to the authors of *The American Voter*, "The questions we have used to classify respondents according to their expectations about the election have referred to the contest *in the nation as a whole* . . . the analysis of answers to a question referring to the presidential race within the respondent's state indicates that it is the election *as a whole* that has cognitive and motivational significance, despite the existence of the electoral college."[30]

These findings are not easy to reconcile with our own. It could be that differences in the behavior of highly motivated voters from place to place are indeed an important source of local variations in rates of registration, but it does not seem likely that this is true, and it would not account for our result in any case if such voters do not pay attention to the closeness of the presidential race in their states. It could also be, and this seems more probable, that the factor intervening between the greater competitiveness of a state's party politics and higher turnout is not, for most voters, any conscious assessment of the likely outcome of the current election (such as is assumed by the analysis of *The American Voter*) but rather generalized feelings about how much votes have counted in the past; these generalized feelings may in turn be shaped by campaigning as this typically varies from state to state. Such an hypothesis would be consistent with data which show that Southern voters attribute less efficacy to voting than do Northerners,[31] and not inconsistent with either our own findings or those of Campbell and his co-authors. Finally, it could be that differences in rates of registration between cities of competitive and non-competitive states should be attributed largely to the actions of party activists; they undoubtedly are quite aware both of the level of party competition in a state and of its significance for the value of efforts to entice voters to register.

Factors affecting costs of registration. The four variables we inserted in Regression I.1 in order to examine the relationship between rates of registration and practices or procedures affecting the costs of registering were indices especially constructed for that purpose.[32] All were so scaled as to lead us to predict positive correlations of each variable with the percentage of the population of voting age registered to vote. While all showed the predicted relationship, it was statistically significant in two cases only.

The use of literacy tests was associated with lower rates of registration, as those who put provisions for such tests into election codes doubtless intended it to be.[33] In William Riker's words, "Eighteen states have adopted the [literacy test], seven to disfranchise Negroes, five to disfranchise Indians and Mexicans and Orientals, and six to disfranchise European immigrants."[34] The disfranchising effect of literacy tests appears to have been considerably less severe in cities outside the South, however, than in Southern cities. In one regression involving data from non-Southern cities only, literacy tests continued to be correlated with lower rates of registration, but the relationship was no longer significant even at a level of confidence of 90 per cent.

A more striking finding is the extremely strong relationship between the date at which registration rolls are closed and the percentage of the population of voting age that is registered.[35] This variable had the largest "t" value of any of the twelve in Regression I.1, and the second largest "t" value in Regression I.2. Its regression coefficient of .15 in Regression I.2 implies that extending the closing date for registration from, say, one month to one week prior to election day would tend to increase the percentage of the population registered by about 3.6 per cent. For politicians, varying the closing date for registration would thus appear to be a very effective way in which to manipulate the size of the potential electorate.

Why this should be so can be suggested here, if not demonstrated. A longer period in which one may register increases considerably the convenience of doing so, of course, but we doubt that that is all there is to the matter. A late closing date for registration also probably tends to increase rates of registration because it allows the campaign to serve as a reminder to weakly motivated voters that they need to register and as a stimulus to find out from others how they can do so. Such an interpretation of our findings would be consistent with the results of Gosnell's experimental efforts to stimulate registration in Chicago, and with his observation that ". . . if all the adult citizens in the city had been properly informed regarding registration dates, 10 per cent more of them would have registered."[36]

Even though the index we constructed in an effort to assess the effect on rates of registration of differences in systems of registration (permanent or periodic) failed to show a statistically significant relationship to variations in percentages of the population of voting age registered to vote, we are unwilling to deprecate the importance of such differences. Though it is by no means wholly persuasive, there is other evidence that systems of permanent registration are associated with higher rates of registration than are systems of periodic registration.[37] Moreover, our examination of these relationships could not in the nature of the case be very conclusive. For one thing, only fifteen of the cities in our sample had a system of periodic registration or its equivalent. For another, variations in systems of registration were highly correlated with variations in closing dates for registration (+.64). With both these factors working to obscure any relationship that our registration-systems variable might have to rates of registration, that relationship nonetheless just missed significance at a level of confidence of 90 per cent.

The variable labeled "times and places of registration" failed to correlate significantly with rates of registration in the full sample of cities. Our index was constructed to reflect the relative difficulty that the average citizen in each city would face in finding a registration place open at hours convenient to him. In constructing it, however, we did not take into account the fact that cities face different tasks in registering voters, depending on whether they use systems of permanent, or periodic, registration. In cities with periodic registration, about one-half of the adult population succeeds in registering, on the average. Cities with permanent registration, again on the average, do not have to deal with anything like this many people; in such cities, at any given time, most potential registrants are already registered. Thus, the convenience of equal facilities in cities having registration systems of the two different sorts cannot be equated. We therefore decided to analyze the effect of variations in the times and facilities for registration in cities using systems of permanent registration—that is, in a set of cities facing really comparable problems in registering voters. The results of that analysis are reported below.

We found that differences among cities in rates of registration were not significantly related to differences in the length of residence in states and localities required of voters. This finding is surprising. No other aspect of the legal provisions relevant to voting has received nearly so much attention from students of voting as residence requirements; indeed, some writers have seemed to regard residence requirements as proto-typical of requirements of registration.[38] We may have obtained these results because differences from place to place in requirements of residence were not sufficiently great to make any great difference in the relative percentages of the population of voting age qualified to vote; or it may have been that the differences in the proportion of recent migrants in the populations of our sample of cities were not great enough to affect rates of registration.

It seems to us, however, that some aspects of the reasoning that leads one to expect residence requirements to make a difference in registration rates may be faulty. It is a fact that, in any given year in the United States, many people change residence and are therefore disqualified for voting in many localities. It is true also that respondents to opinion surveys will frequently cite an inability to meet local requirements of residence in explanation of their failure to vote or register,[39] and that survey data show recency of residential change to be negatively correlated with turnout in elections. It does not follow from these facts that residence requirements keep large numbers of adults from voting who would vote if such requirements did not exist. Residence requirements may disqualify recent migrants as voters, but there are other reasons why they might not vote, some peculiar to their status as recent migrants and some not. Moreover, their own explanations of their conduct can hardly be taken at face value; inability to meet legal qualifications is a "good" reason for not voting and one that is therefore likely to be invoked frequently. Thus, we may have exaggerated the significance of residence requirements not only for differences among cities in rates of registration but also as a cause of non-voting and non-registration.

Findings with Respect to Cities with Systems of Permanent Registration.

The results of our analysis of registration in the 89 cities of our sample having systems of permanent registration are given in Table 2. The twelve independent variables included in Regression II.1 account for 70 per cent of the variation in rates of registration among these cities; the five variables retained in Regression II.2 account for 65 per cent of the variation.

For reasons already cited, we included in this analysis a variable not included in Regression I.1: methods of purging registration rolls. To "purge" a registration roll is to remove from it the names of voters no longer qualified to vote. State laws usually specify the circumstances in which a voter's name is to be purged; in most states it will be purged when a voter dies, moves away, or fails to vote within a certain period of time. Both the reasons for purging a voter's name and the procedures for discovering whether there is cause for purging the name of any particular voter, however, vary considerably from city to city. We expected such variations to be related to differences among cities in rates of registration, but they were not significantly related, as Table 2 indicates.[40]

Variations in our index of the convenience of the times and places of registration were significantly related to variations in rates of registration. The relationship was significant at the 95 per cent level of confidence in Regression II.1 and at the 99 per cent level of confidence in Regression II.2. This finding is important, for it suggests that local officials, by varying the convenience of registration procedures, may be able to affect appreciably not only the size, but also the composition, of local electorates.

The education variable explained much less of the variation in rates of registration among cities with systems of permanent registration than it did among the cities in our full sample. In our analysis of registration in cities with systems of permanent registration, the regression coefficient of this variable was not

■ **Table 2.** Regression analysis of differences in rates of registration among cities with systems of permanent registration (89 cities, 1960)

Variables[a]	Ex-pected sign	Regression II.1[b]			Regression II.2[c]		
		b	(s)	t	b	(s)	t
Independent Variables							
Socio-economic factors							
Age (per cent 20–34)	–	−0.42	(0.22)	1.94*	−0.19	(0.18)	1.05
Sex (per cent male)	+	−0.13	(0.71)	0.18			
Race (per cent non-white)	–	−0.17	(0.08)	2.26*	−0.25	(0.07)	3.74**
Education (median years completed)	+	1.11	(1.10)	1.01			
Income ($100/yr.)	+	0.26	(0.18)	1.46			
Length of residence (per cent from out of state)	–	−0.19	(0.16)	1.23			
Factors affecting the value of the vote							
Inter-party competition (per cent)	–	−0.28	(0.14)	2.05*	−0.51	(0.09)	5.54**
Factors affecting the costs of registration[d]							
Provisions regarding literacy tests	+	0.07	(0.06)	1.21			
Closing date for registration	+	0.15	(0.05)	3.43**	0.17	(0.04)	4.09**
Times and places of registration	+	7.86	(3.67)	2.14*	9.71	(3.31)	2.93**
Other factors[d]							
Methods of purging registration rolls	+	0.004	(0.05)	0.08			
Residence requirements	+	0.05	(0.05)	1.01			
Dependent Variable: Percentage of population of voting age registered to vote							
Mean		76.3			76.3		
Standard deviation		(11.6)			(11.6)		
F-ratio		14.80			31.00		
Standard error of estimate		6.8			7.0		
Number of cities		89			89		
R^2		.70**			.65**		

(Footnote on p. 263)

significant even at the 90 per cent level of confidence. Moreover, changes in its value were associated with changes in rates of registration only about half as great as in Regression I.1.

These last two findings—together with analyses of registration of Northern cities, in cities with rates of registration above 78 per cent, and in cities with late closing dates for registration—lead us to propose the following generalization: When the costs of registering are generally high, differences from place to place in the value of variables affecting the motivation to vote—education, for example —will account for a considerable part of the variation in rates of registration; when the costs of registering are generally low, differences from place to place in the value of such variables will be relatively less important, and differences in the convenience of arrangements for registration relatively more important, in their effects on rates of registration.

Controlling for the Effects of Region.

A classification by region of the 104 cities of our sample reveals a considerable difference among the cities of the various regions in average rates of registration. Those averages were as follows:

Region	Average rate of registration
Midwest	82.5
West	80.7
Northeast	76.1
Border	70.7
South	55.9

In order to discover if these differences might stem from some difference in the culture of regions rather than from regional variations in the values of the variables discussed so far, we re-computed Regressions I.1 and I.2 with a set of regional dummy variables included. (That is, we re-computed these regressions after having denoted whether a city was in, or not in, each of the five regions by assigning a "1" in the first case and a "0" in the second.) Following is the matrix

Notation: b = net (partial) regression coefficient; (s) = standard error of regression coefficient; t = t-value of regression coefficient (t-value may differ from $b/(s)$ ratios in table because of rounding); ** = significant at 99 per cent; * = significant at 95 per cent;
[a] Defined in Appendix I.
[b] Included all variables listed.
[c] Includes only variables significant at 95 per cent level in Regression II.1.
[d] As we indicate in Appendix I, these sets of variables are measured by indices whose scales are arbitrary. Thus, no units of measurement are shown in parentheses, and no meaning can be attached to the absolute values of the regression coefficients of these variables without bearing in mind how each index was scaled. The "t" values can, however, be interpreted in the usual way as indicators of statistical significance.

of *t*-values needed to show in which instances the regional dummies were significantly different from each other:[41]

	West	Northeast	Border	South	Midwest
West	—	1.63	2.23*	0.81	0.70
Northeast	1.63	—	0.99	0.43	1.53
Border	2.23*	0.99	—	1.25	1.97
South	0.81	0.43	1.25	—	0.37
Midwest	0.70	1.53	1.97*	0.37	—

*   Significant at the 95 per cent level of confidence.

Two findings revealed by this matrix warrant comment. First of all, the relationship of the South dummy to registration was not significantly different from that of any of the other four regional dummies. This result is important, because it implies that the low rates of registration characteristic of Southern cities (on the average, 17.4 per cent below the mean registration rate for all 104 cities) can be explained mainly in terms of the variables included in Regression I.1.

Secondly, only two pairs of regional dummies did differ significantly from each other in their relationship to registration, Border-West and Border-Midwest. The regression coefficients for the regional dummies shown in Table 3 (Regression III.1) indicate that our regression equation over-predicts the rate of registration in the cities of the Border states by about seven percentage points relative to that in Midwestern cities and by about 10.5 percentage points relative to that of Western cities. The equation also tends to under-predict registration in Western cities relative to registration in the rest of the country. We have no ready explanation. It may be that statutes which on their face are not particularly discouraging to registration are administered in a way that does discourage registration in the cities of the Border states. It may also be that voters in the West are more likely than those elsewhere to regard voting as a civic duty. These are mere conjectures, however, which cannot be tested with the data available to us.

Comparisons of the regressions reported in Tables 1 and 3 indicate one additional fact of importance: When regional dummies are included in the regression, the explanatory value of the age and education variables is appreciably lessened. A part of the apparent effect on registration of these two variables thus seems to be associated with factors varying by region that were not taken into account in Regressions I.1 and I.2. For the rest, however, findings already reported can stand without further qualification.

Results for Particular Cities and the Pattern of Residual Variance.

Figure 1 shows the relationship between the actual rates of registration for the cities of our full sample and the rates of registration predicted on the basis of

Regression I.2. If the predictions had been perfect, all of the 104 observations would lie on the 45 degree line. They do not, but it is encouraging that the regression equation predicts about equally well over the whole range of values for the dependent variable.

■ **Table 3.** Regression analysis of differences among cities in percentages of the population of voting age registered to vote, with regional variables (104 cities, 1960)

Variables[a]	Ex-pected sign	Regression III.1[b]			Regression III.2[c]		
		b	(s)	t	b	(s)	t
Independent Variables							
Socio-economic factors							
Age (per cent 20–34)	−	−0.39	(0.21)	1.89	−0.43	(0.18)	2.36*
Sex (per cent male)	+	−0.38	(0.66)	0.57			
Race (per cent non-white)	−	−0.17	(0.08)	2.25*	−0.18	(0.07)	2.52*
Education (median years completed)	+	1.07	(1.16)	0.92	2.13	(0.91)	2.36*
Income ($100/year)	+	0.19	(0.18)	1.08			
Length of residence (per cent out of state)	−	−0.25	(0.16)	1.58			
Factors affecting the value of the vote							
Inter-party competition (per cent)	−	−0.29	(0.12)	2.37*	−0.37	(0.08)	4.68**
Factors affecting the costs of registration[d]							
Provisions regarding literacy tests	+	0.10	(0.04)	2.39*	0.14	(0.04)	3.73**
Closing date for registration	+	0.15	(0.04)	3.83**	0.16	(0.04)	4.62**
Times and places of registration	+	1.50	(2.12)	0.71			
Registration system (permanent or periodic)	+	0.04	(0.04)	0.93			
Other factors[d]							
Residence requirements	+	0.02	(0.05)	0.38			
Regions							
West		2.20	(3.15)	0.70	3.06	(2.53)	1.21
Northeast		−3.56	(2.32)	1.53*			
Border		−7.05	(3.58)	1.97*	−5.50	(3.04)	1.81
South		−1.66	(4.48)	0.37			

Variables[a]	Ex-pected sign	Regression III.1[b]			Regression III.2[c]		
		b	(s)	t	b	(s)	t
Dependent Variable: Percentage of the population of voting age registered to vote							
Mean		73.3			73.3		
Standard deviation		(14.3)			(14.3)		
F-ratio		22.09			40.99		
Intercept		67.5			48.2		
Standard error of estimate		6.9			7.0		
Number of cities		104			104		
R^2				.80**			.78**

Notation: b = Net (partial) regression coefficient; (s) = standard error of regression coefficient; t = t-value of regression coefficient; ** = significant at 99 per cent; * = significant at 95 per cent.
[a] Defined in Appendix I.
[b] Includes all variables listed.
[c] Includes only variables significant at 95 per cent level in Regression I.1, plus the two regional dummies whose coefficients were significantly different from each other.
[d] As we indicate in Appendix I, these sets of variables are measured by indices whose scales are arbitrary. Thus, no units of measurement are shown in parentheses, and no meaning can be attached to the absolute values of the regression coefficients of these variables without bearing in mind how each index was scaled. The "t" values can be interpreted in the usual way as indicators of statistical significance.

Table 4 reports actual and predicted rates of registration for each of the cities of the full sample. Cities are listed according to the size of their residuals, starting with Memphis, which had the largest positive residual, and ending with Wichita, which had the largest negative one. The reader may use this table, as we did, as a starting point for efforts to think of variables that will account for the pattern of residual variance.

We found two variables that seem to account for a very small part of it. The regression equation led us to under-predict registration in cities with large percentages of Catholics in their populations.[42] It also led us to over-predict registration in the relatively few cities where there were substantial number of resident aliens.[43]

By far the most important statement we can make about our effort to explain the pattern of residual variance, however, is simply this: Not much came of it. The size or sign of a city's residual had little if any relation to the size of the city,[44] the state in which it was located, its provisions for absentee registration,[45] the percentage of its population that was foreign born,[46] or whether or not it had less stringent residence requirements for voting in presidential elections than it did for voting in state and local elections. There were no substantial differences in the residuals of Southern cities as between those with larger or smaller concentrations of Negroes.[47] Our predictions were neither markedly better nor markedly worse for cities that used roving deputy registrars or mobile registration units and those that did not, for cities with high and low percentages of college graduates in their populations,[48] and cities with the most and the least stable populations.[49] Finally, cities with unusually small or unusually large concentrations of young voters, males, and non-white residents showed no common tendency, and neither did cities whose populations had an unusually high or low median educational attainment. Thus, it seems that our simplifying assumption of linear relationships between these variables and the rate of registration did not lead to serious error.

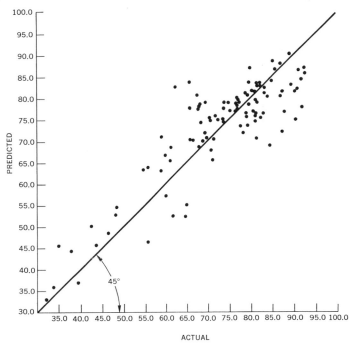

1   Relationship of Actual Rates of Registration to Predicted Rates (104 cities 1960).

III. Concluding Observations

One conclusion to be drawn from our study of registration can be put as follows: Local differences in the turnout for elections are to a large extent related to local differences in rates of registration, and these in turn reflect to a considerable degree local differences in the rules governing, and arrangements for handling, the registering of voters. Some of our other conclusions may be of greater interest to practicing politicians, but this one contributes most to a better understanding of the electoral process.

■ **Table 4.** Actual and predicted registration rates, and residuals (104 cities)

City	Actual	Predicted	Residual
1. Memphis	84.7	69.3	15.4
2. Berkeley	90.5	75.2	15.3
3. Gary	87.3	72.4	14.9
4. Detroit	92.0	78.2	13.8
5. South Bend	96.4	83.5	12.9
6. Baton Rouge	64.7	52.4	12.3
7. Torrance	87.7	76.9	10.8
8. Camden	81.3	70.8	10.5
9. Dallas	65.0	55.1	9.9
10. Seattle	92.0	82.5	9.5
11. New Orleans	55.6	46.4	9.2
12. Corpus Christi	61.8	52.8	9.0
13. Houston	60.0	57.3	8.7
14. Scranton	90.4	81.7	8.7
15. Lansing	91.9	84.6	7.3
16. New Bedford	82.4	75.6	6.8
17. Tacoma	87.3	80.6	6.7
18. Des Moines	92.6	86.0	6.6
19. Jersey City	81.1	74.7	6.4
20. Buffalo	83.0	76.7	6.3
21. Albany	88.4	82.2	6.2
22. Spokane	89.4	83.4	6.0
23. Cincinnati	79.4	73.8	5.6
24. Peoria	87.4	81.8	5.6
25. Minneapolis	92.5	87.2	5.3
26. Winston-Salem	71.2	65.9	5.3
27. Youngstown	81.0	76.0	5.0
28. Fresno	81.1	76.8	4.3
29. St. Paul	91.2	86.9	4.3
30. Philadelphia	77.6	73.6	4.0
31. Canton	80.9	77.0	3.9
32. New Haven	79.2	75.8	3.4
33. Trenton	75.8	72.4	3.4
34. Hammond	84.0	80.7	3.3
35. Chattanooga	70.7	68.1	2.6
36. Birmingham	39.1	36.8	2.3
37. Waterbury	81.4	79.2	2.2
38. Kansas City (Kans.)	78.9	76.7	2.2
39. Pasadena	83.2	81.5	1.7
40. Pittsburgh	81.2	79.6	1.6
41. Flint	79.6	78.6	1.0
42. Glendale	84.9	84.2	0.7
43. Grand Rapids	83.2	82.9	0.3

City	Actual	Predicted	Residual
44. Cleveland	71.5	71.6	−0.1
45. Baltimore	68.1	68.7	−0.6
46. Tulsa	82.4	83.0	−0.6
47. Columbus (Ga.)	32.1	32.7	−0.6
48. Worcester	81.0	81.6	−0.6
49. Los Angeles	77.0	77.7	−0.7
50. San Diego	73.9	74.7	−0.8
51. Charlotte	69.9	70.9	−1.0
52. Dearborn	89.3	90.3	−1.0
53. Portland (Ore.)	85.8	86.9	−1.1
54. Salt Lake City	87.0	88.2	−1.2
55. Fort Wayne	81.7	82.9	−1.2
56. Oklahoma City	80.4	81.7	−1.3
57. Topeka	81.9	83.3	−1.4
58. Tampa	68.8	70.2	−1.4
59. Elizabeth	75.6	77.1	−1.5
60. Dayton	73.6	75.1	−1.5
61. Rockford	82.0	83.5	−1.5
62. Syracuse	79.3	81.0	−1.7
63. Akron	77.0	78.7	−1.7
64. Sacramento	77.3	79.1	−1.8
65. Toledo	76.9	78.7	−1.8
66. Richmond	46.5	48.5	−2.0
67. Atlanta	33.8	35.8	−2.0
68. Norfolk	43.6	45.8	−2.2
69. Santa Ana	75.1	77.3	−2.2
70. Erie	78.8	81.2	−2.4
71. Utica	77.1	79.8	−2.7
72. Columbus (O.)	72.4	75.2	−2.8
73. Springfield	77.1	80.1	−3.0
74. Duluth	85.1	88.8	−3.7
75. Greensboro	66.6	70.4	−3.8
76. Patterson	68.4	72.2	−3.8
77. Cambridge (Mass.)	73.8	77.8	−4.0
78. Oakland	71.9	76.0	−4.1
79. Louisville	59.0	63.2	−4.2
80. Little Rock	61.2	65.5	−4.3
81. Hartford	70.7	75.0	−4.3
82. Lincoln	79.4	83.7	−4.3
83. Rochester	74.9	79.3	−4.4
84. Austin	48.3	52.8	−4.5
85. Bridgeport	70.6	75.6	−5.0
86. Boston	74.0	79.2	−5.2

City	Actual	Predicted	Residual
87. St. Louis	68.5	74.7	−6.2
88. Portsmouth	38.0	44.3	−6.3
89. Fort Worth	48.4	54.7	−6.3
90. Honolulu	60.0	66.9	−6.9
91. Newark	61.4	68.6	−7.2
92. Omaha	79.8	87.1	−7.3
93. San Antonio	42.6	50.1	−7.5
94. Nashville	55.9	64.0	−8.1
95. Jacksonville	54.9	63.5	−8.6
96. St. Petersburg	69.7	79.4	−9.7
97. San Francisco	68.0	78.4	−10.4
98. Newport News	35.0	45.5	−10.5
99. Niagara Falls	67.7	78.6	−10.9
100. Miami	59.2	71.1	−11.9
101. New York	65.7	77.7	−12.0
102. Allentown	67.7	80.6	−13.0
103. Kansas City (Mo.)	65.8	83.8	−18.0
104. Wichita	62.2	82.7	−20.5

This conclusion lends support, first of all, to Gosnell's explanation for the difference in the normal rates of turnout of voters in the United States, on the one hand, and in other democracies, on the other. This difference, one that has produced considerable commentary on the civic virtues of Americans relative to those of other peoples, was thought by Gosnell to be due in large measure to differing practices in the registration of voters:

■ In the European countries studied, a citizen who is entitled to vote does not, as a rule, have to make any effort to see that his name is on the list of eligible voters. The inconvenience of registering for voting in this country has caused many citizens to become non-voters.[50] ■

The probable accuracy of this observation is strongly suggested not only by findings that we have already reported but also by a comparison of turnout rates in Canada, France, and Great Britain (all of which have systems of automatic registration) with those in the cities of our sample where more than 90 per cent of those of voting age were registered to vote. In 1960 the rate of turnout of registered voters in such cities was, on the average, 78.5 per cent. In post-war elections in Canada, France, and Great Britain it has been, again on the average, 74.3, 77.4, and 77.6 per cent, respectively.[51]

Secondly, our findings regarding the interrelation of turnout, registration, and registration procedures suggest the solution to a problem discussed by V. O. Key:

■ A major question posed by the trend of voting [in U.S. presidential elec-tions] is why the decline in electoral interest since the 1890's. The blunt truth is that nobody knows the answer. A frequent explanation has been that the enfranchisement of women in 1920 brought into the electorate large numbers of persons not in the habit of voting. Yet popular interest began to shrink before the adoption of the women suffrage amendment.[52] ■

We suspect that a major part of the explanation for the trend of voting in presi-dential elections lies in the following facts: In the latter half of the nineteenth century, when the turnout of eligible voters was between 75 and 85 per cent, voters were not required to register in many parts of the country, and in many places where they were, there were systems of automatic registration. In the period from 1896 to 1924, when the turnout declined almost steadily, state after state enacted registration laws which typically required registration annually and in person of all voters in the nation's large cities; the registration procedures of this era have been described by one student of registration practices as "expen-sive, cumbersome, and inconvenient to the voter."[53] In the period from 1924 until the present, during which time the turnout has gradually risen, more and more states have been liberalizing their registration laws, particularly as these apply to the larger cities. In short, turnout in presidential elections in the United States may have declined and then risen again, not because of changes in the *interest* of voters in elections, but because of changes in the *interest demanded* of them.

Thirdly, our findings suggest a quite different view of the electorate from that implicit or explicit in many discussions of voting. It is fair to say that the electorate is treated by many students of voting, especially Lazarsfeld, Berelson, and their co-authors, as if it were the product of socio-economic forces. In *The People's Choice* they conclude that ". . . three-quarters of the non-voters stayed away from the polls deliberately because they were thoroughly uncon-cerned with the election. . . . A long range program of civic education would be needed to draw such people into the orbit of political life. . . ."[54] In *Voting* they observe that "It is often a mistake to give purely political explanations for non-participation. . . . Non-voting is related to persistent social conditions having little to do with the candidates or the issues of the moment."[55]

While no one could quarrel with the above statement if enough weight were put on the "purely," our study indicates, not only that electorates are much more the product of political forces than many have appreciated, but also that, to a considerable extent, they can be *political artifacts*. Within limits, they can be constructed to a size and composition deemed desirable by those in power. Our matrix of simple correlations (Appendix II), for instance, shows a definite associ-ation between restrictive rules and procedures for registration and limited com-petition between major parties in the states in which the cities of our sample are located. Presumably, it is easier for a party in power to pursue a restrictive policy toward registration if its opposition is weak. Conversely, success in restricting registration presumably indicates some success in influencing the composition of the population of registered voters, which in turn makes it easier for the party in power to stay in power. While the abilities of Southern politicians to construct electorates have long been appreciated, relatively little curiosity has been shown about any similar endeavors on the part of their Northern colleagues. It seems unlikely that the latter, any more than the former, have always acted without design in establishing rules for registration.[56]

Finally, the findings of this study have a bearing on the continuing debate between those who favor and those who oppose efforts to get out the vote. A frequent objection to such efforts is that voters not interested enough to vote are not apt to vote wisely and so should be left alone. This view recalls the statement of a New York voter regarding the adequacy of the facilities for registering in New York City in 1964: "I sure do want to vote against that man [Senator Barry Goldwater], but I don't think I hate him enough to stand on that line all day long."[57] How much interest should a voter have to qualify him for voting? Enough to stand in line all day? For half a day? For two days? We cannot say, but those who think voting should be limited to the "interested" ought to be prepared to do so.

APPENDIX I

Definitions of Variables and Sources of Data

1.   *Age:* the number of persons in the age group 20 to 34 divided by the number of persons over 21 years of age. Source: U.S. Department of Commerce, Bureau of the Census, *1960 Census of Population: Characteristics of the Population.* Table 20.

2.   *Education:* median school years completed by persons over 25 years of age. Source: U.S. Department of Commerce, Bureau of the Census, *County and City Data Book 1962,* Table 6.

3.   *Race:* percentage of non-whites in the population. Source: U.S. Department of Commerce, Bureau of the Census, *County and City Data Book 1962,* Table 6.

4.   *Income:* dollars received per year per family unit divided by 100. Source: U.S. Department of Commerce, Bureau of the Census, *County and City Data Book 1962,* Table 6.

5.   *Sex:* percentage of males in the population over 21 years of age. Source: U.S. Department of Commerce, Bureau of the Census, *1960 Census of Population: Characteristics of the Population,* Table 20.

6.   *Length of residence:* the number of persons over five years of age in the state economic area in which a city is located who resided in another state in 1955, divided by the total number of persons over five years of age in the state economic

area in which that city is located. "State economic areas" are as defined in our source for these data: U.S. Department of Commerce, Bureau of the Census, *U.S. Census of Population 1960: Selected Area Reports, State Economic Areas*, Table 2.

7. *Offices at stake:* the number of contests for the offices of President, U.S. Senator, U.S. Representative, Governor, and Mayor in which any one voter might vote. Source: Richard M. Scammon, *ed., America Votes 4* (Pittsburgh: University of Pittsburgh Press, 1962).

8. *Inter-party competition:* the difference between 50 and the average percentage of the two-party vote received by Democratic candidates in elections for Governor from 1956 to 1960 inclusive and for President in 1956 and 1960. Source: Richard M. Scammon, *ed., America Votes 4* (Pittsburgh: University of Pittsburgh Press, 1962).

9. *Provisions regarding literacy tests:* values of this variable were assigned as follows: test of literacy lending itself to discriminatory administration, 20; simple and straightforward test of literacy, 80; no test of literacy, 100. Where a "20" was assigned, the test required a registrant to show "understanding" or give a "reasonable interpretation" of sections of the U.S. Constitution or state constitutions or to make application without "aid, suggestions or memorandum"; or a registrant might qualify without showing literacy provided he was of "good character" or owned a stated amount and kind of property. Where an "80" was assigned, registrants were not required to interpret passages from the Constitution, and members of minority groups were not at a disadvantage in qualifying for any exemptions to the requirements of literacy. Source: Constance E. Smith, *Voting and Election Laws* (New York: Oceana Publications, Inc., 1960), and the election codes of the relevant states.

10. *Closing date for registration:* in all cases in which registration (or period in which the poll tax could be paid) closed 100 or fewer days before the election, the value assigned was the number of days before the election at which registration was closed subtracted from 100. In all other cases, the value assigned was zero. Source: Constance E. Smith, *op. cit.*, election codes of relevant states, and answers to questionnaires sent to local boards of elections.

11. *Registration system:* values for this variable were assigned as follows: annual payment of cumulative poll tax required, 10; annual payment of a non-cumulative poll tax required, 25; annual personal registration required (with no requirement for the payment of a poll tax), 34; system of permanent registration, 100. Source: Constance E. Smith, *op., cit.*, election codes of the relevant states, and answers to questionnaires sent to local boards of election.

12. *Times and places of registration:* assignment of values for this variable involved calculating an index of convenience for each *kind* of registration place open in 1960 and summing the values of such indices to arrive at a convenience

score for the registration facilities of the city as a whole. For example, a value for the index of convenience for precinct registration places alone was arrived at by adding the number of hours that precinct registration places were open in 1960 during working hours to two times the number of hours that they were open during the non-working hours, multiplying this number by the number of precinct registration places, and dividing the whole by the number of persons of voting age. Other kinds of registration places for which we calculated indices of convenience were central (e.g. County Court House or City Hall); branch; ward; hospital, plant, or other institutions; mobile units; and roving deputy registrars. "Non-working" hours were defined as hours before 8 a.m. or after 6 p.m. on week days and all hours on Saturday and Sunday. We also treated all hours during which mobile units were in service, all hours put in by roving deputies, and all hours in hospitals, plants, and other institutions as "non-working hours." Sources: Constance Smith, *op. cit.*, election codes of relevant states, answers to questionnaires sent to local Leagues of Women Voters and local Boards of Elections, and telephone interviews with officials of local Boards of Elections.

13. *Residence requirements:* the values of this variable were assigned as follows: residence of two years or more required in the state, 20; residence of one year required in the state and of more than three months in the county or city, 56; residence of one year required in the state and of three months or less in the county or city, 60; residence of six months required in the state and of more than thirty days in the county or city, 96; residence of six months required in the state and of thirty days or less in the county or city, 100. Source: Constance E. Smith, *op. cit.*, and the election codes of the relevant states.

14. *Methods of purging registration rolls:* high values of this variable were assigned to cities where it is easy for a voter to keep his name on the registration rolls, low values to cities where it is not. Two steps were involved in assigning values. An initial score was assigned as follows: provision is made for a mandatory general canvass *or* for a mandatory canvass by mail *or* for public agencies to notify boards of elections of deaths and changes of residence *and* a voter's name is removed upon his failure to vote during a period of less than four years, 15; provisions as just stated except that a voter's name is removed upon his failure to vote during a period of four years or more, 25; provision is made for an optional general canvass *or* for an optional canvass by mail *and/or* for public agencies to notify boards of elections of deaths but not of changes of residence *and* a voter's name is removed upon his failure to vote during a period of less than four years, 45; provisions are as just stated except that a voter's name is removed upon his failure to vote during a period of four years or more, 55; provision is made for an optional general canvass *or* for an optional canvass by mail *and/or* there is no provision for public agencies to notify boards of elections of deaths or changes or residence *and* a voter's name is removed upon his failure

to vote during a period of less than four years, 65; provisions are as just stated except that a voter's name is removed upon his failure to vote during a period of four years or more, 75; no provision is made for a canvass, either general or selective, optional or mandatory, *and* there is no provision for public agencies to notify boards of elections of deaths or changes of residence *and* a voter's name is removed upon his failure to vote during a period of less than four years, 90; provisions are as just stated except that a voter's name is removed upon his failure to vote during a period of four years or more *or* there are no provisions of any kind with respect to canvasses, notification of boards of deaths and changes of residence, or removal of names for non-voting, 100.

Scores assigned as follows were then *substracted* from scores assigned in accordance with the scheme just described: provision is made for removing the names of all nonvoters, deceased persons, and those who have changed residence automatically and there is no requirement that notice be given the person whose name is being removed, 15; provisions are as just stated except that boards of elections are required to give notice to persons whose names are being removed for a change of residence *and* such persons must apply in person to prevent the removal of their names, 12; provisions are as just stated except that those alleged to have changed residence may testify to the contrary by mail and so prevent removal of their names, 10; boards of elections are required to give notice to persons whose names are being removed either for an alleged change of residence or for non-voting and such persons must apply in person to prevent removal of their names, 7; provisions as just stated except persons whose names are being removed may prevent such action by applying for reinstatement by mail, 5; provisions as just stated except boards of election are required to give notice twice to persons whose names are being removed, 0.

Source: Constance Smith, *op. cit.*, election codes of the relevant states, answers to questionnaires sent to local boards of elections and local Leagues of Women Voters, telephone interviews with officials of local Boards of Elections.

15. *Region—West:* Montana, Idaho, Wyoming, Colorado, Utah, Nevada, New Mexico, Arizona, Washington, Oregon, California, Alaska, Hawaii.

16. *Region—Northeast:* Maine, New Hampshire, Vermont, Massachusetts, Rhode Island, Connecticut, New York, New Jersey, Pennsylvania.

17. *Region—Border:* Delaware, Maryland, West Virginia, Kentucky, Missouri, Oklahoma.

18. *Region—South:* Virginia, North Carolina, South Carolina, Georgia, Florida, Tennessee, Alabama, Mississippi, Arkansas, Louisiana, Texas.

19. *Region—Midwest:* Ohio, Michigan, Indiana, Illinois, Wisconsin, Minnesota, Iowa, Nebraska, Kansas, North Dakota, South Dakota.

■ **Appendix II.** Regression I.1: Matrix of simple correlations (104 cities, 1960)

	1	2	3	4	5
1. Registration	1.00	−0.46	−0.05	−0.54	0.26
2. Age (per cent 20–34)	−0.46	1.00	0.39	0.34	0.21
3. Sex (per cent male)	−0.05	0.39	1.00	0.05	0.12
4. Race (per cent non-white)	−0.54	0.34	0.05	1.00	−0.29
5. Education (median years completed)	0.26	0.21	0.12	−0.29	1.00
6. Income	0.57	−0.11	0.30	−0.41	0.54
7. Length of residence	−0.28	0.15	0.23	0.23	0.19
8. Inter-party competition	−0.71	0.38	−0.18	0.39	−0.00
9. Residence requirements	0.40	−0.11	0.11	−0.22	0.08
10. Literacy tests	0.56	−0.32	−0.08	−0.36	0.02
11. Closing date	0.66	−0.33	−0.12	−0.22	0.08
12. Times and places of registration	−0.10	0.13	0.06	−0.10	0.19
13. Registration system	0.57	−0.32	−0.15	−0.17	0.01

■ **Appendix III.** Partial correlation coefficients and Beta-weights

	Regression			
	I.1		I.2	
Variables	p	β	p	β
Age (per cent 20–34)	−.24	−.16	−.27	−.17
Sex (per cent male)	−.03	−.02		
Race (per cent non-white)	−.21	−.13	−.24	−.15
Education (median years completed)	.22	.17	.38	.22
Income ($100/yr.)	.15	.12		
Length of residence (per cent from out of state)	−.14	−.08		
Inter-party competition	−.30	−.26	−.49	−.36
Provisions regarding literacy tests	.22	.14	.32	.19
Closing date for registration	.34	.24	.40	.28
Times and places of registration	.11	.06		
Registration system	.16	.12		
Residence requirements	.10	.05		
Purging methods				
South				
West				
Northeast				
Border				

6	7	8	9	10	11	12	13
0.57	−0.28	−0.71	0.40	0.56	−0.10	0.66	0.57
−0.11	0.15	0.38	−0.11	−0.32	−0.33	0.13	−0.32
0.30	0.23	−0.18	0.11	−0.08	−0.12	0.06	−0.15
−0.41	0.23	0.39	−0.22	−0.36	−0.22	−0.10	−0.17
0.54	0.19	−0.00	0.08	0.02	0.08	0.19	0.01
1.00	−0.17	−0.55	0.30	0.19	0.27	0.02	0.27
−0.17	1.00	0.24	−0.07	−0.24	−0.18	0.03	−0.04
−0.55	0.24	1.00	−0.39	−0.39	−0.56	0.28	−0.55
0.30	−0.07	−0.39	1.00	0.43	0.28	−0.14	0.23
0.19	−0.24	−0.39	0.43	1.00	0.43	0.07	0.37
0.27	−0.18	−0.56	0.28	0.43	1.00	−0.31	0.64
0.02	0.03	0.28	−0.14	0.07	−0.31	1.00	−0.32
0.27	−0.04	−0.55	0.23	0.37	0.64	−0.32	1.00

Regression

II.1		II.2		III.1		III.2	
p	β	p	β	p	β	p	β
−.22	−.16	−.11	.07	−.20	−.13	−.24	−.14
−.02	−.02			−.06	−.04		
−.25	−.19	−.38	−.28	−.23	−.15	−.25	−.16
.12	.11			.10	.08	.24	.17
.17	.17			.11	.10		
−.14	−.09			−.17	−.10		
−.23	−.24	−.52	−.44	−.25	−.25	−.43	−.33
.14	.11			.25	.16	.36	.22
.37	.25	.41	.28	.38	.28	.43	.30
.24	.16	.31	.19	.08	.04		
				.10	.08		
.12	.08			.04	.03		
.01	.005						
				−.04	−.05		
				.07	.06	.12	.08
				−.16	−.11		
				−.21	−.12	−.18	−.09

Notation: p = partial correlation coefficient; $β$ = Beta-weight.

NOTES

1.   We are indebted to a great many people for help given us in the course of this study. The staff of the project included Mr. Paul Corcoran, Duke University; Mrs. Ronald Gebhardt; Mr. Charles J. Peischl, University of Pennsylvania Law School; and Mr. Lawrence C. Petrowski, Columbia University Law School. We were given valuable information, suggestions, and other forms of assistance by Dr. George Graham, The Brookings Institution; Mrs. Alice Hamm, League of Women Voters of the United States; Messrs. Lloyd Bentsen and Jonathan Holman, Stanford Business School; Professor John Kessel, Allegheny College; Mr. Michael McClister, Democratic National Committee; Mr. Thomas G. McHale, U.S. Bureau of the Census; Professors Warren Miller and Donald Stokes, University of Michigan; Professor Ralph Miwa, University of Hawaii; Professor John Strange, Duke University; Mr. Michael Traugott, University of Michigan; Mrs. Rosalie Feltenstein, Princeton University; and Representative Frank Thompson, Fourth District, New Jersey. The aid of local Leagues of Women Voters and Boards of Election was indispensable to the success of the project, and so, too, was that of the Roger W. Strauss Council of Human Relations of Princeton University, which provided the financial support for our research. In the course of our work substantial use was made of computer facilities supported in part by National Science Foundation Grant, NSF-GP579.

2.   Charles E. Merriam and Harold G. Gosnell, *Non-Voting: Causes and Methods of Control* (Chicago: University of Chicago Press, 1924), p. 251.

3.   *Ibid.*, p. 232.

4.   Angus Campbell and his associates at the Survey Research Center of the University of Michigan discuss the relation of voting to certain of the legal arrangements governing suffrage in *The American Voter* (New York: John Wiley and Sons, 1960), 276–286, and Warren Miller has reported additional findings on the subject in a memorandum to the President's Commission on Registration and Voting Participation. V. O. Key examined the effect of poll taxes on voting in his *Southern Politics* (New York: Alfred A. Knopf, 1950), 599–618, and Howard Freeman, Arnold Simmel, and Murray Gendell discuss the turnout of registered voters in William N. McPhee and William A. Glaser, *Public Opinion and Congressional Elections* (Glencoe: The Free Press, 1962), 240–250. Donald R. Matthews and James W. Prothro report findings about rates of registration among Negroes in the South in two articles: "Social and Economic Factors and Negro Voter Registration in the South," *The American Political Science Review 57* (March, 1963), 24–44, and "Political Factors and Negro Voter Registration in the South," *ibid.* (June, 1963), 355–367.

     Much earlier, Gosnell presented some interesting information on the relation of registration procedures to turnout in elections in *Getting Out the Vote* (Chicago: University of Chicago Press, 1927) and *Why Europe Votes* (Chicago: University of Chicago Press, 1930), as did Joseph P. Harris at about the same time in his *Registration of Voters in the United States* (Washington: The Brookings Institution, 1929), 106–108. There are of course comments on the relation of registration to voting in words not cited here, but very few additional sources of systematic information about that relationship.

5. For a list of the cities included in our sample, see p. 268 below. Originally we planned to study factors affecting rates of registration in all cities in the United States with populations above 100,000; we were unable to proceed as planned, however, because we were unable to secure information about registration or registration procedures in some of these cities. Most commonly we could not secure accurate data regarding the percentage of the population of voting age registered to vote or verify the accuracy of such data as we could get. This was the case for 16 cities: Mobile, Montgomery, Tucson, Savannah, Chicago, Evansville, Indianapolis, Shreveport, Jackson, Albuquerque, Knoxville, Amarillo, Beaumont, El Paso, Lubbock, and Wichita Falls. We could not get accurate information regarding times and physical arrangements for registration in eight additional cities: Phoenix, Anaheim, Long Beach, San Jose, Denver, Providence, Madison, and Milwaukee. A figure for the percentage of recent migrants from out of state was missing for Yonkers, New York. Washington, D.C. had no procedures for registering voters in 1960, since, at that time, it had no voters.

6. Anthony Downs, *An Economic Theory of Democracy* (New York: Harper and Brothers, 1927), p. 260.

7. Merriam and Gosnell reported that a substantial number of the non-voters they studied had given fear of loss of income through loss of time away from work as an important reason for not voting; see *Non-Voting*, 86–95.

8. Literacy tests tend to lower registration, of course, not only because they are a bother but also because they disqualify a certain number of voters.

9. The most important have been race, place of residence, education, age, income, marital status, sex, ethnic group affiliation, occupation, geographical mobility, intensity of partisan preferences, perceived closeness of the election, interest in the campaign, concern with the outcome of the election, sense of the efficacy of voting, sense of civic duty, attitudes with respect to issues of public policy, attitudes toward candidates, and level of political information.

10. Nor could we study the relationship of urban and rural residence to rates of registration, since we limited ourselves to the study of registration in large cities.

11. See Anthony Downs, *op. cit.*, 232–236, 260–273.

12. *Ibid.*, p. 235, and Seymour Martin Lipset, *Political Man* (New York: Doubleday, 1960), p. 205.

13. Angus Campbell, Philip Converse, Warren Miller and Donald Stokes, *The American Voter*, p. 476.

14. See particularly Seymour Martin Lipset, *op. cit.*, 202, 209–211; Robert Lane *Political Life* (Glencoe: The Free Press, 1959), 48–49; Angus Campbell *et al.*, *The American Voter*, 496–497; and Lester W. Milbrath, *Political Participation* (Chicago: Rand McNally and Company, 1965), p. 135.

15. See Seymour Martin Lipset, *op. cit.*, 202–208.

16. The F-ratio for the regression was 361.39.

17. The regression coefficient of the rate of registration in this regression was .96, its standard error was .05, and its "t" value was 19.01.

18. The results in all of our text tables are reported in terms of partial regression co-efficients, standard errors of these coefficients, and t-values. Appendix III contains partial correlation coefficients and Beta-weights.

19. The R^2's reported in Table I are not corrected for degrees of freedom; the R^2's for Regression I.1 must therefore be larger than the R^2 for Regression I.2, since the latter contains only six of the twelve independent variables included in the former. Actually, as the F-ratios indicate, Regression I.2 gets higher marks on the statistical significance scale than does Regression I.1, although it is important to remember that we already knew something about the behavior of the variables included in Regression I.2 before it was run. A "t" value significant at the 95 per cent level in Regression I.1 was the criterion for the inclusion of variables in Regression I.2, and in such circumstances the meaningfulness of standard significance tests is open to some question.

20. Precise definitions of these and other variables are given in Appendix I in order of which the variables are discussed below.

21. See Appendix II for the matrix of simple correlations.

22. Angus Campbell, *et al.*, *The American Voter*, 475–476.

23. *Ibid.*, p. 487.

24. Because of the way this variable was measured (See Appendix I), low values imply a high level of competition in a state's party politics; hence, the correlation between the variable and rates of registration is negative.

25. See especially Harold F. Gosnell, *Why Europe Votes*, 182–183, 199–203; Lester W. Milbrath, "Political Participation in the States," p. 43 in Herbert Jacob and Kenneth N. Vines (eds.), *Politics in the American States* (Boston: Little, Brown and Company, 1965); and Herbert Tingsten, *Political Behaviour* (London: P. S. King and Son, 1937), p. 216.

26. Robert Lane, *op. cit.*, p. 310.

27. Lane's data for the election of 1950 are as reported in H. G. Nicholas, *The British General Election of 1950* (London: Macmillan, 1951), p. 318; Gosnell's data were for the election of 1924.

28. Robert Lane, *op. cit.*, p. 309.

29. It does have meaning for the value of the vote in county elections, of course; and if county elections were held in years when major state and national offices were not at stake, one would expect to find a relationship between the competitiveness of a county's politics and the turnout of voters.

30. Angus Campbell, *et al.*, *The American Voter*, p. 100 *f.n.*

31. Angus Campbell, Gerald Gurin, and Warren E. Miller, *The Voter Decides* (Evanston: Row, Peterson and Company, 1954), p. 193.
A re-arrangement of data presented in *The American Voter*, Table 17.4, p. 479, yields the following results:

Sense of political efficacy	Non-South	South
	%	%
High	43	32
Medium	28	24
Low	30	44

32. The assignment of values in these indices was arbitrary, as has been indicated in the notes to Table 1, but a few words about the kind of arbitrariness involved are in order here. This can best be done, perhaps, by indicating how we arrive at the scale of values for one of these indices, that for the variable we have called "registration system." The four positions on that index were assigned values of 10, 25, 34, and 100. This set of values was chosen because it was our guess that a system of permanent registration (valued at 100) was ten times less demanding on voters than a system which combines a cumulative poll tax with annual registration (valued at 10), four times less demanding than a system of annual registration coupled with a non-cumulative poll tax (valued at 25), and three times less demanding than a system of annual personal registration (valued at 34).

   In a moment of less boldness, we eschewed estimates of how much more restrictive one system was than another and constructed a simple ordinal scale which involved only guesses as to which systems had a greater, and which had a lesser, tendency to restrict registration. The substitution of the ordinal indices had little effect on our results. The cardinal indices showed somewhat stronger relationships to registration than those with ordinal scales, but if one of our cardinal indices was significantly related to registration, so was its ordinal equivalent, and if one of our cardinal indices was not significantly related to registration, neither was its ordinal equivalent.

33. Cf. Lester Milbrath, "Political Participation in the States," p. 48 in Jacob and Vines, op. cit., and Donald R. Matthews and James W. Prothro, "Political Factors and Negro Voter Registration in the South," The American Political Science Review 57 (June, 1963,) at p. 358.

34. William H. Riker, Democracy in the United States (New York: Macmillan, 1953), p. 66.

35. To the best of our knowledge only Warren Miller has previously presented systematic evidence tending to show non-voting to be related to an early closing date for registration. In his memorandum to the President's Commission on Registration and Voting Participation, Miller reported that "One out of every four or five citizens lives in a state where registration closes in September, before an election campaign is well under way. . . . Non-voting by two or three per cent of the population is associated with the September closing dates, both North and South."

36. Harold F. Gosnell, Getting Out the Vote, p. 104.

37. See Joseph P. Harris, op. cit., 106–108, and Robert Lane, op. cit., p. 315. Warren Miller reported to the President's Commission on Registration and Voting Participation that "The absence of any prevoting registration requirements and the provision for permanent registration are clearly associated with higher turnout at

the polls." V. O. Key has shown the poll tax to depress turnout in *Southern Politics*, 599–618.

38. This seems to be the sense of Lipset's statement that he does not wish to consider the effects of "legal and technical restrictions like residence requirements, poll taxes and property qualifications, literacy tests (often used as a cover for racial discrimination) and burdensome registration requirements" on the ground that his interest is in *voluntary* (his emphasis) non-voting, (See Seymour Martin Lipset, *op. cit.*, p. 181 *f.n.*) But for the greatest numbers of those who fail to register, non-registration is just as voluntary or non-voluntary as is failure to vote.

39. See Angus Campbell, *et. al.*, *The Voter Decides*, p. 37; Charles E. Merriam and Harold F. Gosnell, *op. cit.*, 79–86; and Phillips Bradley and Alfred H. Cope, "A Community Registration Survey," *The American Political Science Review 45* (September, 1951), at p. 777.

40. It is possible, of course, that the index we constructed did not reflect with sufficient exactness the actual differences in purging practices that exist from city to city. The procedures for purging were difficult to document.

41. These "t" values were obtained by running five versions of Regression III.1, dropping a different regional dummy each time, and using the t's for the other dummies to find whether or not they are significantly different from the omitted dummy.

42. Actually, for cities in *counties* with large percentages of Catholics in their populations. Our source was National Council of the Churches of Christ in the United State of America, *Churches and Church Membership in the United States*, New York, 1956–1958.

43. Our source for percentages of aliens in the population of our cities was U.S. Department of Commerce, Bureau of the Census, *U.S. Census of Population 1960: Characteristics of the Population*, Table 55.

44. To avoid forcing a linear pattern on this variable, we used a set of dummy variables; however, none had a "t" value as high as 1.00.

45. *Cf.* Lester W. Milbrath, "Political Participation in the States," p. 47 in Jacob and Vines, *op. cit.*

46. This variable had the expected negative sign, but the "t" value of its regression coefficient was only 1.19.

47. *Cf.* Donald R. Matthews and James W. Prothro, "Social and Economic Factors and Negro Voter Registration in the South," *The American Political Science Review 57* (March, 1963), 28–32.

48. Our source for this variable (actually the percentage of those over 25 years of age who are college graduates) was U.S. Department of Commerce, Bureau of the Census, *County and City Data Book 1962*, Table 6.

49. Stability of population was measured by the percentage of persons in a city's population over five years of age that were living in the same house in 1960 as they had in 1955. The source for these figures was U.S. Department of Commerce, Bureau of the Census, *County and City Data Book 1962*, Table 6.

50. Harold F. Gosnell, *Why Europe Votes*, p. 185. That differences in turnout for elections in Europe and America may be largely a function of differences in systems of registration has also been suggested by Seymour Martin Lipset, *op. cit.*, p. 181 *f.n.*, and Philip E. Converse and George Dupeux, "Politicization of the Electorate in France and the United States," *Public Opinion Quarterly* (Spring, 1962), 8–9 *f.n.*

51. These averages were for six post-war Canadian elections (1945, 1949, 1953, 1957, 1958, 1963), five post-war elections for the French National Assembly (1946, 1951, 1956, 1958, 1962), and six post-war elections in Great Britain (1945, 1950, 1951, 1955, 1959, 1964). The average rate of turnout of registered voters in the cities of our full sample was 81.6 per cent, and in Northern cities only it was 84.6 per cent.

52. V. O. Key, *Politics, Parties, and Pressure Groups* (New York: Thomas Y. Crowell, 1964), fifth edition, p. 578.

53. Joseph P. Harris, *op. cit.*, p. 89.

54. Paul F. Lazarsfeld, Bernard Berelson, and Helen Gaudet, *The People's Choice* (New York: Columbia University Press, 1948), p. 47. This conclusion is not well supported even by the data adduced as evidence for it. Some 27 per cent of the voters who said they had no interest at all in the campaign nonetheless voted. See *Ibid.*, p. 46.

55. Bernard Berelson, Paul F. Lazarsfeld, and William N. McPhee, *Voting* (Chicago: University of Chicago Press, 1954), p. 32.

56. One of the authors of the present study found, for instance, that there was a very high positive correlation between an index of the convenience of registering in Chicago wards and differences among wards in the Democratic percentage of the two-party vote, a fact which suggests that Mayor Richard J. Daley's organization is alert to the possibilities of manipulating the composition of Chicago's registered voters: See Richard E. Ayres, *Registration 1960: Key to Democratic Victory?* (Princeton University senior thesis, 1964), 34–35.

57. New York *Times*, September 6, 1964.

4 / SURVEY DATA

RELATION OF SCHOOL
FACTORS TO ACHIEVEMENT
AND
INTEGRATION AND ACHIEVEMENT

JAMES S. COLEMAN   ERNEST Q. CAMPBELL
CAROL J. HOBSON   JAMES McPARTLAND
ALEXANDER M. MOOD   FREDERIC D. WEINFELD
ROBERT L. YORK

3.2 RELATION OF SCHOOL FACTORS TO ACHIEVEMENT

... Differences in educational outcomes of minority groups and whites in standard tests ... may be viewed as one measure of educational disadvantage suffered by these groups—a disadvantage stemming partly from the schools, partly from the community, partly from the home. There can be no doubt that this deficiency is a real and serious disadvantage, since these tests measure some of the major skills necessary for further education and for occupational advancement in modern society.

The amount of educational disadvantage is large indeed. It is largest for Negroes and Puerto Ricans, and smallest for Orientals. For Negroes, it is largest in the South outside metropolitan areas, and in those areas where it is largest, the amount of disadvantage grows notably as the child goes from grade 1 to grade 12. These facts themselves suggest something about the sources of difference in achievement, for it is in the parts of the country where schools have least resources that the educational disadvantage is largest to begin with and continues to grow. However, these results give only bare indications of the sources of disadvantage. How much arises from the home? How much arises from the community? How much arises from the school? What are the elements in the home and in the school that put some minority group children at such a disadvantage?

These questions will be studied by examining, within each of the racial and ethnic groups, the sources of educational disadvantage. In the analysis, a child's achievement is related to various possible explanatory factors in his school, as well as to other factors that are ordinarily related to achievement, such as his home background and his attitudes. Before examining the results, it is necessary to present briefly the manner in which statistical analysis relates achievement to a given factor when a number of other factors are operating at the same time. Figure 3.2.1. shows hypothetical data on pupil achievement scores. There are

Reprinted from *Equality of Educational Opportunity* (Washington: Office of Education, U.S. Department of Health, Education, and Welfare, 1966), 290–333. The present version has been slightly abridged by the editor.

only a few scores given because the only purpose of this figure is to illustrate the method. The points are marked a, b, c, d, e, f, g, and h; and each one, let us assume, represents a score of a pupil from a different school with the height of the point above the horizontal line being the score (marked on the left vertical line). A great many factors cause these scores to be different; the pupil's ability and motivation, family interest and background, school characteristics, attitudes of the pupil's peers, his alertness on the day of the test, community attitudes which support education, and so on.

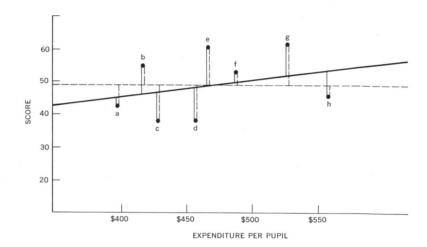

Fig. 3.2.1.

Now let us assume we wish to measure the relation of one factor out of many to these scores, and in particular the factor expenditure per pupil by the school. That factor becomes the scale of the lower horizontal line and the points are placed above that scale according to the expenditure of the school which the pupil attends. Thus the point marked "c" indicates that this pupil (with score of 38) attended a school with a per pupil expenditure of $430 per year; the point "f" represents a pupil in a school which spends $490 per pupil per year, whose score was 52. The overall variability (or variance) of these scores is measured by drawing the horizontal dashed line at their average value (49 in this illustration) and using the distances (vertical dashed lines) of the scores from that average line. The common index of variability or variance is the sum of the squares of these distances.

The next step is to construct a slant line in such a way that the squares of the vertical distances of the points from the slant line are collectively as small as possible. The squares of these vertical distances—shown by the solid lines joining the points to the slant line—will, collectively, be smaller than the squares of the vertical dashed lines. The per cent by which they are smaller is said to be the "amount of variability" or the "amount of variance" "explained" or "accounted for" by the factor. Thus in Figure 3.2.1., if the squares of the solid vertical distances from the solid line were 95 per cent as large, collectively, as the squares of the dashed vertical distances from the horizontal dashed line, then one would state that "5 per cent of the variance in pupil scores is accounted for by the school's expenditure per pupil." To illustrate better the rationale for this kind of analysis, there is shown in Figure 3.2.2. a case in which a single (hypothetical) factor accounts for practically the whole of the variance between scores; the solid vertical lines are, collectively, only a small fraction of the length of the dashed vertical lines collectively. Similarly, for example, if all children in schools with high per-pupil expenditure achieved very highly, and all those in schools with low per-pupil expenditure achieved very poorly, then the statistical analysis would show that per pupil expenditure accounts for a very large part of the variation in achievement.

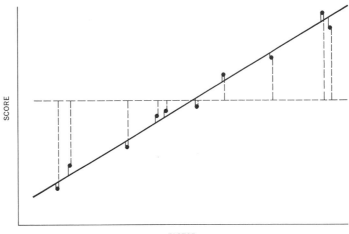

Fig. 3.2.2.

SCORE

FACTOR

There are a variety of precautions necessary in interpreting the results of such analyses. They do not prove that the factor caused the variation; they merely indicate that the two are related. For example, if we found that per-pupil expenditure accounted for much of the variation in achievement, the relation might nevertheless be a result of factors which are themselves associated with both achievement and expenditure, such as the economic level of the families from which these children come. In many cases these factors can be statistically controlled; but cautions in interpretation remain necessary. A technical appendix to Section 3.2 has been included, and a review of that appendix will aid in interpretation of the results in this section.

Had a number of years been available for this survey, a quite different way of assessing effects of school characteristics would have been possible; that is, examination of the educational growth over a period of time of children in schools with different characteristics. This is an alternative and in some ways preferable method of assessing the effects of school characteristics. It, too, requires caution in interpretation, because the various factors that could account for differences in growth are usually themselves associated, and also because the rate of growth bears a complex relation to the initial state.

It should be recognized that the results of such an analysis of growth might differ in some ways from the results of the present analysis. If the sources of variations in achievement were less complex, the results would not differ; but here, as for most matters of human behavior, relationships are complex. Thus, the present analysis should be complemented by others that explore changes in achievement over a large span of time.

3.21 The Criterion of Achievement

The criterion of achievement used throughout most of this examination of school effects is the student's score on the verbal ability test, a vocabulary test measuring verbal skills. The decision to use this criterion was arrived at only after an extensive comparison of this test with others administered in the survey. In the investigations that led to this decision, certain results about performance on these tests were obtained. While some of these results are recognized by some educators, they are far from universally recognized. To understand these results, it is useful first to examine the two purposes for which such tests are used in schools.

Some standardized tests used in schools are ordinarily labeled "achievement tests," and others are labeled "ability tests," with the former used to measure what a child has learned, and the latter used to measure his ability to learn. Schools characteristically use "achievement tests" as a measure of how well the child has learned the material of a specific course. Schools characteristically use "ability tests" as ways of assigning students to classes, using the test as a measure of the child's preparation and capacity to learn the material of a specific course.

The ability tests have been in the past, and are often still, termed "intelligence tests" or "IQ tests," and seen as measures of more fundamental and stable mental abilities, but recent research does not support that view. Ability tests are simply broader and more general measures of education, while achievement tests are narrower measures directed to a restricted subject area. The findings of this survey provide additional evidence that the "ability" tests are at least as much affected by school differences as are the "achievement" tests.

The specific results are as follows:

1. If the variation in individual test scores is separated into two components, that within schools, and that between, a greater effect of school factors should show up as greater between-school variance. As Table 3.21.1 shows, the per cent of variance that lies between schools is slightly greater for the "ability" tests than for the "achievement" tests.

As the table shows, school-to-school variance is generally greatest for the verbal ability test, next for the nonverbal ability test, next for reading comprehension, and mathematics achievement. This is indirect evidence that variations among schools have as much or more effect on the "ability test" scores as on the "achievement test" scores.

■ **Table 3.21.1.** Per cent of variation in achievement between schools for each ethnic group (average over 4 grades at which all 4 tests were given, grades 3–12)

	Non-verbal ability	Verbal ability	Reading compre-hension	Mathe-matics achieve-ment
Mexican-Americans	20.91	23.05	20.63	19.30
Puerto Ricans	25.62	25.66	22.55	21.63
Indian Americans	21.52	28.00	23.17	21.68
Oriental Americans	18.54	16.58	15.76	17.51
Negroes				
North	11.78	15.50	13.17	11.75
South	19.33	21.57	17.08	14.92
Whites				
North	6.81	9.80	7.88	8.63
South	10.66	11.84	9.26	9.42

2. Some considerable part of the school-to-school variation shown in table 3.21.1 is attributable to differences in the composition of the student body in different schools, and not to differences in school effectiveness. Such initial student body differences should show up most strongly in the early grades, and the results of school effects most strongly in the later grades. Consequently, if a school's primary effect were upon achievement test scores, the school-to-school variation in achievement test scores should be larger, relative to that of the ability test scores, in later years in school. But Table 3.21.2 shows that it is the "achievement tests" which show most decline from grade 3 to grade 12 in school-to-school differences. This suggests that the "ability tests" are even more responsive to school differences than are the "achievement tests." (The fact of a decline itself, such as between grades 6 and 9, is a point that will be examined in the next section. Grades cannot be directly compared in the absolute size of their school-to-school variation, because of different sizes of schools at elementary and secondary levels.)

3. When we attempt to explain the variance in individual achievement by use of school characteristics, holding family background constant, a higher proportion of the ability test score is explained than that of the achievement test score. This is shown for grade 12, Negroes and whites in Table 3.21.3.

This table provides more direct evidence that school variations have more effect on the ability scores than on the achievement scores, for more variation in ability test scores is accounted for, in every case, than in either of the achievement test scores.

■ **Table 3.21.2.** School-to-school variations (as per cent of the total variation in achievement) at each grade level (averages for Mexican Americans, Puerto Ricans, Indian Americans, Oriental Americans, Northern and Southern Negroes, and Northern and Southern whites)

	12	9	6	3	1
Nonverbal ability	13.99	13.97	22.29	17.33	18.16
Verbal ability	16.61	15.61	21.36	22.41	17.78
Reading comprehension	13.24	11.98	18.54	20.86	—
Mathematics achievement	10.55	11.97	18.41	21.48	—

■ **Table 3.21.3.** Per cent of variation explained in scores on 4 tests by selected school characteristics for Negroes and whites, after student background effects are controlled, for grade 12. (Background variables controlled are shown in Table 3.221.1)

	Negroes				Whites			
	Verbal	Non-verbal	Read-ing	Math	Verbal	Non-verbal	Read-ing	Math
10 teacher variables	7.21	5.21	4.46	2.06	1.29	1.19	0.23	0.61
18 school variables	6.54	5.78	5.00	2.12	2.02	.81	.62	.90

4.   If school factors affected reading comprehension scores more than verbal ability scores, then holding verbal ability constant should not reduce greatly the variance in reading comprehension explained by school factors. Thus a direct comparison was made, using reading comprehension with and without verbal ability constant, and verbal ability with and without reading comprehension constant. In all cases, family background factors were held constant. . . .

For both Negroes and whites, the variance explained in reading comprehension is reduced proportionately more by controlling for verbal ability than is the variance in verbal ability reduced by controlling for reading comprehension.

5.   One may ask finally whether schools are exerting more influence independent of family background on reading comprehension than on verbal skills measured in the verbal-ability test. If this were so, the relation between family background factors and reading comprehension should decline more over the years of school than the relation between family background and verbal ability. However, this is not the case; the change in the relation of background to reading comprehension parallels directly the changes that will be shown in table 3.221.3 for verbal skills. It appears clear that schools affect verbal skills measured by both tests, and affect them to a similar degree, except that the differences between schools show up somewhat more clearly in performance on the verbal-skills test.

The result of this investigation in its implications for testing and classification of students is clear: The scores on ability tests are at least as much affected by school differences on surveyed characteristics as are scores on achievement tests.

What is the explanation for the fact that the ability test scores show more school-to-school variation, and appear to be more affected by differences in school characteristics than achievement test scores? The answer seems to lie in the fact that achievement tests cover material that is nearly the same in all school curriculums, toward which all schools teach alike, while the ability tests cover material that the school teaches more incidentally, and thus with more differential success. Consequently, student bodies that differ at the beginning of school become slightly more alike with respect to the skills most directly related to a standard curriculum, but do not with the skills in which the curriculum is less standard.

The difference between these two types of tests appears more fully in table 3.21.5, in which the school-to-school component of variation is corrected for the number of schools, to give an estimate of the school-to-school component of the variance relative to the sum of both variance components.

The similarities between schools tend to compress the school-to-school component of variance in subjects toward which the curriculum is directed; the differences between schools became evident in the things their students learn, covered in ability tests, that are not as directly related to the curriculum. This does not mean that the school affects less their learning of these latter skills, for they are learned differently in different schools, as the relatively higher school-to-school component of variance in table 3.21.5 shows.

The effects of school differences should then show up, as the preceding tables indicate they do, not so much in school differences in achievement on tests toward which curriculum is directed, as in school differences in achievement on tests less directly related to the curriculum. As a consequence of this, the verbal-ability test constitutes the best measure of differences in achievement affected by differences between schools.

Other related points also confirm the use of this test score for assessing the apparent effects of schools. It showed the highest correlations, at all grade levels and for all racial and ethnic groups studied in the survey, with other test scores. It appeared, consequently, to measure much of what the other tests measure, but to be more reliable in doing so. Thus the verbal-ability test, in reality a verbal-achievement test, will be used as the criterion of achievement throughout the subsequent sections.

■ **Table 3.21.5** School-to-school component of total variance expressed as per cent of both variance components at each grade level. Averages for Mexican Americans, Puerto Ricans, Indian Americans, Oriental Americans, Northern and Southern Negroes, and Northern and Southern whites (corrected for number of degrees of freedom due to number of schools)

	Grades				
	12	9	6	3	1
Nonverbal ability	11.89	12.14	23.92	14.89	17.20
Verbal ability	16.25	14.70	21.27	23.56	16.54
Reading comprehension	10.80	9.02	16.29	20.70	—
Mathematics achievement	6.72	9.00	15.74	20.94	—

3.22 School-to-School Variations in Achievement

The question of first and most immediate importance to this survey in the study of school effects is how much variation exists between the achievement of students in one school and those of students in another. For if there were no variation between schools in pupils' achievement, it would be fruitless to search for effects of different kinds of schools upon achievement.

Thus the variation in achievement that exists between schools represents an upper limit to the effect of factors that distinguish one school from another in its ability to produce achievement. But other factors as well may be responsible for these variations in achievement from school to school. It may be useful to list possible factors that could be involved in school-to-school achievement differences.

Possible sources of school-to-school variation in achievement are—

1. Differences from one school to another in school factors affecting achievement.
2. Differences from one community to another in family backgrounds of individual including abilities of students.
3. Differences from one community to another in influences outside school, apart from the student's own family.

Possible sources of within-school variation in achievement—

1. Differences in pupils' abilities in the same school.
2. Differences in family backgrounds of the pupils in the same school.
3. Differences in school experience among students within the same school (i.e., different teachers, different courses, etc.).
4. Different influences within the community on different students toward achievement (such as community attitudes which may discourage high achievement among lower status children, and encourage it among higher status children).

These two lists indicate that the finding of school-to-school variation in achievement is neither a necessary nor a sufficient basis for inferring the effect of school factors; other factors can cause variations among schools, and school factors can cause variations within a school. Nevertheless, when we find school-to-school variations in achievement, we can proceed with the use of the appropriate techniques, one step toward the identification of school factors producing different levels of achievement in different schools.

The effect of school factors in producing variations within a school cannot be assessed in this study, because data were not gathered on the differential experiences within school, such as the particular set of teachers in a school who had taught each student (except for those experiences that are highly dependent on a student's achievement itself; for example, the number of mathematics courses he has taken).

Thus the effects of school factors studied in this survey must manifest themselves in school-to-school variation in achievement. The task becomes one of separating the three possible sources of such variation, so that some idea can be gained of the magnitude of school effects.

Ordinarily, when one finds that the level of achievement in one school is much higher than the achievement in another, there comes to his mind these sources of difference: The different students with which the school begins, the different community settings, or student body climates which encourage or fail to encourage high achievement, and the differences in the school itself. When we find school-to-school variation in achievement, we shall keep these same sources of variation in mind. Part of the subsequent analysis will be an attempt to separate them out, so that some assessment of the effect of each can be made.

For each racial and ethnic group there is a total variation of test scores that can be divided into two parts: (1) a part consisting of the variations of individual scores of pupils in a school about the average score of his ethnic group in the school—this is the within-school variance; (2) a part consisting of the variations of the school averages about the average score for the Nation or region—this is the school-to-school or the between-school variance. Table 3.22.1 exhibits the percentage that the between-school variance is of the total variance. Examination of the figures shows that the between-school part of the variance is about 5 per cent to 35 per cent of the total variance.

■ **Table 3.22.1.** Per cent of total variance in individual verbal achievement scores that lies between schools*

	Grades				
	12	9	6	3	1
Mexican-Americans	20.20	15.87	28.18	24.35	23.22
Puerto Rican	22.35	21.00	31.30	26.65	16.74
Indian Americans	30.97	24.44	30.29	37.92	19.29
Oriental Americans	5.07	5.64	22.47	16.25	9.54
Negro South	22.54	20.17	22.64	34.68	23.21
Negro North	10.92	12.67	13.89	19.47	10.63
White South	10.11	9.13	11.05	17.73	18.64
White North	7.84	8.69	10.32	11.42	11.07

*   Corrected for degrees of freedom.

This table leads to the first important result in the assessment of school factors associated with achievement: School to school variations in achievement, from whatever source (community differences, variations in the average home background of the student body, or variations in school factors), are much smaller than individual variations within the school, at all grade levels, for all racial and ethnic groups. This means that most of the variation in achievement could not possibly be accounted for by school differences, since most of it lies within the school. The table presents only the results for verbal achievement, but as section 3.21 indicated, the results hold equally or even more strongly for other test scores. This result indicates that despite the wide range of diversity of school facilities, curriculum, and teachers, and despite the wide diversity among student bodies in different schools, over 70 per cent of the variation in achievement for each group is variation within the same student body. The school-to-school difference is even less than overall figures for all groups indicate, because the school-to-school differences are generally least for Negroes and whites, and it is these groups which are numerically greatest. Consequently, only about 10 to 20 per cent of the total variation in achievement for the groups that are numerically most important lies between different schools.

A further examination of Table 3.22.1 gives some indication of the possible sources of the school-to-school differences. The existence of variations among schools gives no indication of whether these differences are related to school factors, community differences in support of school achievement, or background differences. However, if these variations were largely a result of either school factors or community differences in support of school achievement, then the school-to-school differences would increase over the grades in school. (Because of different school sizes in elementary and secondary schools, direct comparison can be made only up through grade 6.) However, this is not the case; there is no consistent increase for all groups in grades 1-6, and only a slight increase when an average of all groups is taken. Grade 1 is the crucial case here, because the tests were given shortly after the beginning of school, and thus school factors could have had little effect—nor could community factors outside the family have had much effect (except insofar as they acted through the family). Thus, the school-to-school component of test score variance at grade 1 is almost wholly a measure of the skills with which children in different schools begin school. And as Table 3.22.1 indicates, this school-to-school component is already large at grade 1, for whites as large as that at grade 3. Thus the larger part of school-to-school variation in achievement appears to be not a consequence of effects of school variations at all, but of variations in family backgrounds of the entering student bodies.

A reasonable conclusion is, then, that our schools have great uniformity insofar as their effect on the learning of pupils is concerned. The data suggest that variations in school quality are not highly related to variations in achievement of pupils. Section 3.1 showed this indirectly, in that achievement of those minority groups with poorest family backgrounds not only began lowest but remained so. Here, the comparison is wholly within each group, and indicates that the relative lack of effect of the school which is suggested by comparison among ethnic groups is true for variations in achievement within each group as well. The present data suggest why the minorities that begin with an educational disadvantage continue to exhibit this disadvantage throughout the twelve grades of school: The school appears unable to exert independent influences to make achievement levels less dependent on the child's background—and this is true within each ethnic group, just as it is between groups.

There are differences among the different ethnic groups in school-to-school variation in achievement. First, comparison of Negroes and whites shows important differences. The school-to-school variations in achievement are larger in the South than in the North for both Negroes and whites. However, it is among the Negroes that these school-to-school variations are especially high in the South. This result, coupled with the fact that for the Negroes and the other minority groups, the school-to-school component of variance increases from grade 1 to grade 3, while it does not for whites, leads to a third important result of the section. Indirect evidence suggests that school factors make more difference in achievement for minority group members than for whites; for Negroes, this is especially true in the South. This result suggests that insofar as variations in school factors are related to variations in achievement, they make most difference for children of minority groups. The evidence is only indirect here, and the point requires further examination when school factors are explicitly studied in a later section. But at this point the indirect evidence suggests that it is those children who come least prepared to school, and whose achievement in school is generally low, for whom the characteristics of a school make the most difference.

These results suggest (and subsequent sections will reinforce this suggestion) that these children may be thought of as differing in sensitivity to variations in school quality. The data indicate that the least sensitive are in general those children from groups where achievement is highest at the beginning of school (and remains so), and the most sensitive are those with lowest initial levels of achievement. A rough order of the sensitivity to school effects can be obtained by inspection of Table 3.22.1, giving perhaps the following order from high to low sensitivity:

Puerto Rican	Negro, North
Indian American	Oriental American
Mexican-American	White, South
Negro, South	White, North

Since it is important to assess whether in fact there is this general difference in sensitivity to school effects, the data in succeeding tables will be presented in the order indicated above. Thus if there is a general difference in sensitivity to school effects, the size of the relationship to school factors shown in subsequent tables should tend to become progressively less, moving down the table.

The overall results of this examination of school-to-school variations in achievement can be summed up in three statements:

1.   For each group, by far the largest part of the variation in student achievement lies within the same school, and not between schools.
2.   Comparison of school-to-school variations in achievement at the beginning of grade 1 with later years indicates that only a small part of it is the result of school factors, in contrast to family background differences between communities.
3.   There is indirect evidence that school factors are more important in affecting the achievement of minority group students; among Negroes, this appears especially so in the South. This leads to the notion of differential sensitivity to school variations, with the lowest achieving minority groups showing highest sensitivity.

In examining the ability of school variations to account for variance in individual achievement, these school-to-school variations in Table 3.22.1 will constitute a kind of upper limit. Thus, in some cases, it will be useful to study the variance accounted for by a given factor relative to this upper limit, as well as to the overall variation in achievement. Two different questions are being answered: When the total variation in individual achievement is the standard, the question is what part of individual achievement can this variable account for? When the school-to-school variation from Table 3.22.1 is the standard, the question is what part of the school-to-school variation in achievement does the variable account for?

To continue the focus on the overall effectiveness of particular factors, the subsequent tables will report per cent of individual variance accounted for.

Obviously, the amount accounted for will be quite low, since the upper limit is itself low. To determine the proportion of school-to-school variance accounted for, the numbers in Table 3.22.1 may be taken as upper limits.

3.22.1   The influence of student background factors on achievements.   Before examining the relation of school characteristics to student achievement, it is useful to examine the influence of student background characteristics. Because these background differences are prior to school influence, and shape the child before he reaches school, they will, to the extent we have succeeded in measuring them, be controlled when examining the effect of school factors. This means that the achievement differences among schools which are due only to differences in student input can be in part controlled, to allow for more accurate examination of the apparent effects of differences in school or teacher factors themselves.

It is useful, then, at the outset, to examine the relation of these background factors to achievement, to get a view of some of the family factors that predispose children to learn well or poorly in school. The survey cannot investigate the effects of background factors in detail, but it is critically important to control as much of their effect as possible before examining school factors.

A preliminary analysis of the relation of particular background factors to achievement showed that family background differences measured in this survey could be clustered into eight variables. The relation of these variables to achievement will be examined only at grades 12, 9, and 6, since several of the questions were not (and most could not have successfully been) asked of the children at grades 3 and 1. (Except where indicated below, the question numbers refer to the 12th and 9th grade questionnaires. If the question content differs for the sixth grade, indication will be made.)

A   (1) (Grades 9 and 12) Urbanism of background (based on Q6 and Q21 about community in which self and mother grew up); (2) (Grade 6) Migration (based on Q3 and Q13 about own and mother's birthplace).

B   Parents' education (based on Q19 and Q20 about mother's and father's education).

C   Structural integrity of the home (based on Q18 and Q17 about mother and father in the home).

D   Smallness of family (number of brothers and sisters, in a negative direction) (based on Q10).

E   Items in home (based on Q31, Q32, Q33, Q34, Q37, and Q38: TV, telephone, record player, refrigerator, automobile, vacuum cleaner).

F   Reading material in home (based on Q35, Q36, Q39, Q41, and Q42: Dictionary, encyclopedia, daily newspaper, magazines, books. Last two items missing in 6th grade).

G   Parents' interest (based on Q26 and Q30: Talk with parents about school; anyone read to you when small).

H   Parents' educational desires (based on Q24, Q25, Q27, Q28, and Q29: How good a student do mother and father want child to be; how far in school do mother and father want child to go; attendance at PTA. Last three items missing in 6th grade).

These clusters of variables range from factors in the parents' background (father's and mother's education, urbanism of background) to factors which describe the present interest in his school work that his parents show. In all cases, the data are based on the child's report, which may include distortions or mis-perceptions or absence of information, especially at grade 6.

One way of examining the influence of background factors on achievement is to examine the per cent of within-school variance and the per cent of school-to-school variance accounted for by these family factors. First, taking the school-to-school variations as given, and examining the added variance accounted for by family background characteristics shows what portion of the within-school variance may be accounted for by these factors. This is a severe restriction, because from Table 3.221.2 it appears that much of the school-to-school variance is itself a result of family background differences. Table 3.221.1 shows at grades 12, 9, and 6, the variation accounted for at each of these stages, first by the ob-jective conditions in the home, as reported by the child, then by these plus "subjective" background factors, and finally, in addition, by his own attitudes. The table shows that at each grade level, the amount of within school-variance accounted for by these factors taken together is of the same order of magnitude as the variance associated with school-to-school factors. For whites and for Oriental Americans especially, the percent of within-school variance accounted for by objective family conditions (b), and those plus subjective family con-ditions (c) is very great. For all groups, the total variance accounted for, including the school-to-school variation (column a) and the within-school variation ex-plained by background and attitudes, is between 30 per cent and 50 per cent of the total variance in achievement.

Second, we may ask about the proportion of school-to-school variance accounted for by background factors. Taking the variance in column (2) of Table 3.221.1 as the total variance to be explained, the question becomes what per cent of this school-to-school variance is accounted for by these same back-ground factors? Table 3.221.2 shows the per cent of school-to-school variance (of which the total as a per cent of individual variance is given in column (a) of Table 3.221.1) is accounted for by the same background factors as in the third column of Table 3.221.1. Much of the effect of these individual background factors is within schools, as shown by Table 3.221.1, but Table 3.221.2 shows that an additional amount is associated with school-to-school differences in achieve-

---

*   The first column is only an estimate of the school-to-school variations in achieve-ment for each group, obtained by regressing individual achievement on overall school mean achievement (for all groups together) and proportion white. These two measures together (except for the presence of third groups in the school) provide an estimate of the group's mean score in the school under the assumption that differences between the the white mean and the group mean are constant over all schools.

■ **Table 3.221.1.** Percent of variance accounted for in verbal achievement at grades 6, 9, and 12, by successively adding additional factors

[A: Variance associated with school-to-school differences (Measured and unmeasured;* B: objective background factors (as reported by student) added (A through F); C: subjective background factors added (G and H); D: child's attitudes added (1) interest (in school, (2) self-concept, (3) control of environment]

	A	A + B	A + B + C	A + B + C + D
Grade 12				
Puerto Ricans	23.40	24.69	26.75	31.54
Indian Americans	24.13	30.73	34.81	43.61
Mexican Americans	20.07	22.60	26.09	34.33
Negro, South	22.15	26.17	28.18	38.97
Negro, North	11.19	15.34	18.85	31.04
Oriental Americans	2.33	13.65	21.99	32.04
White, South	10.39	18.14	24.06	39.07
White, North	8.25	17.24	27.12	40.09
Negroes, total	20.90	24.73	27.31	38.18
Whites, total	9.49	17.93	26.42	39.80
Grade 9				
Puerto Ricans	16.77	19.11	21.88	30.41
Indian Americans	19.75	25.89	29.31	36.64
Mexican Americans	20.28	25.26	27.79	34.10
Negro, South	18.55	22.84	26.93	38.88
Negro, North	8.96	13.84	17.73	30.48
Oriental Americans	7.36	17.58	27.66	34.93
White, South	10.50	21.54	26.63	42.09
White, North	8.31	19.32	25.55	39.56
Negroes, total	17.43	21.68	25.47	37.21
Whites, total	10.00	20.78	26.57	40.90
Grade 6				
Puerto Ricans	22.49	34.25	36.40	40.35
Indian Americans	26.67	33.93	35.05	41.20
Mexican Americans	37.60	35.79	37.74	45.04
Negro, South	22.25	27.95	28.89	37.69
Negro, North	11.86	16.97	17.93	26.39
Oriental Americans	24.31	41.20	42.25	51.76
White, South	12.33	21.58	23.52	34.61
White, North	12.77	19.95	21.70	35.77
Negroes, total	19.77	24.83	25.77	34.12
Whites, total	13.71	21.25	23.06	35.95

(Footnote on p. 298)

ment. This table, together with the following one, shows the strength of background factors in accounting for the variation in achievement, both within and among schools.

The overall variance in verbal achievement including both within- and between-school related to these background factors is shown in Table 3.221.3. Three colums are shown in the table for each grade, the first consisting of the variance accounted for by the first six background factors alone, excluding the parents' interest and aspirations (as reported by the child). The second column shows the variance accounted for by all eight, and the third column is the difference between the first two, showing the added variance accounted for by parents' interest and aspirations for the child.

■ **Table 3.221.2.** Per cent of school-to-school variance in verbal achievement (approximated by mean school achievement, controlling on proportion white in school) accounted for by eight background factors (see (B) and (C) in Table 3.221.1). Variance explained is a per cent of that shown in column (A) of Table 3.221.1

	Grade 12	Grade 9	Grade 6
Puerto Ricans	3.05	4.74	7.54
Indian Americans	2.96	3.41	7.28
Mexican Americans	11.56	10.49	6.55
Negro, South	32.69	23.47	12.37
Negro, North	12.25	7.37	6.75
Oriental Americans	5.67	7.24	28.36
White, South	28.86	23.82	19.96
White, North	15.99	14.42	10.99
Negroes, total	29.05	21.82	12.80
Whites, total	21.89	21.28	17.09

The table shows that overall, the background factors measured by these six or eight variables account for about 10 per cent to 25 per cent of variance in individual achievement. There are, of course, many other aspects of the child's background that are not measured here; thus the variance accounted for by these variables can be interpreted as a kind of lower limit to the actual effects of background differences. (This is the opposite situation to that for school-to-school variation, where the variation between schools constituted an upper limit to the amount that could be related to school differences.)

The data show a number of variations among grade levels and among different groups. First, the six measures of objective conditions in the home account for more of the variance in achievement at earlier grades than at later ones. The decline from grade 6 to 12 is very slight for Negroes and whites, and larger for some of the other groups.

This decline is especially noteworthy because of the lesser reliability of reporting of family background at earlier grades, which would reduce the observed relationship. Thus, the true decline in the relationship between objective conditions in the home and achievement is probably greater than the slight observed decline.

■ **Table 3.221.3.** Per cent of variance in verbal achievement accounted for at grades 12. 9, and 6, by six and by eight background factors

	Grade 12			Grade 9			Grade 6		
	Six	Eight	Eight-Six	Six	Eight	Eight-Six	Six	Eight	Eight-Six
Puerto Ricans	3.64	4.69	1.05	3.89	6.18	2.29	23.71	25.51	1.80
Indian Americans	18.89	22.07	3.18	13.92	16.30	2.38	18.40	19.65	1.25
Mexican Americans	7.92	10.23	2.31	12.79	14.25	1.46	21.82	23.07	1.25
Negro, South	14.41	15.79	1.38	12.27	15.69	3.42	14.66	15.44	.78
Negro, North	7.53	10.96	3.43	7.68	11.41	3.73	9.51	10.25	.74
Oriental Americans	11.81	19.45	7.64	12.75	22.81	10.06	34.77	36.16	1.39
White, South	14.75	20.13	5.38	18.40	23.12	4.72	18.14	19.91	1.77
White, North	14.28	24.56	10.28	16.49	22.78	6.29	14.10	15.57	1.47
Negroes, total	13.48	15.14	1.66	12.15	14.99	2.84	14.01	14.62	.61
Whites, total	14.71	23.03	8.32	17.81	23.28	5.47	16.20	17.64	1.44

Two rather simple models of the impact of family background on achievement are *a priori* reasonable: (1) The family's impact on the child has its greatest effect in earliest years, so that family-to-family differences in achievement should decline after the beginning of school; and (2) the family's impact on the child affects his receptivity to later experience, so that family-to-family differences in achievement should increase over the years of school. The data from objective conditions of the home appear to support the first of these models, because of the decline (probably underestimated) in the relation of these conditions to achievement from grade 6 to 12.[1]

A second point to be observed in the table is that the measures of the subjective home conditions show the opposite trend over grades: Their relation to achievement increases over the grades 6 to 12. The third column at each grade level shows the amount added to the accounted-for-variance by the two measures of parents' interest. This column shows an increase from grades 6 to 12. The increase indicates either that the older students perceive their parents' interest more accurately than the younger ones, or that their parents' interest has more impact on their achievement in the later years of school.

A third point from this table is of more direct relevance to this study. This is the difference in the relation of subjective home conditions to achievement for the different groups. For whites and Oriental Americans, parents' interest accounts for much more variation than it does for any of the other groups. This result may be due to either of two conditions: Either a given amount of parents' interest has the same effect for all groups, but there is more variation in parents' interest for these two groups, or it in fact does have a greater effect for these two groups. To decide between these two interpretations, the unique contribution of these two measures (from the third column at each grade level in Table 3.221.3), was divided by the variance of the one variable H in the list above) that accounts for nearly all the added variance in all groups. The data show that almost none of the variation in achievement accounted for is related to the different variances in each group, and nearly all of it is related to different strength of the effect of parents' interest. This leads to an important result:

Either (a) Negro, Mexican American, Puerto Rican, and Indian American children fail to perceive their parents' interest or lack of interest in their schooling as fully as do whites and Oriental Americans; or (b) the parents of these minority group children are less able to translate their interest into effective support for the child's learning than are white or Oriental American parents.

■ **Table 3.221.4.** Relative strength of influence of subjective home conditions upon achievement. For each grade, left column shows the variance of parents' desires for child's education, right column shows added variance explained by last two factors divided by left column (and multiplied by 100)

	Grade 12		Grade 9		Grade 6	
Puerto Ricans	103.59	1.01	95.63	2.39	84.64	2.13
Indian Americans	95.55	3.33	99.14	2.40	91.99	1.36
Mexican Americans	90.23	2.56	89.36	1.63	87.10	1.44
Negro, South	60.28	2.29	67.52	5.07	71.28	1.09
Negro, North	69.94	4.90	73.94	5.04	79.03	.94
Oriental Americans	79.98	9.55	81.09	12.41	78.75	1.77
White, South	65.22	8.25	66.70	7.08	68.26	2.59
White, North	71.22	14.43	67.09	9.38	64.05	2.30
Negroes, total	65.40	2.54	70.85	4.01	75.34	.81
Whites, total	69.71	11.94	66.98	8.17	65.40	2.20

There is some evidence to support both of these possibilities. Earlier in section 3.1, the greater unreality of Negro children's aspirations was evident; this suggests that the same lack of realism may inflate his report of his parents' interest. At the same time, Negro parents do show a greater interest in their child's education and greater aspirations for his success in education than do white parents of the same economic level. Thus, the children may be reporting reliably. If so, the data in Table 3.221.3 suggest that Negro and other minority parents are not able effectively to translate their interest into practices that support the child's achievement.

A somewhat more detailed view of the factors in the child's background that are most highly associated with verbal achievement is given in Table 3.221.5. The proportions of variance in achievement accounted for by each of the six variables were ranked, and the rank orders for each group at each grade level are listed in the table. The (–) preceding the rank indicates a negative relation between achievement and the variable.

The table shows that in the sixth grade, the child's report of items in his home, indicating its economic level, has the highest relation to achievement for all minority groups, while parents' education has the highest relation for whites. In later years, parents' education comes to have the highest relation for nearly all groups. For Negroes at grade 12, the length of time in an urban environment and the (small) size of his family show approximately the same importance as parents' education. Contrary to much that has been written, the structural integrity of the home (principally the father's presence or absence) shows very little relation to achievement for Negroes. It does, however, show a strong relation to achievement for the other minority groups.

In general, each of the groups under study shows its own pattern of relative importance of background variables. It appears that the relative importance of educationally related attributes of the home (parents' education, reading matter) compared to indicators of the economic level is greater for white children than for minority group children. . . .

3.23 Student Body Characteristics

In examining the relation of school characteristics to achievement of children in each group, the first caution is provided by the results of section 3.22. The pattern of school-to-school differences in achievement at the different grade levels indicated small relation to school factors. Yet some idea of the possible effects of school factors can be gained by a few simple examinations. It is convenient to separate school characteristics into three groups, as was done in part 2: First, facilities, curriculum, and other characteristics of the school itself. Second, characteristics of the teaching staff; and third, those of the student body.[2]

Subsequent sections will examine variables within each of these broad classifications, to study their relation to achievement. However, if that were done without an initial view of all three together, the relative strength of the

■ **Table 3.221.5.** Rank by size of standardized regression coefficients for 6 background factors* grades 12. 9, 6 (1 is high, 6 is low)

	Grade 12					
	A	B	C	D	E	F
Puerto Ricans	2	1	(−)4	5	(−)3	6
Indian Americans	5	1	6	2	3	4
Mexican Americans	2	1	3	4	6	5
Negro, South	2	3	6	1	5	4
Negro, North	3	1	4	2	6	5
Oriental Americans	(−)5	3	1	4	(−)6	2
White, South	3	1	6	4	(−)5	2
White, North	4	1	5	3	6	2
Negroes, total	1	2	6	3	4	5
Whites, total	4	1	5	3	(−)6	2

*   Code:
A = (Grades 9 and 12) urbanism of background.   E = Items in home.
A = (Grade 6) migration.   F = Reading material in home.
B = Parents' education.   G = Parents' interest.
C = Structural integrity of the home.   H = Parents' educational desires.
D = Smallness of family.

three, and thus an important result, would be overlooked. The principal result, based on a variety of analyses, is as follows:

Attributes of other students account for far more variation in the achievement of minority group children than do any attributes of school facilities and slightly more than do attributes of staff.

In general, as the educational aspirations and backgrounds of fellow students increase, the achievement of minority group children increases. Such a result must be subject to special scrutiny, because it may be confounded by the student's own educational background and aspirations, which will generally be similar to those of his fellow students. For this reason, throughout the analysis except where indicated, his own background characteristics are controlled to reduce such an effect.

It is useful to examine two tables which provide some of the evidence on which this result is based. One (Table 3.23.1) presents the results of regression analyses using eight variables. The eight variables consist of three to represent student backgrounds and attitudes; two to represent school factors; two to represent teacher factors, and one to represent student body qualities. The three background variables are control variables and their effect is not shown. The unique parts of variance accounted for by the other five are shown individually

Grade 9						Grade 6					
A	B	C	D	E	F	A	B	C	D	E	F
3	4	2	(−)6	(−)5	1	(−)6	5	2	4	1	3
(−)4	1	3	5	2	6	3	4	2	6	1	5
(−)6	3	2	5	1	4	(−)6	4	3	5	1	2
5	1	4	3	2	6	6	2	5	4	1	3
6	2	3	1	5	4	6	3	5	4	1	2
(−)6	4	2	3	5	1	6	3	2	4	1	5
6	1	5	3	4	2	(−)5	1	6	3	2	4
6	1	4	2	5	3	(−)5	1	6	4	3	2
4	1	5	2	3	6	6	2	5	4	1	3
6	1	4	3	5	2	(−)5	1	6	4	2	3

in the table. The unique part associated with a single variable is calculated by obtaining the variance accounted for by all eight variables and then independently obtaining the variance accounted for by seven variables (omitting the single variable); the difference between the two variances thus obtained is the unique contribution (to the accounting for of variance) of the single variable.

The first column shows the part of the variance (over and above the part accounted for by the three background control variables) for which the whole set of five variables accounts together. The second column is the "common" part of the five; it is calculated by subtracting the sum of the unique per cents of variance from the joint per cent. (Grades 1 and 3 are not shown here because extremely small proportions of the variance are accounted for by any of the five school characteristics.)

The table shows vanishingly small unique contributions of school and teacher characteristics, but very large unique contributions of student body characteristics. In addition, the second column of the table shows the variance that is explained in common; that is, variance that could alternatively be explained by more than one of the five variables. Some of this variance is of course attributable to school or teacher variables, and we shall see later that most of it

■ **Table 3.23.1.** Per cent of variance in verbal achievement uniquely accounted for by one variable representing each of: school facilities (A), curriculum (B), teacher quality (C), teacher attitudes (D), student body quality (E), at grades 12, 9 and 6

| | Joint ABCDE | Unique | | | | | |
		Common	A	B	C	D	E
Grade 12							
Puerto Ricans	21.83	11.93	1.00	0.01	0.44	0.89	8.55
Indian Americans	10.60	3.56	.31	.52	0	2.77	3.44
Mexican Americans	15.70	7.45	.22	.20	.27	.42	7.14
Negro, South	11.06	2.80	0	0	.01	.18	8.07
Negro, North	7.59	3.58	.13	.04	0	.17	3.67
Oriental Americans	1.18	.44	.03	.03	.18	.09	.41
White, South	3.02	.25	.02	0	0	.24	2.34
White, North	1.58	.25	.02	0	0	0	1.31
Negro, total	12.43	5.58	.02	1.01	.02	.03	6.77
White, total	2.52	.50	.01	0	0	0	2.01
Grade 9							
Puerto Ricans	14.46	2.95	.13	.23	.05	.31	10.79
Indian Americans	8.69	2.39	.89	.16	.19	.30	4.76
Mexican Americans	9.22	3.88	.05	.19	.28	1.18	3.64
Negro, South	8.84	3.40	0	0	.07	.02	5.35
Negro, North	3.37	1.38	.07	.01	.01	.24	1.66
Oriental Americans	3.79	−.34	.05	.20	.27	.13	3.48
White, South	2.05	.15	.03	.03	.01	.05	1.78
White, North	1.23	.01	.01	.12	.08	.01	1.10
Negro, total	8.21	3.99	.01	0	.08	.08	4.05
White, total	1.88	−.06	.02	.08	.06	.09	1.69
Grade 6							
Puerto Ricans	12.01	4.07	.01	.02	.03	.02	7.86
Indian Americans	9.14	2.28	.54	.09	.40	.34	5.49
Mexican Americans	12.91	4.91	0	.01	.10	.22	7.67
Negro, South	9.48	3.22	.05	.03	.06	.04	6.12
Negro, North	4.81	.87	0	.05	.19	.01	3.69
Oriental Americans	4.99	1.39	.15	.42	.08	.04	2.91
White, South	2.13	−.02	.03	0	0	.01	2.11
White, North	4.56	.02	.15	0	.08	0	4.31
Negro, total	9.38	2.85	0	.03	0	.01	6.49
White, total	4.37	−.06	.03	0	.05	.09	4.26

is to be attributed to teacher variables. In any case, an impressive per cent of variance is accounted for by student body characteristics.

A different way of viewing the relative importance of school and fellow-student variables for achievement is to give a special advantage to school variables, by letting them account for as much variance as possible, and then introducing characteristics of fellow students to account for whatever additional variance they will. This was done in another analysis, in which the student's own background was statistically controlled. The result is shown in Table 3.23.2 for each grade level. At grades 3 and 1, little variance is accounted for either by school characteristics or student body characteristics. This result, in which no variables account for much of the variance in achievement, is true throughout the analysis for grades 3 and 1, despite the large school-to-school variations shown in Tables 3.22.1 and 3.22.2.

However, in grades 12, 9, and 6, the greater importance of student body characteristics becomes evident. Even when they are added after school characteristics, they more than double the explained variance for many groups, and sharply increase it for all groups.

These demonstrations could be supplemented by many others; in the many analyses that have been carried out, nearly any student body characteristic is more effective in accounting for variations in individual achievement than is any characteristic of the school itself.

A second general result indicated by Tables 3.23.1 and 3.23.2 is that the highest achieving groups, whites and Oriental Americans, show generally least dependency of achievement on characteristics of fellow students. This statement assumes that the differences shown in Table 3.23.1 and Table 3.23.2 are not due to lesser variation in characteristics of fellow students for Oriental Americans and whites. The variances for student body characteristics (as used in Table 3.23.1) and for encyclopedia and students' college plans (the two variables that account for most of the variance at grades 9 and 12 in Table 3.23.2) are slightly smaller for these groups. However, when these variances are divided into the numbers in Tables 3.23.1 and 3.23.2 the difference still holds with nearly the same strength. This means that a given difference in characteristics of fellow students makes less difference in achievement of these two groups. This indicates, as in previous data, a lesser sensitivity to school environments for children in these groups. It suggests also, as in previous data, that family background which encourages achievement reduces sensitivity to variations in schools. The school, including the student body, apparently has less differential effect upon achievement of children from such backgrounds.

The results suggest, then, that the environment provided by the student body is asymmetric in its effects, that it has its greatest effects on those from educationally deficient backgrounds. The matter is of course more complex than this simple relation, doubtless depending on the relative number of high and low achieving students in the school, and on other factors.

Another result from the data of Tables 3.23.1 and 3.23.2, which is consistent

■ **Table 3.23.2.** Per cent of variance in verbal achievement accounted for by school characteristics (A) and by school characteristics plus student body characteristics (A + B). Background characteristics controlled are the first six appearing in Table 3.221.5

	Grade 12			Grade 9		
	A*	A + B†	Gain	A*	A + B†	Gain
Puerto Ricans	6.67	22.59	15.92	4.07	15.70	11.63
Indian Americans	11.48	22.78	11.30	2.59	9.98	7.39
Mexican Americans	6.59	15.90	9.31	2.82	10.68	7.86
Negro, South	8.64	12.69	4.05	7.52	12.66	5.14
Negro, North	3.14	7.73	4.59	1.45	4.62	3.17
Oriental Americans	3.83	4.40	.57	5.66	11.12	5.46
White, South	3.16	4.61	1.45	1.60	2.82	1.22
White, North	1.87	2.94	1.07	.73	2.34	1.61
Negroes, total	6.96	12.82	5.86	5.19	10.59	5.40
Whites, total	2.53	3.69	1.16	1.15	2.44	1.29

*   School characteristics are:
Per pupil expenditure on staff
Volumes per student in library
Science lab facilities (9 and 12 only)
Extracurricular activities (9 and 12 only)
Presence of accelerated curriculum (9 and 12 only)
Comprehensiveness of curriculum (9 and 12 only)
Use of tracking (9 and 12 only)
Movement between tracks (9 and 12 only)
Size
Guidance counselors (9 and 12 only)
School location (city suburb, town, country)

with the general difference in sensitivity shown earlier, concerns differences among Negroes. It is those Negroes who are in the South whose achievement appears to vary most greatly with variations in the characteristics of their fellow students. Here, where the most educationally disadvantaged backgrounds are found, and where achievement is lowest, is where student body characteristics make most differences for Negro achievement. It is in these more stable, less urban areas where exposure to children of different educational backgrounds and aspirations has in the past been least possible for Negro children.

Particular student body characteristics. Having noted the generally strong relation of student body qualities to achievement, the next question becomes what qualities? First, it can be said that student body characteristics measuring the general educational backgrounds of the student body, and those measuring

Grade 6			Grade 3			Grade 1		
A*	A + B†	Gain	A*	A + B†	Gain	A*	A + B†	Gain
3.21	11.83	8.62	2.27	8.18	5.91	4.52	6.26	1.74
5.64	9.25	3.61	4.04	5.35	1.31	3.62	5.75	2.13
1.47	11.92	10.45	3.50	6.76	3.26	5.64	6.10	.46
4.90	7.77	2.87	.80	1.40	.60	2.14	2.93	.79
.77	2.73	1.96	2.96	5.13	2.17	2.38	3.28	.90
9.06	12.10	3.04	2.62	7.28	4.66	3.88	6.45	2.57
.57	1.92	1.35	.83	1.91	1.08	.96	1.53	.57
.32	3.63	3.31	.33	1.46	1.13	.83	2.35	1.52
2.77	5.48	2.71	2.26	2.96	.70	.72	1.76	1.04
.47	3.13	2.66	.33	1.28	.95	.32	1.33	1.01

† Student body characteristics are:
Proportion whose families own encyclopedias
Number of student transfers
Attendance
Proportion planning to attend college (9 and 12 only)
Teachers' perception of student-body quality (1, 3, 6 only)
Average hours of homework (9 and 12 only).

the educational aspirations are highly correlated. That is, a general dimension along which student bodies can be placed is the "average educational level"—either in terms of backgrounds or realistic aspirations—of students. In examining the importance of that dimension, two variables were used; one as a measure of background and the other as a measure of aspirations. The first is the proportion of students who said in the questionnaire that they have an encyclopedia in the home, and the second is the proportion with definite plans to attend college. For grade 6, the latter measure was not available, and a measure of student body quality was constructed from the presence or absence of student-derived problems in the school, as reported by the teachers.

Three measures of present characteristics of the student body were used as follows:

1. A measure of student mobility, derived from the principal's report of the per cent of students who were transfers in or out of school last year.
2. A measure of student attendance, from the principal's report.
3. The average hours of homework, from the student's report (for grades 9 and 12 only).

The relation of these student body measures to individual student achievement is examined in Table 3.23.3 under three conditions, all of which control the student's own background. The first condition controls also the per pupil instructional expenditure in school, the second controls as well 10 school facility and curriculum measures (themselves to be examined in the next section), and the third controls as well as the other student body measures introduced here.

■ **Table 3.23.3.** Additional variance in verbal achievement accounted for by student body factors under 3 conditions: per-pupil instructional expenditure (A); with 10 school variables added (B)†; and with other student body characteristics added (C).‡ (Six background factors controlled)

Item	Grade 12		
	A	A + B	A + B + C
Negro total			
Total explained*	(2.17)	(2.77)	((15.48))
Encyclopedia	8.03	4.26	1.93
Mobility	(−).22	(−).37	(−).11
Attendance	.68	1.04	.29
College (9, 12)	6.52	3.18	.09
Teachers' report (6)	—	—	—
Homework	.11	.08	(−).01
White total			
Total explained*	(.36)	(.47)	((3.13))
Encyclopedia	1.02	.48	.12
Mobility	.00	(−).04	(−).01
Attendance	.12	.23	.10
College (9, 12)	1.52	.90	.48
Teachers' report (6)	—	—	—
Homework	.12	.04	(−).02
Negro, North			
Total explained*	(.14)	(.77)	((2.73))
Encyclopedia	4.71	2.25	.55
Mobility	(−).94	(−).97	(−).36
Attendance	1.29	1.04	.23
College (9, 12)	5.35	3.09	1.36
Teachers' report (6)	—	—	—
Homework	.20	.05	(−).13

There are several results that derive from the table. The first general result that is supported by several aspects of the table is this: The educational backgrounds and aspirations of fellow students appear to provide a facilitating or amplifying effect on the achievement of a student independent of his own background.

Some of the evidence related to this result in Table 3.23.3 follows: In grade 12, both the level of background and aspirations of fellow students relate strongly to achievement, and neither's relation to achievement is wholly accounted for when the other is controlled. Second, at the ninth grade, the relation to background is about the same, though the level of educational aspirations of fellow students relates much less strongly to verbal achievement.

Grade 9			Grade 6		
A	A + B	A + B + C	A	A + B	A + B + C
(2.55)	(5.19)	((10.59))	(2.62)	(6.96)	((12.82))
6.36	4.68	3.82	2.16	2.00	1.32
(−).35	(−).36	(−).35	.01	.01	.01
.75	.97	.12	1.00	.98	.38
.52	.26	(−).11	—	—	—
—	—	—	.12	.47	.28
.32	.40	.10	—	—	—
(.64)	(1.15)	((2.44))	(.80)	(2.53)	((3.69))
1.11	.98	.80	1.13	1.22	.27
(−).01	(−).03	.00	.02	.04	.14
.37	.36	.24	.37	.36	.08
.13	.07	.00	—	—	—
—	—	—	2.16	2.15	1.21
(−).01	(−).02	(−).07	—⁚	—	—
(.02)	(1.45)	((4.62))	(.09)	(3.14)	((7.73))
1.82	1.61	1.26	1.36	1.31	.65
(−).92	(−).84	(−).74	(−).16	.05	.00
1.02	1.04	.25	.44	.41	.08
.22	.10	.34	—	—	—
—	—	—	1.37	1.10	.48
.63	.51	.14	—	—	—

| | Grade 12 | | |
Item	A	A + B	A + B + C
Negro, South			
Total explained*	(3.49)	(4.90)	((7.77))
Encyclopedia	7.04	2.90	1.54
Mobility	.10	.07	.05
Attendance	.29	.48	.30
College (9, 12)	5.58	1.90	.62
Teachers' report (6)	—	—	—
Homework	.64	.09	.16
White, North			
Total explained*	(.05)	(.32)	((3.63))
Encyclopedia	.76	.39	.08
Mobility	(−).10	(−).19	(−).11
Attendance	.16	.19	.04
College (9, 12)	1.04	.79	.40
Teachers' report (6)	—	—	—
Homework	.13	.02	(−).02
White, South			
Total explained*	(.15)	(.57)	((1.92))
Encyclopedia	1.69	.54	.06
Mobility	.50	.17	.23
Attendance	.01	.28	.22
College (9, 12)	2.53	.95	.45
Teachers' report (6)	—	—	—
Homework	.35	.12	.01

*   The total explained variance under columns A and A + B (marked by parentheses) does not include the contributions of the listed items. Under column A + B + C (that marked by double parentheses) does include their contributions.
†   School characteristics are:
Per pupil expenditure on staff
Volumes per student in library
Science lab facilities (9 and 12 only)
Extracurricular activities (9 and 12 only)
Presence of accelerated curriculum (9 and 12 only)
Comprehensiveness of curriculum (9 and 12 only)
Use of tracking (9 and 12 only)
Movement between tracks (9 and 12 only)
Size
Guidance counselors (9 and 12 only)
School location (city suburb, town, country)

Grade 9			Grade 6		
A	A + B	A + B + C	A	A + B	A + B + C
(2.89)	(7.52)	((12.66))	(2.98)	(8.64)	((12.69))
7.99	4.66	3.29	2.64	1.86	.94
.06	.05	.00	1.03	.84	.28
.39	.85	.57	1.09	1.18	.51
.40	.02	(−).09	—	—	—
—	—	—	.08	.13	.18
.80	1.03	(−).06	—	—	—
(.14)	(.73)	((2.34))	(.29)	(1.87)	((2.94))
.82	.83	.75	1.29	1.36	.16
(−).15	(−).16	(−).03	.04	.10	.30
.81	.69	.57	.32	.25	.02
.00	.00	(−).09	—	—	—
—	—	—	2.80	2.82	1.67
(−).01	(−).05	(−).06	—	—	—
(.21)	(1.60)	((2.82))	(.06)	(3.16)	((4.61))
1.56	.86	.62	.67	.44	.08
.39	.15	.06	.01	.00	.01
(−).04	.02	.00	.53	.57	.32
.95	.36	.17	—	—	—
—	—	—	1.04	.86	.52
.19	.24	.04	—	—	—

(−) preceding the number indicates that the partial relationship of the attitude to achievement is negative.

‡   Student body characteristics are:

Proportion whose families own encyclopedias
Number of student transfers
Attendance
Proportion planning to attend college (9 and 12 only)
Teachers' perception of student-body quality (1, 3, 6, only)
Average hours of homework (9 and 12 only)

In the North, it is the level of fellow-students' aspirations that relates more strongly, while in the South, it is their backgrounds. At the sixth grade, the student body quality as perceived by the teacher relates about as strongly to achievement as the measure of student body background (for whites and for Negroes in the North, more strongly; for Negroes in the South, less strongly).

Another general measure of the student body's affinity for school, which derives partly from general characteristics of the community and partly from management of the school, is attendance. For all groups, it relates moderately to achievement, both before and after other student body factors are controlled.[3]

A final result from this table concerns mobility. In the North, for both whites and Negroes, achievement is lower where student mobility is high; in the South achievement is higher where student mobility is high.

This reversed relation in the North and South is very likely an urban-rural difference. In cities, certain schools have very high student turnover, and this apparently limits the ability of such schools to produce achievement. But in rural areas, mobility is much lower, and it appears to be those schools which are most fixed and stable in student population that have lowest achievement.

There is one special characteristic of the student body for which the regression analysis provides some additional evidence. This is the racial composition of the student body. The problem of assessing its effect is vastly complicated by the fact that students of both races in racially heterogeneous schools are not representative of all students of their race, but are often highly unrepresentative. Nevertheless, with this caution it is useful to examine the achievement of students of each race in schools of varying different racial composition.

The question of performance of children in schools of different racial composition is often confused by not separating several different components:

i. Effects due to different facilities and curriculum in the school itself.

ii. Effects due to differences in educational deficiency or proficiency of fellow students that are correlated with race, though not universally so.

iii. Effects due to racial composition of the student body apart from its level of educational proficiency.

Some insight into these effects may be gained by examining what the racial composition of the student body can tell us about the achievement of students of each race under different levels of prior information, as follows (under all conditions, his own family background characteristics are controlled):

A) In the first instance, if we know nothing about the school except its per-pupil instructional expenditure;

B) In the second case, if we know also a variety of school facility and curriculum characteristics;

C) In the third case, if we know also several characteristics of the student body, such as those examined in the preceding section.

In all these cases, we ask what does the racial composition of the student body (measured as proportion of students that are white and not Puerto Rican or Mexican American) tell us in addition about the achievement of a student of a given racial or ethnic group. These various conditions are presented in Table 3.23.4 for grades 3, 6, 9, and 12. It is worth remarking that the added variance accounted for under some of the conditions is large indeed, relative to the variance explained by most school factors. There are a few other student body variables that add more to the explained variance, but not much more. These numbers must also be viewed relative to the total between-school variance, which is less than 20 per cent for Negroes and less than 10 per cent for whites. (See Table 3.22.1.)

The first quite general result in this table is that as the proportion white in a school increases, the achievement of students in each racial group increases. This does not yet separate out the effects i, ii, and iii. We shall raise the question shortly about which of these effects appear to be most important.

The second general result is that this relationship increases as grade in school increases. The relationship is absent at grade 3, and strongest at grade 9, and 12. This gives some assurance that the relation is not due to associated factors, which should produce an apparent effect at all grades alike.

A third point to note is that the additional knowledge of school characteristics (condition A + B compared to A) reduces only slightly the added influence of racial composition. This leads to the third important result: The higher achievement of all racial and ethnic groups in schools with greater proportions of white students is not accounted for by better facilities and curriculum in these schools (to the extent these were measured by our questionnaires). But a comparison of this condition with the next (A + B + C) which includes information about the student body's educational background and aspirations shows that the latter characteristics do sharply reduce the added variance explained by racial composition. (As explained in section 3.2A, an appearance of sharp reduction in apparent effect is likely to mean in reality complete absence of effect.) This leads to still another important result: The higher achievement of all racial and ethnic groups in schools with greater proportions of white students is largely, perhaps wholly, related to effects associated with the student body's educational background and aspirations. This means that the apparent beneficial effect of a student body with a high proportion of white students comes not from racial composition per se, but from the better educational background and higher educational aspirations that are, on the average, found among white students. The effects of the student body environment upon a student's achievement appear to lie in the educational proficiency possessed by that student body, whatever its racial or ethnic composition.[4]

This result does, however, give some insight into the way in which achievement levels of two groups can remain quite different over a long period of time. If a large part of the effect of a school on a student is accounted for by the achievement level of other students in the school, then in a segregated system, if one group begins at an educationally impoverished level, it will tend to remain at that level.

■ **Table 3.23.4.** Additional per cent of variance in achievement explained by proportion white in school under different prior states of information: (6 variables in student's own background controlled), per pupil expenditures on staff in the school (A); additional facilities and curriculum characteristics of school (B) characteristics of student body (C); effect is toward higher achievement except where (−) precedes number.

	Grade 12			Grade 9		
	A	A + B	A + B + C	A	A + B	A + B + C
Puerto Ricans	17.06	13.53	3.98	7.76	8.45	0.81
Indian Americans	12.61	6.93	.15	8.50	11.21	5.19
Mexican American	12.51	9.45	1.87	11.50	11.52	4.20
Negro, South	1.52	1.67	.39	2.35	1.62	.34
Negro, North	2.90	1.83	.41	2.41	1.36	.82
Oriental Americans	.77	1.70	(*)	.89	.30	(*)
White, South	.00	.01	(−).01	.00	.04	.00
White, North	.56	.81	.21	1.40	1.40	.41
Negro total	3.29	3.54	.68	3.01	1.54	.67
White total	.29	.29	.13	.69	.91	.25

	Grade 6			Grade 3		
	A	A + B	A + B + C	A	A + B	A + B + C
Puerto Ricans	6.34	6.66	0.78	5.24	5.02	1.51
Indian Americans	2.83	4.59	2.02	2.60	1.91	.96
Mexican American	9.70	9.06	1.67	3.08	3.52	1.00
Negro, South	1.31	1.62	.56	(−).23	(−).18	(−).28
Negro, North	1.46	1.36	.37	.09	.14	(−).07
Oriental Americans	.06	.09	.04	3.52	2.25	.52
White, South	.34	.39	.15	.19	.16	.04
White, North	1.50	1.38	.34	.01	.04	(−).05
Negro, total	1.12	1.54	.40	(−).01	.00	(−).07
White total	1.06	1.04	.23	.04	.06	(−).01

*   The regression had insufficient data for estimation.

Ordinarily, one has a conception of school's effect as consisting of a strong stimulus from the outside, independent of the immediate social context of the students. In view of the results of this section, it appears that a more appropriate conception may be that of a self-reproducing system, in which most of the effects are not independent of the social context, but are, rather, internal ones.

3.23.1. Two comments on the analysis. The results of the preceding sections are enough at variance with common beliefs that a number of questions are likely to be raised about the analysis.

One such question is this: Why are the racial and ethnic groups separated in the analysis? Let us suppose that all Negroes go to equally bad schools and all whites go to equally good schools, or vice versa. Then the analysis which keeps the groups separate will show no effectiveness of school characteristics, because for each racial or ethnic group, the schools are uniformly bad or good.

First, it is important to make clear why the racial groups were kept separate in the analysis. When achievement differs as much as it does between these groups, then to analyze the groups together, without controlling for race or ethnicity of the student, would cause any school characteristics highly associated with race or ethnicity to show a spurious relation to achievement. For example, race of teacher, which is highly correlated with the student's own race, would show a high relation to achievement if the student's race were not controlled. In short, it would not be good methodology to fail to control on a variable—race or ethnicity in this case—which is known to have a high and stable relation to the dependent variable, independently of characteristics of the school attended by the student.

An examination was carried out, without controlling for race, of whether school factors might appear to account for large portions of the variance.[5] It used the five school average variables shown in Table 3.23.1, together with the same three individual student variables used in that analysis: Family economic background, family educational background and interest, the student's attitude. The five variables characterizing the school were school facilities, school curriculum, teacher qualities, teacher attitudes, and student body characteristics. Table 3.231.1 shows the unique contribution of each of these five, in a regression containing all eight variables, as well as the unique contribution of all five together, at grades 3, 6, 9, and 12. The table shows that the school and staff factors make very small unique contributions to the variance, just as in the case when the racial and ethnic groups were treated separately (Table 3.23.1). The one variable at the level of the school that does make a strong unique contribution is the educational backgrounds and aspirations of fellow-students—the student body variable. It may be noted parenthetically that even the meager contribution of teacher attitudes may be largely a result of the correlation of these attitudes with the race or ethnicity of the student in the school.

Also it must be emphasized that with respect to teacher quality we deal only with school averages. The variance of pupil achievement accounted for differences between teachers in the same school cannot be explored by means of the data of the survey.

A second question will likely be raised for which the data of the survey provide less direct evidence. The question can be posed in this way: School effects were not evident because no measurement of educational growth was carried out. Had it been, then some schools might have shown much greater growth rates of students than would others and these rates might have been highly correlated with school characteristics.

■ **Table 3.231.1.** Unique per cent of variance in verbal achievement accounted for by characteristics of schoolteachers, and student body, in regression with 2 family background factors and 1 individual attitude.

	Grades			
	12	9	6	3
Unique contribution to variance accounted for by—				
School facilities	0	0	0	0
School curriculum	0	.2	0	0
Teacher qualities	0	0	0	.1
Teacher attitudes	.8	.9	.4	.3
Student body characteristics	4.7	4.9	8.2	1.4
Unique of all 5 jointly	9.6	8.1	10.9	2.5
Total by all 8	35.4	38.1	37.7	12.9

If this were the case, then one of the strongest implications would be that the correlation between family background and achievement should show a decrease over the years of school roughly proportioned to the school effect, and correspondingly, school factors should show an increase in correlation with achievement. Only if family background were homogeneous within schools, and if the school's effect were highly correlated with family background, would a school effect maintain a high correlation of achievement to family background. But it has already been shown that schools appear to have an effect that is dependent upon the average family background in the school—an effect through the student body not through the characteristics of the school itself. Thus, the question posed above can only be meaningful if it refers to an effect independent of the student body composition. And such an effect, as indicated above, would reduce the correlation between family background factors and achievement, and increase the relation of school factors with achievement. Yet there is little increase in the variance in achievement explained by school characteristics, though there is some increase in variance explained by teacher characteristics (as section 3.25 will show), and more increase in variance explained by student body characteristics. Also, Table 3.221.3 showed that considering both subjective and objective background, the multiple correlation between background factors and achievement remains constant or increases over grades 6 to 12 for Negroes, and whites. (Grades 1 and 3 could not be included in the comparison because several family background measures were not obtained at the grades 1 and 3). It is likely that measurement was not as good at grade 6, which makes precise comparison not possible; but it is clear that no strong outside stimulus is making its impact felt in such a way as to interfere with the general relation of background to achievement; that is, it is clear that schools are not acting as a strong stimulus independent of the child's background, or the level of the student body. For if they were, there would be a decline in this correlation, proportional to the strength of such stimulus. This is not to say, of course, that schools have no effect, but rather that what effects they do have are highly correlated with the individual student's background, and with the educational background of the student body in the school; that is, the effects appear to arise not principally from factors that the school system controls, but from factors outside the school proper. The stimulus arising from variables independent of the student background factors appears to be a relatively weak one.

3.24 School Facilities and Curriculum

The study of characteristics of school facilities and curriculum must take as its starting point the surprisingly small amount of variation in student achievement accounted for by variations in these characteristics. Nevertheless, something can be learned about achievement in schools with differing characteristics by proceeding somewhat arbitrarily to introduce successively selected school characteristics to examine what aid they give in accounting for variance in achievement. In carrying out this examination of particular school factors, the comparatively small samples of groups other than Negro and white make results from these groups quite variable, and of little value in learning the achievement associated with given school characteristics. Thus, only Negroes and whites, for the country as a whole and for North and South separately, will be examined. The overall per pupil expenditure on staff is introduced first, as an overall measure of the community's input of resources into the school. Even at this initial point, however, student background differences are controlled so that the results will not be masked by the community's input of students into the school. Hence, the residual relationship shows the higher achievement of children who report similar backgrounds in schools with high per pupil expenditure. The data from this examination are presented in Table 3.24.1, and they lead to the first result of this section: For schools attended by Negroes in the South, but among no other groups, high per pupil expenditure is associated with higher achievement, at grades 6, 9, and 12, after background differences of students are controlled. This result means that for Negroes in the South, achievement is appreciably lower in schools with low per pupil expenditure than in schools with high expenditure. Another comparison makes the differences between this group and others even sharper: the variance in per pupil expenditure among Negroes and whites in the South is only a tenth to a third as great as that for other groups. Consequently, the contrast between this relationship for Southern Negroes and its relative absence elsewhere is even more marked.

This is not to say by any means that expenditure differences in themselves create such differences in achievement for Southern Negroes. This measure very likely represents other differences in the community. As section 3.23 showed, when student body characteristics are taken into account, the variance accounted for by a facilities measure (which includes per pupil expenditure) is very small indeed. In fact, if adjustments had been made to remove student body factors in the present analysis, together with facilities and curriculum measures, the unique contribution of per pupil expenditure for Southern Negroes would have nearly vanished.

■ **Table 3.24.1.** Variance accounted for by per pupil instructional expenditure grades 12, 9, 6, after 6 background variables are controlled

	12	9	6
Negro, South	2.98	2.89	3.49
Negro, North	.09	.02	.14
White, South	.06	.21	.15
White, North	.29	.14	.05
Negroes, total	2.62	2.55	2.17
Whites, total	.80	.64	.36

The next step in the examination is to introduce certain selected facilities and curriculum measures which gave evidence in early analyses of showing most relation to achievement or appear to be intrinsically important in school policy (such as grouping or tracking). Some facilities measures, such as the pupil/teacher ratio in instruction, are not included because they showed a consistent lack of relation to achievement among all groups under all conditions.

The facilities and curriculum measures are—

volumes per student in school library
science laboratory facilities (9 and 12 only)
number of extracurricular activities (9 and 12 only)
presence of an accelerated curriculum
comprehensiveness of the curriculum (9 and 12 only)
strictness in promotion of slow learners (6 only)
use of grouping or tracking (9 and 12 only)
movement between tracks (9 and 12 only)
school size
number of guidance counselors (9 and 12 only)
urbanism of school's location.

For all Negroes and all whites, and for each race in the North and the South separately the analysis allows us to examine the added variance that any one of these measures would account for under two different conditions—when only knowledge of student background and per pupil instructional expenditure of the school is given, and when in addition knowledge of all the other facilities and curriculum measures is given. That is, under the first condition, only the measures of student input and financial input into the school are controlled; under the second condition, a variety of other facilities and curriculum measures are also controlled. The data are given in Table 3.24.2.

Variations among grades. The general comparison between grades shows that the facilities and curriculum measures account for an increasingly larger amount of variance in achievement from the 6th to the 12th grades. Very little of the variance is accounted for at the 6th grade by most measures, somewhat more at the 9th, and still more at the 12th. The absence of relation for most items at grade 6 is a result of the low variation among schools with respect to these facilities in elementary schools.

Variations between Negroes and whites. The generally lesser variance accounted for by school-to-school differences for whites is evident here. For whites, less variance is accounted for by all characteristics, and little or none is accounted for by many.

Variation between regions. For both Negroes and whites, and for nearly all measures, more variance is accounted for by school differences in the South than by school differences in the North. This result accords with previous results that show the greater relation of achievement to school differences in the South than in the North.

Particular facilities and curriculum measures. One variable that explains a relatively large amount of variance at grades 9 and 12 under the first condition (A) is school size. (The lack of relation at grade 6 may be a result of the lesser variation in size of elementary schools.) The relation is strongest for Negroes in the South, but not absent for whites in the South. However, most of its apparent effect vanishes if various facilities and curricular differences are controlled. That is, the higher achievement in larger schools is largely accounted for by the additional facilities they include. There is some evidence, among the whites in the North, that school size may have a reverse effect, perhaps for the largest schools. The indication that the effects of size may differ in rural areas where the size of schools is quite small and in urban ones where the size is quite large is given further support by Table 3.24.3, which separates each race into metropolitan and nonmetropolitan areas, and shows the amount of explained variance added by introducing school size. (This measure of variance added is under the condition that all characteristics above it in Table 3.24.2 had been controlled. Thus, it is with A plus most of B controlled.)

■ **Table 3.24.2.** Unique percentage contributions to variance in verbal achievement by individual facilities and curricular measures, given knowledge of student background (6 background variables controlled) and per pupil expenditure (A), and given knowledge of A plus 10 facilities and curriculum measures (B)

	Grade 12		Grade 9		Grade 6	
	A	A + B	A	A + B	A	A + B
Negro total						
Total variance accounted for*	(2.62)	((6.96))	(2.55)	((5.19))	(2.17)	((2.77))
Expenditure	—	.54	—	.87	—	1.62
Volumes	.04	.05	(−).04	0	(−).01	.02
Laboratories	1.61	.42	.04	.07	—	—
Extracurricular	1.64	.10	.12	.01	—	—
Accelerated	.59	.11	.11	.04	.08	.07
Comprehensiveness (12, 9)	.61	0	.08	(−).01	—	—
Promotion strictness (6)	—	—	—	—	.25	.22
Grouping or tracking	(−).01	.10	(−).14	(−).01	—	—
Movement between tracks	(−).40	(−).19	(−)1.14	(−).88	—	—
Size	2.55	.16	1.32	.09	0	.04
Guidance	2.61	.06	1.25	.06	—	—
Urbanism	2.12	.11	.88	.15	.23	.28
White total						
Total variance accounted for*	(0.80)	((2.53))	(0.64)	((1.15))	(0.36))	((0.47))
Expenditure	—	.54	—	.87	—	1.62
Volumes	(−).11	(−).12	.06	.03	.01	.01
Laboratories	.62	.20	0	(−).05	—	—
Extracurricular	.04	.93	.07	.02	—	—
Accelerated	.67	.33	.01	0	.02	.02
Comprehensiveness (12, 9)	0	(−).02	(−).14	(−).13	—	—
Promotion strictness (6)	—	—	—	—	.05	.05
Grouping or tracking	(−).02	0	(−).01	0	—	—
Movement between tracks	.02	0	(−).02	0	—	—
Size	(−).22	(−).19	.04	.04	0	0
Guidance	.16	.81	.22	.17	—	—
Urbanism	.04	.28	.08	0	(−).03	.03

*   Total variance accounted for under condition A ( ) does not include in the regression the listed facilities. Under condition A + B (( )), it does include these facilities.

■ **Table 3.24.3.** Unique percentage contributions of school size to explained variance in verbal achievement, when student background factors, per pupil instructional expenditure, selected facilities, and selected curriculum factors are controlled.

	Grade 12	Grade 9	Grade 6
Negro			
North	(−)0.01	0.21	(−)0.01
South	1.59	1.12	.02
In metropolitan area	.07	.13	(−).02
Outside metropolitan area	2.87	1.59	(−).01
White			
North	(−).27	(−).04	(−).01
South	.33	.23	.22
In metropolitan area	(−).43	.01	.01
Outside metropolitan area	.08	.00	.00

This shows a slightly greater difference between the effects by the urban-rural classification than by the North-South classification, and adds support to the indication that there might be a negative effect of size in metropolitan areas.

A variable which can aid in the interpretation of this relation is urbanism of school's location. In urban areas, this variable expresses the difference in location between city and suburb; outside urban areas, it expresses the difference in location between rural, small town, and larger town locations. For both Negroes and whites this variable is positively related to achievement in the South, where the difference is principally the difference between rural and small or larger town, but it is not positively related to achievements in the North, where the variable difference measures principally suburb versus city. This again suggests that quite apart from facilities and curriculum, the smallest and most rural schools have lower achievement than larger and more urban schools, but the largest and most urban do not have higher achievement than those of middle size and again, that this is most true for Negroes.

Several of the measures in Table 3.24.2 can be dismissed rather quickly. Tracking shows no relation to achievement, and thus the apparent relation of movement between tracks to achievement cannot be meaningfully interpreted.

Comprehensiveness of the curriculum shows small and inconsistent relations to achievement. The existence of an accelerated program in the curriculum does, however, show a consistent relation to achievement at grade 12, particularly in the North, both before and after other curriculum and facilities measures have been controlled. It is not possible to tell conclusively, however, whether the accelerated program is truly effective in providing additional opportunity, or merely an additional indicator of a student body with high achievement or of a community with high educational interest.

The number of volumes per student in the school library shows small and inconsistent relations to achievement. However, both the number of science laboratories and the number of extracurricular activities have a consistent relation of moderate size to achievement. The number of extracurricular activities accounts for more variation in achievement before other school factors are controlled, but it accounts for less than laboratories after they are controlled. This indicates that extracurricular activities are more highly associated with other attributes found in schools with high achievement, but that the existence of laboratories has a more intrinsic relation to high achievement.

The general picture that all these results give of schools that come closest to taking full advantage of their student input is one with generally greater resources. The relations are not large, but they are all in the direction of somewhat higher achievement: higher per pupil instructional expenditure, a curriculum that offers greater challenges, more laboratories and more activities. However, probably the most important result is the one stated in the preceding section: that characteristics of facilities and curriculum are much less highly related to achievement than are the attributes of a child's fellow students in school.

It is clear that the other variations among the schools in this survey have almost overwhelmed any effects of variations in the curriculum. A more intensive study, more fully focussed on these curricular variables alone, would be necessary to discover their effects. But this fact alone is important: Differences in school facilities and curriculum, which are the major variables by which attempts are made to improve schools, are so little related to differences in achievement levels of students that, with few exceptions, their effects fail to appear even in a survey of this magnitude.

3.25 Teachers' Characteristics

Teachers of these students differed in a number of ways. Most Negroes are taught by Negro teachers, whites are almost always taught by whites; teachers of Negroes tend to have more positive attitudes toward school integration, and less often express a preference for teaching middle class, white-collar workers' children. Teachers of Negroes scored lower on the vocabulary test taken by teachers; and there were other differences as well—all indicated as in part 2.

In assessing the effect of teachers' characteristics upon achievement, teachers in a school were aggregated to obtain averages for the teaching staff in that school. For grades 1, 3, and 6, aggregation was done only over teachers who taught grades 1–6; for grade 9, aggregation was done only over teachers who taught grades 7–12; and for grade 12, aggregation was done only over teachers who taught grades 9–12.

Altogether, variation in school averages of teachers' characteristics accounted for higher proportion of variation in student achievement than did all other aspects of the school combined, excluding the student body characteristics. Several teachers' characteristics were selected for special examination, after eliminating a number of characteristics that appeared, in early regressions, to have little effect. Other variables were eliminated because they were highly correlated with one or more of those remaining, and thus their effects could not easily be distinguished. The variables which remain must be regarded in part as surrogates for other variables that are related to them. Thus, as with any investigation into a complex set of relations, the results must be interpreted with caution because of the many factors that could not be simultaneously held constant.

The teacher variables selected for special examination were—

1) The average educational level of the teachers' families (mother's education was used).
2) Average years of experience in teaching.
3) The localism of the teachers in the school: whether they had attended high school and college in the area, and had lived there most of their lives.
4) The average level of education of the teachers themselves.
5) The average score on vocabulary test self-administered by the teachers.
6) The teachers' preference for teaching middle-class, white-collar students.
7) The proportion of teachers in the school who were white.

The first important result from this examination is that the effect of teacher's characteristics shows a sharp increase over the years of school. The variance in achievement explained by variation in average teacher characteristics is very small at lower grades and increases for higher grades. This effect is shown in Table 3.25.1. In this table, attention should be focused particularly on shifts from grades 6 to 12, since analyses in earlier sections have shown the generally lesser relation of any variables to achievement at grades 1 and 3. When grades 6, 9, and 12 are considered, there is a general increase for whites and Negroes in both regions. The other minority groups show less consistency; however, the relation is greatest at grade 12 for nearly all groups.

The table shows a second important result. The apparent effect of average teacher characteristics for children in a given group is directly related to the "sensitivity" of the group to the school environment. In particular, Southern Negroes appear to be more affected than Northern Negroes, and whites appear least affected of all groups.[6]

This result is an extremely important one, for it suggests that good teachers matter more for children from minority groups which have educationally deficient backgrounds. It suggests as well that for any groups whether minority or not, the effect of good teachers is greatest upon the children who suffer most educational disadvantage in their background, and that a given investment in upgrading teacher quality will have most effect on achievement in underprivileged areas.

The specific teacher variables selected for examination show the contribution of each of these variables to explanation of the overall variance. These effects

■ **Table 3.25.1.** Per cent of variance in verbal achievement accounted for by 7 selected teacher variables at grades 12, 9, 6, 3, and 1, with background factors controlled*

	Grade 12	Grade 9	Grade 6	Grade 3	Grade 1
Puerto Ricans	18.38	9.70	8.11	2.60	4.70
Indian Americans	15.75	7.25	17.95	3.71	10.97
Mexican-Americans	14.63	11.71	12.59	2.31	2.18
Negroes, South	9.97	7.72	5.29	1.73	.91
Negroes, North	4.35	1.58	2.19	2.38	1.38
Oriental Americans	1.77	3.18	4.19	3.92	6.04
Whites, South	2.07	2.49	1.12	1.08	.46
Whites, North	1.89	1.02	1.67	.85	.87
Negroes, total	9.53	6.77	3.52	2.83	.52
Whites, total	1.82	1.03	1.23	.59	.37

*   Only the 4 background variables 1, 2, 5, and 6 from Table 3.221.1, measured in all 5 grades, were controlled in grades 1 and 3; for comparability with secs. 3.23 and 3.24, 6 background variables were controlled in grades 6, 9, 12.

are shown for Negroes and whites at each grade level in Table 3.25.2. The table shows the cumulative amount of variance explained as each of these variables is added, in the order indicated above.

These data show again the strikingly stronger effect of teacher variables for Negroes than for whites. For whites, none of these characteristics of teachers show much effect at any grade level. For Negroes, the variables which do show an effect do so increasingly with higher grade levels.

The variables that show most effect are the teachers' family education level (a positive effect), the teachers' own education (positive effect), and the score on the vocabulary test (positive effect). Teachers' attitudes show a slight effect in some grades (negative effect of preference for middle-class students); as does experience (positive effect), while localism and proportion white show little or no effect. For other minority groups, similar results hold, except that teachers' experience shows inconsistent directions of effect, suggesting that it has no effect of its own, teachers' preference for middle-class students has a stronger and consistently negative effect for Mexican Americans, Puerto Ricans, and Indians, and proportion white teachers has a consistently positive effect for these three groups.

The strongest result to derive from these tabulations (beyond the greater effect for groups of high sensitivity to school environments and the greater effect with increasing grade level) is that the teachers' verbal skills have a strong effect, first showing at the sixth grade, indicating that between grades 3 and 6, the verbal

■ **Table 3.25.2.** Cumulative variance in achievement explained for Negroes and whites at each grade level by adding school average of specified teacher variables in order listed (background variables controlled)

Variable added	Grade 12		Grade 9		Grade 6		Grade 3		Grade 1	
	N	W	N	W	N	W	N	W	N	W
Teachers' family educational level	2.26	0.10	1.42	0.14	0.58	0.21	0.03	0.01	0.03	0.00
Years experience	3.37	.12	1.53	.22	.61	.21	1.50	.05	.14	.15
Localism	3.38	.47	1.54	.47	.93	.49	2.34	.21	.26	.19
Teachers' educational level	4.87	1.08	3.20	.60	.93	.51	2.40	.23	.26	.21
Score on vocabulary test	7.05	1.21	5.05	.62	2.82	.67	2.74	.27	.34	.27
Preference for middle class	8.09	2.07	5.42	.69	3.03	.82	2.76	.56	.35	.33
Proportion white	8.23	2.10	5.55	1.04	3.33	1.20	2.83	.59	.52	.37

skills of the teacher are especially important. This result is shown in the table for Negroes, and it holds as well for each of the other minority groups. For each of those groups the jump from grade 3 to grade 6 in added variance explained by teachers' verbal skills is even greater than that for Negroes.

The second, and less strong effect for Negroes, is that the teachers' educational level (both family education and teachers' own education) or some variable for which this is a surrogate, begins to make a difference at grades 9 and 12. (The same general result holds for the other minority groups, except that the teachers' own education shows more variable effects from these groups.)

An overall examination of school, teacher, and student environment variable together is possible, now that all three have been examined individually. This examination is carried out in Table 3.25.3, which shows the variance accounted for by teacher variables, by teacher variables plus the school characteristics examined in section 3.24, and by these two sets of variables plus the student environment variable examined in section 3.23. The third column of this table shows that, altogether, these variables account for nearly all of the school-to-school variation for the groups other than Negroes and whites at grade 12, but considerably less than that for Negroes and whites, and less for all groups at grades 9 and 6. The relative strength of these three acts of variables can be examined by comparing the first column (teacher variables alone) with the first line in the second column of Table 3.24.2 (school characteristics alone) and the second column (teacher plus school characteristics) with the second column of Table 3.23.2 (student environment plus school characteristics). This comparison

■ **Table 3.25.3** Per cent of variance in verbal achievement accounted for by teacher variable (T), these plus school variables (S), and these plus student environment variables (E), grades 12, 9, and 6 (6 background variables controlled)

	Grade 12			Grade 9			Grade 6		
	T	T+S	T+S +E	T	T+S	T+S +E	T	T+S	T+S +E
Puerto Rican	18.38	20.00	26.39	9.70	11.37	16.26	8.11	10.81	13.97
Indian Americans	15.75	19.56	26.33	7.25	10.17	14.04	17.95	19.41	20.95
Mexican Americans	14.63	16.94	19.16	11.71	14.12	15.04	12.59	13.57	16.52
Negro, South	9.97	11.68	13.90	7.72	11.24	13.33	5.29	7.76	9.02
Negro, North	4.35	6.68	8.97	1.58	3.32	5.36	2.19	2.66	4.93
Oriental Americans	1.77	6.63	(*)	3.18	(*)	(*)	4.19	11.99	14.54
White, South	2.07	3.60	4.80	2.49	3.36	3.83	1.12	1.56	2.94
White, North	1.89	3.16	3.82	1.02	2.06	3.07	1.67	2.02	4.84
Negro total	9.53	10.70	13.78	6.67	8.70	11.22	3.52	4.42	6.52
White total	1.82	3.42	4.18	1.03	2.41	3.18	1.23	1.77	4.13

*   The regression had insufficient data for estimation.

shows that the school characteristics are the weakest of the three, and that teachers' characteristics are comparable to but slightly weaker than characteristics of the student environment.

Thus the effects of teacher variables upon student achievement show several important results. Restating these results, they are—

1.   Teacher differences show a cumulative effect over the years in school.

2.   Teacher differences show more relation to difference in achievement of educationally disadvantaged minority groups than to achievement of the white majority. The relation corresponds roughly to the general sensitivity of the minority group to variations in school environments. In addition, teacher differences are over twice as strongly related to achievement of Southern Negroes as to achievement of Northern Negroes.

3.   Teachers' verbal skills have an effect first showing strongly at grade 6 for all minority groups.

4.   Teachers' educational background (own and family's) shows an effect first showing strongly at grade 9, for all minority groups.

3.26 Attitudes of Students

Three expressions of student attitude and motivation were examined in relation to achievement. One was the student's interest in school and his reported pursuit of reading outside school; another was his self-concept, specifically with regard to learning, and success in school; and a third was what we have called his sense of control of the environment.

As indicated in an earlier section, both Negro and white children expressed a high self-concept, as well as high interest in school and learning, compared to the other groups. Negroes, however, were like the other minority groups in expressing a much lower sense of control of the environment than whites.

These attitudes were not measured at all grade levels; the table below shows the questions on which each was based at each grade level. (At grade 3, only one question could be used for each of the first two attitudes, and there were no items for the third. At grade 1, no attitudinal questions were asked. Thus the comparisons are all for grades 6, 9, and 12.)

Grades	Interest in learning and reading	Self-concept	Control of environment
12	q 57, 59, 60, 63	q 91, 108, 109	q 102, 103, 110
9	q 54, 56, 57, 60	q 88, 99, 100	q 93, 94, 103
6	q 36, 51, 28	q 37, 40	q 38

Because questions were not identical between grade 6 and grades 9 and 12, the measures are not exactly the same. Despite this variation between grade 6 and grades 9 and 12, however, one point stands out clearly in the analysis.

Of all the variables measured in the survey, including all measures of family background and all school variables, these attitudes showed the strongest relation to achievement, at all three grade levels. The zero-order correlations of these attitudes with achievement were higher than those of any other variables, in some cases as high as the correlation of some test scores with others (between .4 and .5). Taken alone, these attitudinal variables account for more of the variation in achievement than any other set of variables (all family background variables together, or all school variables together). When added to any other set of variables, they increase the accounted-for variation more than does any other set of variables. Table 3.26.1 and 3.26.2* give a comparison between these attitudes and the eight strongest background variables. Table 3.26.1 shows the amount of variance accounted for by these three attitudes and by the eight background

---

*   [Table 3.26.2 has been omitted in this edition. Ed.]

factors used throughout this analysis. In the 9th and 12th grades, with only two exceptions (Oriental Americans in grade 9, and Indian Americans in grade 12), the attitudes account for more of the variance. In grade 6, the attitudes account for most variance for whites and for Negroes, when North and South are considered separately; background factors account for more variance in the other groups.

■ **Table 3.26.1.** Total variance in verbal skills as a per cent by three attitudes, and by eight background variables, at grades 12, 9, and 6

	Attitudes			Background		
	Grade 12	Grade 9	Grade 6	Grade 12	Grade 9	Grade 6
Puerto Ricans	9.09	13.99	8.97	4.69	6.18	25.51
Indian Americans	21.62	18.81	14.23	22.07	16.30	19.65
Mexican-Americans	14.04	16.32	13.38	10.23	14.25	23.07
Negro, South	17.18	20.84	15.55	15.79	15.69	15.44
Negro, North	17.54	20.77	13.27	10.96	11.41	10.25
Oriental Americans	19.58	21.69	25.78	19.45	22.81	36.16
White, South	26.52	31.53	23.69	20.13	23.18	19.91
White, North	29.14	31.10	24.20	24.56	22.38	15.57
Negroes, total	15.89	20.12	14.16	15.14	14.99	14.62
Whites, total	27.68	31.10	24.26	23.03	23.28	17.64

These tables show that, whatever measure is chosen, the attitudinal variables have the strongest relation to achievement. It is, of course, reasonable that self-concept should be so closely related to achievement, since it represents the individual's own estimate of his ability. (See again the items on which this variable is based, section 3.1). The relation of self-concept to achievement is, from one perspective, merely the accuracy of his estimate of his scholastic skills, and is probably more a consequence than a cause of scholastic achievement. His interest in learning, it can be assumed, partly derives from family background, and partly from his success in school. Thus, it is partly a cause of achievement in school. Of the three attitudinal variables, however, it is the weakest, especially among minority groups, where it shows inconsistent relations to achievement at grades 9 and 12. The absence of a consistent relation for Negroes, along with the data presented in section 3.1 which showed Negroes even more interested in learning than white, gives a picture of students who report high interest in academic achievement, but whose reported interest is not translated through effective action into achievement. Thus the causal sequence which is usually assumed to occur, in which interest leads to effort and thereby to achievement, appears not to occur in this way for Negroes and other minority groups.

Clues to the causal sequence that may occur are provided by the relation of the two other attitudes to achievement. One of these clues lies in the second important result of this section: At grade 12, for whites and Oriental Americans, self-concept is more highly related to verbal skills before or after background is controlled than is control of environment; for all the other minority groups, the relative importance is reversed: the child's sense of control of environment is most strongly related to achievement.

■ **Table 3.26.3.** Unique contributions to accounted for variance in verbal skills of self-concept and control of environment at 12th grade, in conjunction with one other attitude, with and without eight background factors included.

[Total variance accounted for in regression at left is given in Table 3.26.1, in regression at right in Table 3.26.2]

Group and region	Without background		With background	
	Self concept	Control of environment	Self concept	Control of environment
Puerto Ricans	2.59	3.00	2.09	2.18
Indian Americans	4.94	9.69	2.91	5.06
Mexican-Americans	1.43	8.64	0.70	7.29
Negro, South	3.64	8.36	3.06	5.76
Negro, North	5.30	6.41	3.72	5.07
Orientals	6.46	3.60	5.20	1.59
White, South	10.97	1.29	7.67	0.69
White, North	8.50	2.55	5.02	1.55
Negroes, total	3.61	7.88	2.91	5.33
Whites, total	9.31	1.99	5.82	1.26

Table 3.26.3 shows this comparison. This result is particularly impressive because this attitude has no direct logical relation to achievement in school or to ability. The three questions on which it is based are a statement that "good luck is more important than hard work for success," a statement that "every time I try to get ahead, something or someone stops me," and a statement that "people like me don't have much of a chance to be successful in life." Yet for minority groups which achieve least well, responses to these statements (individually or together) are more strongly related than any other variable to achievement. It was evident earlier in section 3.1 that children from these groups are

much more likely to respond to these statements in terms showing a sense of lack of control of the environment. Now the present data show that children in these minority groups who do exhibit a sense of control of the environment have considerably higher achievement than those who do not. The causal sequence in this relation is not implied by the relationship itself. It may very well be two-directional, with both the attitude and the achievement affecting each other. Yet in the absence of specific evidence about causal direction, it is useful to examine one direction at length—the possible effect of such an attitude; that is, feeling a high or low sense of control of the environment, on achievement.[7]

Table 3.26.4 shows, for each minority group, and separately for Negroes and whites in the North and South, the average verbal achievement scores for boys and girls who answer "good luck" and those who answered "hard work" on one of those questions. Those minority group students who give "hard work" or "control" responses score higher on the tests than do whites who give "no control" responses.

■ **Table 3.26.4.** Verbal achievement scores of grade-9 pupils who have differing responses to the question: "Agree or disagree: Good luck is more important than hard work for success"

Group and region	Agree (good luck)	Disagree (hard work)
Mexican American	38.6	46.8
Puerto Rican	38.5	45.5
Indian American	39.9	47.3
Oriental	44.0	52.5
Negro, South	36.6	43.3
Negro, North	40.0	47.1
White, South	42.9	52.5
White, North	45.4	54.8

The special importance of a sense of control of environment for achievement of minority-group children and perhaps for disadvantaged whites as well suggests a different set of predispositional factors operating to create low or high achievement for children from disadvantaged groups than for children from advantaged groups. For children from advantaged groups, achievement or lack of it appears closely related to their self-concept: what they believe about themselves. For children from disadvantaged groups, achievement or lack of achievement appears closely related to what they believe about their environment: whether they believe the environment will respond to reasonable efforts, or whether they believe it is instead merely random or immovable. In different words, it appears that children from advantaged groups assume that the environment will respond if they are able enough to affect it; children from disadvantaged groups do not make this assumption, but in many cases assume that nothing they will do can affect the environment—it will give benefits or withhold them but not as a consequence of their own action.

One may speculate that these conceptions reasonably derive from the different experiences that these children have had. A child from an advantaged family most often has had all his needs satisfied, has lived in a responsive environment, and hence can assume that the environment will continue to be responsive if only he acts appropriately. A child from a disadvantaged family has had few of his needs satisfied, has lived in an unresponsive environment, both within the family (where other demands pressed upon his mother) and outside the family, in an outside and often unfriendly world.[8] Thus he cannot assume that the environment will respond to his actions. Such a state of affairs could be expected to lead to passivity, with a general belief in luck, a belief that that world is hostile, and also a belief that nothing he could ever do would change things. He has not yet come to see that he can affect his environment, for it has never been so in his previous experience.

Thus, for many disadvantaged children, a major obstacle to achievement may arise from the very way they confront the environment. Having experienced an unresponsive environment, the virtues of hard work, of diligent and extended effort toward achievement appear to such a child unlikely to be rewarding. As a consequence, he is likely to merely "adjust" to his environment, finding satisfaction in passive pursuits.

It may well be, then, that one of the keys toward success for minorities which have experienced disadvantage and a particularly unresponsive environment— either in the home or the larger society—is a change in this conception.

There is a further result in these data which could provide some clues about the differential dynamics of these attitudes among children from disadvantaged and advantaged groups, or from different kinds of families. When all three attitudes are examined together as predictors of verbal achievement, then the following shifts from grade 6 to 9 and 12 occur: (a) At grade 6, professed interest in school is related to achievement for all groups; but this relation vanishes at grades 9 and 12 except for Oriental Americans and whites; (b) control of environment is strongly related to achievement for all groups at grade 6; but this relation declines for Oriental Americans and whites in grades 9 and 12, while it increases for the other minority groups. These relationships can be seen in Table 3.26.5, which shows the unique contributions to variance of the three attitudes at the three grade levels.[9]

These data indicating changes in the relationships must be viewed with caution, since some differences existed between grade 6 and grades 9 and 12 in the measures themselves. However, the data suggest that the child's sense of control of his environment (which, as section 3.1 showed, is lower at grade 6, and increases with age) is important in the early achievement of children from all groups, but that it is these children from disadvantaged groups whose sense of control of environment continues to be associated with an important difference in later achievement. These results of course are only suggestive, and indicate the need for further investigations of the dynamics of attitudes and achievement among disadvantaged groups in society. Because of the likely mutual dependence of these attitudes and achievement, such investigations will require special care on determining the extent to which each influences the other.

■ **Table 3.26.5.** Unique contributions to accounted for variance of verbal achievement at grades 12, 9, and 6*

[Total variance given in table 3.3.1]

Group and region	Grade 12			Grade 9			Grade 6		
	Interest	Self-con-cept	Con-trol	Interest	Self-con-cept	Con-trol	Inter-est	Self-con-cept	Con-trol
Puerto Ricans	(−)6.25	2.59	3.00	(−)0.15	1.54	8.59	5.10	0.42	2.30
Indian Americans	.05	4.94	9.69	.31	2.45	9.20	5.81	1.40	4.35
Mexican-Americans	(−).11	1.43	8.64	.64	.64	9.26	3.30	2.11	4.77
Negro, South	(−).07	3.64	8.36	.51	1.26	13.09	4.11	1.60	6.32
Negro, North	0	5.30	6.41	.19	2.84	10.03	1.91	1.94	6.37
Oriental Americans	1.09	6.46	3.60	3.62	2.38	5.39	6.15	2.53	7.33
White, South	2.24	10.97	1.29	2.78	5.93	7.08	3.83	5.06	5.18
White, North	3.97	8.50	2.25	3.86	5.31	4.87	2.67	6.96	5.33
Negro total	.25	3.61	7.88	.08	1.70	12.30	2.60	1.55	6.93
White total	3.02	9.31	1.99	3.13	5.71	5.74	3.05	6.30	5.38

*   (−) preceding the number indicates that the partial relationship of the attitude to achievement is negative.

It is useful to inquire about the factors in the school and the home which affect children's self-concept and sense of control of the environment. First, this study provides little evidence concerning the effect of school factors on these attitudes. If family background characteristics are controlled, almost none of the remaining variance in self-concept and control of environment is accounted for by the school factors measured in this survey. One variable, however, is consistently related to control of environment and self-concept. For each group, as the proportion white in the school increases, the child's sense of control of environment increases, and his self-concept decreases. This suggests the possibility that school integration has conflicting effects on attitudes of minority group children: it increases their sense of control of the environment or their sense of opportunity, but decreases their self-concept. This relationship may well be an artifact, since the achievement level of the student body increases with per cent white, and may be the proximate cause of these opposite relationships. If so, these effects are merely effects or achievements and motivations of fellow students, rather than direct effects of integration. Whatever the time structure of causation, the relations, though consistent, are in all cases small.

It appears reasonable that these attitudes depend more on the home than the school. Reference was made earlier to a study which suggests that a mother's sense of control of the environment affects her young child's cognitive skills. It appears likely that her child's sense of control of environment depends similarly on her own. Such inquiry into the source of these attitudes can best be carried out by such intensive studies on a smaller scale than the present survey. However, some results from the present survey may be stated as clues to the sources of these attitudes.

At grades 6, 9, and 12, the simultaneous relation of eight family background factors to the two attitudes was studied. These background factors are:

Structural integrity of the home (father's presence, primarily).
Number of brothers and sisters.
Length of residence in an urban area.
Parents' education.
Economic level of home environment.
Reading material in home.
Parents' interest in child's schooling.
Parents' desires for child's further education.

The pattern of relationships between these factors and the two attitudes is similar for all groups in the survey with minor exceptions noted below. First, only a small fraction of the variance in these attitudes, averaging less than 10 per cent, is accounted for by all these background factors, combined. For minority groups other than Negroes, control of environment is better accounted for by these background factors than is self-concept. For Negroes, both are about the same; and for whites self-concept is better accounted for than control of environment.

For both attitudes and for all groups, the parents' desires for the child's further education have the largest unique contribution to positive self-concept and a sense of control of environment. For self-concept, the only other variables which show a consistent relation (positive) are parents' education and the amount of reading material in the home. For the child's sense of control of the environment, there is in addition a consistent relation to the economic level of the home and the structural integrity of the home. That is, children from homes with a higher economic level, and children from homes where the father is present, show a higher sense of control of the environment than do children from homes with lower economic level or children from homes where the father is absent.

These results can be seen only as minor indications of the source of these attitudes in children's backgrounds. The major result of this section, which appears of considerable importance and warrants further investigation, is the different role these two attitudes appear to play for children from advantaged and disadvantaged backgrounds.

Implications of the results of section 3.2 for equality of educational opportunity. Of the many implications of this study of school effects on achievement, one appears to be of overriding importance. This is the implication that stems from the following results taken together:

1. The great importance of family background for achievement;
2. The fact that the relation of family background to achievement does not diminish over the years of school;
3. The relatively small amount of school-to-school variation that is not accounted for by differences in family background, indicating the small independent effect of variations in school facilities, curriculum, and staff upon achievement;
4. The small amount of variance in achievement explicitly accounted for by variations in facilities and curriculum;
5. Given the fact that no school factors account for much variation in achievement, teachers' characteristics account for more than any other—taken together with the results from section 2.3, which show that teachers tend to be socially and racially similar to the students they teach;
6. The fact that the social composition of the student body is more highly related to achievement, independently of the student's own social background, than is any school factor;
7. The fact that attitudes such as a sense of control of the environment, or a belief in the responsiveness of the environment, are extremely highly related to achievement, but appear to be little influenced by variations in school characteristics.

Taking all these results together, one implication stands out above all: That schools bring little influence to bear on a child's achievement that is independent of his background and general social context; and that this very lack of an independent effect means that the inequalities imposed on children by their home, neighborhood, and peer environment are carried along to become the inequalities with which they confront adult life at the end of school. For equality of educational opportunity through the schools must imply a strong effect of schools that is independent of the child's immediate social environment, and that strong independent effect is not present in American schools.

TECHNICAL APPENDIX TO SECTION 3.2

Measurement of variance. First, the measurement of school-to-school variation requires some attention. If the total variation between pupils is labeled SS,
then SS can be partitioned, $SS = SS_w + SS_b$, where SS_w is the variation within
and SS_b the variation between schools. Here the term "variation in achievement"
refers to the sum of squared deviations from the mean achievement. This sum
can be partitioned into one component expressing the sum of deviations of school
mean achievements from the overall mean, and a component expressing the sum
of squared deviations of individual scores within a school from the school mean.
The overall mean for each group other than Negroes and whites is the national
mean for that group. For Negroes and whites, it is the group mean in the North
and that in the South. For all groups other than Negroes and whites, there was
some evidence that response unreliability in racial identification resulted in
measurement error. To reduce this, the measurement of school-to-school variation excluded students who identified themselves as members of these groups
in schools where at most one other student of the same group was found in
that grade.

The latter component, SS_b, is that which stands ready to be accounted for by
factors that differ from one school or community to another. We will refer to this
as the proportion of variation that lies between schools. The value of SS_b,
expressed as a percentage of SS for each of the groups, for verbal achievement in
grades 1, 3, 6, 9, 12, is given in Table 3.2A.1.

However, as a true measure of the relative impact of factors that vary from
school to school (or community to community), and factors that vary among
individuals within a school, this measure SS_b requires correction.

If we think of the individual's test score as made up of a component that is
the average for his racial or ethnic group (A_g), a component that is the average
of his group in his school (A_s), and a component that is individually associated
with him (A_i), then his score can be seen as composed of the sum of these components: Score $= A_g + A_s + A_i$.

Our question about between-school variation relative to within-school variation can thus be resolved to a question of the relative sizes of typical values of
A_s and A_i. Table 3.22.1 presents, for each group and for each grade level, the
relative sizes of A_s and A_i, by exhibiting the per cent that the variance of A_s
is of the sum of the variances of A_s and A_i.

Problems in the assessment of relationships. The analyses reported above
deal with the relationships between tested achievement and the classes of factors
we conceive of as partially measurable and contributing to its development:
Home background, community, school facilities, curriculum, and teachers.

There are three central facts to be remembered throughout any analysis of
the sort here conducted:

1.   The measurement of either any single variable or any class of variables is at best partial and incomplete.

2.   When two variables (or two sets of variables) are statistically associated, for reasons that may be either irrelevant or closely related to the study, an apparent relationship of another variable to one of them may result from an actual relationship of that variable to the other. (If this occurs, we are likely to speak of the first as a surrogate for the second, and to try to uncover the effect by studying the joint relationship of our response with both variables or sets of variables.)

3.   Even if association of the variables we are studying with some "explanatory" variable is firmly established, this establishment cannot of itself settle the question of causation (though strong evidence would be provided if the time order were known); either variable may "cause" the other, or both may share a common cause. In many cases, continuing studies of the development of these variables over time can untangle such a question of "What causes what?" In the present case, studies of change in achievement level could give more direct evidence than the present cross-sectional survey.

■ **Table 3.2A.1.** Per cent of total variance in individual verbal achievement score that lies between schools (uncorrected for degrees of freedom)*

	Grade				
	12	9	6	3	1
Mexican American	22.02	17.92	27.63	24.61	23.04
Puerto Rican	24.02	22.10	29.46	27.07	20.45
Indian American	27.59	24.69	28.19	31.52	18.79
Oriental American	9.21	11.18	24.79	21.12	18.76
Negro, South	19.92	17.98	21.14	27.23	20.34
Negro, North	12.37	13.37	16.92	19.33	12.50
White, South	9.96	9.12	11.82	16.47	16.77
White, North	7.76	8.51	10.96	11.95	11.58

*   Because of possible misclassification due to response error, which could contaminate greatly the small minorities, schools with 2 or fewer members at a grade level of each of the 4 minorities other than Negroes were excluded in calculating these variances. This and the fact that these results were calculated from the total sample, weighted appropriately, while the regression data were calculated from appropriately weighted samples of 1,000 students in each of the 20 strata at each grade level, makes the calculation of between school variance in this section, and the partitioning of the variance through regression in later sections not directly comparable.

To neglect any of these central difficulties is to lay oneself open to very serious risk of error. Yet, to fail to use such evidence in making judgments and taking action is to lay oneself open to the often more serious dangers of unwarranted inaction, or of action based merely upon rumor and ill-founded opinion. We must recognize and deal with the three difficulties, using care in interpretation.

Point (1), incompleteness of measurement, is not often a major issue in assessing whether the variable incompletely measured is associated with the variable being studied. Incompleteness of measurement will lead to underestimation of the amount of effect. While this fact must be kept in mind, it does not often become crucial, since even incomplete measures, so long as they reflect or are reasonably highly correlated with the true variable, ordinarily serve to establish the existence and proper direction of a real effect. (In combination with point (2), as we shall shortly see, point (1) can be very crucial.)

There is, however, one instance in the present study where it may be that measurement is so incomplete as to give rise to dangers of misinterpretation. This is in connection with school facilities and curriculums, both of which combine formal conditions easy to describe and measure with informal conditions that can at present only be judged by personal inspection and involvement. In comparing Negroes and whites, for example, we can anticipate that social pressures toward equality of opportunity, both in segregated and integrated school systems, will have concentrated its effects on the formal conditions. As a consequence, the close parallelism between the formal facilities available to the two races, as reported in part 2, may easily mask wide differences in the informal conditions. If this were so, the true effects of such school characteristics might be underestimated.

Point (2), the danger of unconsidered surrogates, is of central importance, as we can easily see from instances in the present study. Let us suppose that community attitudes toward the importance and quality of education have substantial effects on the development of student achievement. What would we expect about the apparent relation between achievement and teacher characteristics? Surely we would expect that communities more concerned with education and educational quality would—(1) be more selective in hiring teachers, and (2) pay higher salaries, thus attracting better candidates. As a consequence we might expect an apparent relationship between development of achievement and measurable teacher characteristics to be generated as a surrogate for an underlying relationship between development of achievement and community regard for education, even if teacher characteristics themselves had no effect on achievement.

The joint action of points (1) and (2), if not adequately considered, can lead to seriously misleading conclusions. Consider the development of achievement in the presence of two sets of student body variables: Student bodies of different background and motivation, and student bodies of different racial composition. Suppose that while student body background exerts major direct effects upon the development of achievement, racial composition has no direct effect. It will still be so that higher percent white will be associated with development of achievement, although only through its concomitant, higher student body background and motivation.

The simplest mistake is to forget about student body background while studying the relation of achievement to per cent white. This is a pure point (2) mistake. The appropriate solution is to attempt to compare achievement among schools with the same student body quality. If student body background were measured exactly (and if the usual statistical devices used to approximate a comparison for equal values of student body background are adequate), then this comparison would show no apparent effect of per cent white upon achievement.

But if measurement were imprecise, as it is in this study, or if the usual statistical techniques[10] are inadequate, the result of "controlling" student body background will not be to make the apparent effect of per cent white vanish, but rather to make it very much smaller with the same sign but not zero.

Therefore, whenever "controlling" a third variable greatly reduces but does not annihilate the apparent effect of a second variable upon a first, we should be able to recognize the possibility that the second variable has a small effect on the first variable, although the effect has not been demonstrated.

Point (3) is a point of very general application that must be borne in mind in all kinds of studies. Answers about causation are too often unclear, even when a clear answer as to cause may be essential in assessing the likely value of a proposed corrective measure. The relation between attitude and achievement, as discussed in section 3.26 above, offers a clear instance of the difficulties, which are perhaps greatest when each of two variables "causes", at least to a degree, the development of the other.

Problems in assessing strength of relationships. Almost all studies of socially organized phenomena face a common difficulty: The untangling and expression of the amounts of effect of many variables upon the response variable (in this case verbal achievement) in one or several groups. While the last section treated some of the qualitative problems of untangling influences, this section will examine the quantitative problems of expressing the size of these influences.

A careful regression study involves the development of sequences (perhaps one, usually more) of more and more inclusive "regressions" in which those linear combinations of more and more variables are found which predict as well as possible, in the data being analyzed, the value of the responses from the values of certain other variables.

It is convenient to use numerical names as follows:

First variable = the response being studied.

Second variable(s) = the variable or variables the amount and direction of whose direct effect on the first variable is being sought out.

Third variables = variables entered into the regression before the second variable is so entered.

Fourth variable = variables not entered into the regression before the second variable.

The last section pointed out that an indirect effect of the second variable via some other intermediate variable remains an apparent effect of that second variable if this intermediate variable remains a fourth variable, but that this indirect effect would be greatly reduced (in the ideal case nullified) if the intermediate variable were made a third variable. There is an important partial converse to this result. If there is another variable which affects the second, but whose effect on the first variable is only through the direct effect of the second variable, then keeping this second-variable-affecting variable a fourth variable helps us to properly assess the amount and direction of the second variable's direct effect, while admitting such a variable as a third variable would confuse and bias this estimation.

Accordingly, there is no simple path to careful estimation of a direct effect. Some variables should be used as third variables, others definitely should not. Which is which depends upon the finer details of how the various variables are related to one another.

Even the numerical expression of amount of dependence deserves attention if the reader is to receive an appropriate impression. We are engaged from many, though not all, points of view, in describing what fraction of the variability of a first variable is sensibly associated with a second variable. This means that we must choose a scale upon which to measure variability. No choice of scale always gives simple and neat results. However, one scale does this more often than any other we know. This is the scale on which variability is measured by variance— by the equivalent quantities:

1. Average square of deviation of individual from the mean.

2. One-half the average squared difference between two individuals.

This is a squared scale, and tends to make numbers appear somewhat more extreme than they might otherwise appear. To speak of 10 per cent contribution to the variance may appear to speak of little, yet this is to speak of a correlation $\sqrt{0.10} = 0.32$ which is far from negligible.

Use of "per cent accounted for" and "unique contribution." Having fixed upon a scale of measurement, and having chosen appropriate first and second variables, many different numerical answers are still possible. This is so because different choices of a third variable can lead to a quite different per cent of the original variance of the first variable being absorbed by regression on the second variable.

Where the point of the analysis is to estimate roughly how much variability can be ascribed to a given second variable, the analysis frequently offers a choice among several sets of third variables. Where the point is the relative amount of variability absorbed by various more-or-less competing variables, matters are more complex. In part due to pressure of time, the choice, almost uniformly made, has been to show the so-called "unique contributions" of the several variables, namely the contributions of each when all the others concerned (as well as perhaps still others) are present as third variables. This choice is usually what might be termed "formally conservative," since it is likely to give a smaller number for the per cent accounted for than when fewer variables are treated as third variables. (Adding a third variable need not reduce the per cent accounted for, and sometimes does not, but a reduction seems empirically much more common than an increase.)

However, to know the per cent of variance in the first variable accounted for (uniquely) by a second does not give a complete picture of the strength of the relationship. In the first place, the variance of the first variable might be quite different in the two groups. Since in the present study, the dependent variable is nearly always verbal achievement, and the variances for different groups are nearly alike, this is not here a matter of substantial importance, and we shall not discuss alternative ways to deal with such a situation. However, even when the variances of the first variable are all about the same, the variances of the second variable may differ, and we must consider what effect this has on the interpretation of a different per cent accounted for in the two (or more) groups.

It is easiest to discuss this problem in the simplified case where (i) the variance of the first variable is exactly the same (say, 100 per cent $= 1.00$) for each group; (ii) there are no third variables; and (iii) the apparent effect of the second variable is the same as its direct effect. Discussion of this case will suffice to deal with the issue, since the presence of third variables does nothing to alter the essentials of the situation.

In the jth body or group of data, let the variance of the second variable be σ_{2j}^2 and let the regression coefficient be b_j. The amount of variance in the dependent variable accounted for will thus be $b_j^2 \sigma_{2j}^2$ which is also the unique contribution (in group j), which we will abbreviate as "unique for j," when no other variables are to be considered.

The question arises then, concerning how one may interpret differences among different groups in the variance accounted for, since it depends both on the regression coefficient b_j and the variance of the second variable σ_{2j}^2.

At one extreme, differences in amounts accounted for may arise when the b_j are the same for the different groups j and the σ_{2j}^2 are quite different.

From a purely scientific standpoint, since b_j are the same, which means that the average effect on the first variable from a given change in the second variable is the same in all groups, we would usually say that the relation of the second variable to the first variable is everywhere the same. More practically, the change to be expected in the value of the first variable from a given change in the mean value of the second variable is the same in all groups (though we might find it somewhat easier to obtain this change in mean value in those groups for which σ_{2j}^2 is larger).

Another extreme arises when the σ_{2j}^2 are all the same, though b_j vary quite widely. The scientific answer is now that the mechanism of the second variable's effect upon the first variable operates with quite different effectiveness in the different groups. At the more practical level, the change in the first variable to be expected from a given change in the second variable is quite different from one group to another, and we are almost certain to find it worth while to concentrate our corrective measures upon the groups in which b_j is largest.

Both of these extreme situations, as well as the situation between the extremes, could bring about the same differences among groups in per cent of variance accounted for. Thus it is necessary to examine both the per cent accounted for, and the per cent accounted for divided by σ_{2j}^2.[11] The inferences to be drawn by comparisons among groups in these quantities are:

a) Differences between groups j and k in per cent accounted for (or unique contribution to per cent accounted for): "Given the distribution of the second variable as it is found in groups j and k, there are specified differences in the proportion of first-variable variance that the second variable accounts for."

b) Differences in (per cent accounted for)$/\sigma_{2j}^2$: "If the second variable had the same variation in groups j and k, the proportion of first-variable variance that would be accounted for in groups j and k would show specified differences; or, alternatively, if an identical shift in the average value of the second variable occurred in groups j and k, the expected shifts in the first variable would show specified differences."*

The general procedures used in studying the effect of school characteristics. To examine the effect of school characteristics, the data were put in such a form that students' characteristics, such as achievement in test scores and motivation, could be related to the characteristics of schools they attended, including characteristics of teachers, school facilities and curriculum, and characteristics of the student body. For each group other than Negroes and whites, a representative sample of 1,000 students, together with their corresponding school and teacher characteristics, was used in the analysis at each grade level. For Negroes and whites, eight such samples, corresponding to the regional classifications of sections 2 and 3.1. were used. However, weighted aggregation of these strata was carried out to obtain two regional strata, total North and total South (including the Southwest), and the Nation, for both groups.

Achievement and student attitudes were taken as dependent variables in the analysis, and family background, teacher, school, and student body characteristics were taken as independent variables. Most of the analysis reported below proceeded as follows:

First, the relation of achievement to family background factors was studied, both to learn how much of the variation in achievement was accounted for by those background factors measured, and to learn just what factors in student backgrounds showed most relation to achievement. The results of this analysis are reported in section 3.221. The background factors measured in the survey cover factors such as the economic and educational level of the home, and parents' interest in education, as seen by the child. They do not include differences in native endowment, which of course must also be considered part of family background, though an unmeasured part.

Then the relation of teacher and school factors to achievement was examined, after taking out the variation in achievement explained by the measured family background factors. This was done to reduce the differences in achievement which resulted from student background differences, so that the influence of school factors themselves, apart from the influence of family background, could be isolated. Since the student's background is clearly prior to, and independent of, any influence from school factors, these background factors can and should be held constant in studying the effects of school variables. Thus the variation in achievement and attitudes to be explained by school variables is that left after variation explained by family background differences is taken out.

It is not so clear among the school and teacher variables which are to be considered prior and thus to be taken account of first. Many of the school and teacher variables included in this survey are highly correlated: schools with high per pupil expenditure tend to have teachers with more training, to have more laboratories and other facilities, to have a more complete curriculum, to have remedial and accelerated programs, and other characteristics. Thus, it is usually not possible to study separately the effects of a large number of factors, when they are highly correlated.

Given this difficulty, an order of variables which appeared reasonable and justifiable was used in the analysis, and the addition at each point to accounted-for variance in the dependent variable was noted. This meant that factors which were added early had more opportunity to explain variance in the dependent variable than those added late. Insofar as the latter were correlated with those added early, they will explain less variance than if they had been added early. In the report of the analysis, when a particular order is used, the above points should be kept in mind in interpretation.

There are a number of technical problems associated with an analysis with variables at two levels, such as carried out here. The most important is that the variables at the school level can account only for variance that exists between schools, and not for variance of the individual characteristics (such as achievement) within schools. For this reason, at the outset of the analysis, the portion of variance that lies between, rather than within, schools is examined.

It must always be remembered in interpreting the results of such an analysis that the effective number of units for studying school effects is not the number of individuals, but the number of schools. Consequently, although the sample of students is quite large, the sample of schools is not large for statistical analysis, and thus investigation of effects of highly specific school factors is not possible. It is true, however, that analyses of these data that go considerably beyond that reported here can be carried out, to examine questions of less immediate importance to the present mandate.

3.3 INTEGRATION AND ACHIEVEMENT

Section 3.23 showed that the proportion white in a school was positively related to individual performance. This effect appeared to be less than, and largely accounted for by, other characteristics of the student body than the racial composition of the school per se. The magnitudes of the relations may be seen by comparing the results for Negro students reported in Table 3.23.2 in the columns headed "Gain" with Table 3.23.4 in the column headed A + B. This shows that, given the facilities and curriculum characteristics of the school, the amount of additional variance explained by the general aspects of the student environment is 4.0 and 4.6 per cent in grade 12, and that explained by proportion white is 1.7 and 1.8 per cent. Tabulations were performed to give further information about the relation of racial composition to achievement, by considering the average test performance of groups of Negro students who had attended classes last year with different proportions of white fellow students.

For the Metropolitan Northeast and Midwest Table 3.3.1 shows the average scores on two achievement tests received by Negro students who had attended classes of different racial composition at grades 6, 9, and 12. Comparing the averages in each row, in every case but one the highest average score is recorded for the Negro pupils who had a majority of white classmates. In reading the rows from left to right, the general pattern is an increase in average test performance as the proportion of white classmates increases, although in many cases the average for the Negro students in totally segregated classes is higher than the average for those in classes where half or less of the students were white.

Table 3.3.2 was constructed to observe whether there is any tendency for Negro students who have spent more years in integrated schools to exhibit higher average achievement. Those students who first entered desegregated schools in the early grades do generally show slightly higher average scores than the students who first came to desegregated schools in later grades.[12]

In the Metropolitan Northeast the average score for students who have only attended segregated schools is consistently lower than those groups of students with other experiences. However, in the Metropolitan Midwest, the average scores of Negroes who have only experienced segregated schooling may exceed the averages recorded for those students who first came to desegregated schools in the later grades. In these cases, one would need to look at the learning experience of these children coming late to desegregation to see whether their relatively poorer achievement is due to lack of preparation for a more competitive situation, to continued segregation within the desegregated school itself, or to some other factor.

Not only is the test average somewhat higher for Negro students in classes where most of the students are white, but also test performance varies more in these clases. Table 3.3.3 gives the standard deviations of the test scores received by Negro students from classes with different racial compositions. Twice the standard deviation of the test scores is a range which includes about two-thirds

■ **Table 3.3.1.** Average reading comprehension and math achievement test scores of Negro pupils, by grade, region, and proportion of white classmates last year

Grade	Region	Reading comprehension—proportion of white classmates last year				Math achievement—proportion of white classmates last year			
		None	Less than half	Half	More than half	None	Less than half	Half	More than half
12	Metropolitan Northeast	46.0 (474)	43.7 (1,215)	44.5 (1,207)	47.5 (1,468)	41.5 (474)	40.6 (1,215)	41.1 (1,207)	44.5 (1,468)
12	Metropolitan Midwest	46.4 (646)	43.2 (321)	44.0 (507)	46.7 (790)	43.8 (646)	42.6 (321)	42.9 (507)	44.8 (790)
9	Metropolitan Northeast	44.2 (2,297)	44.8 (2,929)	44.8 (1,233)	47.1 (1,676)	43.1 (2,297)	43.5 (2,929)	43.7 (1,233)	47.2 (1,676)
9	Metropolitan Midwest	45.3 (1,356)	45.2 (1,070)	45.3 (434)	46.4 (636)	44.4 (1,356)	44.3 (1,070)	44.1 (434)	46.6 (636)
6	Metropolitan Northeast	46.0 (2,108)	45.4 (1,992)	45.8 (794)	46.6 (1,224)	44.0 (2,108)	43.4 (1,992)	43.6 (794)	45.6 (1,224)
6	Metropolitan Midwest	46.0 (1,651)	44.7 (1,439)	44.9 (353)	45.1 (550)	43.8 (1,651)	42.8 (1,439)	42.9 (353)	44.1 (550)

Number in parentheses is the number of cases on which the average was calculated.

Table 3.3.2. Average reading comprehension test scores of Negro pupils, by grade, region, proportion of white classmates last year, and first grade in class with white pupils.

Grade	Region and first grade with majority pupils	Proportion of white classmates last year					Total
		None	Less than half	Half	More than half		
9	Metropolitan Northeast						
	1, 2, or 3	45.9 (871)	46.7 (1,596)	46.9 (701)	48.1 (977)		46.8 (4,221)
	4, 5, or 6	45.2 (340)	43.3 (446)	44.4 (155)	44.4 (232)		44.8 (1,203)
	7, 8, or 9	43.5 (572)	42.9 (509)	44.6 (227)	45.0 (280)		44.0 (1,618)
	Never	43.2 (327)	—	—	—		43.2 (327)
9	Metropolitan Midwest						
	1, 2, or 3	45.4 (516)	46.6 (677)	46.4 (677)	48.6 (344)		46.7 (1,882)
	4, 5, or 6	44.4 (231)	44.1 (149)	45.3 (70)	46.7 (101)		44.5 (561)
	7, 8, or 9	44.4 (173)	43.3 (137)	43.3 (66)	45.2 (111)		43.7 (496)
	Never	46.5 (70)	—	—	—		46.5 (370)
12	Metropolitan Northeast						
	1, 2, or 3	40.8 (73)	43.6 (297)	45.2 (282)	48.6 (462)		46.2 (1,231)
	4, 5, or 6	46.7 (268)	45.1 (627)	44.9 (622)	46.7 (586)		45.6 (2,241)
	7, 8, or 9	42.2 (46)	43.5 (109)	43.8 (134)	49.7 (201)		48.2 (535)
	10, 11, or 12	42.2 (52)	41.1 (118)	43.2 (117)	46.6 (131)		44.1 (451)
	Never	40.9 (19)	—	—	—		40.9 (19)
12	Metropolitan Midwest						
	1, 2, or 3	47.4 (143)	44.3 (137)	45.6 (187)	48.3 (288)		46.7 (818)
	4, 5, or 6	46.1 (161)	43.0 (117)	43.5 (221)	46.4 (320)		45.4 (882)
	7, 8, or 9	46.6 (112)	40.8 (39)	42.3 (48)	45.6 (97)		45.3 (314)
	10, 11, or 12	44.8 (88)	39.5 (20)	43.5 (21)	44.9 (44)		44.3 (188)
	Never	47.2 (121)	—	—	—		47.2 (121)

Number in parentheses is the number of cases on which the average was calculated.

■ **Table 3.3.3.** Standard deviation of test scores for Negro students grouped by the proportion of white classmates last year, by test, grade, and region

Grade	Region	Reading achievement—proportion of white classmates last year					Math achievement—proportion of white classmates last year				
		None	Less than half	Half	More than half	All	None	Less than half	Half	More than half	All
12	Metropolitan Northeast	9.35 (474)	9.65 (1,215)	9.06 (1,207)	13.53 (1,338)	32.54 (130)	9.73 (474)	9.65 (1,215)	9.73 (1,207)	14.02 (1,338)	23.64 (130)
12	Metropolitan Midwest	9.04 (646)	8.95 (321)	9.23 (507)	9.27 (723)	9.45 (67)	9.49 (646)	9.22 (321)	9.25 (507)	9.73 (723)	11.12 (67)
9	Metropolitan Northeast	8.81 (2,297)	8.68 (2,929)	8.67 (1,233)	9.23 (1,429)	10.61 (247)	9.11 (2,297)	8.87 (2,929)	8.98 (1,233)	8.95 (1,429)	10.61 (247)
9	Metropolitan Midwest	8.31 (1,356)	8.33 (1,070)	8.98 (434)	9.07 (508)	10.83 (128)	8.53 (1,356)	8.42 (1,070)	9.66 (434)	9.47 (508)	10.90 (128)
6	Metropolitan Northeast	7.99 (2,108)	8.15 (1,992)	8.05 (794)	9.11 (1,020)	8.05 (204)	7.91 (2,108)	7.85 (1,992)	8.00 (794)	8.80 (1,020)	8.92 (204)
6	Metropolitan Midwest	7.52 (1,651)	7.70 (1,439)	7.75 (353)	8.12 (409)	8.42 (141)	7.51 (1,651)	7.16 (1,439)	7.79 (353)	7.92 (409)	9.47 (141)

Number in parentheses is the number of cases on which the standard deviation was calculated.

of the scores. Thus the value 9.35 in the upper left-hand corner has the following meaning: The average score of the 474 scores represented here is 46.0 (given by Table 3.3.1) and two-thirds of the 474 scores fall between $46.0 - 9.35 = 36.65$ and $46.0 + 9.35 = 55.35$. The greatest variability in test performance in each grade occurs for the groups of Negro students who had all white classmates or more than half white classmates.

■ **Table 3.3.4.** Per cent of white students who would choose all white close friends; by first grade in class with nonwhites, present grade and region

Grade	Region	First grade attended with nonwhites				
		1, 2, or 3	4, 5, or 6	7, 8, or 9	10, 11, or 12	Never
9	Metropolitan Northeast	30.4	32.3	36.0	—	36.8
9	Metropolitan Midwest	27.5	34.2	31.8	—	41.4
12	Metropolitan Northeast	28.9	37.1	35.1	36.5	35.8
12	Metropolitan Midwest	37.8	43.0	44.0	47.5	47.4

■ **Table 3.3.5.** Per cent of white students who would choose all white class; by first time in class with nonwhites, present grade and region

Grade	Region	First class attended with nonwhites				
		1, 2, or 3	4, 5, or 6	7, 8, or 9	10, 11, or 12	Never
9	Metropolitan Northeast	21.5	24.4	25.2	—	28.0
9	Metropolitan Midwest	33.8	40.2	37.7	—	45.9
12	Metropolitan Northeast	18.3	25.5	21.7	22.9	26.5
12	Metropolitan Midwest	26.0	32.9	30.0	34.6	38.5

These differences in the variability of performance imply that if one only knew the racial composition of the class which a Negro attends, he could be more confident in using a mean of the scores of all Negroes from such classes to predict a given Negro performance if class had a majority of Negroes than if the Negroes were in a minority in the class. For in the latter case it is most likely that a given Negro student would have a particularly high score or a particularly low score.

This variability in performance may be due to either differences in the background and previous training of the individual Negro students in mostly white classes, or to differences in the conditions of schools in which these classes exist, such as the degree to which the Negro students are accepted into the formal and informal activities of the school.[13]

The survey data also show that white students who first attended integrated schools early in their school careers are likely to value their association with Negro students. Tables 3.3.3 and 3.3.4 show that the smallest percentage of white students who would choose all white classes or all white friends are those who first attend classes with nonwhites in the early grades.

NOTES

1. It should be noted, however, that in grades 1 and 3 these conditions (incompletely measured) show a lower relation to achievement than in any of the three grades examined here. This is true for the relation of all variables to achievement at these two grades. While this may result from incompleteness and unreliability of response at these grade levels, it may indicate that the relation does in fact increase over time.

2. The general finding of the importance of student body characteristics for educational outcomes has been shown by several investigators. One of the first systematic investigations is repored in Alan B. Wilson, "Residential Segregation of Social, Classes and Aspirations of High School Boys." *American Sociological Review* v. 24, 1959, pp. 836–845.

3. It is important to note that neither the student's own attendance nor his college aspirations are controlled in this analysis, though six variables in his background are. Thus, there is some confounding of the effect of the environment provided by fellow students with his own characteristics, which are related to them. However, the strength of the fellow-student background measure, when the same background characteristic is controlled for the student himself, and the considerations discussed earlier in this section, indicates that this confounding does not seriously distort inferences from the data.

4. The data show a lesser residual relationship (column A + B + C) for whites than Negroes and for Southern whites than for Northern ones. However, this is largely due to the lesser variation in racial composition of student body for whites than for Negroes, and for Southern whites than Northern ones.

5. If any school factors were highly associated with race, they would certainly account spuriously for a large fraction of the variance in achievement. Thus, an apparent school effect would not necessarily represent a true school effect.

6. To determine whether this differential relation is merely a result of greater variation in teachers' characteristics for Southern Negroes compared to Northern ones, or in fact a greater effect of a given amount of variation, the variances of the three most important variables, teachers' verbal ability, family educational background, and own education, were examined. These variances are approximately the same

for Northern and Southern Negroes, indicating that it is not a difference in variability of teachers, but a difference in the effect of a given degree of variability that is responsible for the different relation.

7. In this regard, a recent social-psychological experiment is relevant. Negro and white adults were offered an alternative between a risky situation in which the outcome depended on chance, and one in which the outcome, though no more favorable altogether, was contingent on their own response. Negro adults less often chose the alternative contingent on their own behavior, more often chose the chance alternative, as compared to whites. Herbert M. Lefcourt, "Risk-Taking in Negro and White Adults," *Journal of Personality and Social Psychology* 2, 1965, pp. 765–770.

8. Recent research on Negro mothers and their 4-year-old children has shown that those mothers with a sense of futility relative to the environment have children with lower scores on Stanford-Binet IQ tests, after other aspects of the mother's behavior, including her own IQ score, are statistically controlled. See Roberta M. Bear, Robert D. Hess, and Virginia C. Shipman, "Social class difference in maternal attitudes toward school and the consequences for cognitive development in the young child," mimeographed, 1966, Urban Child Center, University of Chicago.

9. An investigation of the relative sizes of the variances of these attitudes for the different groups shows that it is not the different amount of variation in the attitudes that is responsible for the different relations to achievement among the different groups, for the attitude variances do not differ widely. It is instead the different relation that a given amount of attitude difference has to achievement in these groups.

10. This refers to either "partialing out," often conducted by the successive addition of variables to a regression, or to "controlling" on variables by confining our attention to comparisons within broad categories.

11. Only when there is a single second variable and when the variance of the first variable equals unity is (the per cent accounted for)$/\sigma_{2}^{2}$, equal to b_{j}^{2}. In multiple regression, it is not equal to the square of the multiple regression coefficient.

12. No account is taken in the tabulation for Tables 3.3.1 and 3.3.2 of the fact that the various groups of pupils may have come from different backgrounds. Further exploration of the question by cross-tabulations on indicators of socioeconomic status showed that the differences shown in these Tables are not accounted for by family background.

13. Irwin Katz reviews several experiments performed with Negro subjects in interracial environments, and suggests a model of the conditions under which the performance of Negroes is likely to either benefit or suffer in the company of whites. Irwin Katz, "Review of Evidence Relating to Effects of Desegregation on the Intellectual Performance of Negroes," *American Psychologist*, June 1964.

SOME DYNAMIC ELEMENTS OF
CONTESTS FOR THE PRESIDENCY

DONALD E. STOKES

Despite the measured pace of American elections, there have now been a number of presidential campaigns since the advent of survey studies of voting. However sparingly, political history slowly has added to the set of distinct configurations of men and events which comprise a contest for the Presidency. The set is still small, whatever the impression created by massed thousands of interviews or by the accompanying files of election returns. Yet it is now large enough to be pressed hard for evidence about the sources of electoral change.

A primary virtue of measurements extended over a series of elections is that they can throw light on the problem of change. So long as the earliest voting studies were confined to cross-sectional relationships, they could deal only very inadequately with changes superimposed on these relationships or with changes in the relationships themselves. In the case of Lazarsfeld's enormously influential Erie County study in 1940, the natural limitations of a single-election study were compounded by the investigators' misfortune in choosing a campaign whose dominant personality and principal issues differed little from those of preceding elections. I have often wondered whether the static social determinism of *The People's Choice* would have emerged from a campaign in which the tides of short-term change were more nearly at flood.[1]

I shall examine here some sources of change which are richly evident in the presidential elections of the last two decades. In doing so I shall utilize several time series which can be extracted from the Survey Research Center's interview studies of the American electorate. The presidential contest of 1964 marked the fourth occasion on which the Center's national electoral studies have recorded the public's response to the issues and personalities of a presidential campaign.

This lengthening interval of electoral history contains material enough for the analyst of change. From the Eisenhower victories of the early 1950's, the high-point of presidential Republicanism since the Great Depression overwhelmed Hoover's party, the strength of Eisenhower's successors ebbed away in 1960 and sank in 1964 to a level which can only be regarded as one of the extreme lows of American national party competition. I shall examine some of the attitudinal factors in this extraordinary decline, focusing especially on the importance of changes in the issues and leaders which the electorate is asked to appraise. The

Reprinted by permission of the author and the American Political Science Association from *The American Political Science Review* **60** (March, 1966), 19–28.

relation of these "inputs" to the "output" of the presidential vote is exceedingly complex, but the moral of my piece is that this relationship introduces more dynamism into contests for the Presidency than the stability of party identification or of the social bases of party preference might lead us to expect.

In the course of the discussion I shall utilize a statistical model which has proved useful for measuring various attitudinal forces on the nation's vote. Dealing with a type of behavior which is notoriously subject to multiple influences, this model seeks to discern the relative importance of several dimensions of attitude both for individual choice and for the nation's collective decision.[2] The model treats the behavior of the individual voter as governed in an immediate sense by the direction and strength of his attitudes toward the several political objects he is asked to appraise, attitudes which we have probed in these presidential elections by asking a series of free-answer questions about the parties and presidential candidates. Since a presidential campaign confronts the voter with four main objects—the two parties and the two candidates—it is natural to place each respondent along four dimensions of attitude, and many of the findings reported below will rely on such a four-dimensional model. For other purposes, however, it is more revealing of the content of political attitude to place each respondent along six attitudinal dimensions: (1) attitude toward the Democratic candidate as a person; (2) attitude toward the Republican candidate as a person; (3) attitude toward the parties and candidates which relates to the benefit of various groups; (4) attitude toward the parties and candidates which relates to domestic policy; (5) attitude which relates to foreign policy; and (6) attitude which relates to the general performance of the parties in the nation's affairs. A detailed account of the procedure by which respondents are assimilated to these several dimensions appears in the appended note.

The appendix also describes the statistical operations by which we obtain definite estimates of each dimension's contribution to the winning majority—the means by which, in effect, the nation's collective decision is resolved into a set of attitudinal components. These methods must of course be regarded as approximate, for reasons of sampling if no other, and I advance no claim to exact measurement; none is really necessary to the central conclusion which I shall draw from the analysis. Nevertheless, the model's success in estimating the direction and size of the winning majority in each of a series of elections does increase our confidence that we have measured dimensions of popular feeling which are deeply involved in changes of party fortune.

The several dimensions of attitude, however, have by no means been equally involved in electoral change. Just as the various components of electoral decision can be very different in their direction and strength at a given point in time, they can exhibit a very different tendency to change over time. In the period of our research some have been relatively stable, others not. By examining the role of each attitude component over twelve years we form several time series which are extraordinarily suggestive of the sources of change during this interval of our national politics.

The Attitudinal Components over Time

The curves described by the components of the six-dimensional model arrange themselves into three interesting pairs. The first of these is a pair whose values have consistently favored the Democrats over the entire period. As shown by Figure 1, partisan evaluations relating to domestic issues and to group benefit have uniformly helped the Democrats more than the Republicans, although the extent of this aid has fluctuated from year to year.[3] To an unusual degree these elements of the party images have roots in the past, extending back at least to the Roosevelt New Deal. Indeed, the benefit to the Democrats from their party's sponsorship of disadvantaged elements of American society is an antique theme of our party politics. Even in the mid-1950's and the early 1960's the volume of comment approving the Democrats and disapproving the Republicans in terms of the interests of the common man was impressive. In the two most recent elections, however, these class-related comments were diminished somewhat and were accompanied by references to religious and racial groups in which the arithmetic of group size was less favorable to the Democrats. For these reasons the group curve in Figure 1 shows the party's advantage to be somewhat less in 1960 and 1964.

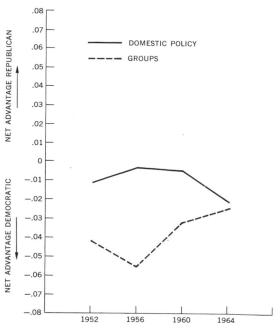

1 Continuing Democratic advantage: groups and domestic policy.

It will be apparent that the concept of "group" is defined here in a very inclusive manner. Likewise, our net has been cast very widely in coding references relating to domestic issues. In particular, many of the comments giving substance to the domestic issue dimension are "valence" or "image" issues, in which the parties or candidates are linked with something which is uniformly approved or disapproved ("the Republicans are the party of depression") rather than "position" issues on which there are genuine differences of party policy. The leading image issue of domestic politics throughout this period was the association of the Democrats with good times, the Republicans with bad. This association, which probably had weakened steadily from the height of the Great Depression to the election of 1952, was further attenuated by the prosperity of Eisenhower's first term. But it revived again in the recession of 1958, before the Republican administration had left office, and it has been given fresh substance by the rising prosperity of the Kennedy and Johnston years.

The domestic issue dimension has not, however, been altogether lacking in genuine position issues. One of the peculiar qualities of the Goldwater candidacy is that it converted into position issues a number of image issues on which ᴀ broad consensus had hitherto existed between the parties. This fact was not lost upon the general public. Under the Goldwater challenge, the Democrats were rewarded more generously in 1964 than in any of the three prior elections for their sponsorship of social security and of the circle of other social and economic welfare policies which had wide popular approval. Primarily for this reason the domestic issue curve of Figure 1 shows a greater Democratic advantage in 1964 than in the years before.

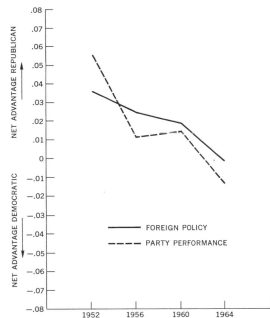

2   Decaying Republican advantage: foreign policy and party performance.

A second pair of curves is traced by the movement of two components in which a strong initial Republican advantage is seen to have vanished over these four elections. As shown by Figure 2, the Republican party under Eisenhower enjoyed a substantial lead over the Democrats on foreign affairs—preeminently in terms of the great image issue of peace and war. This lead was not greatly lessened when Eisenhower's deputy sought the Presidency in 1960, but Nixon's legacy dissolved altogether in the contest of Goldwater and Johnson. It would be a misreading of the 1964 value, however, to suppose that widely-held foreign policy beliefs consistent with Goldwater's were nicely balanced by widely-held beliefs consistent with Johnson's. According to our evidence, foreign affairs did intrude on the public's consciousness in the 1964 campaign more than in any election since 1952, but popular references to foreign issues in 1964 still had only about a fourth the frequency of references to domestic issues. The loss of Republican advantage on this dimension was due to the final collapse of the belief that the party under Goldwater was more likely to bring peace than were the Democrats under Johnson.[4]

The loss of Republican advantage in foreign affairs is paralleled by the decay of the party's advantage in popular assessments of party performance. The Republicans began this series of elections immensely aided by the mood for a change in 1952. There is no more striking element in all of our attitudinal materials than the public's anger and frustration with the outgoing Democratic administration in that year. Whatever the validity of the public's grievance, it was real enough in motivational terms and contributed handsomely to Eisenhower's first victory. The force of this feeling was easily spent, however, once the Democrats had been driven from office. Yet in 1956 and again in 1960 the Republicans still enjoyed an edge in terms of the electorate's general evaluations of current party performance, a fact which is the more remarkable in view of the stronger hold of the Democrats on the nation's underlying party identifications.[5] By 1964, however, this lingering advantage had been swept away, and the Democrats by a modest margin were now seen as the party better qualified to conduct the country's affairs.

The third pair of curves is traced by the components having to do with popular reactions to the personal attributes of the candidates. As shown in Figure 3, there has been remarkable variety in the appeal of the Republican candidates. The values of this component in 1952 and 1956 attest to General Eisenhower's personal hold on the electorate, an attraction which, if anything, was even more wholly personal after Eisenhower had served four years as President. Mr. Nixon's appeal in 1960 was somewhat less, although his personal appeal to the electorate, especially the sense of his broad experience, was marked. If the eventual account given by the political histories is that Nixon was a weak candidate in 1960, it will be largely myth.

The response to Goldwater, however, was something else again. Whereas Nixon's personal stature helped bring his party to the verge of a third presidential victory against a party enjoying a clear advantage in the country's partisan identifications, popular reaction to Goldwater contributed to his party's electoral ruin. The detailed references to Goldwater are an impressive amalgam of doubts—a wild and erratic campaigner, muddled and unclear, unstable, poorly educated, and so on—with these themes very little offset by references to the advertised qualities of integrity, sincerity, and decisiveness. If our estimates are right, the transition from Nixon to Goldwater cost the Republicans something like 7 per cent of the total vote.

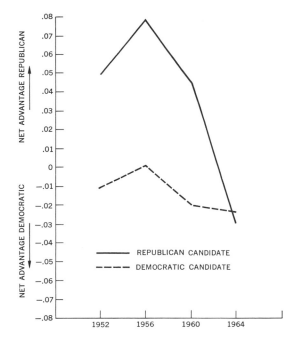

3   Greatest variation: appeal of candidates.

Despite immense differences of personal style, the appeal of three successive Democratic candidates was much more nearly equal. And except for Stevenson's second campaign, the response to each of these candidates added to his strength at the polls. Certainly the movement of the Democratic curve in Figure 3 shows Johnson to have been an asset to his own candidacy in 1964: the response to Johnson's attributes apparently did the Democrats about as much good as the response to Goldwater's did. The combined effect of both appears to have moved the two-party vote roughly 5 percentage points toward Johnson.

To emphasize the dynamic implications for party competition of pairing successive candidates for President, Figure 4 combines the effect of the personal appeals of the two men seeking the office in each of these elections.[6] The variation of this summary curve is impressive indeed. From a maximum Republican advantage of nearly 8 per cent in the rematch of Eisenhower and Stevenson, the curve falls through more than 13 percentage points to a maximum Democratic advantage of more than 5 per cent in the contest of Johnson and Goldwater. A more eloquent statistical comment on the personal contribution which candidates for President can make to electoral change could hardly be given.

It would be a mistake to read into these figures too simple an explanation of the impact of candidate personality on the mass public. Certainly it would be grossly wrong to suppose that the properties of these "stimulus objects" are somehow immediately and directly impressed on the electorate's response. The relation of stimulus and response is remarkably complex, involving an interplay of several quite different factors. Before drawing some general conclusions about the problem of change, it would be well to consider the interaction of the "actual" properties of the stimuli to which the electorate responds, certain response dispositions which the electorate has already learned, and some properties of the communication processes by which the electorate is informed of the objects of presidential politics.

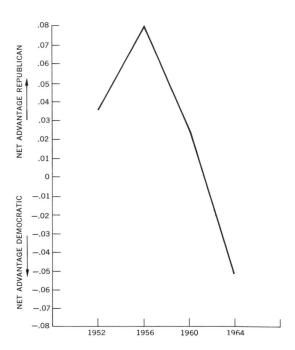

4   Net impact of candidates.

Stimulus Properties and Response Dispositions in the Attitude Components

Although the comments below extend to the full range of stimuli to which the public is exposed, some of the subtleties of electoral response can most readily be observed in connection with candidate effects. The men seeking the Presidency bring to a campaign certain "real" properties as stimulus objects. Some of these belong to the past—the candidate's role as war hero, his success as governor or senator, his marital difficulties, and so on—although the communication of these things to much of the public may lie ahead. Other properties have to do with appearance, behavior, and personal style—the candidate's smile, the timbre of his voice, his smoothness in dealing with the teleprompter, his willingness to suffer fools gladly—knowledge of which can reach the electorate in numberless ways.

Impressions of these things, however, do not fall on wholly unprepared ground. Voters display a variety of response dispositions as they form their evaluations of the candidates. One type of response disposition is so evident as to require little comment. A wealth of research evidence, as well as familiar observation, attests the profound influence which partisan loyalties may have on the voter's perceptions of the men seeking office. The stronger the voter's party bias, the more likely he is to see the candidate of his own party as hero, the candidate of the other party as villain. No one who has talked with a sample of voters during a presidential campaign can have failed to note at every hand the processes by which cognitive balance is achieved.[7]

The voter's perceptual predispositions are not, however, limited to party bias. We are confronted at times by striking evidence of other identifications exerting a like influence on candidate images. A vivid example of these is the influence of religion on perceptions of John F. Kennedy during the 1960 election campaign. Because Kennedy was the Democratic candidate, voters identifying with the Democratic party tended to view him more favorably than did voters identifying with the Republican party. But Kennedy was seen by the electorate not only as a Democrat; he was seen as a Catholic as well. As a result, at every point along the party identification continuum, Catholics tended to perceive Kennedy in a more favorable light than did Protestants.

A demonstration of the joint biasing effects of religion and party in 1960 may be found in Figure 5. In that campaign we placed each of our sample respondents along a standard party identification scale, represented here by five ordered groups: Strong Republicans, Weak Republicans, Independents, Weak Democrats, and Strong Democrats. At the same time we placed each of our Protestant and Catholic respondents on a scale of religious identification defined here by four ordered groups: persons strongly identified with a Protestant Church, persons weakly identified with such a church, persons weakly identified with the Catholic Church, and persons strongly identified with the Catholic Church. These two forms of psychological identification are moderately correlated in American society (that is, Catholics are more likely than Protestants to be Democratic) but not more than moderately so. Crossing the two here yields twenty groups defined by religion and party at once in which we may examine the distribution of attitude toward Kennedy. Figure 5 displays the mean attitude toward Kennedy within each of these twenty groups.[8]

The means exhibit a remarkable pattern. The fact that the curve for each religious group slopes upward to the right shows that, whatever the voter's religious identification, he is more likely to have perceived Kennedy favorably the closer he was to the Democratic end of the party identification dimension. And the march of the four religious curves up the figure shows that, whatever the voter's party identification, he is more likely to have perceived Kennedy positively the closer he was to the Catholic end of the religious dimension. There is even a pattern to the partial discontinuities: the regularity of the curves for weak Protestants and weak Catholics suggests that the biasing tendencies of party identification were generally effective among the mildly religious while the irregularity of the curves for strong Protestants and strong Catholics suggests that party loyalty could have a marked impact on the strongly religious only if a party faith were itself strongly held.

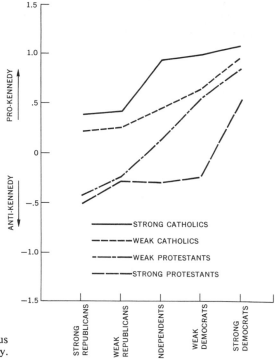

5   Influence of party and religious identifications on perceptions of Kennedy.

Figure 5 is so rich in evidence of selective perception that we may easily miss what it has to say about the element of Kennedy's image which was not the result of response dispositions based on religion and party. The fact that this element was a favorable one ought not to be obscured by the strong pattern of the figure. Any reasonable operation by which we might seek to reconstruct a mean attitude among persons who are religiously and politically neutral would show that Kennedy was likely to be positively seen when his image did not fall prey to strong negative bias. For example, persons who were politically independent perceived Kennedy favorably even if they were weakly identified with a Protestant church.

We ought not to conclude from this that partisan and religious dispositions were the only response biases involved in the electorate's response to Kennedy or that, these dispositions aside, Kennedy was in some absolute sense an attractive candidate. In 1960, as any campaign year, many other kinds of response dispositions underlay the private impressions of the candidates formed by tens of millions of voters. We have identified two of the most important. It would not be difficult to suggest other factors which may have predisposed voters to react positively or negatively to something in the youthful, vigorous, Ivy-educated, Boston-accented stimulus which Kennedy presented.

Perhaps this point can be stated even more forcefully in terms of popular reaction to General Eisenhower, the most attractive presidential candidate since Franklin Roosevelt. The point is simply that "attractive" implies more than something about the candidate himself; it also implies something about the response dispositions of the electorate. Given the dominant values of contemporary American society, Eisenhower was enormously appealing. But we can at least imagine his having done very badly before an electorate less resonant to the military conqueror and less susceptible to the charm of a supremely other-directed personality who nevertheless evoked many of the traditional virtues. We might suppose, for example, that Eisenhower would have done very badly indeed before an electorate whose dominant values are those of American university faculties of social science.

Attitudes already formed toward some political objects are of course among the dispositions which can influence response to others. This seems especially true in the case of attitudes toward the candidates. When one rival for the Presidency already is well known, as an incumbent President will always be, the public's attitude toward his opponent will inevitably be colored by its response to the established figure. Thus, in 1940, Roosevelt-haters were quick to discover the virtues of Wendell Willkie when he was thrust onto the presidential stage, as Roosevelt's partisans were quick to discern Willkie's vices. And in the early 1950's, Adlai Stevenson had the misfortune to be paired with a much better-established rival who already enjoyed the highest public regard.[9]

Of course the complex relation of candidate stimulus to the public's response also involves important communication factors. In a sense, the only real candidate stimuli are those which reach the voter via the mass media and interpersonal conversation, stimuli which only rarely are complemented by direct voter contact with the candidate. Therefore, the benefit or harm done to a candidate's cause by his actual personal attributes is mediated not only by the response dispositions of the electorate; it is mediated as well by the manner in which these attributes are communicated to the electorate. It is not hard to believe that some of the disarray of Goldwater's popular image was due to his extraordinarily bad press. The candidate properties communicated to the public are not a pure fiction of the media. But neither are they a pure reflection of the candidate himself, as he might have been seen at home in the desert.

What has been said of candidates can be said of any object which has electoral effects. Certainly the political role of domestic and foreign issues involves a similar interplay of stimulus properties, response tendencies, and communication processes. The Korean War's immense profit for the Republicans in 1952, for example, depended on much more than a set of objective events in the Far East and the parties' stand on those events. It depended too on a welter of response dispositions in the electorate—general isolationist or internationalist attitudes, hostility to communism, latent militarist tendencies, the anxieties of farmers over having sons away at harvest time, and the like—as well as the way in which the public was informed by the communications media of what was happening half a world away.

If the political effects of issues and personalities in the wider environment depend partly on what the electorate hears and how it is disposed to react to what it hears, it follows that changes in communication and response tendencies can at times alter the political effects of a stimulus which has not itself changed. A clear example of this is the rapid build-up of a candidate by the mass media when he steps into the charmed circle of leading contenders—or the opposite experience, which many potential candidates have had, of falling through the medias' trap door to oblivion. Instances of marked change of response dispositions while political objects remain unchanged are more difficult to discern, but they undoubtedly occur. Herbert Hoover's high starched collars, a symbol of middle class prosperity in the booming twenties, probably looked quite different from the bread-lines of 1932.

Although changes of communication and of response dispositions can alter the electorate's response to a given political object, it is nevertheless true that a turnover of objects—of the personalities, issues, and events of national politics—is the more important source of short-term electoral change. This is the more true since a stimulus object can affect communication and response dispositions themselves. For example, quite apart from the sort of man he "really" is, a candidate can have wide influence on his treatment by the mass media. If the newspapers gave Mr. Goldwater extraordinarily rough treatment for a Republican candidate, Goldwater's own posture toward the press was part of the reason. Similarly, different candidates engage different response dispositions in the mass public. Unlike any Democratic candidate since Al Smith, Kennedy activated response dispositions based on Catholic and Protestant religious identifications, as we have seen. And candidates can lead the electorate to learn new dispositions, as Kennedy helped make the country receptive to a whole new generation of youthful, vigorous candidates for national and state office.

This type of change is vividly mirrored in the components of electoral decision given here for the past four presidential elections. The evidence of the changing personal impact of the candidates is especially impressive. Yet in a presidential system the turnover of candidates has implications reaching beyond sheer personal appeal. A candidate for the nation's great office is a focus for popular feeling about issues and questions of group benefit as well, and our measurements should be extended to take this fact into account.

Relative Change in Candidate and Party Attitude

It is hardly surprising that candidates for the Presidency should attract attitudes which are somewhat distinct from those attaching to the parties themselves. The platforms adopted by the nominating conventions are much less binding than the election manifestoes of a British party, for example, and a presidential candidate is notoriously at liberty to take his own stands on major issues and the problems of major social groupings. Equally, on matters requiring congressional action he is free to contradict positions taken by his party in the Senate and House. And on matters of foreign policy, the country is largely dependent on the candidate's record and views to know what his administration would be likely to do in the world. This is the stuff of which a presidential system is made.

Therefore, it is of interest to compare the variability of attitudes toward the parties and their presidential candidates. Neither has been constant over the period of our research, but the two have shown vastly different propensities to change. When we turn from a six-to a four-dimensional model, summarizing popular feeling according to the party or candidate toward which it is directed whether or not it concerns domestic or foreign issues, questions of group benefit, or other matters, the candidate components are found to have moved much more strongly from Republican to Democratic advantage.

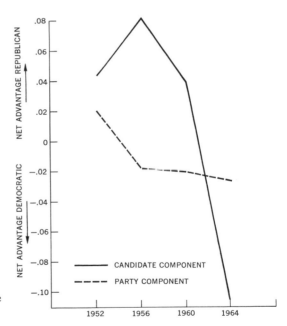

6   Variation of party and candidate components.

This contrast is shown by Figure 6, in which each pair of party and candidate components of the four-dimensional model is added together at each election. The combined party curve has not by any means stood still. The public's full assessment of the parties showed a marked Republican advantage in the mood of 1952. But by 1956 the comparison of parties had moved to the Democrats' benefit, and this trend continued over the later two elections.

The combined candidate curve, however, describes a very much greater change. The public's full assessment of Eisenhower and Stevenson, including issue and group perceptions as well as perceptions of personal qualities, was strongly Republican in 1952 and even more decisively so four years later. In the 1960 election, the comparison of candidates still favored the Republicans, although much more moderately. But between the Kennedy-Nixon campaign and the Johnson–Goldwater campaign the combined candidate component moved a most remarkable distance to the Democrats' advantage. In each contest the candidate curve was the farther removed from the zero-point: indeed, its average displacement from the neutral point has been more than 6 per cent, whereas the average displacement of the party curve has been about 2 per cent. But the really arresting comparison has to do with relative change: over these elections the variance of the candidate curve has exceeded that of the party curve by more than 10 to 1.

It is therefore evident that the dynamism of popular attitude is peculiarly tied to the emergence of new candidates for the Presidency. The attitudes toward the parties are not inert. The shift in the relative assessment of the parties over the period of this research has been enough to alter the parties' strength by something like six million votes on a turnout equal to that of 1964. But this change, impressive as it is, nevertheless is moderate by comparison with the change induced by succeeding pairs of candidates. The fluctuations of electoral attitudes over these elections have to a remarkable degree focused on the candidates themselves.

All of this is quite out of keeping with the static perspective of the earliest studies of voting. Even if our findings are no more than approximately true, they argue strongly the dynamic implications of changes of the stimulus objects of national politics. This source of change has in fact brought spectacular shifts of presidential voting despite the fact that over the same period there has been almost no perceptible shift in the single most important type of response disposition, the electorate's enduring party loyalties. It may also be noted that the variations of attitude recorded here have been largely independent of secular changes in the structure of American society, although, as we have seen, a turnover of stimulus objects can alter dramatically the facts of social structure which are relevant to political choice. Taken together, changes in the several stimulus objects of presidential politics in this span of years have been quite enough to bring a change of party control, indeed to have induced a drastic transformation of party fortune in the contest for the Presidency.

APPENDIX

A Note on the Statistical Model

Since the number of positive and negative comments which a given voter makes about a given political object depends on the direction and strength of his feeling toward the object, we have placed a respondent on any given attitude dimension by forming the arithmetic difference of his pro-Republican and pro-Democratic responses whose content relates to the dimension. A pleasing variety of evidence can be marshaled to support the assumptions involved in this technique. That the resulting scales measure the intensity of attitude is borne out by the monotonic (indeed linear) relationships they exhibit with a host of other partisan variables, including the vote itself. That the neutral point is correctly located is indicated by the fact that a majority of those placed at the first scale position to the pro-Democratic side of the zero-point of each dimension do in fact vote Democratic; a majority of those at the first scale position to the pro-Republican side, Republican. The correct location of the neutral point is also attested by the model's success in estimating the direction and magnitude of the winning majority, as explained below. That the distances between scale positions are roughly equal (an assumption necessary to the further statistical operations) is also supported by the linearity of the relationship between the attitude scales and individual voting choice. Indeed, the proportion of the variance of the vote explained when individual choice is treated as a linear regression (as measured by the square of the product moment correlation) is almost identical with the proportion of the variance due to differences between the scale classes (as measured by the correlation ratio). That only a modest amount of error is involved in forming these relative-frequency measures of the direction and intensity of attitude is indicated by the success of the scales in accounting statistically for voting choice. Interestingly, the possibility that large errors have resulted from differences of verbal behavior can be partially discounted on the basis of experimental permutations of the order in which respondents were invited to comment on the two parties and the two candidates. Despite the reasonableness of the suspicion that either "warm-up" or "fatigue" effects might produce large differences in the volume of response according to the order in which the parties and candidates were presented, changes of order in fact seem not to make a particle of difference.

A linear probability model is used to describe the relation of these scales to voting choice, with a Republican vote scored 1 and a Democratic vote 0. If the probability of voting Republican, $\Pr(R)$, is expressed as a linear regression on the dimensions $X_1, \ldots, X_I$:

$$\Pr(R) = b_0 + b_1 X_1 + \cdots + b_I x_I, \tag{1}$$

where I is either four or six according to the model used, the coefficients $b_1, \ldots, b_I$, of this linear combination measure the relative dependence of partisan choice on each of the dimensions. For some purposes it is useful to standardize these coefficients by measuring each attitude dimension in terms of sample standard deviations, yielding a new set of coefficients $b_1^*, \ldots, b_I^*$, as defined in a manner:

$$b_i^* = b_i s_i \quad (i = 1, \ldots, I) \tag{2}$$

which removes the effect of differences in the extent of variation along each of the dimensions. These standardized coefficients are not, however, the familiar beta coefficients of a regression equation in which both the dependent and independent variates are measured in sample standard deviations about their respective means. Scoring the dependent variable 0 and 1 is necessary to the probability interpretation of estimated scores. And each attitude scale is measured about its neutral point since this constitutes a theoretically meaningful origin.

The multiple correlation of the several predictors with partisan choice has varied in the range of .72 to .75 over the four presidential elections studied. There is reason to believe that most of the remaining "error" variance is due to the dichotomous nature of the dependent variate and that the multiple correlation of the attitude dimensions with some underlying *propensity* to vote Republican or Democratic would be substantially higher. Of the alternative ways of describing this relationship, I have given most attention to a multivariate probit model under which the probability of voting Republican varies according to the cumulative normal ogive. Such a model has aesthetically pleasing formal properties, especially the fact that it will never give probability estimates less than zero or exceeding unity. In practice, however, its performance differs little from that of the model used, since the relation of voting choice to the several dimensions is so nearly linear over the range of attitude actually found in our samples. The distribution of the electorate along an attitude dimension is much more easily summarized under the linear model, a fact which counts greatly in its favor.

To estimate the average amount by which a given dimension has increased (or lessened) the probability of the individual's voting Republican, we combine the information about its relation to voting choice, as measured by the multiple regression coefficient, with information about the mean location of voters on the dimension, as measured by the displacement of the observed mean from the theoretical neutral point, forming for each attitude dimension the product

$$b_i(\bar{X}_i - X_i^0) = b_i^* \frac{\bar{X}_i - X_i^0}{s_i} \tag{3}$$

where b_i and b_i^* are as defined above and X_i^0 is the neutral point of the *i*th dimension. If the neutral point is taken as the origin, this product of course simplifies to

$$b_i\bar{X}_i = b_i^* \frac{\bar{X}_i}{s_i}. \tag{4}$$

It is these quantities which I have called "attitudinal components" of the vote. The rationale for taking account of the mean's displacement from the neutral point is of course that a given dimension will benefit one party or the other only as its mean departs from the neutral point.

On the assumption that a dead heat would be the outcome of an election in which neither party was advantaged along any of the dimensions of attitude, the test of the model's ability to estimate the winning majority consists in seeing how well this relation is satisfied by the actual vote:

$$P_R - .5 = \sum_{i=1}^{I} b_i \bar{X}_i \qquad (5)$$

where P_R is the proportion of the two-party vote actually polled by the Republican candidate for President and each attitude factor X_i is measured about its theoretical neutral point. Over the four elections studied the maximum departure of this relation from equality has been about two per cent, despite the fact that the Republican proportion of the two-party vote has varied over an interval from 58 per cent to less than 40 per cent. Indeed, the correlation of estimated and actual majorities over these four contests is .98, a figure which increases our confidence that we have faithfully measured many of the immediate attitudinal forces on the electorate's decision.

NOTES

1. Paul F. Lazarsfeld, Bernard Berelson, and Hazel Gaudet, *The People's Choice* (New York: Duell, Sloan and Pearce, 1944). It is paradoxical that Lazarsfeld and his associates should have come to so static a view of party preference, since the desire to observe changes of preference was so central to their original intentions. Had they worked within the context of an election such as that of 1952 it is entirely unlikely that they could have ignored the presence of massive inter-election change, overlaid on the social bases of preference summarized in the Index of Political Predisposition.

2. For a report of the application of this model to the Eisenhower elections see Donald E. Stokes, Angus Campbell, and Warren E. Miller, "Components of Electoral Decision," *The American Political Science Review* **52** (June 1958), 367–387.

3. The vertical coordinate of Figure 1, as well as of Figures 2 and 3, gives the value of the quantity

    $$b_i(\bar{X}_i - X_i^0)$$

    defined in the appendix. As explained there, this quantity may be interpreted either at the individual level as the average amount by which a given dimension has increased (or lessened, in the case of negative values) the probability of the individual's voting Republican or at the level of the whole electorate as the proportion of the total two-party vote by which a given dimension has increased (or lessened) the Republican share.

4. For direct additional evidence on this point see Philip E. Converse, Aage R. Clausen, and Warren E. Miller, "Electoral Myth and Reality: The 1964 Election," *The American Political Science Review* **59** (June 1965), p. 332.

5. For evidence on the distribution of party identification in this period see "The Concept of the 'Normal Vote'," in A. Campbell, P. Converse, W. Miller, and D. Stokes, *Elections and the Political Order* (New York, 1966), Ch. 1.

6. The individual and aggregate interpretations of the quantity represented by the vertical coordinate of Figure 4 are the same as before, but the quantity itself is the sum of the components measuring the increment or decrement to Republican strength due to personal attributes of the Republican and Democratic candidates.

7. Certainly evidence of it is plentiful enough in the Center's studies. See, for example, Angus Campbell, Philip E. Converse, Warren E. Miller and Donald E. Stokes, *The American Voter* (New York: John Wiley and Sons, 1960), pp. 120–145. An excellent general review of the achievement of cognitive congruence in political attitudes is given by Robert E. Lane and David O. Sears in their *Public Opinion* (Englewood Cliffs, N. J.: Prentice-Hall, 1964). An interesting application of these concepts to attitude change may be found in Denis G. Sullivan, "Psychological Balance and Reactions to the Presidential Nominations in 1960," in M. Kent Jennings and L. Harmon Zeigler, (eds.) *The Electoral Process* (Englewood Cliffs, N. J., 1966), pp. 238–264.

8. In order to standardize the metric used in these comparisons, I have divided each of these means by the sample standard deviation of attitude toward Kennedy. Because the sample contained only seven Weak Catholic Weak Republicans and only seven Weak Catholic Independents the means for these two groups have been adjusted to reduce the probable effect of sampling error.

9. The voter's attitude toward a given political object may be influenced by the presence of other objects in his perceptual field even when no question of order is involved in the formation of attitude. In such a case, however, it is more reasonable to think of these effects as belonging to the configuration of stimulus objects, rather than to the voter's response dispositions.

5 / DATA ANALYSIS AND RESEARCH DESIGN

DATA ANALYSIS AND STATISTICS: TECHNIQUES AND APPROACHES

J. W. TUKEY
M. B. WILK

1. Introduction

Data analysis is not a new subject. It has accompanied productive experimentation and observation for hundreds of years. At times, as in the work of Kepler, it has produced dramatic results.

As in any other science, what is done in data analysis is very much a product of each day's technology. Every external technological development of major relevance—organized tables of functions, knowledge of the mathematical consequences of the Gaussian law of error, desk calculators, stored-program electronic computers, graphical display facilities—has been accompanied by a tendency to rediscover the importance and identity of data analysis.

Today, as in the past, data analysis is usually difficult, cumbersome, and complex—and often very time consuming, both in man-hours and in elapsed time. It is also of mushrooming importance in business, politics, science, and technology.

The basic intent of data analysis is simply stated: to seek through a body of data for interesting relationships and information and to exhibit the results in such a way as to make them recognizable to the data analyzer and recordable for posterity. Its creative task is to be productively descriptive, with as much attention as possible to previous knowledge, and thus to contribute to the mysterious process called insight.

Four major influences act on data analysis today:

1) the formal theory of statistics,
2) revolutionary developments in computers and display devices,
3) the challenge, in many fields, of more and ever larger bodies of data,
4) the accelerating emphasis on quantification in an ever wider variety of disciplines.

The last few decades have seen the rise of formal theories of statistics, "legitimizing" variation by confining it by assumption to random sampling, often assumed to involve tightly specified distributions, and restoring the appearance of security by emphasizing narrowly optimized techniques and claiming to

Reprinted by permission of the authors from *Proceedings of the Symposium on Information Processing in Sight Sensory Systems*, November 1–3, 1965, California Institute of Technology.

make statements with "known" probabilities of error. While some of the influences of statistical theory on data analysis have been helpful, others have not.

Exposure, the effective laying open of the data to display the unanticipated, is to us a major portion of data analysis. Formal statistics has given almost no guidance to exposure; indeed, it is not clear how the informality and flexibility appropriate to the exploratory character of exposure can be fitted into any of the structures of formal statistics so far proposed.

On the other hand, some facets of formal statistics are more nearly appropriate, and have proved much more useful, in dealing with the many bodies of data that require routine handling, not data analysis, and that can be rightly approached with specific narrow questions.

As a discipline, data analysis is a very difficult field. It must adapt itself to what people can and need to do with data. In the sense that biology is more complex than physics, and the behavioral sciences are more complex than either, it is likely that the general problems of data analysis are more complex than those of all three. It is too much to ask for close and effective guidance for data analysis from *any* highly formalized structure, either now or in the near future.

Data analysis can gain much from formal statistics, but only if the connection is kept adequately loose.

The impact on data analysis of developments in the availability of computer hardware and in the understanding of computer software has been unduly delayed. Not only has the development of appropriate computing systems been slow, but the necessary rethinking of data analysis itself has hardly been begun.

The revolutionary computer and display developments now taking place will inevitably stimulate major extensions and departures in data analysis, whose beginnings are already visible. Today's first task is not to invent wholly new techniques, though these are needed. Rather we need most vitally to recognize and reorganize the essentials of old techniques, to make easy their assembly in new ways, and to modify their external appearances to fit the new opportunities.

Data has typically been easier to gather than to analyze, though there are outstanding exceptions. Despite the gains in computation and display—perhaps because of them—this is increasingly true. In so many fields, the accumulation of large volumes of data is becoming irresistibly practical and economical. As in the past, much, perhaps most, of even carefully collected data will not be adequately analyzed. In part this is because facts are usually more complex than the hopes which have led to their accumulation; in part because the accumulation of data dampens experimental excitement; in part because collecting data simply serves to keep the experimenter busy while he designs a more adequate experimental setup or develops a needed point of view; but also, in part, because the technology of data analysis is still unsystematized and many of those who could put its tools to good use are unable to do so effectively.

Increasingly, most disciplines are evolving towards increased quantification and mathematization. Many of them (e.g., medicine) have had long histories of being descriptive and relatively qualitative largely because of the complexities of their phenomena and systems.

The wider variety of problems thus brought to data analysis increases the importance of recognizing general elements in diverse problems and untangling these elements from more specific ones. The need is to recognize and understand the similarities and differences of data analyses in nuclear physics, in the physiology of cell nuclei, in cloud-seeding, in the assay of antiviral agents, in chemical engineering, and in opinion polling, to select but a few.

2. Data Analysis Is Like Doing Experiments

Far too many people have persisted in regarding statistics, and even data analysis, as a branch of probability theory, nestled deep within modern mathematics. Happily this view is increasingly out of favor. Statistical data analysis is much more appropriately associated with the sciences and with the experimental process in general.

The general purposes of conducting experiments and analyzing data match, point by point. For experimentation, these purposes include: (1) more adequate description of experience and quantification of some areas of knowledge; (2) discovery or invention of new phenomena and relations; (3) confirmation, or labeling for change, of previous assumptions, expectations, and hypotheses; (4) generation of ideas for further useful experiments; and (5) keeping the experimenter relevantly occupied while he thinks.

Comparable objectives in data analysis are: (1) to achieve more specific description of what is loosely known or suspected; (2) to find unanticipated aspects in the data, and to suggest unthought-of models for the data's summarization and exposure; (3) to employ the data to assess the (always incomplete) adequacy of a contemplated model; (4) to provide both incentives and guidance for further analysis of the data; and (5) to keep the investigator usefully stimulated while he absorbs the feeling of his data and considers what to do next.

Among the important characteristics shared by data analysis and the experimental process are these:

1) Some prior presumed structure, some guidance, some objectives, in short some ideas of a model, are virtually essential, yet these must not be taken too seriously. Models must be used but must never be believed. As T. C. Chamberlain said, "Science is the holding of multiple working hypotheses."

2) Our approach needs to be multifaceted and open-minded. In data analysis as in experimentation, discovery is usually more exciting and sometimes much more important than confirmation.

3) It is valuable to construct techniques that are likely to reveal such complications as: assumptions whose consequences are inappropriate in a specific instance, numerical inaccuracies, or difficulties of interpretation of what is found.

4) In both good data analysis and good experimentation, the findings often appear to be obvious—but generally only after the fact.

5) It is often more productive to begin by obtaining and trying to explain specific findings, rather than by attempting to catalog all possible findings and explanations.

6) While detailed deduction of anticipated consequences is likely to be useful when two or more models are to be compared, it is often more productive to study the results before carrying out these detailed deductions.

7) There is a great need to do obvious things quickly and routinely, but with care and thoroughness.

8) Insightfulness is generally more important than so-called objectivity. Requirements for specifiable probabilities of error must not prevent repeated analysis of data, just as requirements for impossibly perfect controls are not allowed to bring experimentation to a halt.

9) Interaction, feedback, trial and error are all essential; convenience is dramatically helpful.

10) There can be great gains from adding sophistication and ingenuity—subtle concepts, complicated experimental setups, robust models, delicate electronic devices, fast or accurate algorithms—to our kit of tools, just so long as simpler and more obvious approaches are not neglected.

11) Finally, most of the work actually done turns out to be nonconsequential, uninteresting, or of no operational value. Yet it is an essential aspect of both processes to recognize and accept this feature, with its momentary embarrassments and disappointments. A broad perspective on objectives and expected difficulties is often required to muster the necessary persistence.

In summary, data analysis, like experimentation, must be considered as an open-ended, highly interactive, iterative process, whose actual steps are selected segments of a stubbily branching, tree-like pattern of possible actions.

3. The Key to Effective Data Analysis

The iterative and interactive interplay of summarizing by fit and exposing by residuals is vital to effective data analysis. Summarizing and exposing are complementary and pervasive.

If certain aspects of the data have been effectively summarized by fitting a straight line, then we can improve exposure by building on this summarization. The plot of y against x is likely to be dominated by what has been summarized by the straight line. A plot of the residuals from the fit against x (or other variables) exposes to view only what has not been summarized, thus avoiding unnecessary distraction and permitting attention to finer details.

Even when used for confirmation alone, data analysis is a process of first summarizing according to the hypothesized model and then exposing what remains, in a cogent way, as a basis for judging the adequacy of this model or the precision of this summary, or both.

Techniques for summarizing are, fortunately, often useful for exposing and vice versa. For example, a half-normal plot[1] of contrasts in a 2^n experiment may serve as an effective summary of the data, with identification of interesting effects. It may also serve as an exposing technique in indicating, for instance, the unanticipated existence of two error terms.

This process of summarizing and exposing is intrinsically iterative. No step is clearly the last before it is taken.

Exposure of what has not yet been summarized often leads us to recognize behavior or problems not yet allowed for—and then to plan and obtain a revised summary, starting a new cycle.

Summarizing data is always a process of constrained and partial description —a process that essentially and inevitably corresponds both to some sort of fitting and to the production of residuals, though it need not necessarily involve formal criteria or well-defined computations.

Recognition of the iterative character of the relationship of exposing and summarizing makes it clear that there is usually much value in fitting, even if what is fitted is neither believed nor satisfactorily close.

4. Using Residuals Effectively

When the fit has a sufficiently arithmetic character, there is a natural way to express what the fit has not described. Additive residuals defined by

observation = fit + residual

are widely used.

There are exceptions to the use of additive residuals. Multiplicative residuals or residual factors defined by

observation = (fit) × (residual factor)

are sometimes useful, but are usually easily reduced to additive residuals by the taking of logarithms.

In other circumstances, it may be appropriate to express residuals in still other ways.

One of the truly incisive tools of exposure is the computation and adequate examination of residuals. Perhaps because of the blinding effects of unrealistic optimism about assumptions, perhaps because of the difficulties of computational practice during the era before modern computing evolved, residuals have not received the attention and use they richly deserve.

There is no substitute for examining the collection of detailed individual residuals in diverse ways. It is almost always a sad inadequacy (though far better than nothing) to try to summarize the exposing information in a body of residuals by a mean square error. Even the computation of the individual residuals and their examination as an unstructured mass is not enough. Several graphs of residuals are usually in order. Calculation of suitable numerical summaries, which answer specific questions more stringently but more general questions hardly at all, can also be useful.[2,3]

Kinds of plots of residuals that are very often valuable include: (i) plots against fitted, or possible values; (ii) plots against variables which have been employed as a basis for the summarizing fit; (iii) plots against variables which were not used in the fit, e.g., time; (iv) plots which display residuals identified according to some meaningful characteristic, e.g., according to whether the residual is or is not from an observation which was used in developing the fitted summary; (v) probability plots of ordered residuals, including empirical cumulative distribution plots and plots of empirical quantiles against quantiles of reference distributions, such as the unit normal. While all such plots provide indications of the spread of the body of residuals, it is far more important that they combine palatable summaries of individual residuals with sensitive indications of distributional peculiarities of the entire collection of residuals.[4]

Residuals may fail to reveal deficiencies of a summarizing model when these are too varied and general, or when the data points are few in number or badly distributed.

An example of this is the behavior of residuals from an additive fit in a two-way classification table, where the effects of the two outliers can combine[5] to conceal any obvious peculiarities, so long as the individual residuals are examined as an unstructured set of numbers (although more subtle examination may succeed in identifying them). It is not difficult to visualize similar happenings in fitting straight lines and the like.

5. The Strategy of Data Analysis

In addition to the two-pronged use of summarization and exposure, including careful attention to residuals, three of the main strategies of data analysis are:

 i) graphical presentation,
ii) provision of flexibility in viewpoint and in facilities, and
iii) intensive search for parsimony and simplicity, including careful reformation of variables and bending the data to fit simple techniques.

Some people are apparently able to absorb broad information from tables of numbers.[6] Most of us can only appreciate matters with full insight by looking at graphical representations. For large scale data analysis, there is really no alternative to plotting techniques, properly exploited. A picture is not merely worth a thousand words, it is much more likely to be scrutinized than words are to be read. Wisely used, graphical representation can be extremely effective in making large amounts of certain kinds of numerical information rapidly available to people.

Another major weapon in the strategy of data analysis is flexibility in viewpoint and in facilities, which must be built into both the general technology and the individual techniques. In particular we must have flexibility, not only of the choice of a model for summarization, but also in the selection of the data to be employed in computing the summary, as well as in choosing the fitting procedures to be used and the terms in which the variables are to be expressed. Here, as we shall reiterate in connection with individual topics, flexibility in assembly and reassembly of techniques is crucial.

Using human judgment in selection of parts of the data for analysis, or in cleaning up the data by partial or complete suppression of apparently aberrant values is natural, sensible, and essential. Data is often dirty. Unless the dirt is either removed or decolorized, it can hide much that we would like to learn.

Just because values have been suppressed in fitting is no reason for their residuals from the fit to be forgotten. Not every suppression will have suppressed mere dirt. Some will have suppressed clean data, others will have suppressed diamonds.

The importance of parsimony in data analysis can hardly be overstated. By parsimony we mean *both* the use of few numerical constants and *also* the avoidance of undue complexity of form in summarizing and displaying. The need for parsimony is both esthetic and practical.

In general, parsimony and simplicity will be achieved in the summary description either at the price of inadequacy of description or at the price of complexity in the model or in the analysis. Typically those who insist on doing only primitive analyses must often be satisfied with complex—not parsimonious—summaries which often miss important points.

One further aspect of great strategic importance in data analysis involves the transformation, better called reformation, of variables. Especially insightful choices of modes of expression underlie much of physical science. Changing from raw values to their square roots or logarithms before the data is analyzed is often astonishingly effective. Equally important is the evolution and use of techniques of analysis by which the data itself may be employed to indicate useful transformations.

It is almost always easier, and usually better, to "unbend" data to fit known analysis techniques than to bend the techniques to fit the data.

6. Fitting, the Workhorse of Data Analysis, Has Varied Objectives

The single most important process of data analysis is fitting. It is helpful in summarizing, exposing, and communicating. Each fit (i) gives a summary description; (ii) provides a basis for exposure based on the residuals; and (iii) may have the parsimony needed for effective communication.

Fitting inevitably raises questions concerning classes of models to be used, selection of criteria of fit, choices of mode of expression for observations, as well as questions of numerical and logical algorithms. The answers to all these questions depend upon the diversity of the objectives of fitting, their character, and the differences amongst them.

These objectives include:

1) Pure description, in the sense of drawing, possibly hastily, a curve across the page and saying y appears to depend on x just about this way. If this is our only aim, we do want the curve to fit well, but we do not care at all whether its functional form is more than an accident. Finding, for instance, that a cubic polynomial fits our data well enough is not, at this level, to be thought of as giving any particular support for a cubic "law."

2) Local prediction, in the sense that, so long as the situation "remains the same," we should like to do well by substituting x's into the fit and regarding the result as predicting the value of y.

3) Global prediction of local change, in the sense that we can use our fit to assess the result (averaged over fluctuations) of changing one or more x's moderately, even when both the start and the finish of this change are far from the circumstances for which the fit was developed. If this is to be accomplished successfully, the general situation must be favorable, and theory, or insight, or broad experience must have been responsible for choosing the form of the fit and the nature of the y-variables; the data before us can rarely be used to narrow things down enough to provide such good prediction, even of changes, elsewhere.

4) Global prediction of values, in the sense that we can use our fit to predict y given x far outside the range of the data on which it was based. Reliance upon outside information (including insight) is now even greater, and the chances of success are correspondingly diminished.

5) Using a fit depending on several mathematical variables (some of which may be functions of the same physical variable) to tell us which variables have influences and which do not (which can include telling us about the forms of the dependencies). This is sometimes possible, but nowhere nearly as often as is commonly hoped. Very frequently several alternative sets of variables will each give a satisfactory fit.

6) Using the fit to estimate values having the general character of physical constants. Both a careful description of what is to be varied and what is to be held constant are essential before there is any hope of doing this effectively. "Heat capacity," for example, is not an adequate name. Heat capacity at constant volume differs substantially, both in meaning and value, from heat capacity at constant pressure. In most circumstances, indeed, constants to be assessed are not even as simply defined as heat capacity, rather they are only defined in terms of specific, rather complex functional forms.

These six objectives are centered on what has been fitted rather than on the other essential ingredient of fitting, what remains after the fit. We need to give equal attention to the varieties of use of residuals. They have two quite distinct sorts of uses. Residuals can be used as an immediate basis for further summarization, as in:

1) Providing adjusted values for further study, as when economic series are seasonally adjusted, or when the analysis of covariance is applied.

2) Providing a basis for immediate further fitting, as when residuals from an eye-fitted straight line are fitted by either a further straight line or a quadratic. (So-called stepwise regression procedures operate in this general way, though they tend, perhaps too frequently, to omit the calculation of actual residuals.)

The more usual objectives for residuals are equally vital. They emphasize exposure, and include:

1) Examining and exposing with a view to learning about the inadequacy of the fit.

2) Examining and exposing with a view to identifying "peculiar values" either for study in their own right or for suppression, partial or complete, from further analysis.

We need not assess the relative value and frequency of these specific objectives of fitting—the real need is to identify and distinguish the varied objectives (of which these ten are not all), to recognize their diversity, their tendency to occur one or a few at a time, and the consequent great variety of different demands that are made, both upon the fitting process itself and upon such associated procedures as plotting of residuals. No one fitting-and-residuals procedure can serve all our purposes.

7. Reexpressing Variables

When is one expression better than another *for analysis*? Basically, when the data are more simply described, since this implies easier and more familiar manipulations during analysis and, even more to the point, easier and more thorough understanding of the results.

The usual goals of better expression include:

1) additivity of effects,
2) constancy of variance,
3) normality (Gaussianity) of distribution,
4) linearity of relationship.

Widespread and clear understanding of the relative desirability among the first three goals has been impeded by a happy fact—one that only appears accidental: All three tend to come together. In the rarer instances where a choice has to be made among these three, additivity is to be preferred above all, with constancy of variance second. Indeed, the importance and naturalness of additivity is so great that it now serves[7] as the base for a second kind of fundamental measurement, conjoint measurement.

Some ways of seeking out desirable expressions are:

1) explicit trial of various alternatives, whose evaluation is usually best done in terms of corresponding residuals.[3,8]
2) use of numerical guides to the next choice.[2,3]
3) use of computer iteration to seek that monotone change of expression which produces the greatest amount of additivity.[9]

The gains from reforming individual variables by reexpressing them are likely to be substantial. More major gains come from such efforts than from any other data-analytic step.

8. Scaling in Data Analysis

Even starting with a weak measure of similarity and dissimilarity, we may be able to define interesting and useful variables by "scaling."

The basic idea is to convert measures of dissimilarity into measures of "distance" by some specific rule, and then seek point systems, in some suitable metric space (often a Euclidean space of an appropriate number of dimensions), whose distances would mimic these "distances." It was converted into a tool of practical importance by the work of Shepard[10,11,12] and Kruskal,[13,14] who pioneered the use of an arbitrary relation, obtained by computer iteration, between dissimilarity and "distance."

A guide to a variety of other structures for "scaling" has been provided by Coombs[15] and Torgersen.[16]

9. New Linear Combinations for Old

Much more needs to be said than there is space to say here about objectives and techniques when linearly combining given expressions of given variables into new variables. We can only summarize some of the important aspects of unbending the data.

The computations classically used for calculating canonical correlation coefficients and canonical variates can be used in much more general situations to provide an ordered family of linear combinations of the original working variables, guided by the ability of initial subsets of this family to describe, through linear regression, the behavior of one or more guide variables.

Orthogonalization, exact or approximate, often avoids computational difficulties. In particular, orthogonal polynomials, in other than the usual order, may be useful.

Rotation of an initial coordinate system to a more useful position can be helpful, but automatic rotation[17] requires quite explicit information about the advantages and disadvantages of specific choices in order to be useful.

Procedures of stepwise, screening or "steered" regression[18,19,20] cannot be expected to be perfect, if perfection means always reaching the "best" subset.

They may often be useful, particularly if the uncertainties and inadequacies of the objectives and the results are clearly recognized.

10. General Considerations in Graphical Presentation

Graphical presentation appears to be at the very heart of insightful data analysis. For most people, graphs convey more of a message than tables and do so more persuasively and attractively. Graphical presentation continues to hold its pre-eminent place despite feeble understanding of the reasons for its power and appeal and severe limitations on the variety and character of its techniques, the latter stemming both from past technological limitations and from continuing inadequacies of imagination. Why?

Some reasons are easily found: Graphical displays can be very flexible. The human eye and brain are speedy and proficient in recognizing certain types of geometric configurations. "Smoothness" seems to be very much a geometric concept. The eye seems much more able to comprehend nonunderstood graphs than nonunderstood numbers. Quite large volumes of data can be displayed economically and comprehensibly. And the same graph can transfer effectively either a very compressed summary or an extensive amount of detail, as well as many intermediate packages of information.

Before we discuss some of these reasons in more detail, one key point must be made. While it is often most helpful to "plot the data," this is rarely enough. We need also to "plot the results of analysis" as a routine matter. (There is often more analysis than there was data.)

The innate flexibility of graphical displays is many-sided. It is not merely that we can choose to do many different things graphically. If one expects (or only contemplates the possibility) that y is approximately linear in x, a simple plot will confirm this when it is so and be even more instructive when it is not. If one has no clear anticipation, the same simple plot is likely to reveal whichever one of many alternative structures appears to be present, even though these structures are nowhere collected in a list.

A scatter diagram with 100 or 500 points need not be more difficult to scan than one with 10 or 50. The same is often true with 1,000 or 5,000 points (possibly with 10,000 or 50,000). Tables of numbers simply cannot be expanded comparably without tremendous increases in difficulty of examination and understanding.

Almost all graphical techniques are based upon one or more natural reference situations and serve best to reveal differences between data and reference. Graphs are most effective when these reference situations, usually conceptually simple, produce simple configurations, *above all when reference situations produce straight lines*. (This has important implications about the redesign of histograms.[21])

"Smoothness" seems to be an essentially geometrical concept for which we do not yet seem to have a reasonable analytical approximation. "Smooth" extrapolation and interpolation, especially with irregularly spaced data, continues to be easier and more persuasive when conducted and exhibited graphically rather than numerically.

One great virtue of good graphical representation is that it can serve to display clearly and effectively a message carried by quantities whose calculation or observation is far from simple. Many kinds of spectra, analog and numerical, illustrate this principle. The far infrared spectrum of a complex molecule undoubtedly speaks to us, probably in a quite contorted way, about the structure of that molecule, but even in 1965 we understand little of what is said. Yet we have little difficulty in using the complex of peaks as a "fingerprint" for the organic compound. The computational procedures useful in obtaining an estimated numerical spectrum for some process appear complex. Yet the appearance of a peak in the estimated spectrum often carries a clear message to those who have not even tried to gain an understanding of the computational procedure.

This phenomenon can be even more noticeable in the cepstrum, where the ideas underlying the spectrum are twice used.[22]

11. Kinds of Two-Variable Graphs

Some of these questions are: What are the main styles of two-variable graphs? How can we classify the characteristics of what is plotted? How should these issues relate to each other and to the attitude of mind with which the graphs should be approached?

1) *Point plots*, where only isolated points appear.

2) *Linked plots*, where the individual points are both identified and linked to one another by line segments.

3) *Curve plots*, where the intent is to represent a smooth functional dependence. (The fact that automatic plotters presently use line segments to delineate curves is only a practical detail.)

4) *Comparative plots*, where individual points and a nearby curve are displayed in obvious comparison.

To these major styles we may add:

5) *Smoothed-connection plots*, which may be regarded as a modification of either (2) or (4), where individual points are displayed against a chain of links joining a smoothed sequence of points, as when running moving averages of a time series are connected up and shown together with the original points.

6) *Step plots*, in which a connected trace is made up of alternating horizontal and vertical segments, as in the most common way of presenting empirical cumulative distributions.

7) *Tick plots*, where the links of a linked plot are reduced to ticks starting out from each point. (In general, it seems likely that the ticks should be shorter

the longer the x- (or y-) spacing of the points. Consequently, the ticks corresponding to sufficiently short spacings will be so long that each pair of such ticks blends into a link.

The proper choice of plot style can often determine what one learns from a plot. The simplest important question is when, and when not, to join data points by lines.

In discussing this, it will help to distinguish among:

1) *Point clouds*, where x and y enter on an equal footing and the main message is a pattern of distribution. (Both the case "x and y original observations on (different) response variables" and the case "x and y residuals of original observations on (different) response variables" are common.)

2) *Scatter displays*, where the dependence of the behavior of y upon the value of x is the focus of the display, but there is no thought of x being "prior" to y (as would, for instance, be the case if there were a recognized and relevant logical possibility that a value of x, or something associated with this value, might "cause" some of the value of y); this sort of plot arises, for example, when y is the residual corresponding to the fitted value x (or, perhaps even better, when x is the fitted or original value of a variable observed alongside, but not prior to, the variable defining y).

3) *Progressive patterns*, where the interpretation "y is, at least in part, caused by x, or by something associated with x" is *one* interpretation that can be contemplated. Almost all time series are examples of progressive patterns.

These distinctions are important both in the appropriate choice of style of a graph and in the attitude of mind in which the graph is examined. Other features also play an important role:

1) The "character" of the available points, as expressed, for example, by the regularity of the spacings of the x-values and by the closeness of these spacings, as compared to the general behavior of the pattern.
2) The quality of the data, in the sense of reasonable anticipations concerning the presence and frequency of "outliers" or "blunders" in the observations.
3) Whether variabilities in various regions are expected to be similar.
4) Whether the statistical fluctuations associated with individual points are reasonably taken to be uncorrelated or correlated.
5) The character of these correlations where present.

12. Linking Up Points and Related Issues

If a plot represents a point cloud, it is most unlikely that linking up the points into a chain is either sensible or useful. The information sought is likely to be conveyed in terms of the general pattern and extent of the cloud.

If we have many, many points, this sort of plot should go over into some adequate display concerning the density of a two-dimensional distribution.

Possibilities include: (i) "spider-webs" in which each cell contains (approximately) the same number of points, (ii) contouring of apparent densities, and (iii) variable intensity representations, such as are used in "speech spectrograms."

For a scatter display, it is again quite unlikely that linking up into a chain is sensible and useful. What we are likely to want from a scatter display are indications of tilting, or arching up or sagging down, or of horizontal wedging.

Progressive patterns are quite a different case: there are circumstances where linking up definitely helps, and others where it is unbearable. The spacing of the x-values is now important, especially as it relates to changes in y, as is the character of the (statistical) variability of y, and, of course, the sort of attention we wish to give to the plot.

When one looks at a progressive plot, one basically intercompares wiggles of different "spacings." (Sometimes "waves" is a better word than "wiggles.") Specifically, any of the following alternatives may apply:

1) We may be interested in the "general level" of y, which is a matter of looking at wiggles or waves so long or slow that their effects do not change appreciably in the range covered by the data before us.

2) We are probably most often interested in the next smaller things: trends up, trends down, archings up and saggings down. In other words our interest is in long waves or slow wiggles, sometimes in their existence or character, and sometimes in their magnitude.

3) If the data is dense enough or stable enough to reveal them, we are also likely to be interested in phenomena at the next narrower scale of variation: in more-or-less local peaks and valleys, perhaps even in relatively sharp "lines" (that either stick up or canyon down). Any or all of their location, existence, character, or magnitude may be relevant.

4) Not infrequently, the general magnitude of the "fast" variations exhibited by the progressive pattern is a matter of considerable interest, either because this variation is thought to reflect observational error in its purest simple form (which need not be very pure) or because the magnitude of the fast variations determines either visibility or interpretation of the slower wiggles or waves.

5) The existence and character of "outliers" is often a matter of interest; however, our need is almost as often to see some other aspects of the plot without obtrusive interference from any wild points that may be present.

6) Finally, in looking at a progressive pattern, the trained eye and trained brain always receive impressions of the roughness and smoothness of the pattern, of the relative amounts of organized and disorganized structure, of the apparently preferred scales of organization. The eye and brain thus combine to do, both much more crudely and somewhat more flexibly, what a spectrum analysis of the plot might try to do.

If the spacing of the x's is close, where closeness is determined by comparison with the features that concern us, irregularity of spacing need not be very important, although it may be well to introduce equally spaced points, replacing all the points in each of a chain of intervals (of relatively equal length) by a single summary point. If, on the other hand, our x-values are sufficiently coarsely spaced, we have little chance to see the features that concern us, whether these spacings are regular or irregular. The difficult case, as always, is a transitional one, here the one where the spacing is neither very close nor very coarse.

If the x-values are quite irregular, the transitional case cannot be handled with linked plots. The misleading features of connecting line segments of widely varying lengths are subtle and treacherous. The increased visual importance of the long links that occur just where the data is weakest is a major contributor, but is probably not the only cause of confusion.

There are other situations where linking up is to be avoided. Prominent among them are these:

1) If wild points are at all common, connecting up points will almost surely lead the eye and brain to focus on these wild points to the exclusion of other features, which is often exactly what we do not want to happen. The simple cure in such a case is to use a point plot.

2) If the intensity (amplitude) of quick wiggles (short waves) is comparable to that of medium wiggles (medium waves), linking up the points tends so much to divert our attention to the quick wiggles as to be often quite misleading. Again point plots are indicated.

These last two cases are not so different in character as they seem at first sight; both correspond to rather flat spectra.

13. The Need for Various Mental Approaches

Given an appropriate plot, we still need an appropriate attitude or "set" for the brain to take toward its message. In this regard, the degree and character of correlations among the fluctuations of the various points are particularly important.

When we plot one point per experiment and each experiment involves a single prechosen value of x—the traditional plot of y against x—the fluctuations of different points are very nearly (almost by definition) independent. This is the type of progressive pattern to which most scientists and engineers are first made accustomed.

Another extreme arises when we plot empirical cumulative distributions. Here each point is dependent, often substantially, on the next point to the left, but not (except through that next point) on any points further to the left. Technically, the fluctuations form a Markov chain of first order. This also often occurs, to a good approximation, when we plot time histories, such as wear curves.

Plots showing ordered eigenvalues or canonical correlations, as well as more complicated time histories, are intrinsically more complicated, since the fluctuations of each point depend (statistically) upon the fluctuations of all other points. So far no one is used to examining progressive patterns of this third sort.

Three-variable graphs. Visual presentation of $z = f(x, y)$ is far from easy, yet badly needed. Of three classes of possibilities—contours, families of cross sections, and isometric views—the first seems, so far, most likely to be effective, though direct-interaction graphical consoles may offer other possibilities.

14. Guidance and Models

As has already been frequently stressed, data analysis cannot be effectively conducted without guidance, without some sort of model, whether implicit and vague or detailed and explicit.

1) *Data analysis has to be guided, but its guides, whether a simple faith in smoothness or knowledge of the complex consequences of assumed normality and independence, must not be taken too seriously.*

Contemplation of raw observations with an empty mind, even when it is possible, is often hardly more beneficial than not studying them at all. This fact may help to account for the fraction, regrettably substantial, of cases in which a large, carefully collected body of data is not looked at by anyone.

We have grown used to a variety of structures for description, from the simplicity of "y increases as x increases" to the complication of "y may reasonably be regarded as differing from a quadratic in x by independent errors drawn from a normal (Gaussian) distribution of such and such a variance" and beyond. All intelligent data analysis uses some of these structures, both as a guide in looking and as parts of a shopping list of what can easily be looked for.

Some of these guiding structures come from deeper theoretical understanding, as when the logarithm of the rate of reaction is related to the reciprocal of the absolute temperature. Some come from bitter experience. Others come from formal statistical study of highly formalized situations, expressed in terms of formal mathematical models. Taken at face value, such formal models can often be dangerously misleading. If we are careful, however, they can give a great deal of help provided they are used as suggestive bases for guidance, as leading cases as it were, without constraint to using only one model and with an ever-present and piercing concern with how important the actual differences between real and formal situations are to just what we are doing at the moment.

In the sense in which we here use the word "model"—a means of guidance without implication of belief or reality—all the structures that guide data analysis, however weak and nonspecific, are models even when they are not explicitly mathematical. Without them we are almost certainly lost (and surely completely primitive); were we to accept them unquestioningly we would be equally lost in a different morass; taking them as guidance we may, however, succeed in finding some of what the data conceals. As Francis Bacon so well said, "Truth arises more easily from error than from confusion."

It is not enough to have just any model. Choosing models is not entirely arbitrary; there are useful guidelines.

2) *It may be well to make some analysis neglecting what we thought we knew before we saw the data, but it is silly to make all analyses of any one body of data in this way.*

Workers in certain fields new to quantitative analysis of data tend to ask each experiment to establish anew all the foundations for its analysis. The more anciently quantitative sciences know how foolish this can be. It is *not* the same thing to show that *if* the dependence is linear then the slope *is* 2 as to show *both* that the dependence *is* linear and the slope *is* 2. To make such distinctions is essential. When, for example, there is background reason to believe that the dependence is likely to be roughly linear, it can be quite foolish not to make at least one analysis of the sort that would be highly effective if dependence were linear.

3) *Both for guidance and the encouragement of exploration, it is most desirable that models be loose and noncommittal.*

Definiteness in detailing objectives and assumptions in a single formal model can simplify the mathematical problems and increase the simplicity and impact of the results thus reached but usually at a price far more than we can afford. Although both mathematical convenience and feasibility and clarity of results are desirable in themselves, tightness of detailed specification usually amounts to cloistering the formal model far away from the realities of the data-gathering situation and cloistering our attention away from possibly important phenomena.

Moreover, the price is often unnecessary; looser structures can often do as well in simplicity and clarity of results while retaining robustness and breadth.

For example, the forcible prespecification of those contrasts in a 2^n factorial experiment which are to provide "the error" has been traditional and common. Contrast the rigidities and dangers of such an approach with the flexibilities and the possibilities of learning about other surprises when the same experiment is analyzed graphically through a half-normal plot.[1]

Our models and procedures need to provide a backdrop for viewing "reality" such that unanticipated as well as anticipated features may be displayed.

4) *Using models to analyze data is different from using data to evaluate models.*

Asking questions concerning the adequacy of a model and trying to answer these by the use of data may be interesting and even valuable. But that orientation and attitude often leads one far from techniques which help to reveal informational content of the data. For data analysis, models and techniques are to be thought of and developed as assisting tools—the focus needs to be on the data. The models need not fit perfectly or even adequately to prove usefully insightful. Moreover, we must never believe so deeply in any model as to constrain our insight.

Thus, for example, although the use of half-normal plotting in analysis of 2^n experiments was suggested by the model of equally distributed normal errors, of simple factorial effects, and the "null" hypothesis that these effects vanish, this plot simply uses these assumptions to provide a "backdrop" for exposure. The plot remains both descriptive and instructive in most circumstances when the assumptions fail, even badly. Indeed, the plot itself will often indicate or reveal the inappropriateness of the assumptions. By contrast, methods of analysis based on single numbers (e.g., t or F ratios) and developed to evaluate similarly narrow null hypotheses under similar assumptions could at best yield very little information about any of the aspects of the data that become important when this model fails.

15. Brief Comments about Some Classical Statistical Procedures

Various views and interpretations of classical statistical procedures exist. Actual uses of these procedures, whether by the applied statistician or by the investigator, often bear little resemblance to their textbook descriptions, sometimes without the user explicitly appreciating the gap.

Generally speaking, conventional descriptions and justifications of statistical procedures, such as multiple linear regression analysis, goodness-of-fit procedures, and many procedures of multivariate analysis, have been largely addressed to summarization and confirmation, with virtually no attention to exposure and perhaps minor attention to description. Even in connection with summarization and confirmation, the procedures are presented in terms of very limited, highly formalized, tightly specified models, typically with objectives which, if taken literally and in the indicated frame of reference, are very artificial.

In actual practice, many of these same classical statistical procedures are employed for purposes that are quite productive as data analysis, but very distinct from those customarily used to derive and justify them. A few examples are briefly discussed below.

Multiple linear regression is commonly presented as a means of estimating regression coefficients and/or demonstrating patterns of dependence via hypothesis testing. In fact, the values of coefficients in linear regression models are rather infrequently of interest as such. Typically, multiple linear regression is useful as a generator of residuals and as providing empirical description and summarization.

Analysis of variance is usually presented as a means of testing (rather artificial) null hypotheses of equivalence of treatment factors or effects, in certain sorts of balanced data arrays obtained from experiment. In practical data analysis, the leading value of the analysis of variance table would seem to be as a summary description of patterns of data variability in relation to physically meaningful classifications. The additive decomposition of each individual value into "grand mean" plus one or more "main effects" plus "interactions" of various orders that underlies the calculations of the analysis of variance has many important uses. It can lead us to consider the character, as well as overall size, of effects and interactions. Through analysis of individual residuals (a process not mentioned in most formal presentations of analysis of variance techniques), this decomposition can provide a basis for exposing its own inadequacies, and hence the inadequacy of conventional analysis of variance (as when a few scattered cells behave quite differently from all the others).

Most multivariate analysis procedures are related, in typical textbooks, to problems of hypothesis testing, usually in a quite artificial framework, as for instance in so-called multivariate analysis of variance. Such procedures and purposes provide almost no help whatever in data analysis, though closely related techniques, such as canonical analysis, discriminant analysis, and principal components analysis, are sometimes of considerable use. Some data analytic, graphically oriented procedures for certain multivariable data have been suggested by Wilk and Gnanadesikan.[23,24]

Description of a body of unstructured data by use of moments, histograms, empirical cumulative distributions, probability (quantile) plots, or the fitting of some theoretical distribution is largely bypassed in recent texts on statistical methods. Yet this problem is basic, challenging, and pervasive, since it would appear that almost every procedure of data analysis eventually yields a body of "data" for which one wishes to assess whether its behavior may reasonably be regarded as similar to that of an unstructured sample. Thus one wishes to have both a summary description based on the unstructured viewpoint and a means of exposing inadequacies in that summary. For this, as for many other purposes, the techniques of probability (quantile) plotting and of empirical cumulative distribution plotting are well suited[4] but the informality of their philosophy and the breadth of their uses and objectives seem to have prevented adequate recognition of their value.

Spectrum analysis generalizes the analysis of variability to situations where sinusoidal functions of time may be important, as is always the case when processes or media are (at least approximately) linear and unchanging, and thus have the twin properties of superposability and independence of time origin. As an adjunct to other techniques of time series analysis, the spectrum and related procedures, especially those involving cross-spectra, have been useful both in description and exposure. Perhaps by a happy accident of mathematical complexity, spectrum analysis techniques have not received great emphasis in terms of hypothesis testing or even specific parameter estimation.

Goodness-of-fit procedures given in textbooks, such as the chi-squared test, are largely directed toward producing a single number as a basis for a prescribed judgment on a hypothesis via probability distribution tables. To depend on a single number is, inevitably and in principle, inadequate. The real world requires that evaluation of goodness of fit include an exposing presentation which gives some insight into the character and nature of the departure from fit.

As far as numerically carrying out classical statistical procedures goes, little has been done, until very recently indeed,[25] to attempt to recognize the common arithmetic and logical operations which underlie a great many of the techniques, and which may serve as the lowest-level functional components in a more organized approach to data analysis. Such recognition is desirable for efficiency but, even more, is necessary in order to use these statistical methods with a flexibility and breadth which is required in practice, but toward which textbook presentations have failed to guide us.

ACKNOWLEDGMENT

Prepared in part in connection with research at Princeton University sponsored by the Army Research Office (Durham). Reproduction for any purpose of the U.S. Government is encouraged.

We should like to thank G. A. Barnard, D. R. Cox, R. Gnanadesikan, C. L. Mallows, H. O. Pollak, and D. L. Wallace for their useful comments on earlier drafts of the paper, about half of whose sections appear here.

REFERENCES

1. Daniel, Cuthbert (1959). Use of half-normal plots in interpreting factorial two-level experiments. Technometrics *1*:311–342.

2. Box, G. E. P., and D. R. Cox (1964). An analysis of transformations. J. Roy. Stat. Soc. *26*:211–243.

3. Anscombe, F. J., and J. W. Tukey (1963). The examination and analysis of residuals. Technometrics *5*:141–160.

4. Wilk, M. B., and R. Gnanadesikan (1966). Probability plotting methods for the analysis of data. Unpublished manuscript.

5. Munk, Jane F., and M. B. Wilk (1966). Detecting outliers in a two-way table. Unpublished manuscript.

6. Pearson, E. S. (1956). Some aspects of the geometry of statistics: the use of visual presentation in understanding the theory and application of mathematical statistics. J. Roy. Stat. Soc. (A) *119*:125–149.

7. Luce, R. Duncan, and John W. Tukey (1964). Simultaneous conjoint measurement: a new type of fundamental measurement. J. Math. Psych. *1*:1–27.

8. Moore, Peter G., and John W. Tukey (1954). Answer to Query 112. Biometrika *10*:562–568.

9. Kruskal, J. B. (1965). Analysis of factorial experiments by estimating monotone transformations of the data. J. Roy. Stat. Soc. (B):251–263.

10. Shepard, R. N. (1962a). The analysis of proximities: multidimensional scaling with an unknown distance function. I. Psychometrika *29*:125–140.

11. Shepard, R. N. (1962b). The analysis of proximities: multidimensional scaling with an unknown distance function. II. Psychometrika *29*:219–246.

12. Shepard, R. N. (1963). Analysis of proximities as a technique for the study of information processing in man. Human Factors *5*:33–48.

13. Kruskal, J. B. (1964a). Multidimensional scaling by optimizing goodness of fit to a non-metric hypothesis. Psychometrika *29*:1–27.

14. Kruskal, J. B. (1964b). Non-metric multidimensional scaling: a numerical method. Psychometrika *29*:115–129.

15. Coombs, Clyde C. (1964). A Theory of Data. John Wiley and Sons, New York.

16. Torgersen, Warren S. (1958). Theory and Methods of Scaling. John Wiley and Sons, New York.

17. Harman, Harry H. (1960). Modern Factor Analysis. University of Chicago Press, Chicago, Illinois.

18. Efroymson, M. A. (1960). Multiple regression analysis. *In* Mathematical Models for Digital Computers (A. Ralson and H. S. Wilf, Eds.), pp. 191–203. John Wiley and Sons, New York.

19. Miller, R. G. (1962). Statistical prediction by discriminant analysis. Meteorological Monographs (Boston, American Meteorological Society) *4*, 25. 54 pp.

20. MacDonald, N. J., and F. Ward (1963). The prediction of geomagnetic disturbance indices: 1. the elimination of internally predictable variations. J. Geophys. Res. *68*:3351–3373.

21. Tukey, John W. (1965). The future of processes of data analysis. Proceedings of the 10th Conference on the Design of Experiments in Army Research, Development, and Testing, pp. 691–729. U.S. Army Research Office, Durham.

22. Noll, A. M. (1964). Short-time spectrum and "cepstrum" techniques for vocal pitch detection. J. Acoustical Soc. Amer. *36*:298–302.

23. Wilk, M. B., and R. Gnanadesikan (1961). Graphical analysis of multiresponse experimental data using ordered distances. Proc. Nat. Acad. Sci. U.S.A. *47*:1209–1212.

24. Wilk, M. B., and R. Gnanadesikan (1964). Graphical methods for internal comparisons in multiresponse experiments. Ann. Math. Statistics *35*:613–631.

25. Beaton, A. G. (1964). The use of special matrix operations in statistical calculus. Ed. D. Thesis, Grad. School of Education, Harvard Univ.

SOME STATISTICAL PROBLEMS
IN RESEARCH DESIGN*

LESLIE KISH

Statistical inference is an important aspect of scientific inference. The statistical consultant spends much of his time in the borderland between statistics and the other aspects, philosophical and substantive, of the scientific search for explanation. This marginal life is rich both in direct experience and in discussions of fundamentals; these have stimulated my concern with the problems treated here.

I intend to touch on several problems dealing with the interplay of statistics with the more general problems of scientific inference. We can spare elaborate introductions because these problems are well known. Why then discuss them here at all? We do so because, first, they are problems about which there is a great deal of misunderstanding, evident in current research; and, second, they are *statistical* problems on which there is broad agreement among research statisticians—and on which these statisticians generally disagree with much in the current practice of research scientists.[1]

Several problems will be considered briefly, hence incompletely. The aim of this paper is not a profound analysis, but a clear elementary treatment of several related problems. The notes contain references to more thorough treatments. Moreover, these are not *all* the problems in this area, nor even necessarily the most important ones; the reader may find that his favorite, his most annoying problem, has been omitted. The problems selected are a group with a common core, they arise frequently, yet they are widely misunderstood.

Statistical Tests of Survey Data

That correlation does not prove causation is hardly news. Perhaps the wittiest statements on this point are in George Bernard Shaw's preface to *The Doctor's Dilemma*, in the sections on "Statistical Illusions," "The Surprises of Attention and Neglect," "Stealing Credit from Civilization," and "Biometrika." (These attack, alas, the practice of vaccination.) The excellent introductory textbook by Yule and Kendall[2] deals in three separate chapters with the problems of advancing from correlation to causation. Searching for causal factors among survey data is an old, useful sport; and the attempts to separate true explanatory

Reprinted by permission of the author and the American Sociological Association from *American Sociological Review* 24 (June, 1959), 328–338.

variables from extraneous and "spurious" correlations have taxed scientists since antiquity and will undoubtedly continue to do so. Neyman and Simon[3] show that beyond common sense, there are some technical skills involved in tracking down spurious correlations. Econometricians and geneticists have developed great interest and skill in the problems of separating the explanatory variables.[4]

The researcher designates the explanatory variables on the basis of substantive scientific theories. He recognizes the evidence of other *sources of variation* and he needs to separate these from the explanatory variables. Sorting all sources of variation into four classes seems to me a useful simplification. Furthermore, no confusion need result from talking about sorting and treating "variables," instead of "sources of variation."

I. The *explanatory* variables, sometimes called the "experimental" variables, are the objects of the research. They are the variables among which the researcher wishes to find and to measure some specified relationships. They include both the "dependent" and the "independent" variables, that is, the "predictand" and "predictor" variables.[5] With respect to the aims of the research all other variables, of which there are three classes, are extraneous.

II. There are extraneous variables which are *controlled*. The control may be exercised in either or both the selection and the estimation procedures.

III. There may exist extraneous uncontrolled variables which are *confounded* with the Class I variables.

IV. There are extraneous uncontrolled variables which are treated as *randomized* errors. In "ideal" experiments (discussed below) they are actually randomized; in surveys and investigations they are only assumed to be randomized. Randomization may be regarded as a substitute for experimental control or as a form of control.

The aim of efficient design both in experiments and in surveys is to place as many of the extraneous variables as is feasible into the second class. The aim of randomization in experiments is to place all of the third class into the fourth class; in the "ideal" experiment there are no variables in the third class. And it is the aim of controls of various kinds in surveys to separate variables of the third class from those of the first class; these controls may involve the use of repeated cross-tabulations, regression, standardization, matching of units, and so on.

The function of statistical "tests of significance" is to test the effects found among the Class I variables against the effects of the variables of Class IV. An "ideal" experiment here denotes an experiment for which this can be done through randomization without any possible confusion with Class III variables. (The difficulties of reaching this "ideal" are discussed below.) In survey results,

Class III variables are confounded with those of Class I; the statistical tests actually contrast the effects of the random variables of Class IV against the explanatory variables of Class I confounded with unknown effects of Class III variables. In both the ideal experiment and in surveys the statistical tests serve to separate the effects of the random errors of Class IV from the effects of other variables. These, in surveys, are a mixture of explanatory and confounded variables; their separation poses severe problems for logic and for scientific methods; statistics is only one of the tools in this endeavor. The scientist must make many decisions as to which variables are extraneous to his objectives, which should and can be controlled, and what methods of control he should use. He must decide where and how to introduce statistical tests of hypotheses into the analysis.

As a simple example, suppose that from a probability sample survey of adults of the United States we find that the level of political interest is higher in urban than in rural areas. A test of significance will show whether or not the difference in the "levels" is large enough, compared with the sampling error of the difference, to be considered "significant." Better still, the confidence interval of the difference will disclose the limits within which we can expect the "true" population value of the difference to lie.[6] If families had been sent to urban and rural areas respectively, after the randomization of a true experiment, then the sampling error would measure the effects of Class IV variables against the effects of urban *versus* rural residence on political interest; the difference in levels beyond sampling errors could be ascribed (with specified probability) to the effects of urban *versus* rural residence.

Actually, however, residences are not assigned at random. Hence, in survey results, Class III variables may account for some of the difference. If the test of significance rejects the null hypothesis of no difference, *several* hypotheses remain in addition to that of a simple relationship between urban *versus* rural residence and political interest. Could differences in income, in occupation, or in family life cycle account for the difference in the levels? The analyst may try to remove (for example, through cross-tabulation, regression, standardization) the effects due to such variables, which are extraneous to his expressed interest; then he computes the difference, between the urban and rural residents, of the levels of interest now free of several confounding variables. This can be followed by a proper test of significance—or, preferably, by some other form of statistical inference, such as a statement of confidence intervals.

Of course, other variables of Class III may remain to confound the measured relationship between residence and political interest. The separation of Class I from Class III variables should be determined in accord with the nature of the hypothesis with which the researcher is concerned; finding and measuring the effects of confounding variables of Class III tax the ingenuity of research scientists. But this separation is beyond the functions and capacities of the statistical tests, the tests of null hypotheses. Their function is not explanation; they cannot point to causation. Their function is to ask: "Is there anything in the data that *needs* explaining?"—and to answer this question with a certain probability.

Agreement on these ideas can eliminate certain confusion, exemplified by Selvin in a recent article:

■ Statistical tests are unsatisfactory in nonexperimental research for two fundamental reasons: it is almost impossible to design studies that meet the conditions for using the tests, and the situations in which the tests are employed make it difficult to draw correct inferences. The basic difficulty in design is that sociologists are unable to randomize their uncontrolled variables, so that the difference between "experimental" and "control" groups (or their analogs in nonexperimental situations) are a mixture of the effects of the variable being studied and the uncontrolled variables or correlated biases. Since there is no way of knowing, in general, the sizes of these correlated biases and their directions, there is no point in asking for the probability that the observed differences could have been produced by random errors. The place for significance tests is after all relevant correlated biases have been controlled. . . . In design and in interpretation, in principle and in practice, tests of statistical significance are inapplicable in nonexperimental research.[7] ■

Now it is true that in survey results the explanatory variables of Class I are confounded with variables of Class III; but it does not follow that tests of significance should not be used to separate the random variables of Class IV. Insofar as the effects found "are a mixture of the effects of the variable being studied and the uncontrolled variables;" insofar as "there is no way of knowing, in general, the sizes" and directions of these uncontrolled variables, Selvin's logic and advice should lead not only to the rejection of statistical tests; it should lead one to refrain altogether from using survey results for the purposes of finding explanatory variables. *In this sense*, not only tests of significance but any comparisons, any scientific inquiry based on surveys, any scientific inquiry other than an "ideal" experiment, is "inapplicable." That advice is most unrealistic. In the (unlikely) event of its being followed, it would sterilize social research—and other nonexperimental research as well.

Actually, much research—in the social, biological, and physical sciences—must be based on nonexperimental methods. In such cases the rejection of the null hypothesis leads to several alternate hypotheses that may explain the discovered relationships. It is the duty of scientists to search, with painstaking effort and with ingenuity, for bases on which to decide among these hypotheses.

As for Selvin's advice to refrain from making tests of significance until "after all relevant" uncontrolled variables have been controlled—this seems rather farfetched to scientists engaged in empirical work who consider themselves lucky if they can explain 25 or 50 per cent of the total variance. The control of all relevant variables is a goal seldom even approached in practice. To postpone to that distant goal all statistical tests illustrates that often "the perfect is the enemy of the good."[8]

Experiments, Surveys, and Other Investigations

Until now, the theory of sample surveys has been developed chiefly to provide descriptive statistics—especially estimates of means, proportions, and totals. On the other hand, experimental designs have been used primarily to find explanatory variables in the analytical search of data. In many fields, however, including the social sciences, survey data must be used frequently as the analytical tools in the search for explanatory variables. Furthermore, in some research situations, neither experiments nor sample surveys are practical, and other investigations are utilized.

By "experiments" I mean here "ideal" experiments in which all the extraneous variables have been randomized. By "surveys" (or "sample surveys"), I mean probability samples in which all members of a defined population have a known positive probability of selection into the sample. By "investigations" (or "other investigations"), I mean the collection of data—perhaps with care, and even with considerable control—without either the randomization of experiments or the probability sampling of surveys. The differences among experiments, surveys, and investigations are not the consequences of statistical techniques; they result from different methods for introducing the variables and for selecting the population elements (subjects). These problems are ably treated in recent articles by Wold and Campbell.[9]

In considering the larger ends of any scientific research, only part of the total means required for inference can be brought under objective and firm control; another part must be left to more or less vague and subjective—however skillful—judgment. The scientist seeks to maximize the first part, and thus to minimize the second. In assessing the ends, the costs, and the feasible means, he makes a strategic choice of methods. He is faced with the three basic problems of scientific research: measurement, representation, and control. We ignore here the important but vast problems of measurement and deal with representation and control.

Experiments are strong on control through randomization; but they are weak on representation (and sometimes on the "naturalism" of measurement). Surveys are strong on representation, but they are often weak on control. Investigations are weak on control and often on representation; their use is due frequently to convenience or low cost and sometimes to the need for measurements in "natural settings."

Experiments have three chief advantages:
(1) Through randomization of extraneous variables the confounding variables (Class III) are eliminated. (2) Control over the introduction and variation of the "predictor" variables clarifies the *direction* of causation from "predictor" to "predictand" variables. In contrast, in the correlations of many surveys this direction is not clear—for example, between some behaviors and correlated attitudes. (3) The modern design of experiments allows for great flexibility, efficiency, and powerful statistical manipulation, whereas the analytical use of survey data presents special statistical problems.[10]

The advantages of the experimental method are so well known that we need not dwell on them here. It is the scientific method *par excellence*—when feasible. In many situations experiments are not feasible and this is often the case in the social sciences; but it is a mistake to use this situation to separate the social from the physical and biological sciences. Such situations also occur frequently in the physical sciences (in meteorology, astronomy, geology), the biological sciences, medicine, and elsewhere.

The experimental method also has some shortcomings. First, it is often difficult to choose the "control" variables so as to exclude *all* the confounding extraneous variables; that is, it may be difficult or impossible to design an "ideal" experiment. Consider the following examples: The problem of finding a proper control for testing the effects of the Salk polio vaccine led to the use of an adequate "placebo." The Hawthorne experiment demonstrated that the design of a proposed "treatment *versus* control" may turn out to be largely a test of *any* treatment *versus lack* of treatment.[11] Many of the initial successes reported about mental therapy, which later turn into vain hopes, may be due to the hopeful effects of *any* new treatment in contrast with the background of neglect. Shaw, in "The Surprises of Attention and Neglect" writes: "Not until attention has been effectually substituted for neglect as a general rule, will the statistics begin to show the merits of the particular methods of attention adopted."

There is an old joke about the man who drank too much on four different occasions, respectively, of scotch and soda, bourbon and soda, rum and soda, and wine and soda. Because he suffered painful effects on all four occasions, he ascribed, with scientific logic, the common effect to the common cause: "I'll never touch soda again!" Now, to a man (say, from Outer Space) ignorant of the common alcoholic content of the four "treatments" and of the relative physiological effects of alcohol and carbonated water, the subject is not fit for joking, but for further scientific investigation.

Thus, the advantages of experiments over surveys in permitting better control are only relative, not absolute.[12] The design of proper experimental controls is not automatic; it is an art requiring scientific knowledge, foresight in planning the experiment, and hindsight in interpreting the results. Nevertheless, the distinction in control between experiments and surveys is real and considerable; and to emphasize this distinction we refer here to "ideal" experiments in which the control of the random variables is complete.

Second, it is generally difficult to design experiments so as to represent a specified important population. In fact, the questions of sampling, of making the experimental results representative of a specified population, have been largely ignored in experimental design until recently. Both in theory and in practice, experimental research has often neglected the basic truth that causal systems, the distributions of relations—like the distributions of characteristics—exist only within specified universes. The distributions of relationships, as of characteristics, exist only within the framework of specific populations. Probability distributions, like all mathematical models, are abstract systems; their application to the physical world must include the specification of the populations. For example, it is generally accepted that the statement of a value for mean income has meaning only with reference to a specified population; but this is not generally and clearly recognized in the case of regression of assets on income and occupation. Similarly, the *statistical* inferences derived from the experimental testing of several treatments are restricted to the population(s) included in the experimental design.[13] The clarification of the population sampling aspects of experiments is now being tackled vigorously by Wilk and Kempthorne and by Cornfield and Tukey.[14]

Third, for many research aims, especially in the social sciences, contriving the desired "natural setting" for the measurements is not feasible in experimental design. Hence, what social experiments give sometimes are clear answers to questions the meanings of which are vague. That is, the artificially contrived experimental variables *may* have but a tenuous relationship to the variables the researcher would like to investigate.

The second and third weaknesses of experiments point to the advantages of surveys. Not only do probability samples permit clear statistical inferences to defined populations, but the measurements can often be made in the "natural settings" of actual populations. Thus in practical research situations the experimental method, like the survey method, has its distinct problems and drawbacks as well as its advantages. In practice one generally cannot solve simultaneously all of the problems of measurement, representation, and control; rather, one must choose and compromise. In any specific situation one method may be better or more practical than the other; but there is no over-all superiority in all situations for either method. Understanding the advantages and weaknesses of both methods should lead to better choices.

In social research, in preference to both surveys and experiments, frequently some design of controlled investigation is chosen—for reasons of cost or of feasibility or to preserve the "natural setting" of the measurements. Ingenious adaptations of experimental designs have been contrived for these controlled investigations. The statistical framework and analysis of experimental designs are used, but not the randomization of true experiments. These designs are aimed to provide flexibility, efficiency, and, especially, some control over the extraneous variables. They have often been used to improve considerably research with controlled investigations.

These designs are sometimes called "natural experiments." For the sake of clarity, however, it is important to keep clear the distinctions among the methods and to reserve the word "experiment" for designs in which the uncontrolled variables are randomized. This principle is stated clearly by Fisher,[15] and is accepted often in scientific research. Confusion is caused by the use of terms like "ex post facto experiments" to describe surveys or designs of controlled investigations. Sample surveys and controlled investigations have their own justifications, their own virtues; they are not just second-class experiments. I deplore the borrowing of the prestige word "experiment," when it cloaks the use of other methods.

Experiments, surveys, and investigations can all be improved by efforts to overcome their weaknesses. Because the chief weakness of surveys is their low degree of control, researchers should be alert to the collection and use of auxiliary information as controls against confounding variables. They also should take greater advantage of changes introduced into their world by measuring the effects of such changes. They should utilize more often efficient and useful statistics instead of making tabular presentation their only tool.

On the other hand, experiments and controlled investigations can often be improved by efforts to specify their populations more clearly and to make the results more representative of the population. Often more should be done to broaden the area of inference to more important populations. Thus, in many situations the deliberate attempts of the researcher to make his sample more "homogeneous" are misplaced; and if common sense will not dispel the error, reading Fisher may.[16] When he understands this, the researcher can view the population base of his research in terms of efficiency—in terms of costs and variances. He can often avoid basing his research on a comparison of one sampling unit for each "treatment." If he cannot obtain a proper sample of the entire population, frequently he can secure, say, four units for each treatment, or a score for each.[17]

Suppose, for example, that thorough research on one city and one rural county, discloses higher levels of political interest in the former. It is presumtuous (although common practice) to present this result as evidence that urban people in *general* show a higher level. (Unfortunately, I am not beating a dead horse; this nag is pawing daily in the garden of social science.) However, very likely there is a great deal of variation in political interest among different cities, as well as among rural counties; the results of the research will depend heavily on which city and which county the researcher picked as "typical." The research would have a broader base if a city and a rural county would have been chosen in each of say, four different situations—as different as possible (as to region, income, industry, for example); or better still in twenty different situations. A further improvement would result if the stratification and selection of sampling units followed a scientific sample design.

Using more sampling units and spreading them over the breadth of variation in the population has several advantages. First, some measure of the variability of the observed effect may be obtained. From a probability sample, statistical inference to the population can be made. Second, the base of the inference is broadened, as the effect is observed over a variety of situations. Beyond this lies the combination of results from researches over several distinct cultures and periods. Finally, with proper design, the effects of several potentially confounding factors can be tested.

These points are brought out by Keyfitz in an excellent example of controlled investigation (which also uses sampling effectively): "Census enumeration data were used to answer for French farm families of the Province of Quebec the question: Are farm families smaller near cities than far from cities, other things being equal? The sample of 1,056 families was arranged in a 2^6 factorial design which not only controlled 15 extraneous variables (income, education, etc.) but incidentally measured the effect of 5 of these on family size. A significant effect of distance from cities was found, from which is inferred a geographical dimension for the currents of social change."[18] The mean numbers of children per family were found to be 9.5 near and 10.8 far from cities; the difference of 1.3 children has a standard error of 0.28.

Some Misuses of Statistical Tests

Of the many kinds of current misuses this discussion is confined to a few of the most common. There is irony in the circumstance that these are committed usually by the more statistically inclined investigators; they are avoided in research presented in terms of qualitative statements or of simple descriptions.

First, there is "hunting with a shot-gun" for significant differences. Statistical tests are designed for distinguishing results at a predetermined level of improbability (say at $P = .05$) under a specified null hypothesis of random events. A rigorous theory for dealing with individual experiments has been developed by Fisher, the Pearsons, Neyman, Wold, and others. However, the researcher often faces more complicated situations, especially in the analysis of survey results; he is often searching for interesting relationships among a vast number of data. The keen-eyed researcher hunting through the results of one thousand random tosses of perfect coins would discover and display about fifty "significant" results (at the $P = .05$ level).[19] Perhaps the problem has become more acute now that high-speed computers allow hundreds of significance tests to be made. There is no easy answer to this problem. We must be constantly aware of the nature of tests of null hypotheses in searching survey data for interesting results. After finding a result improbable under the null hypothesis the researcher must not accept blindly the hypothesis of "significance" due to a presumed cause. Among the several alternative hypotheses is that of having discovered an improbable random event through sheer diligence. Remedy can be found sometimes by a reformulation of the statistical aims of the research so as to fit the available tests. Unfortunately, the classic statistical tests give clear answers only to some simple decision problems; often these bear but faint resemblance to the complex problems faced by the scientist. In response to these needs the mathematical statisticians are beginning to provide some new statistical tests. Among the most useful are the new "multiple comparison" and "multiple range" tests of Tukey, Duncan, Scheffé,[20] and others. With a greater variety of statistical statements available, it will become easier to choose one without doing great violence either to them or to the research aims.

Second, statistical "significance" is often confused with and substituted for substantive significance. There are instances of research results presented in terms of probability values of "statistical significance" alone, without noting the magnitude and importance of the relationships found. These attempts to use the probability levels of significance tests as measures of the strengths of relationships are very common and very mistaken. The function of statistical tests is merely to answer: Is the variation great enough for us to place some confidence in the result; or, contrarily, may the latter be merely a happenstance of the specific sample on which the test was made? This question is interesting, but it is surely *secondary*, auxiliary, to the main question: Does the result show a relationship which is of substantive interest because of its nature and its magnitude? Better still: Is the result consistent with an assumed relationship of substantive interest?

The results of statistical "tests of significance" are functions not only of the magnitude of the relationships studied but also of the numbers of sampling units used (and the efficiency of design). In small samples significant, that is, meaningful, results may fail to appear "statistically significant." But if the sample is large enough the most insignificant relationships will appear "statistically significant."

Significance should stand for meaning and refer to substantive matter. The statistical tests merely answer the question: Is there a big enough relationship here which *needs* explanation (and is not merely chance fluctuation)? The word *significance* should be attached to another question, a substantive question: Is there a relationship here *worth* explaining (because it is important and meaningful)? As a remedial step I would recommend that statisticians discard the phrase "test of significance," perhaps in favor of the somewhat longer but proper phrase "test against the null hypothesis" or the abbreviation "TANH."

Yates, after praising Fisher's classic *Statistical Methods*, makes the following observations on the use of "tests of significance":

■ Second, and more important, it has caused scientific research workers to pay undue attention to the results of the tests of significance they perform on their data, particularly data derived from experiments, and too little to the estimates of the magnitude of the effects they are investigating.

Nevertheless the occasions, even in research work, in which quantitative data are collected solely with the object of proving or disproving a given hypothesis are relatively rare. Usually quantitative estimates and fiducial limits are required. Tests of significance are preliminary or ancillary.

The emphasis on tests of significance, and the consideration of the results of each experiment in isolation, have had the unfortunate consequence that scientific workers have often regarded the execution of a test of significance on an experiment as the ultimate objective. Results are significant or not significant and this is the end of it.[21] ■

For presenting research results statistical estimation is more frequently appropriate than tests of significance. The estimates should be provided with some measure of sampling variability. For this purpose confidence intervals are used most widely. In large samples, statements of the standard errors provide useful guides to action. These problems need further development by theoretical statisticians.[22]

The responsibility for the current fashions should be shared by the authors of statistical textbooks and ultimately by the mathematical statisticians. As Tukey puts it:

■ *Statistical methods should be tailored to the real needs of the user.* In a number of cases, statisticians have led themselves astray by choosing a problem which they could solve exactly but which was far from the needs of their clients. . . . The broadest class of such cases comes from the choice of significance procedures rather than confidence procedures. It is often much easier to be "exact" about significance procedures than about confidence procedures. By considering only the most null "null hypothesis" many inconvenient possibilities can be avoided.[23] ■

Third, the tests of null hypotheses of *zero* differences, of no relationships, are frequently weak, perhaps trivial statements of the researcher's aims. In place of the test of zero difference (the nullest of null hypotheses), the researcher should often substitute, say, a test for a difference of a specific size based on some specified model. Better still, in many cases, instead of the tests of significance it would be more to the point to measure the magnitudes of the relationships, attaching proper statements of their sampling variation. The magnitudes of relationships cannot be measured in terms of levels of significance; they can be measured in terms of the difference of two means, or of the proportion of the total variance "explained," of coefficients of correlations and of regressions, of measures of association, and so on. These views are shared by many, perhaps most, consulting statisticians—although they have not published full statements of their philosophy. Savage expresses himself forcefully: "Null hypotheses of no difference are usually known to be false before the data are collected; when they are, their rejection or acceptance simply reflects the size of the sample and the power of the test, and is not a contribution to science."[24]

Too much of social research is planned and presented in terms of the mere existence of some relationship, such as: individuals high on variate x are also high on variate y. The *exploratory* stage of research may be well served by statements of this order. But these statements are relatively weak and can serve *only* in the primitive stages of research. Contrary to a common misconception, the more advanced stages of research should be phrased in terms of the quantitative aspects of the relationships. Again, to quote Tukey:

■ *There are normal sequences of growth in immediate ends.* One natural sequence of immediate ends follows the sequence: (1) Description, (2) Significance statements, (3) Estimation, (4) Confidence statement, (5) Evaluation. . . . There are, of course, other normal sequences of immediate ends, leading mainly through various decision procedures, which are appropriate to development research and to operations research, just as the sequence we have just discussed is appropriate to basic research.[25] ■

At one extreme, then, we may find that the contrast between two "treatments" of a labor force results in a difference in productivity of 5 per cent. This difference may appear "statistically significant" in a sample of, say, 1,000 cases. It may also mean a difference of millions of dollars to the company. However, it "explains" only about one per cent of the total variance in productivity. At the other extreme is the far-away land of completely determinate behavior, where every action and attitude is explainable, with nothing left to chance for explanation.

The aims of most basic research in the social sciences, it seems to me, should be somewhere between the two extremes; but too much of it is presented at the first extreme, at the primitive level. This is a matter of over-all strategy for an entire area of any science. It is difficult to make this judgment off-hand regarding any specific piece of research of this kind: the status of research throughout the entire area should be considered. But the superabundance of research aimed at this primitive level seems to imply that the over-all strategy of research errs in this respect. The construction of scientific theories to cover broader fields—the persistent aim of science—is based on the synthesis of the separate research results in those fields. A coherent synthesis cannot be forged from a collection of relationships of unknown strengths and magnitudes. The necessary conditions for a synthesis include an *evaluation* of the results available in the field, a coherent interrelating of the *magnitudes* found in those results, and the construction of models based on those magnitudes.

NOTES

*   This research has been supported by a grant from the Ford Foundation for Development of the Behavioral Sciences. It has benefited from the suggestions and encouragement of John W. Tukey and others. But the author alone is responsible for any controversial opinions.

1.   *Cf.* R. A. Fisher, *The Design of Experiments*, London: Oliver and Boyd, 6th edition, 1953, pp. 1–2: "The statistician cannot evade the responsibility for understanding the processes he applies or recommends. My immediate point is that the questions involved can be disassociated from all that is strictly technical in the statistician's craft, and *when so detached*, are questions only of the right use of human reasoning powers, with which all intelligent people, who hope to be intelligible, are equally concerned, and on which the statistician, as such, speaks with no special authority. The statistician cannot excuse himself from the duty of getting his head clear on the principles of scientific inference, but equally no other thinking man can avoid a like obligation."

2.   G. Undy Yule and M. G. Kendall, *An Introduction to the Theory of Statistics*, London: Griffin, 11th edition, 1937, Chapters 4, 15, and 16.

3.   Jerzy Neyman, *Lectures and Conferences on Mathematical Statistics and Probability*, Washington, D.C.: Graduate School of Department of Agriculture, 1952, pp. 143–154. Herbert A. Simon, "Spurious Correlation: A Causal Interpretation,"

Journal of the American Statistical Association, 49 (September, 1954), pp. 467–479; also in his *Models of Man*, New York: Wiley, 1956.

4. See the excellent and readable article, Herman Wold, "Causal Inference from Observational Data," *Journal of the Royal Statistical Society* (*A*), 119 (Part 1, January, 1956), pp. 28–61. Also the two-part technical article, M. G. Kendall, "Regression, Structure and Functional Relationship," *Biometrika*, 38. (June, 1951), pp. 12–25; and 39 (June, 1952), pp. 96–108. The interesting methods of "path coefficients" in genetics have been developed by Wright for inferring causal factors from regression coefficients. See, in Oscar Kempthorne *et al.*, *Statistics and Mathematics in Biology*, Ames, Iowa: The Iowa State College Press, 1954; Sewall Wright, "The Interpretation of Multi-Variate Systems," Chapter 2; and John W. Tukey, "Causation, Regression and Path Analysis," Chapter 3. Also C. C. Li, "The Concept of Path Coefficient and Its Impact on Population Genetics," *Biometrics*, 12 (June, 1956), pp. 190–209. I do not know whether these methods can be of wide service in current social science research in the presence of numerous factors, of large unexplained variances, and of doubtful directions of causation.

5. Kendall points out that these latter terms are preferable. See his paper cited in note 4, and M. G. Kendall and W. R. Buckland, *A Dictionary of Statistical Terms*, prepared for the International Statistical Institute with assistance of UNESCO, London: Oliver and Boyd, 1957. I have also tried to follow in IV below his distinction of "variate" for random variables from "variables" for the usual (non-random) variable.

6. The sampling error measures the chance fluctuation in the difference of levels due to the sampling operations. The computation of the sampling error must take proper account of the actual sample design, and not blindly follow the standard simple random formulas. See Leslie Kish, "Confidence Intervals for Complex Samples," *American Sociological Review*, 22 (April, 1957), pp. 154–165.

7. Hanan C. Selvin, "A Critique of Tests of Significance in Survey Research," *American Sociological Review*, 22 (October, 1957), p. 527. In a criticism of this article, McGinnis shows that the separation of explanatory from extraneous variables depends on the type of hypothesis at which the research is aimed. Robert McGinnis, "Randomization and Inference in Sociological Research," *American Sociological Review*, 23 (August, 1958), pp. 408–414.

8. Selvin performs a service in pointing to several common mistakes: (a) The mechanical use of "significance tests" can lead to false conclusions. (b) Statistical "significance" should not be confused with substantive importance. (c) The probability levels of the common statistical tests are not appropriate to the practice of "hunting" for a few differences among a mass of results. However, Selvin gives poor advice on what to do about these mistakes; particularly when, in his central thesis, he reiterates that "tests of significance are inapplicable in nonexperimental research," and that "the tests are applicable only when all relevant variables have been controlled." I hope that the benefits of his warnings outweigh the damages of his confusion.

I noticed three misleading references in the article. (a) In the paper which Selvin appears to use as supporting him, Wold (*op. cit.*, p. 39) specifically disagrees with Selvin's central thesis, stating that "The need for testing the statistical inference is no less than when dealing with experimental data, but with observational data other approaches come to the foreground." (b) In discussing problems caused by complex sample designs, Selvin writes that "Such errors are easy enough to discover and remedy" (p. 520), referring to Kish (*op. cit.*). On the contrary, my article pointed out the seriousness of the problem and the difficulties in dealing with it. (c) "Correlated biases" is a poor term for the confounded uncontrolled variables and it is not true that the term is so used in literature. Specifically, the reference to Cochran is misleading, since he is dealing there only with errors of measurement which may be correlated with the "true" value. See William G. Cochran, *Sampling Techniques*, New York: Wiley, 1953, p. 305.

9. Wold, *op. cit.*; Donald T. Campbell, "Factors Relevant to the Validity of Experiments in Social Settings," *Psychological Bulletin*, 54 (July, 1957), pp. 296–312.

10. Kish, *op. cit.*

11. F. J. Roethlisberger and W. J. Dickson, *Management and the Worker*, Cambridge: Harvard University Press, 1939. Troubles with experimental controls misled even the great Pavlov into believing *temporarily* that he had proof of the inheritance of an acquired ability to learn: "In an informal statement made at the time of the Thirteenth International Physiological Congress, Boston, August, 1929, Pavlov explained that in checking up these experiments it was found that the apparent improvement in the ability to learn, on the part of successive generations of mice, was really due to an improvement in the ability to teach, on the part of the experimenter." From B. G. Greenberg, *The Story of Evolution*, New York: Garden City, 1929, p. 327.

12. Jerome Cornfield, "Statistical Relationships and Proof in Medicine," *American Statistician*, 8 (December, 1954), pp. 19–21.

13. McGinnis, *op. cit.*, p. 412, points out that usually "it is not true that one can uncover 'general' relationships by examining some arbitrarily selected population. . . . There is no such thing as a completely general relationship which is independent of population, time, and space. The extent to which a relationship is constant among different populations is an empirical question which can be resolved only by examining different populations at different times in different places."

14. Martin B. Wilk and Oscar Kempthorne, "Some Aspects of the Analysis of Factorial Experiment in a Completely Randomized Design," *Annals of Mathematical Statistics*, 27 (December, 1956), pp. 950–985; and "Fixed, Mixed and Random Models," *Journal of the American Statistical Association*, 50 (December, 1955), pp. 1144–1167. Jerome Cornfield and John W. Tukey, "Average Values of Mean Squares in Factorials," *Annals of Mathematical Statistics*, 27 (December, 1956), pp. 907–949.

15. Fisher, *op. cit.*, pp. 17–20. "Controlled investigation" may not be the best term for these designs. "Controlled observations" might do, but "observation" has more fundamental meanings.

16. *Ibid.*, pp. 99–100. Fisher says: "We have seen that the factorial arrangement possesses two advantages over experiments involving only single factors: (i) Greater *efficiency*, in that these factors are evaluated with the same precision by means of only a quarter of the number of observations that would otherwise be

necessary; and (ii) Greater *comprehensiveness* in that, in addition to the 4 effects of single factors, their 11 possible interactions are evaluated. There is a third advantage which, while less obvious than the former two, has an important bearing upon the utility of the experimental results in their practical application. This is that any conclusion, such as that it is advantageous to increase the quantity of a given ingredient, has a wider inductive basis when inferred from an experiment in which the quantities of other ingredients have been varied, than it would have from any amount of experimentation, in which these had been kept strictly constant. The exact standardization of experimental conditions, which is often thoughtlessly advocated as a panacea, always carried with it the real disadvantage that a highly standardized experiment supplies direct information only in respect of the narrow range of conditions achieved by standardization. Standardization, therefore, weakens rather than strengthens our ground for inferring a like result, when, as is invariably the case in practice, these conditions are somewhat varied."

17. For simplicity the following illustration is a simple contrast between two values of the "explanatory" variable, but the point is more general; and this aspect is similar whether for true experiments or controlled observations. Incidentally, it is poor strategy to "solve" the problem of representation by obtaining a good sample, or complete census, of some small or artificial population. A poor sample of the United States or of Chicago *usually* has more over-all value than the best sample of freshman English classes at X University.

18. Nathan Keyfitz, "A Factorial Arrangement of Comparisons of Family Size," *American Journal of Sociology*, 53 (March, 1953), p. 470.

19. William H. Sewell, "Infant Training and the Personality of the Child," *American Journal of Sociology*, 53 (September, 1952), pp. 150–159. Sewell points to an interesting example: "On the basis of the results of this study, the general null hypothesis that the personality adjustments and traits of children who have undergone varying training experiences do not differ significantly cannot be rejected. Of the 460 chi square tests, only 18 were significant at or beyond the 5 per cent level. Of these, 11 were in the expected direction and 7 were in the opposite direction from that expected on the basis of psychoanalytic writings. . . . Certainly, the results of this study cast serious doubts on the validity of the psychoanalytic claims regarding the importance of the infant disciplines and on the efficacy of prescriptions based on them" (pp. 158–59). Note that by chance alone one would expect 23 "significant" differences at the 5 per cent level. A "hunter" would report either the 11 or the 18 and not the hundreds of "misses."

20. John W. Tukey, "Comparing Individual Means in the Analysis of Variance," *Biometrics*, 5 (June, 1949), pp. 99–114; David B. Duncan, "Multiple Range and Multiple *F* Tests," *Biometrics*, 11 (March, 1955), pp. 1–42; Henry Scheffé, "A Method for Judging All Contrasts in the Analysis of Variance," *Biometrika*, 40 (June, 1953), pp. 87–104.

21. Frank Yates, "The Influence of *Statistical Methods for Research Workers* on the Development of the Science of Statistics," *Journal of the American Statistical Association*, 46 (March, 1951), pp. 32–33.

22. D. R. Cox, "Some Problems Connected with Statistical Inference," *Annals of Mathematical Statistics*, 29 (June, 1958), pp. 357–372.

23. John W. Tukey, "Unsolved Problems of Experimental Statistics," *Journal of the American Statistical Association*, 49 (December, 1954), p. 710. See also D. R. Cox, *op. cit.*, and David B. Duncan, *op. cit.*

24. Richard J. Savage, "Nonparametric Statistics," *Journal of the American Statistical Association*, 52 (September, 1957), pp. 332–333.

25. Tukey, *op. cit.*, pp. 712–713.

EFFICIENT CONVERSION OF
NON-METRIC INFORMATION
INTO METRIC INFORMATION

ROBERT P. ABELSON
JOHN W. TUKEY

The title of this paper may prove misleading. "Conversion of non-metric information into metric information" may sound like getting something for nothing. In fact, we are concerned with getting a convenient modest something for an inconvenient modest something. Further, our methods are thus far limited to a particular class of situations. We do not have anything like a universal recipe for converting the qualitative into the quantitative, though a good deal can be done within the confines of the situations with which we are here concerned.

Consider n points to which we wish to assign numerical values, X_1, $X_2, \ldots, X_n$. Suppose we have insufficient information to provide a natural or "correct" assignment of numerical values; our knowledge is limited to a set of constraints on the values, i.e., a set of inequalities on the X's. (For example, $X_1 \leq X_2 \leq \cdots \leq X_n$).

Consider first the purposes that an assignment of numerical values can serve in such a situation. It has become somewhat fashionable, particularly in certain areas of the behavioral sciences, to frown upon "arbitrary" numerical assignment (scaling) procedures. Some take the position that in the absence of a compelling rationale for numerical assignment, no numerical assignment whatever should be attempted (Stevens, 1951). Thus if a set of points are known only up to a rank order, one is limited to the declaration of an "ordinal scale." Further manipulations using the scale are limited, so the dictum goes, to techniques appropriate to ordinal scales—in particular, to those non-parametric statistical techniques designed for the analysis of rankings. The net effect of this dictum is to restrict the flexibility of statistical analysis severely and unnecessarily.

Reliance in such circumstances upon non-parametric procedures seems to us to be unwise, not because such procedures always lack power (90 per cent power is no cause for disdain), but because they are poorly adapted to the variety of uses one requires for good insight into bodies of data. Often when adaptation to new uses is attempted, it is only at considerable sacrifice of power (as in the situations discussed here). Furthermore, *the typical state of knowledge short of metric information is not rank-order information*; ordinarily, one possesses something more than rank-order information. For example, one may know that

Reprinted by permission of the authors and the American Statistical Association from *Proceedings of the Social Statistics Section of the American Statistical Association* (Washington, 1959), 226–230.

X_1, X_2, and X_3 are ordered and in addition that X_2 is closer to X_3 than it is to X_1. Non-parametric techniques which take full advantage of such types of situations are generally unavailable. We would like to probe more deeply here, to gain some idea of what lies between rank-order scales and metric scales.

Consider now the kind of problem for which a numerical assignment procedure is useful. Suppose that the n points represent levels of an independent variable and that we wish to carry out the regression of a dependent variable (about which we have metric information) upon this independent variable (about which we have only non-metric information). To be even more specific, the independent and dependent variables might be imbedded in an analysis of variance design where we were interested in forming a single degree of freedom contrast among the levels of the independent variable. The appropriate coefficients to use in forming such a contrast would be a direct outcome of an assignment of numerical values.

To sum up thus far: we seek a procedure for assigning numerical values to a set of n entities, given a set of inequalities which the assigned values must obey. The problem is of interest because a) it sheds light upon the nature of knowledge intermediate between rank-order knowledge and metric knowledge, and b) the solution makes powerful regression techniques, particularly the formation of contrasts, applicable to many situations when the entities represent levels or versions of an independent variable.

The Criterion for Good Numerical Assignment

The sequence of n numerical values to be assigned must obey certain inequalities. Likewise, the "ideal" values, the values one would assign if one had full scale knowledge, must obey the same inequalities. That is, both the sequence we choose and the sequence we ought to have chosen lie in the convex set of sequences permitted by the inequalities. Denote the chosen sequence by $[X_1, X_2, \ldots, X_n]$ and the ideal sequence by $[Y_1, Y_2, \ldots, Y_n]$. A convenient and reasonable criterion of the success of our choice is the *square of the formal product-moment correlation between* $[X]$ *and* $[Y]$:

$$r^2 = \frac{\left[\sum_{i=1}^{n} (X_i - \bar{X})(Y_i - \bar{Y}) \right]^2}{\sum_{i=1}^{n} (X_i - \bar{X})^2 \sum_{i=1}^{n} (Y_i - \bar{Y})^2}$$

To avoid confusion, one must note that this correlation coefficient is purely "formal" and is not to be thought of in terms of a bivariate distribution from which points are sampled. This r^2 plays a key role in the specific application discussed earlier. In testing the significance of a contrast, the power of the test increases directly with r^2. The same r^2 is almost ubiquitous in other aspects of regression analysis.

There is an obvious difficulty with r^2 as a criterion: one does not know the ideal sequence, $[Y]$. The sequence $[X]$ is of our choice; but, in our ignorance, $[Y]$ might be any sequence within a certain range of possibilities. A further choice must be made in order to provide a usable criterion. On the one hand, one might make some kind of distributional assumption about the possible $[Y]$'s, and average r^2 over this *a priori* distribution. It is difficult to do this in any reasonable and meaningful way. (Indeed the resulting mathematical problem is rather difficult to attack.) On the other hand, one might make the conservative, fixed assumption that *the Y-sequence may well be such as to minimize r^2 for the chosen X-sequence*. This minimum r^2, for $[Y]$ satisfying the inequalities and $[X]$ fixed is the criterion we have chosen to assess any fixed $[X]$. The mathematical problem then becomes a maximin problem: how should one choose $[X]$ such that the minimum r^2 is maximized?

In other words, we play a "game against Nature" in which we fear the worst. For any choice of numerical assignments for $[X]$, assume that Nature chooses a set of "true" values $[Y]$ which obey the inequalities but yield r^2 min., the lowest possible squared product-moment coefficient with $[X]$. We play the game by choosing $[X]$ such that r^2 min. is maximized. (We refer to this choice as the "maximin sequence," denoted by $[C]$.) This results in a guarantee that r^2 cannot be less than a certain value, denoted as r^2 maximin, so long as Nature obeys the inequalities. The strategy amounts to optimizing the conservative guarantee, rather than maximizing some kind of average value.

Mathematical Properties of the Problem

Since the criterion is correlational, the units and origins of the sequences $[X]$ and $[Y]$ are immaterial to the maximin problem. In what follows, only the relative spacing of the n numerical values is of consequence, while the units and origins are chosen for convenience.

With a given set of inequalities there is associated a special set of sequences which we call "corners," such that any admissible sequence $[Y]$ can be generated as a positive linear combination of the corner sequences. (The name "corner" arises from the geometrical conception of the permissible sequences as a convex set of vectors.) As an example, consider the rank-order case: $Y_1 \leq Y_2 \leq Y_3 \leq Y_4$. Fixing $Y_1 = 0$, a simple set of corners is the triplet:

(0, 0, 0, 1)
(0, 0, 1, 1)
(0, 1, 1, 1)

Any $[Y]$ satisfying rank order (with $Y_1 = 0$) can be expressed as a positive linear combination of these corners.

The corners provide the key to the maximin solution, via the following two theorems proved by Tukey. Proofs are given in our more extended article (Abelson and Tukey, 1963).

Theorem I. *For any fixed* [X], *minimum* r^2 *is reached for* [Y] *equal to one of the corner sequences.* In other words, whatever choice we make for [X], Nature plays her most damaging game at one of the corners. Consider the rank-order case again, and suppose we "play" the equal-interval sequence $- 3, - 1, 1, 3$. Nature achieves r^2 min. $= .600$ by playing $0, 0, 0, 1$ or $0, 1, 1, 1$. No worse than this can be done to us when we play $- 3, - 1, 1, 3$. (However, we have a better play in the maximin sense.)

Theorem II. (Oversimplified). *The maximum* r^2 *min. is achieved by the sequence which correlates equally with all corner sequences.* In the rank-order case with $n = 4$, we need simply find the sequence (C_1, C_2, C_3, C_4) which correlates equally with $(0, 0, 0, 1)$, $(0, 0, 1, 1)$, and $(0, 1, 1, 1)$. This is a matter of simultaneous linear equations in the unknown C's which are readily solved.

Theorem 2 as it has been given here is not correct for all sets of inequalities. In particular, the theorem fails when the sequence which correlates equally with all corners does not itself satisfy the appropriate inequalities. Further complications arise when there are more than $(n - 1)$ corners in a given case. The fuller paper goes into the subtle details involved. The correct but more involved theorem will simply be stated here in passing: For any system of inequalities with its associated corner sequences, there exists one and only one sequence which a) is a positive linear combination of a set of the corner sequences such that b) it correlates equally highly with all these corners and c) more highly with corners not in the set, if any.

Results for the Rank-Order Case

First we present in some detail the results for the rank-order case. Then, more briefly, the results for other cases. Throughout we use for the values of the maximin sequence the convenient normalization

$$\sum_{i=1}^{n} C_i = 0, \qquad \sum_{i=1}^{n} C_i^2 = 1/r^2 \text{ maximin.}$$

The maximin sequence in the rank-order case for $n = 4$ is: $- .866, - .134, .134, .866$. For $n = 8$, the values are: $- .935, - .289, - .144, - .045, .045, .144, .289, .935$. For indefinitely large n, the limiting values for the extreme points are: $- 1.000, - .414, - .318, - .268, \ldots, .268, .318, .414, 1.000$.

The solution is markedly non-linear. The values at the two ends have very large relative separation from the next values inwards. This comes about because the solution is guarding against the possibility that Nature will play $0, 0, \ldots, 0, 0, 0, 1$ or $0, 1, 1, 1, \ldots, 1, 1$. A linear sequence can fail rather badly against these possibilities, especially for large n. However, in practice one is often unwilling to acknowledge sequences as pathological as $a, a, \ldots, a, a, a, b$ as reasonable possibilities for the "true" sequences. If so, then one may attempt to rule out such unusual sequences from Natures' repertoire. This means reformulating the inequalities so that these pathological corners do not occur.

This is possible in a number of ways, all of which require that something more stringent than mere rank order be assumed. When this is done, one finds that the end values of the maximin sequence are not forced to lie so far from the body of the sequence as in the rank-order case, and a linear sequence does not fare as poorly (in the maximin sense) as a basis for numerical assignment. Of this, more later.

The following brief display gives r^2 maximin in the rank-order case for various values of n; by way of comparison, the values of r^2 min. against a linear assignment are shown.

					Values of n					
	5	10	20	50	100	200	500	1,000		m
r^2 maximin	.596	.478	.406	.339	.303	.274	.244	.225		$2/2 + \log (m - 1)$
r^2 min. (linear)		.500	.273	.143	.059	.030	.015	.006	.003	$3/(m + 1)$

Asymptotically, r^2 maximin approaches zero, but very slowly, whilst r^2 min. for a linear sequence approaches zero rather rapidly.

The form of the maximin sequence may be roughly approximated with a simple pattern of integers by the following device: write down a linear sequence with mean zero, quadruple the extreme values and double the next-to-end values. At $n = 8$, for example, this quick approximation to the maximin sequence would be $(- 28, - 10, - 3, 1, 1, 3, 10, 28)$. For n less than 50, the r^2 min. for this approximation is at least 90 per cent as high as r^2 maximin. This scheme, which we dub as the "linear-2-4" sequence, is easily remembered.

If Nature is really playing a near-linear sequence, then of course we would be better off by playing a linear sequence than by guarding against wild behavior of Nature by playing the maximin solution or its surrogate, the linear-2-4. If we would like to achieve higher r^2 in case Nature's behavior is near-linear without risking too great a drop in r^2 below the maximin value in case Nature's behavior is wild, a good hedge for small n is to choose a "linear-2" sequence; that is, a linear sequence with the end values doubled. In passing, it might be mentioned that "rankits," like linear coefficients, fare poorly when Nature is behaving wildly.

Other Orderly Cases

Definitions

I.   Symmetric rank order
$$X_1 \le X_2 \le X_3 \le \cdots \le X_{n-1} \le X_n,$$
$$D_1 = D_{n-1}, D_2 = D_{n-2}, D_3 = D_{n-3}, \ldots$$
where $D_1 = (X_2 - X_1), D_2 = (X_3 - X_2), \ldots, D_{n-1} = (X_n - X_{n-1}).$

II. Symmetric, extremes bunched
$$X_1 \leq X_2 \leq X_3 \leq \cdots \leq X_{n-1} \leq X_n,$$
$$(D_1 = D_{n-1}) \leq (D_2 = D_{n-2}) \leq (D_3 = D_{n-3}) \cdots$$

III. Non-symmetric, extremes bunched
$$X_1 \leq X_2 \leq X_3 \leq \cdots \leq X_{n-1} \leq X_n,$$
$$D_1 \leq D_2 \leq D_3 \cdots D_{n-1} \leq D_{n-2} \leq D_{n-3} \cdots$$

IV. Symmetric, extremes spread
$$X_1 \leq X_2 \leq X_3 \leq \cdots \leq X_{n-1} \leq X_n,$$
$$(D_1 = D_{n-1}) \geq (D_2 = D_{n-2}) \geq (D_3 = D_{n-3}) \cdots$$

V. Non-symmetric, extremes spread
$$X_1 \leq X_2 \leq X_3 \leq \cdots \leq X_{n-1} \leq X_n,$$
$$D_1 \geq D_2 \geq D_3 \geq \cdots D_{n-1} \geq D_{n-2} \geq D_{n-3} \cdots$$

VI. "Diminishing returns" (or mirror image)
$$X_1 \leq X_2 \leq X_3 \leq \cdots \leq X_{n-1} \leq X_n,$$
$$D_1 \geq D_2 \geq D_3 \geq \cdots \geq D_{n-1}$$

Table of Maximin r^2

n	I	II	III	IV	V	VI
3	1.000	1.000	.750	1.000	.750	.933
4	.853	.947	.909	.974	.667	.887
5	.853	.974	.778	.947	.625	.834
6	.786	.940	.874	.922	.599	.827
7	.786	.964	.787	.901	.578	.806
8	.744	.936	.856	.882	.561	.789
9	.744	.958	.791	.865	.548	.774
10	.714	.935	.845	.850	.536	.761
11	.714	.953	.793	.837	.526	.750
12	.692	.935	.838	.826	.517	.740
13	.692	.950	.794	.815	.507	.731
14	.674	.935	.832	.805	.501	.724
15	.674	.949	.795	.796	.492	.716
16	.659	.934	.827	.788	.487	.710
17	.659	.948	.795	.780	.479	.704
18	.646	.934	.825	.773	.475	.699
19	.646	.947	.796	.767	.467	.694
20	.636	.934	.823	.762	.464	.689

Maximin Weights Exemplified: n = 8

	I	II	III	IV	V	VI
C_1	−.707	−.477	−.548	−.707	−.935	−.935
C_2	−.293	−.395	−.418	−.219	−.110	−.160
C_3	−.225	−.312	−.289	−.131	−.055	−.062
C_4	−.189	−.230	−.159	−.044	0	.036
C_5	.189	.230	.159	.044	0	.134
C_6	.225	.312	.289	.131	.055	.231
C_7	.293	.395	.418	.219	.110	.329
C_8	.707	.477	.548	.707	.935	.427

Further Cases for Small n

In the literature on psychological scaling, the case in which the first differences of a ranked sequence are ranked is called an "ordered metric scale" (Coombs, 1950). The cases treated above are a limited coverage of this variety of scale. Next we consider all possible ordered metric scales with $n = 3, 4$, or, 5. Also, we consider for $n = 4$ all possible "higher-ordered metric scales" (Siegel, 1956). These are cases in which *all* differences of a ranked sequence are ranked. In addition, the rank-order case for $n = 3$ and 4 is considered with a numerical constraint on the relative size of the biggest or the smallest interval.

Ordered Metric Scales with n = 3

There is only one case here. We have $X_1 \leq X_2 \leq X_3$ and $X_2 - X_1 \geq X_3 - X_2$. (The other possibility is simply a mirror image of this one.) The maximin sequence can be approximated with the simple integer sequence $(-7, 2, 5)$ with r^2 min. $= .923$.

Ordered Metric Scales with n = 4

Maximin coefficients and maximin r^2, for all cases of $n = 4$ involving only simple inequalities among differences:

1. The three differences $(X_2 - X_1)$, $(X_3 - X_2)$, and $(X_4 - X_3)$ are represented by the digits 1, 2, and 3.

2. When the inequalities specify that a particular difference is greater than another, the larger difference is written first [e.g., the system of inequalities $X_3 - X_2) \geq (X_2 - X_1) \geq (X_4 - X_3) \geq 0$ is written 213].

3. When the relative size of two differences is not specified, they are enclosed in parentheses. [e.g., the system of inequalities $(X_2 - X_1) \geq (X_3 - X_2) \geq 0$; $(X_2 - X_1) \geq (X_4 - X_3) \geq 0$ is written 1(23)].

System	C_1	C_2	C_3	C_4	r^2
(13)2	−87	00	00	87	.667
(12)3	−87	−13	50	50	.789
1(23)	−87	05	27	55	.887
132	−87	05	27	55	.887
123	−87	04	29	54	.887
2(13)	−66	−34	34	66	.909
213	−66	−34	42	58	.941

Ordered Metric Scales with n = 5

System	C_1	C_2	C_3	C_4	C_5	r^2
(124)3	−89	−20	00	20	89	.595
(123)4	−89	−20	00	55	55	.694
(14)(23), (14)23	−89	00	00	00	89	.625
(13)(24), (13)24, (13)42	−89	−10	−10	55	55	.704
(12)(34), (12)34	−89	−20	33	36	40	.801
(23)(14), (23)14	−55	−55	00	55	55	.833
1(234)	−89	00	08	25	57	.840
1(34)2, 1342, 14(23), 1432	−89	01	04	29	55	.843
1(24)3, 1423	−89	−04	12	29	52	.853
1(23)4, 12(34), (12)43, 1324, 1234, 1243	−89	−05	13	32	50	.854
2(134)	−69	−40	16	35	58	.892
2(14)3	−69	−40	26	26	58	.901
24(13)	−61	−49	16	36	58	.914
23(14)	−56	−54	14	40	56	.918
2(34)1, 2341, 2431	−56	−54	16	36	57	.921
2(13)4	−69	−40	18	44	47	.923
2413	−61	−49	21	30	58	.927
21(34), 2134, 2143	−69	−40	21	38	50	.931
2314	−63	−47	19	37	53	.935

Higher-Ordered Metric Scales for n = 4

These cases can be specified as elaborations of ordered metric scales. The notation is as in the previous displays, with the addition of constraints upon the sums of differences. For example (in the abbreviated notation), $1 + 2 \geq 3$ signifies $D_1 + D_2 \geq D_3$.

System	C_1	C_2	C_3	C_4	r^2
123; 1 ≥ 2 + 3	−87	07	36	43	.933
123; 1 ≤ 2 + 3	−73	−19	35	58	.972
132; 1 ≥ 2 + 3	−87	16	16	55	.908
132; 1 ≤ 2 + 3	−72	−10	13	69	.974
213; 2 ≥ 1 + 3	−66	−34	50	50	.952
213; 2 ≤ 1 + 3	−73	−19	35	58	.972

A Further Case with n = 3

Rank order is known, and the ratio of the large D to the smaller D does not exceed K. (We do not know which D is larger, however.)

K	r^2
9	.824
4	.893
2	.964
1.5	.987

The maximin sequence for any K can be represented most simply by $(-1, 0, 1)$.

Similar Cases with n = 4

Rank order is known, and the *largest* D (whichever it is) does not exceed the fraction p of the range.

p	C_1	C_2	C_3	C_4	r^2
.40	−67	−24	24	67	.981
.50	−71	−24	24	71	.893
.60	−71	−26	26	71	.865
.70	−75	−22	22	75	.816
.80	−79	−16	16	79	.765
.90	−83	−14	14	83	.711

Rank order is known, and the *smallest D*, whichever it is, is not less than the fraction q of the range.

q	C_1	C_2	C_3	C_4	r^2
.05	-82	-15	15	82	.723
.10	-78	-16	16	78	.796
.15	-74	-18	18	74	.865
.20	-71	-19	19	71	.924
.25	-69	-20	20	69	.971
.30	-68	-22	22	68	.988

Discussion

Results for a large number of cases have been presented. Many of the maximin r^2's are seen to be in the .80's or .90's. This is quite good for most analytic purposes. Thus a little non-metric information will go a long way when it is converted to metric information. A comparison of cases makes it clear that maximin r^2 is most readily boosted above the rank-order value when the inequalities put bounds upon the external intervals of the sequence. "Extremes bunched" is a more favorable case than "extremes spread"; for $n = 4$ and 5, r^2 is higher when an internal interval is known to be biggest than when an external interval is known to be biggest. Restrictions on the fraction of the total range allotted the biggest interval result in powerful increases in r^2; this comes about because huge external intervals are thereby prohibited. One way to summarize this class of results is to say that scales with big gaps in the middle are more "robust" than scales with big gaps in the tails.

Certain other general conclusions are apparent from the results: symmetry is a fairly powerful condition; higher-ordered metric scales can be very close indeed to numerical scales; and so on.

Nevertheless, many of you are no doubt wondering about the proof of this pudding. How often can maximum sequences actually be put to good use?

The answer is not cut-and-dried. Consider the rank-order case. Here the values of maximin r^2 are only fair; moreover, the maximin sequence has an unfamiliar flavor. The end values are moved far out to guard against wild plays of Nature. Are we seriously recommending that for a rank-order case with, say, $n = 6$, the contrast $(-20, -6, -1, 1, 6, 20)$ be used to capture the single degree of freedom associated with the rank order?

The investigator might reject the appropriateness of this contrast. He might say, "It is too bizarre. Give me straight-forward linear weights, or perhaps rankits. I do not foresee that Nature will play tricks on me." Our reply would be, "If you say your non-metric information is rank order *and nothing more*, then you implicitly acknowledge the possibility of a 'true' sequence of the form

(a, a, a, a, a, b). A conservative man would protect himself against such a possibility. If you say that this possibility is inconceivable, then you really have more non-metric information than mere rank order. If you could define this extra knowledge precisely, it would lead to another maximin sequence, one that might strike you as intuitively more reasonable."

Here lies the heart of the situation. Quite commonly, *when we say we only know rank order, we actually know more than this, but don't know how to express what else it is that we know.* Typically, our excess "knowledge" is to the effect that the scale is no worse than mildly curvilinear, that Nature behaves smoothly in some sense. This is a more vague and general conception than any of the highly specific cases considered in this paper. The maximin method needs extension to this general case, the problem being to specify the inequalities and corners in some reasonable way. The same problem, seen from a different standpoint, has been apperceived by Mosteller (1958). The problem is clear; the solution is not.

The murkiness of the general "rank-order-plus-smoothness" case should not obscure the fact that in a good many practical situations the maximin approach can straightforwardly be used to good effect. Perhaps the leading candidate for a clear-cut case is the ordered metric scale for $n = 3$. Excellent use can be made of the contrast $(-7, 2, 5)$ in the situation where X_2 is known to lie between X_1 and X_3 but nearer to X_3 than to X_1. One instance of the use of this contrast is already in the literature (Sarnoff, 1960). It is hoped that other instances of practical application will make their appearance in the near future.

REFERENCES

Abelson, R. P. and Tukey, J. W. (1963). Efficient utilization of non-numerical information in quantitative analysis: General theory, the case of simple rank order. *Annuals of Mathematical Statistics*, 34, 1347–1369.

Coombs, C. H. (1950). Psychological scaling without a unit of measurement. *Psychol. Rev.*, 57, 145–158.

Mosteller, F. (1958). The mystery of the missing corpus. *Psychometrika*, 23, 279–289.

Sarnoff, I. (1960). Reaction formation and cynicism. *J. Personal.*, 28, No. 1.

Siegel, S. (1956). A method for obtaining an ordered metric scale. *Psychometrika*, 21, 207–216.

Stevens, S. S. (1951). Mathematics, measurement, and psychophysics. In S. S. Stevens (Ed.), *Handbook of experimental psychology*. New York: Wiley.

CORRELATED INDEPENDENT VARIABLES: THE PROBLEM OF MULTICOLLINEARITY

HUBERT M. BLALOCK, Jr.

In the sociological and social psychological literature attempts are often made to separate out or evaluate the relative influences of several interrelated independent variables on some single dependent variable. For example, one may wish to assess the relative effects of occupation and education on political attitudes; or he may try to ascertain whether authoritarianism or alienation is more important in determining ethnic prejudice. The more or less standard practice in such situations is to relate each of the independent variables to the dependent variable, while controlling for the remaining independent variables. The purpose of the present paper is to point to certain difficulties which arise whenever the supposedly independent variables are highly correlated with each other.

In experimental designs the investigator attempts to manipulate his variables in such a way that the major causal factors under study operate independently of one another. For example, he may make use of two-way analysis of variance, or some more complex design, involving equal numbers of replications in all subcells. Randomization may then be used to provide assurance that at least some of the additional but unmeasured variables operating will affect the dependent variable independently of the factors under study. But in using correlational data based on nonexperimental studies one may find that two (or more) "independent" variables are highly correlated. If this turns out to be the case, it will then be extremely difficult to evaluate their relative importance without running the risk of making faulty inferences. Let us first see why this should be the case and then turn to concrete numerical illustrations.

Multicollinearity

This particular kind of difficulty has long been recognized in the econometrics literature under the label of "multicollinearity."[1] Stated in most simple terms, whenever the correlation between two or more independent variables is high, the sampling error of the partial slopes and partial correlations will be quite large. As a result there will be a number of different combinations of regression coefficients, and hence partial correlations, which give almost equally good fittings to the empirical data. In any given case the method of least squares will

Reprinted by permission of the author and the University of North Carolina Press from *Social Forces* **62** (December, 1963), 233–238.

usually yield unique solutions, but with slight modifications of the magnitude that could easily be due to sampling or measurement error, one might obtain estimates which differ considerably from the original set.

In order to see the problem in its extreme form let us imagine we are dealing with a single dependent variable Y and two independent variables X and Z as in the equation

$$Y = a + b_1 X + b_2 Z + e_1 \qquad (1)$$

Suppose, also that X and Z are perfectly related according to the equation

$$X = c + dZ \qquad (2)$$

Since this second equation is exact, we may substitute it into the first. More generally, we may combine the two equations by taking arbitrary linear combinations. As can easily be verified, this in effect means that there will be an infinite number of coefficients that will satsify the first equation.[2]

Let us consider an illustrative set of numerical coefficients:

$$Y = 6 + 5X + 3Z + e_1 \qquad (1')$$

and

$$X = 1 + 2Z \qquad (2')$$

Multiply the second equation by 3 and subtracting from the first we would get

$$Y = 3 + 8X - 3Z + e_1 \qquad (1'')$$

which is mathematically equivalent to equation $(1')$. But there are obviously an indefinitely large number of such equations, and we therefore cannot determine the coefficients uniquely.

As Wold and Jureen point out, an exact relationship between X and Z is but a limiting case of the more general situation in which the two variables are correlated.[3] If we were to add an error term e_2 to the second equation, we would obtain a unique solution with least squares, but such a solution would not have desirable properties. It turns out that the standard errors of the estimates of the slopes b_1 and b_2 may become quite large. Although exact formulas are complex and depend on the nature of certain other assumptions, these sampling errors tend to increase as the relationship between the two independent variables becomes more and more exact. In other words, the higher the correlation between X and Z the less faith we have in the accuracy of the estimates of the partial slopes. In the limiting case where the relationship is exact, we have no faith in the estimates at all since the standard errors of these estimates become infinite.[4]

Translating these facts into practical terms, this means that our estimates of the slopes will vary considerably from one sample to the next. It will be recalled that the coefficients of the least squares estimate of equation (1) are *partial* slopes. They estimate the expected change in Y for a unit change in one independent variable, controlling for the second. Partial correlation coefficients will also have this same undesirable property: they will be highly unstable and sensitive to sampling errors. This means that we can be badly misled if we use partial correlations to measure the degree of relationship between the dependent variable and each of the (highly correlated) independent variables in turn. A number of independent replications are likely to give very different results.

Let us now consider an example taken from the social-psychological literature in which apparently inconsistent results have led to a debate which need not have occurred, and which stems from this high degree of instability of partial correlations in the case of multicollinearity.

Empirical Examples

Anomie, authoritarianism, and prejudice. Leo Srole read a paper, later published as a journal article, in which certain findings of a correlational study apparently implied that the relationship between "anomie" and ethnocentrism or prejudice was more important than that between authoritarianism and prejudice.[5] In fact, the partial correlation between the *F* scale and the *E* scale almost disappeared when anomie was controlled. Roberts and Rokeach obtained data, however, which led to the opposite conclusion.[6] These latter authors inferred that authoritarianism was more important than anomie. McDill, in a third study, found the two independent variables to be almost equally important.[7] The results of the three studies are summarized in Table 1.

■ **Table 1.** Comparison of total and partial correlations among anomie (*A*), authoritarianism (*F*), and prejudice (*E*) for three studies

Variables	Srole ($N = 401$)	Roberts and Rokeach ($N = 86$)	McDill ($N = 266$)
	Total correlations		
A and *F*	.45	.47	.67
E and *F*	.29	.64	.64
A and *E*	.43	.55	.63
	Partial correlations		
EF.A	.12	.53	.38
EA.F	.35	.37	.35

An examination of the total correlations for all three sets of data would seem to indicate that correlations among the three variables are in each case moderate and positive. Differences among the results might very readily be attributed to sampling error, differences among the populations studied, or non-comparability in measurement and analysis procedures. In fact, the results of the three studies appear remarkably similar considering all of the possible reasons why differences might be expected. But when we introduce controls we see that the partials appear quite different, much more so than a more or less common-sense approach would suggest.

In both the Srole and Roberts and Rokeach data the correlations between the two independent variables A and F are only moderately strong. Had they been of the order of magnitude of the correlation found by McDill (i.e., .67), the discrepancy between the partials would have been much more pronounced. Even so, the authors of the first two studies were led to quite different conclusions on the basis of total correlational differences that might very well have been attributed to sampling or measurement error.

■ **Table 2.** Comparison of total and partial correlations with dependent variable Y, for different values of correlations between independent variables X and Z.

Total correlations	Correlations between independent variables X and Z						
	.30	.40	.50	.60	.70	.80	.90
$r_{zy} = .70$	.68*	.63	.58	.53	.49	.46	.46
$r_{zy} = .60$	.57	.49	.40	.32	.22	.09	−.10
$r_{zy} = .60$	.54	.50	.47	.43	.40	.38	.40
$r_{zy} = .50$	.42	.35	.29	.22	.14	.04	−.11
$r_{zy} = .50$	.43	.40	.38	.35	.34	.33	.35
$r_{zy} = .40$	.30	.25	.20	.14	.08	.00	−.13

*   Values within body of table are partial correlations with controls on the remaining independent variable, e.g. for the top left-hand set of figures $r_{zy \cdot z} = .68$ and $r_{zy \cdot x} = .57$.

Numerical comparisons. It is instructive to ask how the numerical values of partial correlations will behave under various conditions in which the correlations between independent variables take on different values. Illustrative examples are given in Table 2. In each case we have paired off total correlations with the dependent variable (e.g., .60 and .50) which are so similar that differences could readily be attributed to sampling or measurement error. Reading across the table, we see that the bottom partial correlations in each pair decrease much more rapidly than do the top correlations. Thus the differences between partials become most striking as the correlation between the two independent variables increases. For example, when the correlation between X and Z is .80 and when the other two correlations are .60 and .50 respectively, one of the two partials is reduced almost to zero (.04) whereas the other remains moderately high (.38). Presumably, in another sample the two total correlations might have been reversed in magnitude, and the results of a partial correlational analysis would have looked strikingly different.

It might be thought that difficulties due to multicollinearity are peculiar to interval scales and partial correlations, but this is not the case. The same problems will arise, for example, using contingency methods of controlling. Some hypothetical results for 2×2 tables are given in Table 3.

In Table 3 the data for the partials were constructed so as to be consistent with the frequencies in the top three tables representing the total relationships, and also with the assumption that there is no interaction involved. The degree of relationship between Z and Y, controlling for X (see bottom tables), is negligible as indicated by an average ϕ of .08. But the partial relationship between X and Y is much stronger ($\bar{\phi} = .29$). Incidentally, we can also compute partial ϕ's using the standard formula for a partial correlation since ϕ is a special case of r. With the formula, the partials turn out to be .29 and .08, results which are identical (to the fourth decimal) to the average ϕ's for the two bottom sets of tables. Again we see that if the total association between the two independent variables is high, the partials are apt to look quite different even where the original relationships with the dependent variables are similar.

Further Comments

Were it not for factors such as measurement and sampling error we could still make reliable inferences even where the correlation between independent variables is moderately high. For example, the relationship between Z and Y might be completely spurious and due to X. We would then have the model $Z \leftarrow X \rightarrow Y$, giving us the empirical prediction that $r_{zy} = r_{xz}r_{xy}$. In such a case, both r_{xz} and r_{xy} should be larger numerically than r_{zy}. The three values might be .80, .60, and .50 respectively, In other words, if it were not for sampling or measurement errors we might validly infer that, say, the relationship between authoritarianism and ethnocentrism is spurious and due to anomie. What we are emphasizing, however, is that the possibility of such errors becomes a crucial factor whenever the two independent variables are highly related.

Presumably we wish to test the hypothesis that one or the other independent variable is spuriously related to the dependent variable, against the alternative that both may be independent causes of Y. In the latter case, neither partial should disappear when we control for the other variable. Gold has proposed a criterion for testing for such independent causation which, if we understand him correctly, will work in some situations but not in others.[8] Gold's suggestion is that we control for the *dependent* variable and relate the two independent variables. If the partial reduces to zero we may have independent causation. As can easily be seen, if X and Z are relatively weakly related to each other (in the appropriate direction) and if X and Z are *both* causes of Y, then r_{xz} may be numerically the smallest of the three coefficients. The partial, controlling for Y, may therefore nearly vanish. For example, if r_{xz} is .30 and the remaining correlations are .50 and .60, the partial $r_{xz \cdot y}$ will be exactly zero.

■ **Table 3.** Multicollinearity in the case of 2 × 2 contingency tables

					Total associations						
	Between X and Z				Between X and Y				Between Z and Y		
	Z				X				Z		
X	80	20	100	Y	70	30	100	Y	65	35	100
	20	80	100		30	70	100		35	65	100
	100	100	200		100	100	200		100	100	200
	$\phi = .60$				$\phi = .40$				$\phi = .30$		

					Partial associations						
					Low Z				High Z		
					X				X		
Between X and Y		Y			57	8	65	Y	13	22	35
					23	12	35		7	58	65
					80	20	100		20	80	100
$\bar\phi = .29$					$\phi = .26$				$\phi = .31$		
					$p < .01$				$p < .01$		
					Low X				High X		
					Z				Z		
Between Z and Y		Y			58	12	70	Y	7	23	30
					22	8	30		13	57	70
					80	20	100		20	80	100
$\bar\phi = .08$					$\phi = .11$				$\phi = .05$		
					$p > .20$				$p > .50$		

But quite clearly Gold's suggestion is inappropriate if the two independent variables happen to be highly related. Likewise, it will not work if the two independent causes of Y are negatively related to each other but each positively related to the dependent variable. In such instances a control for Y will *increase* the magnitude of the correlation between X and Z. For example, if r_{xz} is $-$ .30 and if the remaining correlations are .50 and .60, the partial becomes $-$ .87.

The present writer has perhaps erroneously implied in an earlier paper that comparatively simple ways may be found to evaluate the relative importance of two variables which, though both causes of Y, are intercorrelated.[9] He has failed, however, in several attempts to arrive at satisfactory formulas for breaking the variation in the dependent variable into distinct components attributed to each of the correlated independent variables. Tukey suggests that the problem is highly complex and perhaps not capable of yielding any satisfactory solution.[10]

In view of all these difficulties, we must urge caution in the interpretation of controlling operations in which supposedly independent variables are highly related. Further study is needed in view of the fact that in nonexperimental research such independent variables are quite likely to be intercorrelated. This is particularly the case where personality traits and attitudinal variables are being studied by means of relatively sophisticated techniques such as factor analysis. We strongly suspect that factor analyses are not immune to the same kinds of difficulties, especially where the rotated factors are highly intercorrelated.

NOTES

1. For an earlier discussion of multicollinearity see R. Frisch, *Statistical Confluence Analysis by Means of Complete Regression Systems* (Oslo: University Institute of Economics, 1934). See also H. Wold and L. Jureen, *Demand Analysis* (New York: Wiley, 1953), pp. 46–48; and J. Johnston, *Econometric Methods* (New York: McGraw-Hill, 1963), pp. 201–207.

2. We are dealing, here, with a special case of the more general problem in which the coefficients of an equation cannot be identified uniquely. For discussions of the "identification" problem see W. C. Hood and T. C. Koopmans (eds.), *Studies in Econometric Method* (New York: Wiley, 1953), especially Chap. 2.

3. Wold and Jureen, *op. cit.*, p. 47.

4. *Ibid.*, p. 48.

5. L. Srole, "Social Integration and Certain Corollaries: An Exploratory Study," *American Sociological Review*, Vol. 21 (December 1956), pp. 709–716.

6. A. Roberts and M. Rokeach, "Anomie, Authoritarianism, and Prejudice: A Replication," *American Journal of Sociology*, Vol. 61 (January 1956), pp. 355–358.

7. E. L. McDill, "Anomie, Authoritarianism, Prejudice, and Socio-Economic Status: An Attempt at Clarification," *Social Forces*, Vol. 39 (March 1961), pp. 239–245.

8. D. Gold, "Independent Causation in Multivariate Analysis: The Case of Political Alienation and Attitude Toward a School Bond Issue," *American Sociological Review*, Vol. 27 (February 1962), pp. 85–87.

9. See H. M. Blalock, "Evaluating the Relative Importance of Variables," *American Sociological Review*, Vol. 26 (December 1961), pp. 866–874.

10. J. W. Tukey, "Causation, Regression, and Path Analysis," in O. Kempthorne et al., *Statistics and Mathematics in Biology* (Ames, Iowa: Iowa State College Press, 1954), Chap. 3.

THE CASE OF THE INDIANS
AND THE TEEN-AGE WIDOWS

ANSLEY J. COALE
FREDERICK F. STEPHAN

1. Introduction

This article, for the most part, is a statistical detective story. It analyzes circumstantial evidence drawn from the 1950 Census of Population of the United States [2, 4, 5]. This evidence conclusively shows, we believe, that there were processing errors affecting a tiny fraction of the basic P or $Persons$ punch cards which were sorted to provide most of the tabular results of the population census.

The detective story describes the unraveling of a fairly complex pattern of "clues"—an exercise in deduction that may in itself prove an interesting diversion to some readers, as it did to the authors. The story also has practical implications for users of statistical data. Readers interested in these implications, but not in the somewhat complicated story upon which they are based, are referred to the final section.

2. Anomalous Data on the Marital Status of Teen-agers

Our first clue was the discovery in the 1950 Census of Population of the United States of startling figures about the marital status of teen-agers. There we found a surprising number of widowed fourteen year-old boys and, equally surprising, a decrease in the number of widowed teenage males at older ages. The numbers listed by the Census [4, tables 103 and 104] were 1,670 at age 14; 1,475 at age 15; 1,175, at 16; 810 at 17; 905 at 18; and 630 at age 19. Not until age 22 does the listed number of widowers surpass those at 14. Male divorcés also decrease in number as age increases, from 1,320 at age 14 to 575 at age 17. Smaller numbers of young female widows and divorcées are listed—565 widows and 215 divorcées at age 14. These strange figures, even though they appear in a very minor part of the carefully prepared and widely useful data presented in the Population Census, aroused our curiosity and set us to searching for an explanation.

Our investigation is in no way a reflection on the high quality and established accuracy of the Population Census overall. It merely recognizes that in well organized and competently conducted data collection processes there are still

Reprinted by permission of the authors and the American Statistical Association from *Journal of the American Statistical Association* **57** (June, 1962), 338–347.

possibilities for error and the progress of statistical data collection consists of discovering such errors to the fullest extent possible and correcting them as opportunities permit.

Errors arising either from ignorance or falsification on the part of the respondent or from carelessness or incompetence on the part of the enumerator are to be expected in any survey, including the decennial censuses. For many decades the Bureau of the Census has tried conscientiously to minimize such errors by its field procedures (including extensive pretesting), by careful design of the census questionnaires, and by its training program for enumerators and crew leaders. Moreover, the Bureau has pioneered in systematic attempts to determine the extent of errors in response and coverage, and has served as a model of objective scientific behavior for collectors of data by including extensive statements about sampling variability, and response and coverage errors in its published tabulations [2, 3, 4, *Introduction*]. However, it appears unlikely that the teen-age widowers are the result of errors by the respondent or the enumerator. Why should more false entries (or responses) of widowed be made at age 14 than at 15, or at age 15 than at 16? The strongly declining pattern of widowhood with age was not present in earlier censuses, as would be expected were the source of the anomaly in the behavior of respondents or interviewers.

Having noted the anomaly in listed marital status Stephan conjectured that the source of the error might be a mistake in punching some of the basic *P* or *Persons* cards which were sorted to provide most of the tabular results of the population census. Coale then joined him in searching out the discoverable effects of such mistakes in punching to provide a test of this hypothesis and also to yield an estimate of the number of cards that may have been affected and the probable causes of the punching error.

The *P* card is reproduced in Figure 1. If columns 24 to 28 were punched one position to the right of the proper set of punches, the following changes would take place on the cards affected:

a) *Relationship to head* would become *race*, with these transformations:

Head of household	becomes *White*
Wife	becomes *Negro*
Child	becomes *Indian*
Son or daughter-in-law	becomes *Japanese*
Grandchild	becomes *Chinese*
Parent	becomes *Filipino*
Other relation	becomes *Other race*

b) *Sex* would be determined by the entry in the *race* column, with these transformations:

White	becomes *Male*
Negro	becomes *Female*

The other racial categories would produce entries in the sex column that would result in the card's rejection as erroneously punched. The result of a discovered punching error might have been either the recognition of the shift in columns or the assignment of a "correct" (male or female) punch in the sex column on the basis of entries in other columns.

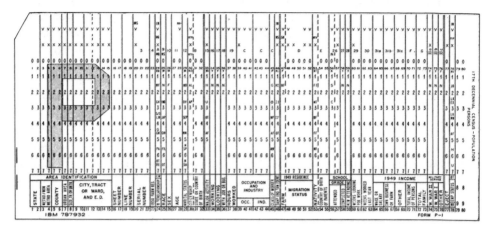

1   The *P* or *Persons* card employed in the 1950 Census of Population.

c)   *the first digit of age* would be determined by *sex*, with these transformations

    Male   becomes *one* (age in the teens)
    Female   becomes *two* (age in the twenties)

d)   *the second digit of age* would be determined by *the first digit of age*.
e)   *Marital status* would be determined by *the second digit of age*. The transformations implied by a column shift here are complicated by the fact that the coding of marital status for persons falling in the twenty-per cent sample was not the same as the coding for non-sample persons. For persons not in the sample, the 1 position in column 29 was to be punched if the person was married, 2 if widowed, 3 if divorced, 4 if separated, and 5 if single.

Additional information regarding presence of spouse was to be coded for married persons in a 20 per cent sample of the population.[1] The information was obtained by examination of adjacent lines on the schedule. For sample cards, then, position one should never have been punched, while position six meant married, spouse present, and position seven meant married, spouse absent.

Thus the following transformations are indicated for cards in the twenty-per cent sample:

---

[1]   The tables showing marital status by age were based on tabulation of twenty-per cent sample cards.

Second age-digit of 2 becomes *widowed*
Second age-digit of 3 becomes *divorced*
Second age-digit of 4 becomes *separated*
Second age-digit of 5 becomes *single*
Second age-digit of 6 becomes *married, spouse present*
Second age-digit of 7 becomes *married, spouse absent*

■ **Table 1.** U.S. ever-married white males 14–17 by marital status, 1950, according to the 1950 census, and to estimates based on the 1940 census

	14	15	16	17
Married				
1950 census	6,195	6,400	*	*
Estimated from 1940 census	1,765	2,465	*	*
Apparent excess in 1950 census	4,430	3,935	*	*
Widowed				
1950 census	1,600	1,355	1,115	720
Estimated from 1940 census	85	85	135	185
Apparent excess in 1950 census	1,515	1,270	980	535
Divorced				
1950 census	1,240	930	730	525
Estimated from 1940 census	85	135	125	255
Apparent excess in 1950 census	1,155	795	605	270

*   At ages 16 and 17 estimated marriages were more than 50 per cent of the census figures, and the estimated error was deemed too unreliable to be published.

It is not clear what would happen to sample cards subject to a shift of column if the second digit of age were 0, 1, 8, or 9. It would have been reasonable to assign the sample cards punched with a 1 (married) to 6 (married, spouse present) or 7 (married, spouse absent) on the grounds that the puncher had incorrectly punched the sample card by the procedure appropriate for non-sample cards. The cards with punches of 0, 8, or 9 could be regarded only as wrongly punched. Two possible actions could have followed: (1) the column shift may have been detected, and a new card punched; or (2) the cards may have been . . ." assigned to the modal marital status category for persons of their age." —*single* for teen-age males [2, p. 50].

3. Erroneously Designated Teen-agers Were Really Middle-Aged Males

If occasionally cards were erroneously punched one column to the right, the source of erroneously listed teen-agers (14–18) would be males in their 40's,

50's, 60's, 70's, or 80's. *Heads of households* would be the source of erroneous *white* teen-agers, while all other relationships to the head would produce erroneous *non-white* teen-agers. White persons would produce *male* teen-agers, Negro persons *female* teen-agers, and all other races would yield an unacceptable punch in the sex column. Persons aged 42 would be listed as widowed 14-year-olds, 52 as widowed 15-year-olds, etc.; while persons aged 43, 53, 63, 73, and 83 would be listed as 14, 15, 16, 17, and 18-year-old divorcés.

In an effort to make a numerical estimate of the errors in classification of marital status, we attempted a rough construction of the number who *should* have been listed as married, widowed, and divorced in some of the teen ages. We might have contemplated an assumption that the proportion in each marital status at each age was the same as in 1940, had there not been a marked increase in the frequency of marriage below age 20 in the decade of the 1940's. We allowed for this increase in early marriage by assuming that the fraction married at ages 14, 15, 16, and 17 for a given color-sex group (e.g., white males) increased by the same multiple as the increase in the fraction married at ages 18 and 19. (The fraction married at these ages in 1950 was not seriously contaminated by the punch-card error, because the source of erroneous cards would be the relatively small number of heads of households in their eighties and nineties.) We also assumed that the widowed and divorced at each age in the range 14–17 changed, as a fraction of the married, in the same proportion as at ages 19 and 20. The resulting estimates of married, widowed and divorced among white males 14–17 are included in Table 1.

Estimates of the "true" number in each marital status based on these assumptions can scarcely be considered precise, and no estimates have been reproduced where the estimated true figure is as much as 50 per cent of the number reported in the census. When the estimated true figure is only a small fraction of the number given in the census, imprecision in the estimate is relatively unimportant. Thus if the true number of 14-year old white male widowers were twice our estimate (implying a 100 per cent mistake in estimation), the estimated 1950 Census error would be reduced only from 1515 to 1430.

Actually, the use of 1940 proportions of widowed/married tends to over-estimate expected widows in 1950, because it neglects reduction in mortality during the decade, especially maternal mortality. The assumption that the fraction married at 14–17 increased to the same degree as those married at age 19 is harder to appraise. The frequency of teen-age marriage undoubtedly increased, but whether or not the increase was greater at very young ages—14 or 15—than at 19 remains a matter of conjecture.

Moreover, it appears that the proportion widowed/married at early teen ages in the 1940 Census was actually overstated. In 1940, the reported *number* widowed increases steadily with age, but the widowed as a *proportion* of the married descends from 14 to age 19 as follows: 50, 34, 29, 17, 9, and 6 per thousand. When allowance is made for the negative socio-economic selection that is probable among those marrying very young, for the likelihood that the young wives are exposed to pregnancy and childbirth at very early ages, and for the doubtless rising probability of widower-remarriage as age of the widower increases from 14 to 19, it is possible to make a case for the validity of figures showing a declining proportion widowed/married as age increases. But the *magnitude* of the reported decline is not credible. Surely most 14-year-old widowers would have been married no more than a year; and the ratio of widowed/married among the 14-year-olds implies a mortality rate 50 to 100 times the rate for adolescent girls in 1940, and 15 to 30 times the maternal mortality rate for white mothers. However, the steeply declining proportion of widowed/married is characteristic of all recent censuses, and the assumption of such a pattern in 1950 may be employed as an approximation not to reality, but to what the census tables would have shown in the absence of a shift of columns in the punching operation.

The persons erroneously classified as white males aged 14, 15, 16, and 17 were presumably white male heads of households in their 40's, 50's, 60's, or 70's. To be reported as a 14-year-old widower, the white male household head would be 42; if 43 he would be reported as a 14-year-old divorcé. No single-year age-distribution by age, sex, color, and relationship to head of household was printed in 1950. However, by interpolation of the proportion by five-year age groups of (white male household heads)/(total white males) it is possible to form a close estimate of such a single-year distribution. We can then estimate what proportion of the punch-cards were subject to the column-shift error. The proportions are shown in Table 2. The proportion "shifted" whose age terminates in 2 appears to be somewhat in excess of those with a terminal digit of 3. The persistent difference in the 40's, 50's, 60's, and 70's could scarcely be explained by chance variations in erroneous punching. Perhaps some other source of error swelled the number reported as widowed; perhaps the erroneous "divorced" were more frequently detected by some sort of editing procedure, or perhaps our technique of "updating" the 1940 Census consistently overestimated the true number of divorcés. In any event, it seems clear that some 14 to 20 per ten thousand of the white male household-head punch cards sorted in the 20 per cent sample were punched (in at least a portion of the columns) one column to the right of proper position.

Persons erroneously classified as *white females* aged 14, 15, 16, and 17 were (if we accept the hypothesis of a shift in columns) Negro heads of households in their 40's, 50's, 60's, and 70's. Because the true number of married, widowed, and divorced is much higher at the young ages among females than among males, it is not possible to estimate nearly as well the number of errors caused by a shift in columns. However, at age 14 if it is assumed that the change in widowed/married since 1940 was the same as at age 19, the true number of widows would be about 80 at age 14, and the number shifted from Negro male households head age 42 would be about 400. This constitutes some 50/10,000 of the estimated 77,000 Negro male household heads aged 42. Similar calculations (still less reliable) indicate an error rate of over 60/10,000 at ages 52 and 62. In short, the proportion of erroneous punch cards for Negro male household heads appears to have been about three times as high as for white male household heads. Of course it is possible that the errors in punching were "bunched," and that the high proportion of errors among cards for Negroes was the result of a fortuitous concentration of errors among cards for geographical areas where Negroes predominate.

■ **Table 2.** Proportion of punch cards apparently subject to shift of column for white male household heads of various ages.

Age of household head	Estimated no. of white male house- hold heads	Reported as	Estimated number erroneously reported	Errors per 10,000 of original cards
42	822,000	widowers age 14	1,515	18.4
52	650,000	widowers age 15	1,270	19.5
62	478,000	widowers age 16	980	20.5
72	244,000	widowers age 17	535	21.9
42, 52, 62, 72	2,194,000	widowers 14–17	4,300	19.6
43	739,000	divorcés age 14	1,155	15.6
53	613,000	divorcés age 15	795	13.0
63	444,000	divorcés age 16	605	13.6
73	212,000	divorcés age 17	270	12.7
43, 53, 63, 73	2,008,000	divorcés 14–17	2,825	14.1
41, 44, 46, 47	2,760,000	married age 14	4,430	16.1
51, 54, 56, 57	2,342,000	married age 15	3,935	16.8

4. White Children of Household Heads Become Young Indians

The figures presented above do not give a completely persuasive explanation of the anomalous data on marital status in the 1950 Census. In support of the hypothesis of the shift in columns while punching there is the fairly consistent proportion of estimated erroneous widowed males to the number of white male household heads at ages 42, 52, 62, and 72, and the similar consistency in the proportion of erroneous divorcés to heads at ages 43, 53, 63, and 73. But the two sets of proportions are different, and the proportions of errors among Negro males appears to be several times higher. No complete explanation of these discrepant error rates presents itself. In fact, an especially skeptical reader might question the whole hypothesis of a shift in columns in view of these varying apparent rates of error. However, there is an independent and wholly conclusive reason for believing that a shift in columns *did* occur.

As was stated earlier, a shift of the punches intended for column 24 into column 25 would translate relationships to head of household (other than household head itself) into races other than white. Specifically a white person when relationship to the head was *child* would be coded as a male Indian, while a Negro child of the household head would be coded as a female Indian. If the white child were male, he would appear as an Indian in his teens; if female, as an Indian in his twenties. Since over 99 per cent of "children" are under 50, and since the shift transfers first digit of age into the second digit, the erroneous Indians would be 10–14 if really male, and 20–24 if really female.

An examination of the age-distribution of the non-white population [5, Table 3] discloses that there are indeed excess Indians at ages 10–14 and 20–24 among both males and females, with more numerous erroneous male than female entries. Moreover, the excess is glaringly apparent in those areas (e.g. Northeastern United States, or North Central Urban) where the true Indian population is a small minority. Thus in the Northeast there are reported 757 male Indians aged 5–9; 1,379 aged 10–14; 668 aged 15–19; 1,297 aged 20–24; and 596 aged 25–29. The erroneous entries at 10–14 and 15–19 are about as numerous in this region as the genuine entries. No "bulges" at 10–14 and 20–24 are to be found in the male Indian population reported in 1940, or in earlier censuses.

5. Excessive Widowhood and Divorce among Indians

As a final confirmation that a shift in columns was the cause of these errors, we find anomalous figures of a sort to be expected on this hypothesis in the reported marital status of the Indian population 14–24, 25–44, and 45 and over [5, Table 10]. Included in the reported 14–24 year olds would be erroneous entries caused by the shift in columns. The source of the erroneous cards would be male persons forty or older whose relation to the head of the household is "child," and female "children" 0–49 years old. The marital status reported for these erroneously entered Indians would depend only on the second digit of age. Those with terminal digits of 2 and 3 would be tabulated as widowed and divorced, with 1, 4, 6, and 7 as married, with 5 as single. If the second digit of age were 0, 8, or 9 the card would be detected as wrongly punched. It could then either have been recognized as subject to a column shift, and a new card punched, or the modal marital status (single) could have been assigned. The marital status anomaly that we expect is an excessive number of widowed and divorced in the age category 14–24, especially among the males. In the whole United States and in every region except the West, where the *true* Indians are most numerous, the widowed and divorced 14–24 year old males are reported (contrary to common sense) as exceeding in number the widowed and divorced females in the 14–24 age group. Moreover, in the Northeast, the reported number of widowed and divorced males 14–24 exceeds those reported at 25–44 by more than two to one.

The number of erroneously reported Indian males 14–24 in the Northeast (substantially equal to those reported as 20–24, since there are so few male "children" in their forties to be shifted into the 14-year-old category) can be estimated by assuming that the ratio of 20–24 year olds to the sum of 15–19 and 25–29 year olds *should* have been the same as in 1940. The estimate on this basis is about 650 erroneously reported. Of these, 2/7 (those with terminal age digits of 2 or 3 rather than 1, 4, 5, 6, or 7) would be reported as widowed or divorced. 2/7 of 650 is about 185. The reported 14–24 year old male widowers and divorcés number 184.

The number of false Indians in the nation can be approximated by the same procedure applied above to the Northeast. The result indicates more than 3,000 white male "children" were erroneously listed as male Indians 10–14, and about 2,000 white female children as male Indians 20–24. These errors constitute more than 15 per cent of the true Indians at these ages, but only about one per ten thousand of the white "children." Errors in the female Indian age distribution at ages 10–14 and 20–24 are sufficient to cause a visible distortion, but are much fewer than among the males—since the source is male and female Negro "children." The error rate among white children is less than one-tenth that found earlier among the cards of white household heads. Part of this difference in error rate is to be expected on the following basis: an x punch was made in column 46 for cards *not* in the 20 per cent sample; cards without the x punch would thus be sorted as sample cards. A shift of columns would put the x punch in column 47 (where it means "same house last year"). Moreover, all of the codes in column 46 except "not working" (code 6) would be translated into acceptable entries in column 47. In short, it appears likely that nearly all of the "shifted" cards would appear in the 20 per cent sample, implying that the error rate on sample tabulations is about 5 times that in tabulations of all cards. The remainder of the 10 times difference could be accounted for by the high proportion of "children's" cards that would be coded 6 (not working) in column 45 and rejected when sorted on column 46. On the other hand, most heads of households would be coded 1 to 5 in column 45 and the card would *not* be rejected when sorted on column 46.

6. Summary and Conclusions

We have found conclusive evidence that several thousand of the basic *Persons* cards used in the tabulations of the 1950 Census of Population were subject to a displacement of columns when being punched. The portion affected ranges from about 1/100 of one per cent among all cards for white females who were children of the household head to about 5/10 of one per cent of the 20 per cent sample cards among Negro male household heads. We can account for some of the variation by noting that all of the shifted cards should have been sorted with the 20 per cent sample, and by the fact that cards coded as "not working" in column 45 would be rejected. But we are left with residual variations in error rate—Negro errors apparently some two-and-a-half to three times the white, for example—that we cannot explain.

These errors were so infrequent that their effect on the number of cards in the groups from which they were drawn is completely negligible. However, in three instances where the groups into which the erroneous cards were sorted were very small, the effect was anything but negligible. For example, the 1950 Census age distribution of American Indians contains more than 15 per cent too many males 10–14 and 20–24; and the number of white males under 17 reported in marital status categories other than "single" was determined more by cards punched in wrong columns than by actual marriages, divorces, and deaths of spouse.

Several practical implications emerge from an appreciation of these errors. First is the importance of the realization that the results of any survey (or indeed of any measurement) must be interpreted in the light of all of the operations— such as interviewing, coding, recording, punching, sorting, and tabulating— that underlie the published figures. It was only through inferring the operational basis of the erroneous classification of teen-age marital status that we were led to anticipate errors in the age-distribution of Indians. We were able to do so only because the Bureau of the Census publishes such a full account of all of its procedures [2], a custom that should be followed by other major data collecting agencies.

A feature of the Census operations that is relevant to the column shift was the verification of punching on a sampling basis by quality control procedures [2, p. 31]. The use of quality control in place of 100 per cent verification of punched cards is amply justified by the savings achieved. One hundred per cent verification would have about doubled the cost of punching. The consequent reallocation of funds would inevitably have caused other more important deficiencies in the census. But quality control, by its nature, permits a very low, unavoidable rate of occurrence of punching errors. In almost all instances these errors are wholly inconsequential. Through the misfortune that some of the very infrequent unavoidably tolerated errors in punching inflated categories which were themselves very rare, a few tabulated results were, in fact, tangibly distorted.

A further implication, then, is that users must scrutinize numbers in small cells of census tabulations with special care. Leon E. Truesdell pointed out this necessity in 1938, citing as an example the possibility that persons for whom no answer is recorded to a question about reading and writing might be recorded as illiterate. Illiteracy was assumed relatively infrequent in his example, so that a small number of "blanks" counted as "no" might double the apparent incidence of illiteracy [1]. Many other examples could be cited of errors of one sort or another that have a visible effect on small cells. One instance can be observed in the listing of years of school in which enrolled, by single years of age, in the United States in 1950 [4, Table 112]. In the first year of elementary school there are shown 7,790 persons 13 years old, 12,765 14 years old, and 8,885 aged 15. In the second year of elementary school the figures at ages 14, 15, and 16 are

6,980, 11,025, and 6,665. It is almost certain that some students in the first year of *high school* (where the modal age is 14) were erroneously listed as in the first year of elementary school.[2] The proportion of such errors was small, but sufficient to produce a large proportionate inflation of the numbers of reported 14-year-olds in the first year of elementary school. In this article we have merely found an additional source—column shifts—of possible error in the numbers in rate categories in tabulations of survey results.

The Bureau of the Census changed over in 1960 to data sensing machinery to transcribe information onto magnetic tape, and the specific problem of a shift in columns is no longer relevant to census operations. The new set of processing operations poses new problems of error control for the Bureau, and may possibly cause misleading figures to show up in new and unsuspected ways in small cells. Users must continue to regard such data with special care.

REFERENCES

1. Truesdell, Leon E. "Residual relationships and velocity of change as pitfalls in the field of statistical forecasting," *Journal of the American Statistical Association*, 33 (1938), 373–9.

2. United States Bureau of the Census. *The 1950 Censuses—How They Were Taken*. Washington, D.C.: Government Printing Office, 1955.

3. United States Bureau of the Census. *The Post-Enumeration Survey: 1950*. Bureau of the Census, Technical Paper No. 4, Washington, D.C., 1960.

4. United States Bureau of the Census. *U.S. Census of Population: 1950, Volume II, Characteristics of the Population*, Part 1, United States Summary. Washington, D.C.: Government Printing Office, 1953.

5. United States Bureau of the Census. *U.S. Census of Population: 1950, Volume IV, Special Reports*, Part 3, Chapter B, "Nonwhite Population by Race." Washington D.C.: Government Printing Office, 1953.

---

2   Enumerators were instructed to code elementary school attendance (in an eight-grade elementary school) as $S1$ to $S8$, and high school attendance as $S9$ to $S12$ [2, p. 55]. An occasional coding of "first year high school" as $S1$ is perfectly understandable.

IMPROVING DATA ANALYSIS
IN POLITICAL SCIENCE*

EDWARD R. TUFTE

I. The Problem

Students of politics use statistical and quantitative techniques to:

summarize a large body of numbers into a small collection of typical values;
confirm (and perhaps sanctify) the results of the analysis by using tests of statistical significance that help protect against sampling and measurement error;
discover what's going on in their data and expose some new relationships; and
inform their audience what's going on in the data.[1]

Most textbooks of social statistics tell us a lot about summarizing and sanctifying in their many chapters on descriptive statistics and significance tests, but they have little to say about how to discover the unanticipated or how to learn something new from the data. Graphical techniques, are for example, among the most powerful procedures for both discovering and informing. Yet most textbooks give only the most humdrum, and often misleading, advice about displaying the data—such as the "necessity" for showing the zero point and for equal class intervals. With this kind of advice, students naturally come away with the impression that the only point of graphing is to make a pie diagram showing how next year's budget is going to be spent. Similarly, most textbook discussions of how to fit straight lines to data—potentially the most powerful technique of data analysis available in many situations—are devoted to explaining how to see whether a particular coefficient is significantly different from zero (sanctification again). Little is said about how to analyze residuals or how to transform the variables entering a regression—techniques that will help us discover patterns in the data far better than any significance test. Finally, almost to guarantee that budding social scientists learn little about discovering and informing, most textbooks of social statistics contain few, if any, actual case histories of data analysis.[2] No wonder most questions concerning data analysis ask whether a scale is "really" an interval scale or whether a one-tailed t-test is appropriate in a particular situation.

Reprinted by permission of Princeton University Press from *World Politics* 21 (July, 1969), 641–654.

The results of all this bad advice show up in many recent quantitative efforts in political science. For example, consider the essays collected in *Quantitative International Politics*, a book representative of many quantitative studies of politics.[3] Instead of residuals off a regression line, we see almost every page littered with the results of significance tests often complete with all the relentless detail of computations, degrees of freedom, test statistics, and probability levels. Residuals (that part of the variation that is "unexplained") are not analyzed in any of the essays simply because no one fitted a line to any data. And even though there is lots of talk about how complicated the world is, no author uses multiple regression, which would allow the inclusion of more than a single explanatory variable. Instead of a sensitive analysis of the problem of multi-collinearity (the difficulty in separating out the independent effects of highly correlated describing variables) and its immediate and profound consequences for testing theories of politics, we see a single correlation matrix twelve pages long in an article that totals twenty-eight pages.

In short, then, much of current political data analysis leaves the impression that the important uses of quantitative methods in the study of politics are either to summarize a large body of data or to sanctify an observed relationship at the .05 level of significance.

How can we do better?

From the point of view of discovering and informing, the following four points help summarize a good approach toward effective data analysis:

1)   Significance tests deserve a secondary role in data analysis. They can be useful, but only after we look at the right things. Significance tests cannot tell us what to think.

2)   The distinction between interval and ordinal measurement is usually of little importance in data analysis. The wise assignment of numbers to ordered categories, coupled with the use of techniques that exploit the properties of numbers, is generally preferable to working with ordered categories.

3)   Looking at correlations is only a partial, first step in the analysis. Correlations are often misleading.

4)   The most effective method of data analysis usually begins by fitting lines to relationships between variables (transformed variables if necessary) and then continues by examining, with the aid of graphs and scatterplots, deviations off the fitted line.

Many people have argued one way or another about the first two points above, and these issues, broadly speaking, are not settled. But if we consider the issue of the utility of significance tests and the problem of levels of measurement from the point of view of discovering and informing—in other words, from the point of view of the pragmatic data analyst—we should find propositions 1 and 2 fairly easy to accept. Let us now look at the four basic points in more detail.

II. The Reconstructed Science of Significance Testing

The overemphasis on significance testing has arisen in part, I think, because some have taken the reconstruction of what scientists do more seriously than actual scientific practice.[4] Thus the rote paradigm of significance testing— Assumptions (Level of Measurement, Model, and Hypothesis); Sampling Distribution; Significance Level and Critical Region; Computing the Test Statistic; and, behold, The Decision—represents a severe and impractical formalization that fails to provide useful guides to effective data analysis. Such a paradigm often serves only to make researchers feel guilty that they have violated one of the unrealistic assumptions of statistical significance tests.

What good are tests of significance, then? Such tests help protect against the possibility that a relationship arises because of happenstance in a random sample.[5] They are also useful as a rough sort of screening device in the analysis of data collected nonrandomly. They may help us adjust our feeling of certainty or uncertainty about a result. Thus the responsible investigator will use tests against the null hypothesis or, often better, confidence intervals to assess the stability of his results. Significance levels are often misused, however, because the dichotomy between "significant" and "nonsignificant" is too sharply drawn and the investigator regards those relationships that reach the .05 level (sometimes the .01 level is the sacred probability) as being the only truly meaningful results. This is bad practice; the relevance of a result does not hinge on its exact significance level. Emphasizing the importance of substantive judgment in interpreting the results of data analysis, one statistician has proposed the "interocular trauma test" of significance: you know what the data mean when the conclusion hits you between the eyes. Edwards, Lindman, and Savage comment further that the "enthusiast's interocular trauma may be the skeptic's random error. A little arithmetic to verify the extent of the trauma can yield great peace of mind for little cost."[6]

Finally, probability levels and test statistics tell us very little about the strength and nothing about the substantive significance of a relationship. The important question is, "Does the result show a relationship which is of substantive interest because of its nature and magnitude?"[7] Significance tests are silent on this matter. Mosteller and Hammel throw light on the problem by noting that when the investigator uses tests of statistical significance, he then faces "the standard difficulty of what to do with the relationships once significance is established. Significance tests have little to say about this. What to do is never made entirely clear, and, as far as we can see, it will be up to the investigator to use his own judgment in appraising and weighting reports that show relations with conditions of observation. Perhaps it will never be possible to improve on individual judgment in such matters; the treatment may be an open statistical problem, or it may be that regression methods could aid the research worker."[8]

In short, then, it seems obvious to suggest that scientific, mathematical, or statistical jargon should not be used merely to sanctify the results of political analysis. Hempel has put the matter clearly: "To say that 'A man M walks down a street S' does not increase the scientific validity of a statement." And to attach a test statistic and a statistical significance level to a statement does not help it much either.

III. Getting out of the Rut of Cross-Tabulations: Pinning Numbers on Ordered Categories

How seriously should a data analyst take the distinction between ordinal and interval measurement? Many have taken the distinction very, very seriously—almost to the point of paralysis. While there is a conceptual distinction between ordinal and interval measurement,[9] the issue that should concern the data analyst is whether this distinction has any practical meaning for his work. One good reason for pinning numbers on ordered categories is that the researcher often knows more about the phenomenon than the mere ordering of observations implies; thus, assigning numbers helps to build that additional information into measurement. For example, if the researcher knows that $A > B > C > D$ and, on the basis of his substantive understanding of the thing being measured, he also knows that D is far from C compared to, say, the difference between A and B, then the measurement should incorporate this information by assigning, for example, the numbers 1, 2, 3, and 9 to the ordered categories. Of course it is arbitrary.[10] The point, as Tukey has put it, is to be *wisely* arbitrary. The argument raises two issues:

1) Should we pin numbers on ordered categories?

2) If yes, just exactly *what* numbers are to be assigned to each category?

From the point of view of doing the detective work of data analysis, we want to assign numbers to orderings. By doing this, we improve measurement by taking advantage of any additional information above and beyond the fact of ordering. Numbers put more substance into measurement. An additional gain is that considerably more powerful techniques can be used in the analysis of the data and thereby increase our chances of learning something new. In the face of these potential gains—better measurement and better analysis—there appears to be very little in the way of potential costs. By sticking rigidly to the distinction between ordinal and interval levels of measurement (a distinction often difficult to make in practice), we are, in effect, censoring the data and shutting off part of what the data could tell us—if we would only let them.[11]

Admitting, then, the possibility that numbers actually should be assigned to ordered categories, just exactly what numbers should be assigned? Several methods have been proposed,[12] but three fairly useful and simple rules are:

1) The assignment should incorporate the investigator's substantive understanding of the thing being measured.

2) The simple linear assignment of numbers to categories (e.g., assigning 1, 2, 3, 4 to four ordered categories) usually won't do. Such a linear assignment is not, in any way, a sounder or more conservative choice than any other assignment. And the chances are that such an assignment is not consistent with the first principle of incorporating substantive information into the measurement.

3) The assignment should often be made so that the distribution of counts begins to look somewhat like a normal distribution.

If the concern is, for example, the magnitude of internal conflict in a society, the measurement might begin with the four ordered categories: (a) petitions against the government, (b) peaceful, massive demonstrations, (c) violent demonstrations, and (d) civil war. Plainly, the category (d) of civil war is in a league by itself so far as internal conflict is concerned. The assignment of numbers to the four categories should take this into account. One such assignment would be the numbers 1, 2, 5, and 17. It would be even better to start with more than four categories—in fact, with as many categories as possible—especially since there is no reason to believe that internal conflict in societies is distributed in four clumps (and certainly not in four equally spaced clumps, as the assignment of 1, 2, 3, and 4 would assume). But, at any rate, we should never work with only two categories. Throwing everything into two bins by dichotomizing the data is just about the most severe form of censorship we could impose on the data. Even with the choice of the optimal cutting point, a major amount of information is lost by dichotomizing the data.

IV. The Pitfalls of Correlations

The correlation coefficient is often used to summarize the relationship between two variables. It is overworked. The contributors to *Quantitative International Politics* report a grand total of about 1,600 correlations in their various essays. Or, taking another example, Thomas Dye's *Politics, Economics, and the Public* includes more than 5,000 correlations. Such coefficients have serious defects; indeed, their faults are often so great that some have recommended that "most correlation coefficients should never be calculated."[13] What are the pitfalls involved in the use of correlations? What are the alternatives to correlation coefficients?

The three scatterplots shown below convey widely divergent information about the relationship between X and Y. The first plot shows no relationship, discounting the extreme outlier on both measures. The second plot suggests a moderately strong linear relationship between X and Y. The third plot reveals a rather marked curvilinear relationship between X and Y, indicating that as X increases, Y gets bigger even faster. Despite the great variation in the visual message, *the correlation between X and Y is the same in all three cases.*

This example shows that a correlation coefficient is a pretty poor way of summarizing the actual data as revealed in the scatterplot. One practical moral

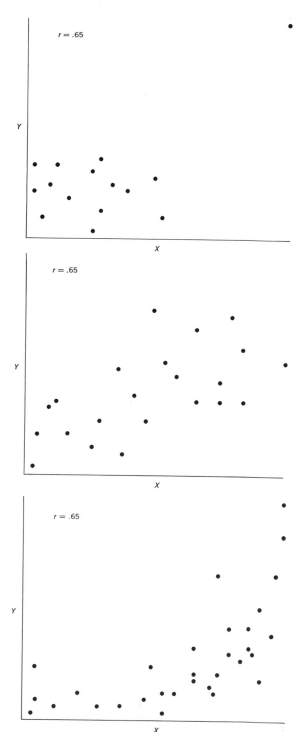

Three different scatterplots with the same correlation (r = .65)

here is that any computer program that produces a correlation matrix should also produce scatterplots of the relationships. A more obvious moral is, of course, that people should use scatterplots more than they do. A major benefit of scatterplots and of most graphical procedures is that they allow the reader to decide for himself how much he wants to learn from the data—instead of having the relationship summarized, and perhaps maimed, by a correlation coefficient or other summary statistic.

Sometimes correlations take us too far away from the substantive matters at hand. For example, consider some hypothetical data relating the number of dollars spent for precinct work on election day and the voter turnout in each precinct. One way to summarize such data is to say, "The correlation between dollars and votes is 0.73." That doesn't say as much as does the statement: "On the average, every $10 produces 1.7 votes." Expressing the result as a correlation coefficient is less informative in this case than is expressing the result as the slope of the line fitting the data. Often both coefficients are informative.

The faults of correlation coefficients do not disappear when correlations are built into a more complex model through the use of partial correlations (as is frequently done in efforts at building "causal models"). While the Simon-Blalock version of causal modeling pays lip service to regression coefficients, most applications of causal modeling never deal with regression coefficients; they are devoted to seeing whether certain partial correlations go to zero.[14] And just as simple correlations can mislead, so can partial correlations.

Finally, it is common practice in using data based on geographic units to "deflate" the values of a variable by dividing it by the population of the geographic unit, and then to correlate the deflated variables. For example, a typical ratio or index correlation (as they are often called) is the correlation between welfare expenditures per capita and income per capita, computed over the fifty states. Similarly, most of the correlations computed in various collections of data for the nations of the world are ratio correlations based on "per-capitized" variables. Ratio correlations can be misleading, and the questions they are designed to answer can be more usefully framed as regression problems.[15]

Often, then, correlation coefficients are very inadequate tools of analysis. Scatterplots and regression coefficients are more useful. Regression coefficients are certainly preferable in situations where increments along the scales of each variable make some sort of substantive sense.[16] In general, the best procedure is to use both correlation and regression coefficients when they are meaningful. Unfortunately, for all the correlation coefficients reported in *Quantitative International Politics* and in *Politics, Economics, and the Public*, no author reported a single regression coefficient.

V. The Importance of Fitting Lines to Data

Political scientists have tended to be diverted by what are essentially secondary issues in data analysis—significance tests and the distinctions among various levels of measurement. Furthermore, I have argued that correlation coefficients have been overworked and their serious defects ignored in most political data analysis. How, then, can we do a better job of data analysis? How can we get out of summarizing and sanctifying and on to discovering and informing?

The answer to these questions, I think, is rarely to be found in a search for new and exotic techniques—especially if we want to communicate our results to more than a tiny fraction of those involved in the discipline. Almost every new issue of a political science journal introduces a new mathematical or statistical technique. At times it appears that new techniques are introduced not because they fit the substantive problem under investigation, but rather because a new computer program is available to produce some results. There is a real and already visible danger of faddishness in applications of quantitative methods. It is not surprising that the limits of such techniques are often underappreciated by their users. Misguided applications of these techniques, however, not only lend a spurious air of certainty to often false conclusions; such misapplications can also lead to an unwarranted distrust of the methods that seem to have produced the conclusions. Both causal modelling and factor analysis may wind up by being the victims of their own advocates. This may be only wishful thinking, however.

All in all, political scientists have tended to ignore the useful regression procedures that fit lines to data. For example, none of the authors in *Quantitative International Politics*, a book that is aggressively quantitative, used even the most elementary kind of regression model. In the remainder of this paper, I want to suggest why multiple regression actually is a useful procedure for data analysis.

Fitting lines to relationships between variables (or variables that are transformed) and then examining the deviations off the fitted line by graphs and scatterplots has a good many virtues:

1) In regression analysis (unlike factor analysis), the research worker must have a fairly specific idea of just what it is he wants to explain. Simply, he has to think in causal terms and know what his response (dependent) and describing (independent) variables are.[17]

2) Fitting lines to data generates residuals, those parts of the variation in the response variable left unexplained by the describing variables. The effective analysis of residuals is a major tool for discovery.

3) The resulting regression coefficients, especially if they are unstandardized, occasionally have substantive meaning and policy implications.

4) Econometricians have built up a large body of useful experience in the application of regression methods to substantive problems. Their advice is sometimes more useful to political scientists than is the advice of other sorts of statisticians.

Finally, let us turn to three important matters in the fitting of lines to data: the analysis of residuals, the transformation of variables, and multicollinearity.

VI. The Analysis of Residuals

Usually the describing variables do not account for all the variation in the response variable. Trying to find something that will explain some of the residual variation helps us discover the unanticipated in a collection of data.

The first step in the analysis of residuals is simply to label them; that is, to calculate the residual for each observation, look at the whole collection of residuals, and see what those observations with residuals of the same size have in common. The next step is to plot the residuals against a wide assortment of things. Here, the computer programmers have let us down a bit, although some regression packages have options for plotting residuals.[18] As far as plotting goes, Tukey and Wilk suggest:

■ Kinds of plots of residuals that are very often valuable include (i) plots against fitted, or possible values; (ii) plots against variables which have been employed as a basis for the summarizing fit; (iii) plots against variables, which were not used in the fit, e.g., time; (iv) plots which display residuals identified according to some meaningful characteristic, e.g., according to whether the residual is or is not from an observation which was used in developing the fitted summary; (v) probability plots of ordered residuals, including empirical cumulative distribution plots and plots of empirical quantiles against quantiles of reference distributions, such as the unit normal. While all such plots provide indications of the spread of the body of residuals, it is far more important that they combine palatable summaries of individual residuals with sensitive indications of distributional peculiarities of the entire collection of residuals.[19] ■

VII. Transformations of Variables

Transformations of variables—that is, any systematic changes in the observed values of the variables made during the course of the analysis—play an important role in the process of fitting lines to data. Transformations are useful because they enable us to use linear techniques to fit rather complicated, non-linear models to the data, because they often point to substantive results, and, finally, because they help the data satisfy certain statistically desirable properties such as normality and stability of variance.[20]

For example, in the analysis of cross-national aggregate data, the logarithm of the variable is often used in place of the actual value of the variable, for convenience and also to meet statistical assumptions. When the variables are logged, moreover, there is an additional gain in terms of the substantive interpretation of the regression analysis. In the two-variable case, with both variables logged, we have

$$\log Y = b \log X + c.$$

It can be shown that b, the estimate of the slope, is the elasticity of Y with respect to X.[21] Thus b estimates the proportional change in Y resulting from a proportional change in X. An increase of 1 per cent in X, then, produces under this model a change of b per cent in Y. This neat interpretation of the slope is an extra benefit of the use of the log transform.

Transformations are also useful in the analysis of percentages. For example, is it always meaningful to assume the difference between 50 and 60 per cent (an increase of 10 per cent) has the same meaning as the 10 per cent difference between 85 and 95 per cent? The research worker should, when it is appropriate, take into account that a 10 per cent increase starting from 85 per cent as the base is actually often a bigger and more important substantive change than the same amount of percentage-change beginning at an initial level of 50 per cent. If this reasoning is correct, then the tails of percentage distributions should be stretched by transformations of percentages. A number of options are available.[22]

VIII. Multicollinearity

If two or more describing variables are highly intercorrelated, then it is difficult and perhaps impossible to assess their independent effects on the response variable. As the correlation between two independent variables approaches unity, it becomes impossible to tell one variable from the other. The difficulty, called multicollinearity, not only affects the estimates of partial slopes and partial correlations in multiple regression procedures; it also similarly weakens inferences based on cross tabulations.[23] While occasionally the use of additional information may alleviate the problem, it often happens that when the social scientist must rely on "experiments" performed by nature, he will be unable to obtain the independent variation necessary to assess the independent effects of his explanatory variables.

The problem of multicollinearity has a number of obvious consequences. Some theories that assert the importance of one variable over another, while theoretically testable, arc actually incapable of being tested if the describing variables are highly intercorrelated. For example, it may be desirable to separate out the independent effects of economic development and social mobilization on a particular response variable such as military intervention in politics. Yet, for cross-section data in Latin America, the correlation between economic development and social mobilization is 0.89, based on twenty-one observations. Under these circumstances it is simply impossible to assess reliably the independent effects of these two variables.[24] No statistical method—cross-tabulation, regression, path coefficients, or what have you—will break this "multicollinearity deadlock."[25]

An additional danger of multicollinearity is that the analysis, in most cases, can be done as usual. The estimates generated when the describing variables are collinear are, however, subject to large instabilities. The following signs, among others, help alert us to the presence of multicollinearity: (1) high correlations among describing variables; (2) a sizable multiple correlation for the

overall regression, but with no particular regression coefficient reaching significance; and (3) large changes in the values of the regression coefficients when
new variables are added to the regression.

IX. Conclusion

We can, I think, learn a great deal about politics and society through the
statistical analysis of the appropriate data. There are now enough good examples
to provide considerable support for this assertion. Techniques of quantitative
analysis can help us inform and discover as well as summarize and confirm.
We must hope that fewer and fewer applications of quantitative methods will
aim only to impress or sanctify.

NOTES

*   I wish to thank Hayward Alker, Jr., Stanley Kelley, Jr., Gerald Kramer, John
McCarthy, Susanne Mueller, Walter Murphy, Dennis Thompson, and John
Tukey for their advice and criticism. I also thank Joseph Verbalis, who constructed
the figures.

1.   For similar categories, see John W. Tukey and M. B. Wilk, "Data Analysis and
Statistics: Techniques and Approaches," in this volume.

2.   An important exception is W. Allen Wallis and Harry V. Roberts, *Statistics: A
New Approach* (Glencoe, Ill. 1956).

3.   J. David Singer, ed. (New York 1968).

4.   See Abraham Kaplan, *The Conduct of Inquiry* (San Francisco 1964), chap. 1.

5.   Leslie Kish, "Some Statistical Problems in Research Design," reprinted in this
volume. Another good discussion of significance tests is William H. Kruskal,
"Tests of Significance," *International Encyclopedia of the Social Sciences* (New
York 1968), vol. 14, 238–50.

6.   Ward Edwards, Harold Lindman, and Leonard J. Savage, "Bayesian Statistical
Inference for Psychological Research," *Psychological Review*, 70 (May 1963), 217.

7.   Kish.

8.   Frederick Mosteller and E. A. Hammel, book review, *Journal of the American
Statistical Association*, 58 (September 1963), 836.

9.   For a recent statement of S. S. Stevens, see his "Measurement, Statistics, and the
Schemapiric View," *Science*, 161 (August 30, 1968), 849–56.

10.   For a discussion of the problem of "being arbitrary," see J. C. Nunnally, *Psychometric Theory* (New York 1967), chap. 1.

11.   One common practice is to convert the numerical values of variables into ordered
ranks before computing measures of association. Such a transformation, presumably made because it somehow seems statistically more conservative (it is not),
may throw away useful information in the data and also sometimes discourage

efforts at multivariate analysis. One other alternative is to employ some of the nonmetric multivariate methods.

12. The discussion here is necessarily rather brief. For more information, see Robert P. Abelson and John W. Tukey, "Efficient Conversion of Non-Metric Information into Metric Information," in this volume; Abelson and Tukey, "Efficient Utilization of Nonnumerical Information in Quantitative Analysis: General Theory and the Case of Simple Order," *Annals of Mathematical Statistics,* 34 (December 1963), 1347–69; and Roger N. Shepard, "Metric Structures in Ordinal Data," *Journal of Mathematical Psychology,* 3 (1966), 287–315.

13. John Tukey, "Causation, Regression, and Path Analysis," in Oscar Kempthorne and others, eds., *Statistics and Mathematics in Biology* (Ames, Iowa 1954), 38.

14. See Hugh Donald Forbes and Edward R. Tufte, "A Note of Caution in Causal Modelling," *American Political Science Review,* LXII (December 1968), 1258–64, and further discussion at 1269–71.

15. See Wallis and Roberts, 546–56, on the hazards of ratios. The problem was discussed by Karl Pearson, "Mathematical Contributions to the Theory of Evolution— On a Form of Spurious Correlation Which May Arise When Indices Are Used in the Measurement of Organs," *Proceedings of the Royal Society of London,* LX (1897), 489–98. See also Edwin Kuh and John R. Meyer, "Correlation and Regression Estimates When the Data are Ratios," *Econometrica,* 23 (October 1955), 400–16; and F. E. A. Briggs, "The Influence of Errors on the Correlation of Ratios," *Econometrica,* 30 (January 1962), 162–77.

16. Tukey, 35–66. Hubert M. Blalock, Jr., makes a similar argument in his "Causal Inferences, Closed Populations, and Measures of Association," *American Political Science Review,* LXI (March 1967), 130–36. Blalock's application of the argument to the Miller-Stokes data, however, is a most inappropriate example. For some useful applications and contrasts between standardized and unstandardized regression coefficients, see Hayward R. Alker, Jr. and Bruce Russett, "Multifactor Explanations of Social Change," in Russett and others, *World Handbook* and *Political and Social Indicators* (New Haven 1964), 311–21.

17. Hayward Alker, "The Long Road to International Relations Theory: Problems of Statistical Nonadditivity," *World Politics,* XVIII (July 1966), at 646–47, has a useful discussion of this point.

18. There are a number of other areas in which current packaged programs are deficient for the needs of social scientists. Two examples here serve to show that we must be careful even though the result came out of the computer. Longley, in a test of commonly used regression programs, found many inaccuracies in the output— including even the wrong sign attached to some coefficients! In this analysis of difficult but real test data (with highly collinear variables), several well-known programs proved accurate to only one or two digits in their estimates of regression coefficients. See James W. Longley, "An Appraisal of Least Squares Programs from the Point of View of the User," *Journal of the American Statistical Association,* 62 (September 1962), 819–41. Second, many cross-tabulation programs have contributed to the frequent misuse of the chi-square test in the analysis of contingency tables. The test is not appropriate for ordered metrics. Of course, it is not entirely the fault of programs when their users dutifully report whatever the printout says.

19. Tukey and Wilk.

20. For converting nonlinear models into linear fit problems, see the useful book by N. R. Draper and H. Smith, *Applied Regression Analysis* (New York 1966), chap. 5. The best place to learn about transformations is in the informative and straightforward essay by Joseph B. Kruskal, "Transformations of Data," *International Encyclopedia of the Social Sciences* (New York 1968), vol. 16, 182–93.

21. See Alker and Russett, 311–13; also J. Johnston, *Econometric Methods* (New York 1963), 44–52.

22 See J. B. Kruskal and the references cited there. Another useful discussion is Carl I. Hovland, Arthur A. Lumsdaine, and Fred D. Sheffield, "A Baseline for Measurement of Percentage Change," in Paul Lazarsfeld and Morris Rosenberg, eds., *The Language of Social Research* (Glencoe, Ill. 1955), 77–82.

23. J. Johnston, 201–07; Hubert M. Blalock, Jr., "Correlated Independent Variables: The Problem of Multicollinearity," in this volume; and Donald E. Farrar and Robert R. Glauber, "Multicollinearity in Regression Analysis: The Problem Revisited," *Review of Economics and Statistics*, 49 (February 1967), 92–107.

24. See Robert D. Putnam, "Toward Explaining Military Intervention in Latin America Politics," *World Politics*, XX (October 1967), 94–95. The finding that economic development is positively correlated with military intervention after the effect of social mobilization is removed is unfortunately not testable because of the high instability of the partial correlation due to multicollinearity. Another example of the problem is discussed in Forbes and Tufte, 1262–64.

25. Johnston, 207. See Farrar and Glauber for discussion of some modest palliatives. In some cases with many variables, collinearity can still present a problem even if there are only modest correlations between the variables.